MANAGEMENT OF NUCLEAR MATERIALS

AUTHORS AND CONTRIBUTORS

The following is a list of all contributors to this volume.
Specific credits appear with each chapter.

GEORGE B. ADKINS

FREDERICK P. BAGGERMAN

ROY G. CARDWELL

GLEN R. CHAMPION

ROBERT W. DOERR

G. L. HANKINSON

ROGER F. HIBBS

DONALD W. HOBA

LYNN K. HURST

H. C. JACKSON

WILLIAM H. JOHNSON

JOHN A. KIRCHER

MATTHEW N. KUEHN

JAMES N. LATIMER

BLAIR S. LEWIS

RALPH F. LUMB

WILLIAM J. MARAMAN

DANIEL F. MCCARTHY

PAUL N. MCCREERY

PAUL K. MORROW

DONALD F. MUSSER

JAMES A. PARSONS

WILBERT A. STANKO

WILLIAM B. THOMAS

FREDERICK H. TINGEY

FRANK P. VANCE

MANAGEMENT OF
NUCLEAR MATERIALS

Edited by

RALPH F. LUMB

Director
Western New York Nuclear Research Center
Buffalo, New York
Formerly Vice President Quantum, Inc.
Wallingford, Connecticut

PREPARED UNDER AUSPICES OF
THE OFFICE OF TECHNICAL INFORMATION,
UNITED STATES ATOMIC ENERGY COMMISSION

D. VAN NOSTRAND COMPANY, INC.
PRINCETON, NEW JERSEY

TORONTO   LONDON
NEW YORK

D. VAN NOSTRAND COMPANY, INC.
120 Alexander St., Princeton, New Jersey (*Principal office*)
24 West 40 Street, New York 18, New York

D. VAN NOSTRAND COMPANY, LTD.
358, Kensington High Street, London, W.14, England

D. VAN NOSTRAND COMPANY (CANADA), LTD.
25 Hollinger Road, Toronto 16, Canada

PRINTED IN THE UNITED STATES OF AMERICA
BY THE COLONIAL PRESS INC., CLINTON, MASS.

PREFACE

In the thirteen years since inception of the U. S. Atomic Energy Commission, there has evolved within its extensive and varied activities a system for maintaining control over nuclear materials. This system reflects the unique characteristics of nuclear materials which generate a combination of considerations not previously encountered by industrial management.

These characteristics include (1) high monetary value because of scarcity and the extensive processing necessary to obtain sufficient purity; (2) high national value because of possible military uses; (3) hazardous radioactivity varying in type and quantity with the kind of material and the kind of processing; and (4) danger of assembling a critical mass which could cause a nuclear reaction. Nuclear materials management has been further complicated by the requirement to process large quantities of these materials on a routine basis with complex, remotely operated equipment.

The methods and techniques developed should be of value not only to private organizations interested in nuclear materials but also to organizations having to control non-nuclear materials of somewhat similar, unique characteristics. The purpose of this book is to accumulate in one place the basic philosophies and practices developed by the Atomic Energy Commission and its contractors so that this experience will be readily available.

The management of nuclear materials consists of a variety of activities pertaining to a few materials that are essential to the atomic energy program. In this book discussion has been restricted to the control of the two nuclear materials, uranium and plutonium. Other nuclear materials are controlled by substantially the same procedures; hence, to avoid repetition, they are not discussed. Control systems for uranium and plutonium are covered separately with little repetition, since differences in their nuclear characteristics and uses require different chemical and physical processing. Also, criticality, health and safety considerations, and control procedures are different.

This book has been prepared to serve as a source book to all who are interested in the management of nuclear materials. It is organized to permit the reader to obtain first a general background and then detailed information on the management of materials in various processes. The first three chapters present the general philosophy and basic considerations pertinent to the control of uranium and plutonium. Subsequent chapters are case histories of the detailed procedures; they present application of the general philosophy and basic considerations.

The case histories were chosen as representative links in the chain of operations from the procurement and processing of uranium ore on through refinement of uranium, separation of isotopes, fabrication of reactor fuel elements, use of these materials in operating reactors, and recovery and utilization of plutonium. The important side streams of scrap recovery and irradiated fuel recovery are also included, as well as the material control aspects of research and development activities.

Since control procedures are constantly subject to change as processes change, the case studies may not present in fully accurate detail the control procedures in effect when this book is read. However, they do illustrate specific ways of applying the general principles and basic considerations to complex operations and thus should serve as a guide to industries interested in similar operations.

I want to express my indebtedness to the contributing authors for their fine cooperation in the preparation of manuscript for this book, and I am indeed grateful that these men agreed to squeeze into already busy schedules the time necessary for the writing.

To Donald F. Musser, former Director of the USAEC's Division of Nuclear Materials Management, I extend heartfelt thanks for his review and comments on the entire manuscript. Special credit should go to James D. Cape, of the Commission's Office of Technical Information, whose suggestions and long hours of dedication to editorial problems had much to do with the final form of this book. Additional credit is due Marian C. Fox, also of the Office of Technical Information, whose help on this manuscript went considerably beyond normal editorial service. The mechanics of putting the many contributions together in a reasonably consistent format has been largely handled by Richard F. Horan, Charles C. Thomas, Jr. and Ann K. Carr, of Quantum, Inc., the organization with which I was associated when most of the work was done on this book.

There are many others too numerous to mention whose suggestions have contributed to the book. To all of these, as well as the foregoing, I owe whatever success may be achieved in presenting this information.

RALPH F. LUMB

Buffalo, New York
July, 1960

CONTENTS

Part One

BASIC MANAGEMENT CONSIDERATIONS

Chapter 1

PHILOSOPHICAL AND PRACTICAL BASIS*

1-1. INTRODUCTION

The term *nuclear materials management* was coined to describe the acquiring, recording, evaluating, and presenting of quantity data necessary for the control of nuclear materials. *Nuclear materials* include natural uranium, thorium, plutonium, and the uranium-233 and uranium-235 isotopes. These are commonly referred to as *SS materials* (i.e. Source and Special nuclear materials as defined by the Atomic Energy Act of 1954). The system of control is referred to as the *SS system,* and the group of people responsible for operating the system is referred to as the *SS Group.*

The SS system is applied to all activities involving SS materials, from receipts, shipments, processing, fabrication, and reactor operation to side streams and recycles. The object of the system is to furnish all quantitative information necessary for prudent and efficient management of SS-material assets.

The SS system is designed around the following activities:

a. An accounting system for recording and reporting SS-material quantity data.

b. A measurements system for generating the data to be accumulated by the accounting system. The accuracy of the measurement system largely determines the usefulness of the reports compiled from the records.

c. A statistical analysis and quality control system for evaluating the validity of the data produced by the measurements system.

Because of the high unit value of many SS materials, the development and use of accurate quantitative data assume more than ordinary importance. Well-defined procedures are essential for determining, recording, and reporting quantities and for evaluating the reliability with which determinations have been made. The SS system provides data on which billings and payments are based, unit costs developed, inventories maintained at the most economical level, process efficiencies determined, and operations scheduled. Indeed, a good SS system is an economic necessity.

* D. F. Musser, Former Director, Division of Nuclear Materials Management, USAEC, Washington, D. C.

3

1-2. SUMMARY

The function of nuclear materials management is an ordinary part of business, surrounded by rather unordinary circumstances. It is not only the newness of nuclear energy industries which distinguishes this function from its counterparts in older industries; there are additional factors not formerly encountered by private industry which set this function apart.

Chief among these factors is the need for a variety of professional disciplines. In a complex plant these may include chemistry, accounting, auditing, physics, engineering, reactor technology, and statistics. The interdependency of these professional skills is an outstanding characteristic of nuclear materials management. The information is primarily technical; hence the emphasis on scientific skills.

The high unit cost of many nuclear materials necessitates scientific evaluation of the means of determining quantities, the importance of isotopic composition plays a role and the prevention of an unintentional assembling of a critical mass must be assured. The information supplied should be of a timeliness and accuracy appropriate to all uses for which it is intended.

For these and other reasons, a single unified system, supplying data to all users, is desirable. Developing a unified system and maintaining it in good repair is best accomplished by centralizing the responsibility in a group reporting directly to the plant manager.

An understanding of the difference between nuclear materials management and more familiar management operations is essential to the proper development of a nuclear materials management system in an industrial organization. Proper operation of the system requires rigorous, positive, and exacting management practices.

1-3. FUNCTIONS OF SS GROUP

In a broad sense, the SS Group has only one function; namely, to provide management with quantitative data with an accuracy and promptness appropriate to the use of the data.

In a more specific sense, the SS Group serves a variety of functions. It prepares reports reflecting the inventory position, utilization of materials, scrap and recycle flows, and operating efficiencies. It determines, in consultation with the users of the data, the optimum frequency for reports, taking into consideration such factors as the type of operation, quantity of material involved, needs for information, and the accuracy required.

The group accumulates and presents in the most useful form information necessary for production evaluation and scheduling. It provides the material quantity data from which unit costs are determined. From time to time unforeseen needs for data arise, and it is the SS Group's responsibility to acquire and assemble these data accurately and efficiently.

The group evaluates the performance of the SS system and maintains a continuing knowledge of the reliability of the quantitative information recorded. It is responsible for making recommendations for improvements in the operation of the system and in the quality of data acquired.

The SS Group's functions often supplement those of other organizational units. For example, in any process involving radioactive or chemically toxic materials, requirements are established to protect the health and safety of the workers and the community from any associated hazards. A Health and Safety Group is generally charged with the responsibility of seeing that these requirements are met. This group is concerned with the measurement of SS material quantities usually too small to be included in the data accumulated by the SS Group, e.g. monitoring the air and checking the hands, feet, and noses of employees. However, the Health and Safety Group's data can be supplemented by the SS Group's data whenever relatively large quantities are involved, e.g. preventing the accumulation of sufficient special nuclear materials* to form a critical mass* that would release large quantities of radiation, or preventing the release of a dangerous amount of SS material to the environment.

1-4. DATA REQUIREMENTS

1-4.1. Receipts, Shipments, and Operations. When SS material is received or shipped, the quantities involved must be determined to meet the needs of the SS systems of both the receiver and shipper. Quantities determined by the shipper may vary from quantities determined by the receiver as a result of differences in methods and accuracy of measurement. Whether these differences are significant is a management decision based on statistical analysis. If the difference is significant and the SS materials are amenable to representative sampling, differences may be resolved by umpire procedures common in business practice. Much of the material, however, is not amenable to sampling—e.g. fuel elements irradiated and removed from the reactor for chemical reprocessing by another company. In such cases, when a receiver lacks satisfactory means of independently determining the quantities involved, the receiver is dependent upon the shipper for a statement of the amount of SS materials involved. When the value of the material warrants, it may be desirable for the receiver to verify quantities by stationing a representative in the shipper's plant with the right to take samples at various stages of fabrication.

The quality of data for receipts and shipments affects not only a company's external financial settlements but also the quality of its internal information.

* See glossary

For example, determination of unit costs makes use of input and output data (synonymous with receipts and shipments) in addition to data accumulated by the SS system for the SS content of finished product, in-process inventory, recycled streams, wastes, etc. The reliability attached to unit costs is therefore dependent upon the reliability of the data furnished by the entire SS system.

Control of process-efficiency factors, such as the quantity of material recycled and process yield, is possible only to the extent that the data provided by the SS system accurately describe what is physically happening to the material.

1-4.2. Inventories and Wastes. Economic considerations dictate that waste side streams and process inventories be kept to a minimum. The dollar value represented by wastes and unnecessary inventory can, by reason of the high unit value of the materials, substantially affect costs of operation.

A statement of the quantities of SS materials on hand is available through measurements made in the course of routine operations. The accuracy of this statement will benefit from independent verification. Accordingly, on a periodic basis (the period depending upon the value of the materials and the type of operation), physical inventory should be taken to verify inventory records. In particular, values should be measured for materials which have been received or changed by processing since the last physical inventory.

1-4.3. Isotopic Composition. One of the characteristics distinguishing uranium from other materials with which industry commonly deals is the variation in value with isotopic composition. Where knowledge of the isotopic composition is important, it is desirable to maintain the necessary facilities for making isotopic determinations. In this way, information can be independently developed concerning the amount of financial liability incurred by receipts, the value of inventory, and financial credit due for shipments. Several basic approaches to isotopic determination and a variety of adaptations and modifications are discussed in the following chapters.

In addition, any operation that handles uranium of more than one isotopic composition must at all times guard against inadvertently blending materials of different isotopic composition. Such blending will result in loss of value owing to the cost of reseparating the isotopes. Isotopic measurement is essential to the prevention and detection of inadvertent blending. The possibility of such blending will be especially troublesome where the same equipment is used successively for fabricating, processing or handling different isotopes of the same elements.

On the other hand, it is quite possible that operational benefits derived from deliberate blending of materials of different isotopic compositions will exceed the loss of value which results. For example, it may be cheaper to dissolve materials of different compositions together and process them together in a chemical plant than it would be to process them separately. Deciding such matters necessitates a knowledge of the quantities and isotopic compositions of the materials so that the decisions may be well-based economically.

1-5. OPERATION OF AN SS SYSTEM

1-5.1. Unified System. The needs for quantitative data are many and varied. In a plant of appreciable size, there will be groups interested in production control, process efficiency, unit costs, etc. To meet their responsibilities, these groups need data in answer to such questions as:

1. How much material is there?
2. Where is it?
3. What form is it in?
4. How accurate is the knowledge of the quantities?
5. What is the monetary value?
6. Has any blending occurred?

Data necessary to answer these questions and many others will normally be obtainable from routine operations. There should be a single unified system to meet the needs for quantitative data. This unified system must be designed to accumulate and evaluate data of varying degrees of complexity, ensure that the user receives needed data in a usable form and on schedule, maintain the reliability of the data, maintain continuing knowledge of the suitability of the unified system, and ensure that inadequacies are brought to managerial attention.

1-5.2. Reliability of Data. Operating efficiencies, unit costs, material losses, and other key information determined by use of the data are reliable only to the extent that the statement of quantities is reliable. Therefore the reliability of the stated quantities must be determined. This can best be achieved by means of mathematical statistics.

Mathematical statistics can be more easily applied when the plant is divided into material balance areas.* This division serves to highlight the parts of the plant where discrepancies occur. The measurements can then be studied to determine whether the discrepancies are caused by inadequate measurements or some other factor.

For a meaningful material balance to be made, the input, output, and inventory must be on a measured basis. In this case, the quantities will not normally balance exactly. There is always some uncertainty in measurements which will be reflected in the balance. Therefore, except for the rare case where all uncertainties compensate, a perfect balance will occur only by some such undesirable mechanism as difference accounting (i.e. measurement of some quantities and subtraction of those quantities from the total to be accounted for, to obtain the remainder by difference). Difference accounting

* See glossary

obscures any losses or errors by burying them in the unmeasured quantities.

Maintained on a measured basis, a material balance provides valuable information concerning the possibility of loss and the reliability of the measurements. Failure to balance spotlights the amount of losses which could have occurred without detection so far as the reliability of the measurements is concerned. If the loss is larger than management feels is acceptable, then the reliability of the measurements must be improved to determine whether the failure to balance is an apparent or real loss.

It cannot be stated whether loss has occurred on the basis of the material balance alone. If the measurements are unreliable to an extent that the quantities handled are overly uncertain, the material balance will reflect this unreliability and provide the motivation for their improvement. Thus, knowledge of material balances leads to knowledge of uncertainties in measurements, and knowledge of uncertainties in measurements leads to improved material balances.

Data may arise in a variety of forms, some of which have narrow application and hence require translation into terms having broader usefulness. It is desirable to convert all basic data to a common form, preferably weight units such as grams or kilograms, and thus avoid a hodge-podge of terms with attendant difficulties. On occasion, the basic data will be difficult to convert accurately. The SS Group is responsible for evaluating the reliability of the conversion.

In most cases, usefulness of data is an inverse function of its age—the older the data, the less its usefulness. It is important, therefore, that the data be provided quickly as well as accurately and efficiently. The most certain way of achieving this result is by means of a unified system, operating under clearly delegated authority and responsibility.

1-5.3. Maintaining the System. Maintaining a unified data system in good operating condition is not an easy task. Deviations from good practice may occur at any point in the system, people may take short cuts in the interest of expediency, operating problems and exigencies may threaten deadlines for data, competitive demands on the available time of personnel often occur, and a host of other things may cause various persons to bring pressure on the SS Group to abridge the system's requirements. The SS Group should be sympathetic to the extent possible but must not permit the system to be abridged in an unnecessary or undesirable manner.

To the SS Group must be assigned clear responsibility for maintaining constant vigilance to see that unauthorized deviations from the system do not occur. Such vigilance is essential if the data are to be of adequate quality for all uses. Deviations result in poor numbers, and poor numbers should not be reported when good numbers are needed and can be furnished. Furthermore, if management does not show interest in good numbers, there is a tendency for the numbers to get poorer and poorer in quality. Thus, failure to stimulate interest in the maximum justifiable accuracy is prejudicial to maintenance of the data necessary to produce more than a rudimentary understanding of plant operations.

Most companies of appreciable size are audited annually by certified public accountants. The audit provides the management with an independent appraisal of the company's accounting performance and ensures the stockholder that the company's material balance statements are fairly presented. A strong SS Group, functionally responsible for review of the adequacy and operation of the SS system, will materially facilitate the work of the auditors.

Except in an activity of small scope, it avails little to limit review to the physical handling of data through the records and reporting system. Every quantity that appears in the records represents a measurement made somewhere in the operations. The measurement may be very simple, such as counting objects, or more complex, such as determining the in-process inventory in a chemical processing plant or the inventory in a reactor. Regardless of simplicity or complexity, it is only by knowing the validity of the measurements that one can know the validity of the records and reports prepared from them.

While the role of an accounting firm conducting an audit may be fulfilled by determining that the company's material balance statements are fairly presented, an additional responsibility devolves upon the company's SS Group. In addition to determining whether the data are fairly presented, the internal reviewers must determine whether the system is designed to turn out valid information with high efficiency (*efficiency* defined as being responsive to all needs for information with a minimum expenditure of effort). Unless that end is accomplished, the system is inadequate no matter how valid the numbers in the records and reports.

In reviewing the system, the SS Group may from time to time encounter data that can and should be more reliable. The best motivation for obtaining reliable data is the personal interest of the data user. However, since the data may be required for a number of purposes, some of which may need greater accuracy or different form than other purposes, it is important that a motivating force exist which ensures that the needs of everyone are met. The SS Group should serve as this motivating force and, when inadequacy of the data results from deviation from the defined system, should be responsible for the discovery, correction, and prevention of a repetition of the deviation.

1-6. SS SYSTEM EXPENDITURE

1-6.1. Criterion. A well-run company governs the extent of its data collection and evaluation activities so that they bear a reasonable relation to the value of the materials. There is no general rule, however, controlling that relationship. A comparatively simple system may suffice even though a relatively large dollar value of material is represented (e.g. an automobile dealer's transactions). At the other end of the scale are activities such as narcotics preparation where a relatively elaborate system is maintained on material that is intrinsically of low value.

The point is that there is no hard-and-fast rule for the amount of effort to be expended in relation to the value of the material. One might, for example, take the approach that the amount of effort should be sufficient to ensure some given reliability (e.g. 1 percent of the material handled). However, problems arise with this approach. For example, part of the material on hand may consist of pure metal stored in a vault. It is easily measurable, and an uncertainty of 1 percent might well mean that discrete items are missing, a situation very likely to be intolerable. Another part of the material might be in heterogeneous process residues, difficult to sample and analyze, where it may be impossible to limit the uncertainty to 1 percent without an inordinate effort.

Other general criteria that might be applied may be subject to similar difficulties. This inability to use a simple rule of thumb is inconvenient but probably beneficial because it forces detailed study.

There is no one measure that fits all situations, but each individual case must be examined to determine the certainty with which the quantities must be known. The principles of mathematical statistics will be of particular value in such determinations since, through the use of statistics, it is possible to calculate the dollar cost of the improved reliability. A judgment can then be made concerning the amount of effort warranted.

Statistical analysis may reveal that too much or too little effort is being made to obtain data. In either case, there is no problem concerning the course of action that should be taken. However, the results of statistical study may be inconclusive; i.e. the data may not show clearly whether the effort expended should be increased, decreased, or allowed to remain at its present level. A decision must then be made whether to gather additional data that may lead to a clear-cut basis for decision or whether to get no more data and maintain the status quo. Different people will make different decisions, depending on their individual judgments. The necessity to exercise such judgment should not be viewed as a shortcoming of the SS system. Supervisors are paid at least partly for ability to make sound judgments; statistics should be recognized as a tool to aid in making those judgments.

1-6.2. Cost. Businesslike operation of an enterprise implies managerial concern over the reasonableness of costs of each phase of operation. The cost of accumulating, evaluating, and presenting data is properly an object of such concern.

The determination of what is chargeable as a cost of the SS system is fundamental. On that point there are two main schools of thought representing the following approaches:

1. Only the additional cost that is occasioned by having an SS system should be chargeable,

2. All costs related to accumulating and presenting data should be charged to the SS system.

A good case can be made for each. The basic philosophy of the first approach is that data necessary for process control, for example, will be accumulated and used regardless of whether there is a unified data system. The same situation is said to hold for measurements of receipts and shipments, for determination of financial responsibility, and usually for all the other data-using functions of the business. Adoption of this approach normally results in a negligible cost for the unified SS system.

There are, of course, problems in determining the incremental costs incurred. Many factors are intangible (e.g. the value gained by increased efficiency in the use of the data) and hence are subject to differences of interpretation. These differences in views, and the difficulties of accurate determination of the components and cost of a system which might exist versus one which does exist, may result in incremental costs that are moderate, zero, or (in the case in which a net saving is thought to result) less than zero. Determination of incremental costs, or savings, is highly subjective, and this alone predisposes many people to reject the incremental cost concept.

The second approach takes the view that the prime reason for having a unified data system is to ensure that all needs for data, regardless of the reason for the need or by whom needed, should be met by a single system. Thus all costs incurred in accumulating, evaluating, and presenting data (as distinct from originating data) to meet those needs should be chargeable to the system.

This view is simple because no determination of incremental costs is necessary, and the relation of the cost of the system to the value of the material is straightforward and readily discernible. If a proposal is made to increase or decrease the quantity or quality of data, the dollar cost or saving in terms of effect on unit price or other yardstick can be determined easily. This point is of particular importance since no system should be considered as a static one to be installed and operated without change. Needs and operating methods change; measurement methods and accounting techniques improve. All these and other factors must constantly be kept in proper focus. A clear knowledge of data costs is helpful in maintaining that focus. Cost awareness will act as a motivation for operating the system at maximum efficiency.

1-7. ORGANIZATION OF SS GROUP

1-7.1. Location of Responsibility. The organizational location of the SS Group should reflect the functions that it must serve and the responsibilities it must meet. In providing quantitative data for a variety of uses, the group deals with all supervisory echelons. To maintain the system in good repair and evaluate the quality of the data, the group must cut across organizational lines. It plays a prime role in supplying information to top management and in implementing top management's wishes regarding any changes desired in the types of information supplied.

Such considerations make it highly advantageous to have the SS Group report directly to the plant manager. From that position the group can ensure efficient operation of a single unified system responsive to all needs for data. It can avoid the tendency which otherwise may exist toward overlapping systems, gaps in data needed, and efforts at cross purposes.

Because of its ready knowledge and accurate information concerning company operations, the SS Group can be of great assistance to management's determination of policy and can ensure that policy, once determined, will be followed properly in regard to data required for evaluation.

The vantage point afforded by the location of the group is of considerable aid in achieving a well-balanced effort in the SS system. Not only must the group see that data are presented in the most useful form, but they must also maintain constant alertness to the possibilities of weeding out information no longer required and of adding new information not formerly needed. The group's role must be an active one; i.e. it must not sit passively by and wait for wants to be made known, but rather it must actively seek out possibilities of adding to, or subtracting from, the information it accumulates and evaluates. Being in a position to see the whole picture lends added stimulus to the incentive to play an active role and materially increases the effectiveness of the SS system.

1-7.2. Personnel. It is very important to provide the SS Group with a proper staff. Development of the system requires clear knowledge and consideration of the importance of accounting and auditing principles, physical and chemical measurements, statistical evaluation of reliability, and plant operations. The SS Group staff should be competent to judge the interplay of these factors, particularly in regard to the resultant reliability of the data and its suitability to the purposes for which it is obtained. In short, the SS Group must be composed of professionally trained people knowledgeable concerning the possible sources of error in data.

This means that the staff should have:

1. Accounting and auditing talent necessary in setting the requirements for and reviewing the performance of the data-handling part of the system.
2. Competence in measurements for proper interpretation of the physical and chemical basis of quantity determination.
3. Professional ability in mathematical statistics for effective treatment of measurement variability.
4. Plant operation know-how to understand the scope and applicability of the SS system.

Where the activity does not warrant full-time employees in particular disciplines, the SS Group should have the required specialists available on a loan or consulting arrangement. However, the use of part-time personnel frequently does not work out well. It may be difficult to borrow people from other branches of the organization, particularly if there is a time conflict with their regular duties; the chain of supervisory command may not be clear to borrowed people, especially in the absence of clear instructions detaching them from their regular assignments; and their time may not be used effectively because they are not familiar enough with the work of the SS Group.

Part-time service by consultants is likely to be subject to the last objection but avoids the earlier difficulties mentioned. All factors considered, it appears that use of full-time personnel is the most satisfactory way of meeting the responsibilities of the SS Group.

Chapter 2

RECORDS, INVENTORIES, AND REPORTS *

2-1. GENERAL PRINCIPLES

The United States Atomic Energy Commission is responsible for procuring large quantities of *valuable* source materials and for putting these materials through many and varied processes. SS materials are withdrawn from the processing chain at specified intervals for use in research projects, reactors, nuclear weapons, and other purposes. Although the Commission is responsible for these functions and supervises them, it does not actually conduct the procuring, processing, and research itself. It enters into contract with various industrial and research organizations to perform these functions for it. Thus the Commission is responsible for extremely valuable quantities of material which are actually in the hands of others. To protect the interest of the Government with respect to use and proper care of these materials, the AEC must initiate and maintain an appropriate system of accounting for the materials.

The AEC requires that prudent, generally accepted accounting principles be used by all contractors in accounting for SS materials. Governing standards are those prescribed by the American Institute of Certified Public Accountants wherever these standards are applicable. Because of the variety and complexity of the processes involved, no specific accounting system is required of contractors for recording SS material transactions. However, contractors are obliged to institute their own systems based upon the following three rules:

1. A double-entry system of accounting must be used in all cases.
2. The system must be adequate to provide information as to the status of SS materials in the contractor's possession at all times.
3. The cost of maintaining the system must bear a reasonable relation to the value of the SS materials handled.

The AEC requires every organization shipping material to measure the quantity being shipped and to indicate the quantity as well as the measurement

---

* D. F. McCarthy, formerly of the Division of Nuclear Materials Management, USAEC, Washington, D. C.

method on the shipping document. It is then the responsibility of the organization receiving the material to independently measure it and to show on its copy of the shipping document the quantity thus derived and the measurement method used. It is not appropriate for the receiver to accept the quantity indicated by the shipper without verification. As a result of these two independent measurements, differences in quantity shipped and quantity received frequently arise. When a difference exceeds recognized limits of measurement uncertainty, it must be investigated and reconciled. When the shipper or the receiver is unable to reconcile the difference, the AEC provides assistance.

The AEC requires each contractor to appoint an SS Representative within his organization. The SS materials accounting system, for which the SS Representative is responsible, operates on a fiscal year that runs from July 1 through June 30.

It has been found highly desirable to simplify SS material control by dividing the plant into material balance areas. A material balance area is usually a geographical area, the material records for which are maintained in such a way that at any time during operations a balance can be taken from the records to show the amount of material for which the area is responsible. These areas are set up only as operationally necessary and usually are defined on the basis of some physical delineation within the plant, type of process, or organizational lines. A custodian is appointed for each area, and he is responsible for all SS materials within his area.

2-2. ACCOUNTING FORMS

The sample forms and records shown in this chapter have been designed to accommodate transactions in the following four assumed material balance areas:

1. Receiving and Shipping Area
2. Processing Area Number 1
3. Processing Area Number 2
4. Laboratory Area

The following forms are normally used by contractors for recording SS material transactions occurring within their plants:

1. Receiving Notice
2. Intraplant Transfer Document
3. Shipping Notice

These represent the minimum number of forms ordinarily used by a typical AEC contractor. Their use will be described in succeeding paragraphs, and samples will be shown.

Two types of quantity information must be recorded for each transaction involving depleted and enriched uranium, total uranium and U^{235} content. Source material is normally reported to the AEC by its contractors in kilograms, and special nuclear material is reported in grams. The forms and records shown in this chapter have been designed to account for depleted or enriched uranium, since these are the most complex from the standpoint of recording transactions. All forms used should be prenumbered in numerical order so that the loss of a form can be recognized promptly.

2-2.1. Receiving Notice. All SS material entering a plant site should be received by only one material balance area. In the system being described, that area is the Receiving and Shipping Area. If transactions are voluminous enough or if shipping and receiving are carried on in separate locations, two material balance areas should be set up, one for receiving and one for shipping.

It is important that SS material received from a source outside the plant be examined (counted, weighed, or otherwise measured) as soon as it is received to assure the receiver that the quantity recorded by the shipper is the correct amount for which he is assuming responsibility. Laboratory analysis, if necessary, should be made as soon as is practicable.

The result of the measurement is then recorded on a Receiving Notice form (see Fig. 2-1), which is completed in duplicate. The original is sent to the SS office, and the duplicate is retained in the Receiving and Shipping Area files. Personnel who are responsible for physically receiving and measuring the SS material should not have access to the transfer document originated by the shipper.

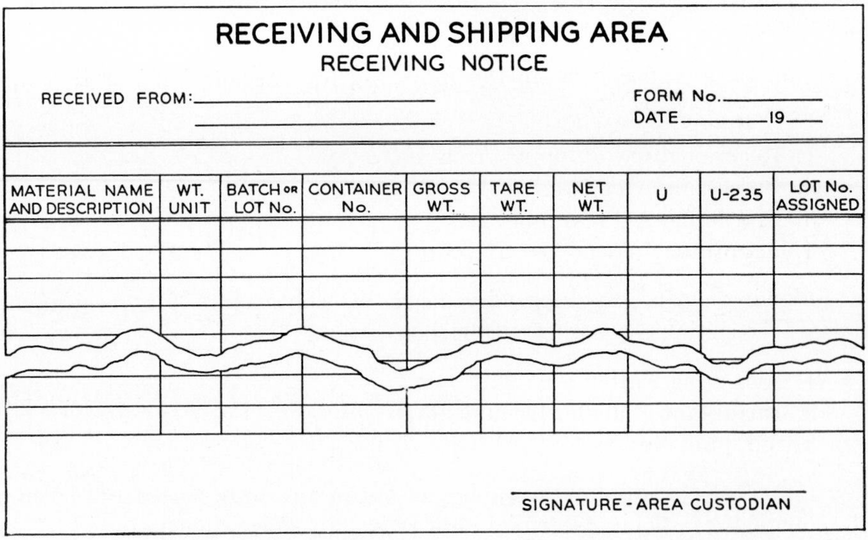

RECEIVING AND SHIPPING AREA
RECEIVING NOTICE

RECEIVED FROM:

FORM No.
DATE 19

MATERIAL NAME AND DESCRIPTION	WT. UNIT	BATCH OR LOT No.	CONTAINER No.	GROSS WT.	TARE WT.	NET WT.	U	U-235	LOT No. ASSIGNED

SIGNATURE - AREA CUSTODIAN

FIG. 2-1 Receiving Notice form.

INTRAPLANT TRANSFER

FROM_____ AREA   FORM No._____

TO_____AREA   DATE_____19____

                                              WEIGHT UNIT_____

LOT OR BATCH No._____

No. OF PIECES OR CONTAINERS_____

NET WEIGHT_____

U_____

U-235_____

SIGNATURE:_____   SIGNATURE:_____
      SHIPPING AREA CUSTODIAN   RECEIVING AREA CUSTODIAN

Fig. 2-2   Intraplant Transfer form.

2-2.2. Intraplant Transfer Document.   Movement of SS material from one material balance area to another is supported by an Intraplant Transfer form (see Fig. 2-2). This form shows the quantity of material for which responsibility passes from one area custodian to another. Thus a form should not be completed unless material is transferred, and no material should be transferred unless an Intraplant Transfer document has been prepared. Each transfer should be represented by one form rather than summarizing several transfers on a single form. No quantity differences between area custodians are permitted on intraplant transfers of SS material.

Each Intraplant Transfer form is prepared by the transferring custodian in triplicate. The original is sent to the SS office, one copy is given to the receiving custodian, and one is retained by the transferring custodian. All three are signed by both custodians.

2-2.3. Shipping Notice.   All SS material being removed to a location outside the plant site should be shipped from only one material balance area, otherwise it will be extremely difficult to maintain adequate control over the material. In the system being described the Receiving and Shipping Area is the only one that handles outside receipts and shipments.

Written instructions to ship material are sent to the shipping area custodian by the SS Representative. A typical form for this purpose is included as Fig. 2-3, Shipping Notice. This is prepared in quadruplicate; one copy is retained by the originator, and three copies are sent to the shipping-area custodian. When the shipment has been accomplished, the shipping-area custodian signs and enters the date on all three copies. One of these is returned

SHIPPING NOTICE

DATE_____19___   FORM No._____

ON_____19__SHIP THE QUANTITY OF NUCLEAR MATERIAL LISTED BELOW TO:

ORGANIZATION_____

ATTENTION_____

DELIVER TO_____

_____

VIA _____

MATERIAL NAME _____

MATERIAL DESCRIPTION_____

_____

QUANTITY_____

SPECIAL SHIPPING INSTRUCTIONS:_____

_____

_____

_____

_____
SS REPRESENTATIVE

ACCOMPLISHED   DATE_____ 19__

LOT No.	CONTAINER No.		GROSS WEIGHT	TARE WEIGHT	NET WEIGHT	U	U-235	

_____
SIGNATURE - SHIPPING AREA CUSTODIAN

FIG. 2-3   Shipping Notice form.

to the SS Representative, one is sent to his accounting group, and one is kept by the shipping-area custodian. At his discretion, the SS Representative may then destroy the original Shipping Notice in his file. The accounting group uses the Shipping Notice to prepare the off-site shipping document.

The procedure described above can have many variations. If an organization has a commitment to ship a given quantity of SS material per day, week, or month, this instruction can be given to the shipping-area custodian in the form of a standing order. In this case the shipping-area custodian prepares the Shipping Notice in triplicate, sending one copy each to the SS Representative and the accounting office and retaining one copy.

Except for routine shipments, the request to send SS material out of the plant probably originates with personnel other than the SS Representative. However, in all cases he should be contacted to originate the Shipping Notice and to prepare whatever shipping instructions are necessary. When this responsibility rests with one person, it is easier to maintain control over the SS material, and it is possible to reduce costly shipping errors.

2-3. ACCOUNTING-OFFICE RECORDS

The accounting office receives a copy of a form for each transaction taking place within the plant. It receives documents from sources outside the plant for receipts from off-site and prepares others for shipments off-site. All these documents are posted into records daily and are summarized monthly so that the organization's position with respect to SS material quantities is known at all times. Records to be kept for the accumulation and summarization of the above-mentioned documents are Off-site Shipping Document, Transfer Journal, Journal Entry Forms, General (and Subsidiary) Ledger.

One set of each of these records must be kept for each SS material handled by the organization. Pages of each are numbered consecutively so that the loss of a page is readily apparent. Although the AEC requires that transactions be reported to it only in whole grams or whole kilograms, some of its contractors keep records of grams and kilograms to tenths or hundredths. In the records exhibited in this chapter, columns have been designed to accommodate these lesser units. These documents and records are described in the succeeding paragraphs.

2-3.1. Off-Site Shipping Document. The off-site shipping document serves two accounting functions: for the recipient it is a record of receipt and for the sender it is a record of shipment. The use of the document in these two capacities is discussed in the following paragraphs.

Record of Receipt. Receipt of every shipment of SS material from a source outside the plant should be certified on the sender's shipping document. For shipments of SS material from one AEC contractor to another, this document is Form AEC-101, shown in Fig. 2-4. This document is received by the recipient's accounting office, where the quantities recorded should be compared with those on the corresponding Receiving Notice (see Fig. 2-1). If differences beyond recognized limits of measurement uncertainty exist, they must be resolved. Information recorded on the Receiving Notice should be entered by the accounting group in the appropriate sections of the shipping form (Form AEC-101) on all copies, and the copies should then be dispatched to all parties

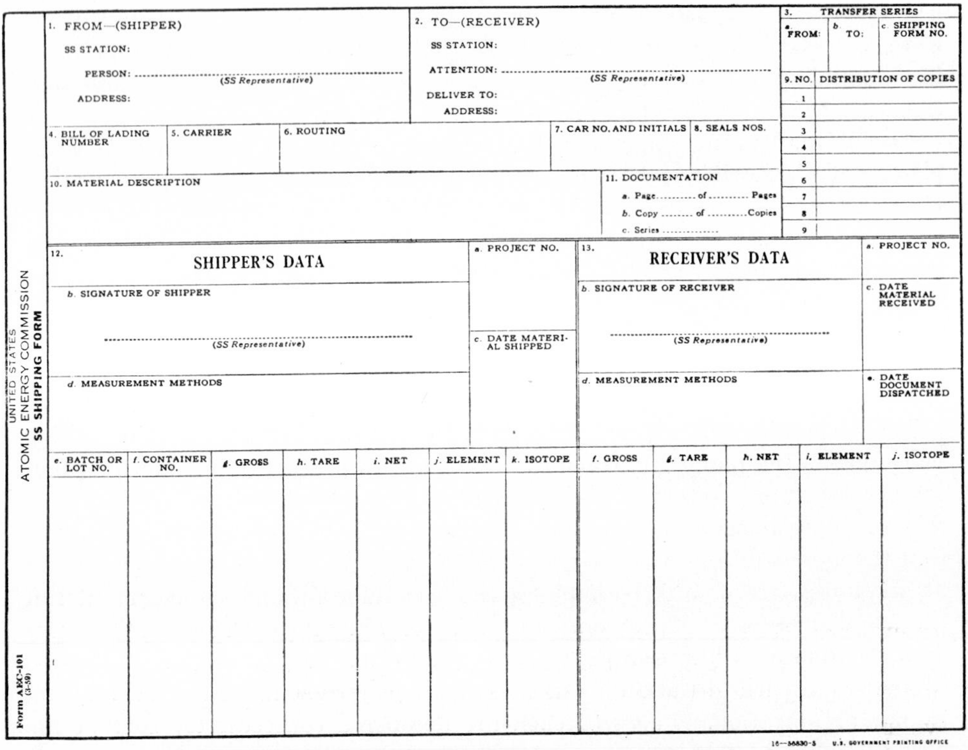

UNITED STATES ATOMIC ENERGY COMMISSION
SS SHIPPING FORM

Form AEC-101 (3-59)

1. FROM—(SHIPPER)
SS STATION:
PERSON: .... (SS Representative)
ADDRESS:

2. TO—(RECEIVER)
SS STATION:
ATTENTION: .... (SS Representative)
DELIVER TO:
ADDRESS:

3. TRANSFER SERIES
a. FROM: b. TO: c. SHIPPING FORM NO.

4. BILL OF LADING NUMBER | 5. CARRIER | 6. ROUTING | 7. CAR NO. AND INITIALS | 8. SEALS NOS.

9. NO. | DISTRIBUTION OF COPIES
1
2
3
4
5
6
7
8
9

10. MATERIAL DESCRIPTION

11. DOCUMENTATION
a. Page .... of .... Pages
b. Copy .... of .... Copies
c. Series ....

12. SHIPPER'S DATA
a. PROJECT NO.
b. SIGNATURE OF SHIPPER
.... (SS Representative)
c. DATE MATERIAL SHIPPED
d. MEASUREMENT METHODS
e. BATCH OR LOT NO. | f. CONTAINER NO. | g. GROSS | h. TARE | i. NET | j. ELEMENT | k. ISOTOPE

13. RECEIVER'S DATA
a. PROJECT NO.
b. SIGNATURE OF RECEIVER
.... (SS Representative)
c. DATE MATERIAL RECEIVED
d. MEASUREMENT METHODS
e. DATE DOCUMENT DISPATCHED
f. GROSS | g. TARE | h. NET | i. ELEMENT | j. ISOTOPE

16—56830-5 U.S. GOVERNMENT PRINTING OFFICE

Fig. 2-4 SS Shipping form (AEC-101).

concerned, in accordance with the distribution indicated on the form. The copy retained by the recipient is the source document for posting to the Transfer Journal. This copy, with the Receiving Notice attached, is placed in the accounting-office files.

Record of Shipment. Evidence that SS material has been shipped off-site comes to the accounting office by means of a Shipping Notice (see Fig. 2-3). This form is used as the basis for preparation of an off-site shipping document (e.g. Form AEC-101, Fig. 2-4). The number of copies to be prepared is governed by the required distribution indicated on the form. The copy retained by the shipper is used as the source document for posting to the Transfer Journal. The form, with the Shipping Notice attached, is filed in the accounting-office "hold" file until the duplicate has been returned by the recipient.

When the duplicate is returned, a comparison is made between the quantities shipped and the quantities received. Differences exceeding recognized limits of measurement uncertainty should be investigated and resolved. The copy of the document showing both the shipper's information and the recipient's information is filed permanently with the Shipping Notice attached. The copy retained in the hold file is then destroyed.

SS MATERIAL TRANSFER JOURNAL

MATERIAL NAME____________

UNIT____________

POSTING REFERENCE			MATERIAL DESCRIPTION	SHIPPER OR RECEIVER	OFF-SITE TRANSFERS		SHIPPING & RCV. AREA		PROCESS. AREA No. 1		PROCESS. AREA No. 2		LABORATORY AREA	
DATE RECEIVED	DATE SHIPPED	DOCUMENT NUMBER			U	U-235	U	U-235	U	U-235	U	U-235	U	U-235

FIG. 2-5 Nuclear Material Transfer Journal form.

2-3.2. Transfer Journal. This record, shown in Fig. 2-5, should be used to summarize off-site receipt and shipment documents and intraplant transfer forms. Where a moderate number of transactions occur, it is quite possible to use this book for all three of these categories. However, where transfers are voluminous, it probably will be necessary to maintain one book each for off-site receipts, off-site shipments, and intraplant transfers. It is also possible, where transactions are few, to dispense with this record and post receipt, removal, and intraplant transfer documents directly to the General (and Subsidiary) Ledger.

At the end of each month, after all entries have been made, the quantity columns of the Transfer Journal are totaled and crossfooted to ensure their being in balance.

Off-Site Transfers. All quantities received from, or shipped to, an off-site location are entered in the Off-Site Transfers columns shown in Fig. 2-5. Because both receipts and shipments are recorded under the same heading to limit the number of columns on the page, receipts (credit entries) should be entered in red ink and removals (debit entries) should be entered in black ink to provide some distinction between receipts and shipments. The offsetting entry to each entry in these columns must be a debit or credit in the Shipping and Receiving Area columns.

The sources of posting to these columns in the Transfer Journal are Forms AEC-101, forms in support of transactions with licensees, or whatever documents record the movement of the SS material into, and out of, the plant.

The column headings on this record can have many variations. If the use of red and black entries is not desirable or is too confusing because of the volume of entries, the Off-Site Transfers column can be subdivided into receipts and shipments. This change would necessitate providing debit and credit categories for each of the material balance area columns. Receipts and shipments can be further subdivided to segregate procurement, receipts from other AEC contractors, receipts from licensees, sales to licensees, leases to licensees, or whatever other categories best describe the organization's routine transactions.

At the end of each month the Off-Site Transfers columns are added to give a net total. Two summaries are made below the total, each of which shows gross receipts by source and type and gross shipments by location and type. One summary shows gross receipts and shipments for the month; the other shows the same information for the fiscal year-to-date. From the summary of transactions for the month, the totals of gross receipts and gross shipments are posted to the General (and Subsidiary) Ledger. The year-to-date totals are not posted.

Intraplant Transfers. Quantities transferred from one material balance area to another are posted only to the material balance area columns of the Transfer Journal.

If there are few intraplant transfers each day, they may be posted individually. If they are voluminous, they should be summarized daily on a work sheet to show the total quantity entering and leaving each material balance area; then these daily totals should be posted to the affected material balance area columns.

When these documents are posted to the Transfer Journal, only one date column need have an entry. The Document Number column need not be filled in unless the documents are entered individually. No entries are required in the Material Description and Shipper or Receiver columns.

Each quantity on a document shown as entering a material balance area is posted to the appropriate columns as a black (or debit) entry. The offsetting red (or credit) entry from the document is posted to the column for the material balance area from which the quantity was removed.

At the end of each month the material balance area columns are added, and the totals are posted to the General (and Subsidiary) Ledger.

2-3.3. Journal Entry Forms. A Journal Entry form, Fig. 2.6, may be used to record any entry on the books for which a form has not been prescribed. Examples of entries normally recorded on Journal Entry forms are discussed in subsequent paragraphs.

Journal Entry forms are usually preprinted with columns for U and U^{235} even though not every SS material requires both types of quantity information. When journal entries for such materials as normal uranium, plutonium, or thorium are prepared, quantity data are usually entered in the U column, leaving the U^{235} column blank. The explanation portion of each journal entry prepared should make reference to the source document or record from which the quantities were obtained and the location of the document or record.

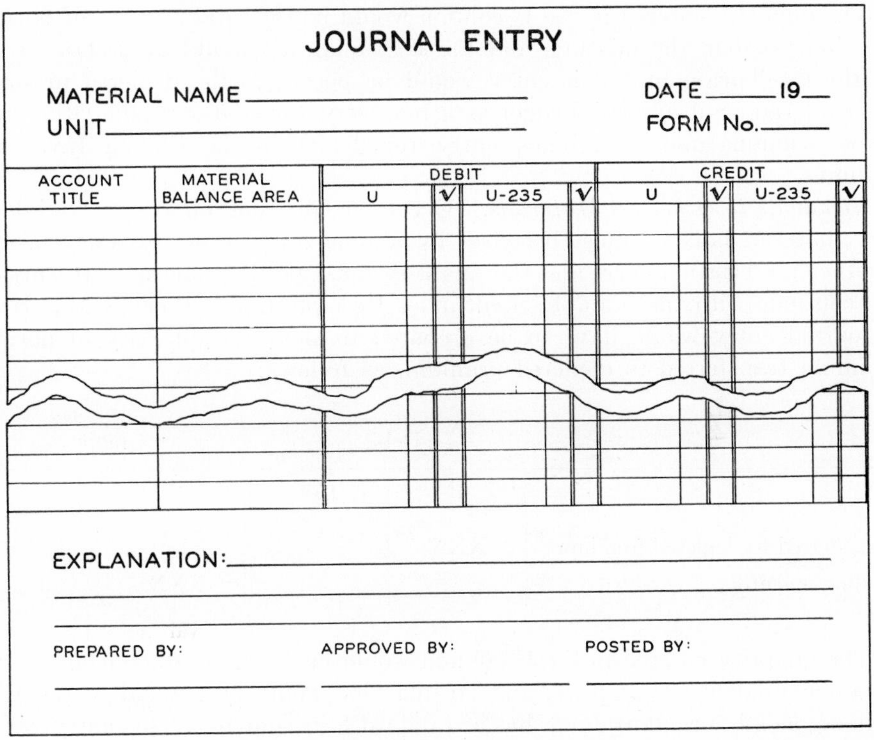

JOURNAL ENTRY

MATERIAL NAME_____   DATE_____19__

UNIT_____   FORM No._____

ACCOUNT TITLE	MATERIAL BALANCE AREA	DEBIT				CREDIT			
		U	V	U-235	V	U	V	U-235	V

EXPLANATION:_____

_____

_____

PREPARED BY: APPROVED BY: POSTED BY:

FIG. 2-6   Typical Journal Entry form.

Not every conceivable type of transaction to be recorded on a Journal Entry form is demonstrated. The principle involved in the samples discussed will prevail for all transactions for which a specific transfer document is not prescribed.

Receipts from Other SS Materials. Occasionally, processing requires the mixing of two or more SS materials, with the result that one or more of them changes into another SS material. For example, a quantity of normal uranium might be combined with a quantity of depleted uranium; the total quantity would be entirely depleted uranium. If a transaction of this type took place, there would be a receipt into the depleted uranium inventory of whatever quantity of normal uranium was used in the mixture. The entry to record this transaction in the depleted uranium balance would be prepared on a Journal Entry form as follows:

	Debit		Credit	
	U	U^{235}	U	U^{235}
Ending inventory	XXX	XXX		
Received from normal uranium			XXX	XXX

The quantity entered in the U column would be the total amount of normal uranium used in the mixture, and the U^{235} quantity would be 0.7115 wt. % of the total uranium. This entry would be posted to the depleted uranium General (and Subsidiary) Ledger as a red entry (or credit) in the Other Receipts columns and as a black entry (or debit) in the Ending Inventory columns.

Removals to Other SS Materials. Every receipt from other SS materials in any material balance must be offset by a removal to other SS materials in another material balance, and the quantity must be the same in both entries. To continue with the example cited under Receipts from Other SS Materials, a journal entry would have to be prepared to show the quantity of normal uranium transferred to depleted uranium, as follows:

	Debit		Credit	
	U	U^{235}	U	U^{235}
Transferred to depleted uranium	XXX			
Ending inventory			XXX	

The quantity entered in the U column would be the total amount of normal uranium used in the mixture, and no quantity would be entered in the U^{235} column, as all normal uranium has a standard U^{235} content. This entry would be posted to the normal uranium General (and Subsidiary) Ledger as a black entry (or debit) in the Other Removals column and as a red entry (or credit) in the Ending Inventory column.

Production. In the SS-materials accounting system the word "production" has a unique meaning. It means bringing into existence an SS material that did not exist previously. This definition is perhaps better clarified by an example. When a quantity of normal uranium is placed in a reactor and subjected to appropriate operating conditions, a new SS material, plutonium, comes into existence. For accounting purposes plutonium is considered to have been produced. Similarly, when thorium is placed in a reactor with enriched uranium, the material "produced" is U^{233}. A Journal Entry form prepared to show plutonium produced over a period of time would appear as follows:

	Debit		Credit	
	U	U^{235}	U	U^{235}
Ending inventory	XXX			
Production			XXX	

This entry would be posted in the plutonium General (and Subsidiary) Ledger as a black entry (or debit) in the Ending Inventory column and as a red entry (or credit) in the Other Receipts column. As explained earlier in this section postings in the plutonium ledger are made to the U column; the U^{235} column is left blank.

In the transaction described above, the quantity of normal uranium placed in the reactor is shown in the records as a transfer from the normal uranium balance to the depleted uranium balance, as discussed previously.

The production of plutonium is the result of the consumption of a portion of the normal uranium used in the process. The loss must be recognized on the books of account and is done so by preparation of a journal entry as follows:

	Debit		Credit	
	U	U^{235}	U	U^{235}
Fission Loss	XXX	XXX		
Ending Inventory			XXX	XXX

The above entry would be posted in the depleted uranium General (and Subsidiary) Ledger as a black entry (or debit) in the Other Removals columns and as a red (or credit) entry in the Ending Inventory columns. It is to be noted that in the entry to record loss by fission the quantity of U^{235} is generally greater than the quantity of U by virtue of the conversion of some U^{235} to U^{236}. The frequency of recording production of plutonium and fission loss of uranium upon the books depends on the significance of the amounts involved. It is not necessary to record these entires more often than monthly, and in the case of a research reactor where small quantities are involved, once a year would probably be adequate.

Information as to the quantity of plutonium produced and the quantity of uranium lost by fission is calculated by technical personnel responsible for operating the reactor. It should be their responsibility to transmit the quantities, in writing, to the accounting office at least once a month. If the calculation is made less frequently than monthly in the ordinary course of reactor operation, then the information should be sent to the accounting office at the time the calculation is made. The transmittal of the data to the accounting office is obviously simple; thus no sample form has been included in this chapter. Duplicates of the technical personnel's calculations, an informal office memorandum, or a form designed by interested personnel at the site can be used to transmit the information to the accounting office.

Approved Inventory Write-Off. Occasionally SS material must be disposed of as waste and removed from inventory. This is usually done when it is not economically feasible to put the material through a recovery process. Permission from the AEC must be obtained by an AEC contractor prior to making such a disposal, and disposal must be accomplished in a manner that provides complete safety for the plant employees as well as the general public. The entry to record such a disposal is made on a Journal Entry form as follows:

	Debit		Credit	
	U	U^{235}	U	U^{235}
Approved inventory write-off	XXX	XXX		
Ending inventory			XXX	XXX

Closing the Books. At the end of each accounting period, usually June 30 of every year, the books are closed or, to be more specific, the General (and Subsidiary) Ledger for each SS material is closed. This is done by preparing the following Journal Entry for each SS material:

	Debit		Credit	
	U	U^{235}	U	U^{235}
Beginning inventory	XXX	XXX		
Off-site receipts	XXX	XXX		
Other receipts	XXX	XXX		
Off-site shipments			XXX	XXX
Other removals			XXX	XXX
Ending inventory			XXX	XXX

Quantities for the entry are the year-to-date totals in the General (and Subsidiary) Ledger taken from the above-named columns of that record. The entry is then posted to the appropriate columns of the General (and Subsidiary) Ledger, and the columns are double ruled to indicate the record has been closed out for the year.

Opening the Books. After the books have been closed at the end of the old fiscal year, they are reopened for the new fiscal year by preparing the following Journal Entry for each SS material:

	Debit		Credit	
	U	U^{235}	U	U^{235}
Ending inventory	XXX	XXX		
Beginning inventory			XXX	XXX

This entry is posted to the above-named columns of the General (and Subsidiary) Ledger and is the first one to be posted at the beginning of each fiscal year. Note that the quantity entered in the Beginning Inventory column by this entry is not changed for the remainder of the fiscal year.

2-3.4. General (and Subsidiary) Ledger. The sources of posting to this record are monthly summary totals, monthly column totals from the Transfer Journal, and entries from Journal Entry forms. However, as mentioned previously, where transactions are so few that the use of a Transfer Journal is not required, entries can be posted here directly from off-site receipt, off-site shipment, and intraplant transfer documents. An example of a General (and Subsidiary) Ledger is illustrated in Fig. 2-7. This ledger has been designed for

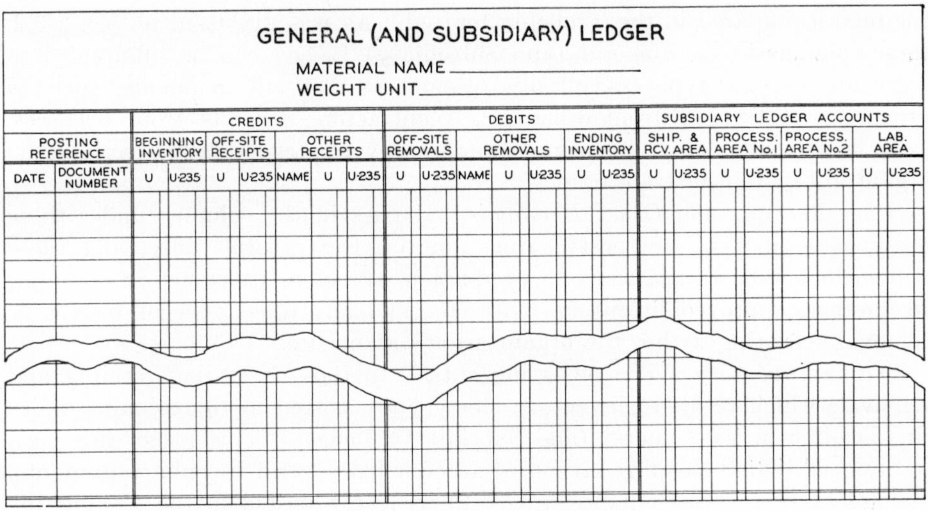

FIG. 2-7 General (and Subsidiary) Ledger.

the use of black ink in posting debit entries and red ink in posting credit entries. However, as mentioned in discussing the Transfer Journal, this method of posting can be changed by providing a debit and a credit column for each account in the General (and Subsidiary) Ledger.

The accounts that normally have debit balances in the SS-materials double-entry system are Ending Inventory and all removals. The accounts that normally have credit balances are Beginning Inventory and all receipts. When a receipt account is credited, the usual offset is a debit to Ending Inventory. When a removal account is debited, the usual offset is a credit to Ending Inventory.

At the end of the second month and at the end of each month thereafter, the monthly entries in each column are added to give a fiscal year-to-date total for each account. This total can be inserted in small pencil figures or can be entered in a color other than black or red. Note that the totals for the Other Receipts and Other Removals columns will have to be in the form of a summary indicating the type of receipt and removal. When the fiscal year-to-date totals have been derived for Off-Site Receipts and Off-Site Removals, their accuracy should be checked to the fiscal year-to-date summary total that was prepared at the end of the month in the Transfer Journal.

Beginning Inventory. In the columns under this heading in Fig. 2-7, the beginning inventory quantity is posted from a Journal Entry form as of July 1 of each fiscal year, and that figure should remain unchanged for the remainder of the fiscal year.

Off-Site Receipts and Off-Site Removals. Entries posted in these columns will come from the summary totals of gross receipts and gross removals for the month prepared in the Transfer Journal. As was discussed in Sec. 2-3.2, these columns in the General (and Subsidiary) Ledger can be subdivided to segregate various types of off-site receipts and off-site removals, such as procurement, receipts from other AEC contractors, receipts from licensees, sales to licensees, leases to licensees, or whatever category best describes the organization's routine transactions.

Other Receipts and Other Removals. Entries in the columns under these headings (Fig. 2-7) are posted from Journal Entry forms only, and these will include such transactions as production, transfers from one SS material to another, approved inventory write-offs, and any other type of receipt or removal occurring within the organization's plant site.

Ending Inventory. The offsetting entries to those recording receipts and removals which result in inventory changes are posted in the columns under this heading in the General (and Subsidiary) Ledger. This ledger has been so designed that the ending inventory account has several subsidiary accounts, one for each material balance area. Every entry posted in the Ending Inventory columns must also be posted to one or more of the Subsidiary Ledger Accounts columns. Thus, at the end of each month after all postings have been made, the sum of the balances in the Subsidiary Ledger columns should always agree with the balance in the Ending Inventory columns. They are added at the end of every month to ensure that agreement exists.

2-4. INVENTORY OF SS MATERIAL

Periodically, a physical inventory must be taken to determine that the quantity of nuclear material shown on the General (and Subsidiary) Ledger is in agreement with the quantity physically on hand. It is not possible to prescribe here the exact frequency with which physical inventories should be taken. In the scope of AEC activities, frequency varies from once each working shift (or three times a day) to once each year.

Frequency must be a decision by management based on the value of the material, the cost of accounting for it, processing conditions, rate of turnover, and other items peculiar to individual situations. Regardless of the situation, a physical inventory should be taken at least once each year.

The physical inventory should be listed completely, extended, and totaled. At least one copy should be turned in to the accounting office for comparison with the quantity from the General (and Subsidiary) Ledger. Standard forms for listing inventory items are commercially available and are quite adequate for this purpose.

If the total from the physical inventory listing differs from the total from the General (and Subsidiary) Ledger, appropriate effort should be expended to locate the difference. If efforts fail to locate the entire difference, an entry should be made on the books to bring them into agreement with the physical listing total. The adjustment should be made on a Journal Entry form as follows:

a. If the physical inventory is greater than the book inventory:

	Debit		Credit	
	U	U^{235}	U	U^{235}
Ending inventory	XXX	XXX		
Book-physical inventory difference			XXX	XXX

b. If the physical inventory is less than the book inventory:

	Debit		Credit	
	U	U^{235}	U	U^{235}
Book-physical inventory difference	XXX	XXX		
Ending inventory			XXX	XXX

When a physical inventory is taken in an entire plant, one of the above entries must be made for each material balance area where a difference exists. However, for any one SS material the adjustment for all affected material balance areas can be entered on one Journal Entry form.

The account, Book-Physical Inventory Difference (B-PID), may be a debit or a credit, depending on whether there is a loss or a gain in inventory. It is common practice to post the B-PID quantity in the Other Removals column of the General (and Subsidiary) Ledger in all cases, even when it is a credit (or gain). This provides a clear portrayal of the cumulative net quantity of B-PID.

Use of the B-PID account is not restricted to inventory adjustments at the end of a month. During the month, if an unusual operating incident occurs or an accident takes place which results in the loss of a significant quantity of SS material, it is the responsibility of the material balance area custodian to inform management immediately and to follow up this notification promptly with a written report describing completely the circumstances resulting in the loss of the material.   The amount of the loss should be determined as soon as possible and made known to personnel in the accounting office, who should remove the quantity from the records by debiting B-PID and crediting Ending Inventory on a Journal Entry form.   This entry should be prepared and posted as of the date of the incident.

2-5. MATERIAL BALANCE REPORTS

At the end of each month every contractor under the jurisdiction of the AEC is required to render an accounting of his SS material transactions on a form entitled Material Balance Report (Fig. 2-8).

Lines 12 through 23 of Fig. 2-8 are restricted to the recording of SS material received from another AEC contractor, and lines 42 through 53 are used to report SS material removed to another AEC contractor.   No contractor uses line 39, Shipper-Receiver Difference.   This line is used only by the AEC in reconciling total shipments and total receipts for the month.   The two columns on the left of the form are used for reporting SS material transactions for the month, and the two columns on the right of the form are used to report cumulative fiscal year-to-date quantities.

A separate report is prepared for each SS material. Quantities for off-site receipts and off-site removals are entered on the report from the month and fiscal year-to-date summaries prepared monthly in the Transfer Journal. Quantities for other receipts, other removals, and beginning and ending inventories for both month and fiscal year-to-date are taken from the General (and Subsidiary) Ledger.

Under Receipts, lines 5 and 10 are Other Receipts; the remainder are Off-Site Receipts.   Under Removals, lines 29 through 34 and 42 through 53 are Off-Site Removals; the remaining lines are Other Removals, except line 39, which was discussed above.

In addition to the important contribution it makes to the AEC's system of internal control, the report has been found quite valuable to contractors for such purposes as production control, providing data for cost-accounting systems, and statistical studies on differences between book and physical inventory quantities.   The Material Balance Report is quite comparable to a statement of profit and loss prepared for financial transactions.

2-6. INTERNAL AUDITS

At the beginning of the chapter it was pointed out that the AEC required the use of generally accepted accounting principles in the maintenance of its SS

Form AEC-577
(Rev. 8-56)

U. S. ATOMIC ENERGY COMMISSION
MATERIAL BALANCE REPORT

(SS Material)

(Station or Operations Office Name)

(Symbol)

(Unit)

MONTH OF_____, 19____

FISCAL YEAR TO DATE

(Total Element)	(Isotope)		(Total Element)	(Isotope)
		1. Beginning Inventory		
		RECEIPTS		
		2. Procurement—Raw Materials		
		3. —From Licensees		
		4. —Miscellaneous		
		5. Production		
		6. Returns—(Albuquerque Use Only)		
		7. —(Albuquerque Use Only)		
		8. —Licensee Program		
		9. —International Cooperation		
		10. From Other SS Material Balances		
		11.		
		12. Operations Office—Albuquerque		
		13. —Chicago		
		14. —Division of Raw Materials		
		15. —Evergreen		
		16. —Grand Junction		
		17. —Hanford		
		18. —Idaho		
		19. —New York		
		20. —Oak Ridge		
		21. —San Francisco		
		22. —Savannah River		
		23. —Schenectady		
		24.		
		25. TOTAL RECEIVED		
		26. TOTAL TO ACCOUNT FOR		
		REMOVALS		
		27. Book-Physical Inventory Difference		
		28. Approved Inventory Write-Offs		
		29. Sales—Licensees		
		30. —International Cooperation		
		31. Leases—Licensees		
		32. —International Cooperation		
		33. Special—(Albuquerque Use Only)		
		34. —(Albuquerque Use Only)		
		35. Expended in AEC Tests		
		36. Routine Tests (Albuquerque and San Francisco)		
		37. Fission Loss		
		38. Tritium Decay		
		39. Shipper-Receiver Difference		
		40. To Other SS Material Balances		
		41.		
		42. Operations Office—Albuquerque		
		43. —Chicago		
		44. —Division of Raw Materials		
		45. —Evergreen		
		46. —Grand Junction		
		47. —Hanford		
		48. —Idaho		
		49. —New York		
		50. —Oak Ridge		
		51. —San Francisco		
		52. —Savannah River		
		53. —Schenectady		
		54.		
		55. TOTAL REMOVALS		
		56. ENDING INVENTORY		
		57. TOTAL ACCOUNTED FOR		

Prepared by (Signature)

Approved by (Signature)

Date

Date

GPO #15396

FIG. 2-8 Material Balance Report (AEC-577).

accounting system.   Industry has long been aware of the advantages provided by an internal auditing staff, which reviews the adequacy and implementation of management policies, as well as the importance of the staff in the organization's system of internal control.   These advantages are equally applicable to nuclear materials management.

2-7. SUMMARY

The reader will recognize the generally accepted accounting principles in the foregoing discussions.   No attempt was made to indicate their application to specific circumstances.   However, this information should materially assist in an understanding of the many factors involved in the development of systems to suit specific processes described in later chapters.   These same simple principles will be found running throughout the description of accounting systems for the many complex operations described.

Chapter 3

MEASUREMENTS AND STATISTICS*

3-1. INTRODUCTION

The data accumulated by the record and reporting system discussed in Chapter 2 are only as good as the accuracy and precision of the measurements used to generate them. A knowledge of the accuracy and precision of these measurements is acquired by statistical evaluation. This chapter discusses the use of measurements and statistics in a record and reporting system.

The principal criterion for the evaluation of a record and reporting system is whether or not the data accumulated have an accuracy and precision appropriate to the value of the material and the uses to be made of the data. Data are accumulated by a measurement system that generally comprises a large number of determinations of mass, volume, chemical composition, and isotopic composition. It must be decided first what degree of accuracy and precision is desired of each measurement method; then the many factors that determine the accuracy and precision of each measurement method must be considered.

Examples of these factors are those involved in the selection of an analytical method: the effect of possible interfering elements; time required for an analysis. These considerations and others, such as availability of equipment, costs, and concentration must all be carefully weighed before the optimum analytical method can be chosen.

After measurement methods are chosen the data generated can be treated statistically to determine whether the desired accuracy and precision are being produced. In addition, the summation of data from all methods can be evaluated to ascertain the appropriateness of the over-all accuracy and precision of the measurement system.

A wide variety of statistical techniques can be employed in this evaluation. Techniques found most useful are discussed here in general terms. There is also a wide variety of measurement methods available for the determination of

* R. F. Lumb, Director, Western New York Nuclear Research Center, Buffalo, N. Y., and G. B. Adkins, Division of Nuclear Materials Management, USAEC, Washington, D. C.

quantities of SS material. The chapter gives the general types of methods most useful in typical chemical and physical processing. Later chapters will discuss specific measurement methods and statistical techniques employed by AEC contractors.

3-2. MEASUREMENT AND SAMPLING SYSTEMS

The beginning point for material control at any plant is the receipt of material from a source of supply. The monetary value of the material is frequently high: uranium hexafluoride enriched to 95 percent U^{235} is valued at $17 per gram of contained U^{235}. Consequently, it is quite important that the receiver know with reasonable centainty whether the quantity received is as stated. This certainty is arrived at through a measurement of the material received. The measurement method chosen depends upon the degree of assurance desired by the receiver that he has received, within acceptable limits, the quantity of material stated by the shipper. Because it is impossible to measure any material with absolute accuracy, it is anticipated that there will be a difference between the quantity as measured by the receiver and the quantity as stated by the shipper.

The history of agreement between the supplier and the receiver concerning quantity and quality, the frequency of receipts from a given supplier, the cost of sampling and measuring, and the value of the material all influence the choice of a system for evaluating receipts. In a case with no previous history of receipts, the initial receipts may be evaluated by measuring each item in the lot. However, with a reasonably long history of agreement, the receiver may elect to sample only enough items to verify that the supplier's quality level is still satisfactory. The decision to employ selective sampling to determine if each lot is acceptable should be based on statistical evidence that the supplier maintains consistent quality control. A sampling plan of this nature involves selecting items from the lot on a random basis, making independent measurements on these items, and comparing them with the values stated by the shipper. If the values agree within acceptable limits, then the shipper's values are accepted. If the values are not in agreement, rejection of the lot may result, or an independent measurement may be made of each item in the lot.

3-2.1. Scale and Balance Control. A control program must be established for all scales and balances used for weighing SS receipts. This program should encompass a periodic recalibration and a determination of the accuracy and precision of each scale and balance by the use of standard weights. Data obtained from weighing the standards periodically are statistically analyzed to obtain the precision, or reproducibility, of the weighing instrument. If a significant bias is determined statistically, the weighing instrument should be recalibrated and then retested.   Statistical control charts are useful in giving a visual indication of the performance of the scale or balance.

3-2.2. Sampling.   Once the weight of incoming material has been determined, a sample must be taken for chemical and isotopic analyses.   The choice of a sampling method will be largely dependent upon the homogeneity and the physical characteristics of the material to be sampled.   If particle size is reasonably small and uniform, the pipe or auger sample is generally satisfactory.   In other cases it may be worth while to pulverize and blend materials so that samples of this type can be utilized.   There are a number of automatic sampling techniques that can also be employed to sample material having small, uniform particle size.   These techniques involve taking a proportional cut from a falling stream of material.   Dip samples generally are impractical because the homogeneity is rarely satisfactory; however, in the case of liquid materials, a dip sample from an adequately agitated vessel may be quite in order.   There are a number of literature sources available which can help in the choice of sampling methods.[1,2]

Once a sampling method has been chosen, the next step is to determine the optimum size and number of samples: too large or too many implies a waste and too small or too few compromises the utility of the results.   Generally, the size of each sample will be determined by its ability to truly represent the lot and by the convenience of sampling.   Special circumstances, e.g. high radioactivity, may override these considerations.

An important factor in determining the size and number of samples necessary is the homogeneity of the material.   A larger sample or more samples will be required for inhomogeneous material than for homogeneous material to meet the same limit of error.   Therefore, the degree of homogeneity must be ascertained, or a reasonable estimate made, before a decision can be made as to the required number and size of samples.   If sufficient history is available on the variability of the material to be sampled, that decision is considerably simplified.

The cost of sampling may be a determining factor in establishing the number of samples to be taken.   If there are sufficient data available on the cost of sampling and sampling variance, it will be possible to optimize the number of samples to be analyzed.[3]   However, if the data are insufficient for the utilization of this optimization technique, the number of samples will be dictated by the factors discussed below.

Perhaps the most important factor in determining the number of samples necessary is the amount of error that can be tolerated in the sample estimates, simply stated as a *limit of error* or *margin of error*.   For a given sampling method of known precision, this limit of error will establish the minimum number of samples to be taken.   An alternative is to reduce this number by im-

---

[1] Numbered references are to be found at the end of the chapter.

proving the sampling precision. However, if no data are available concerning the sampling variance, it becomes necessary to utilize a procedure such as Stein's method of two-stage sampling. First, a small number of samples is taken, the analyses are accomplished, and the variance of the container or lot under consideration is computed. The number of samples necessary to meet the margin of error at the desired risk is determined by inserting this variance in a formula. Then further samples are taken to complete the necessary number of samples.

There is a risk that the results will not be within the limit of error desired. This risk can be made as large or as small as desired. However, a small risk dictates a large number of samples, and, conversely, a large risk will permit a small number. The objective is to select a number of samples such that, within a given risk or probability, the mean or average of these samples does not differ from the true value of the population by an amount equal to, or greater than, the chosen margin of error. Stated in equation form:

$$P_r\{|\overline{X}_s - \overline{X}_p| \geqslant d\} = \alpha \qquad (3.1)$$

where P_r is the probability of rejection, $\overline{X}_s$ is the average value of the sample, and $\overline{X}_p$ is the average value of the population. The margin of error, or difference d, and the risk α can be selected at any values desired. There are numerous equations for the determination of the number of samples taken but each of them depends on the above equation.

There are limitations on the use of the above procedure. For example, the parent population from which the samples are drawn is assumed to be normally distributed; otherwise, the risk of exceeding the chosen limit of error may be affected, or an unnecessarily large number of samples will be analyzed.

The importance of realizing the contribution of sampling uncertainty to the over-all uncertainty for any given measurement cannot be stressed too strongly. In addition, it is important to know the contribution of analytical methods to the total uncertainty in the measurement. The relative contributions by each (sampling variance and analytical variance) can be determined by standard analysis of variance techniques.[4]

In recent years, both the government and private industrial firms have increased their use of statistical sampling plans. Sampling plans are of two basic types: attribute and variable. Attribute sampling plans[5,6] are used when it is sufficient to classify the receipt as either defective or nondefective with respect to a given requirement or set of requirements. Variable sampling plans are used when it is necessary to measure a specified quality characteristic on a continuous scale.

The use of attribute plans requires the establishment of a risk of sampling (i.e. a desired quality level), usually expressed as the probability of accepting bad items and rejecting acceptable items. One of the functions of mathematical statistics is to compute the probabilities of such occurrences so that well-based decisions can be made as to the optimum amount of sampling and analysis necessary to limit such occurrences. A "criterion of acceptability" is established which each item in the sample must meet to be acceptable. This is usually expressed as the maximum deviation from the shipper's values to be expected when the reliability of both parties' measurement methods has been considered. A number of items are then selected at random from the lot through the use of a table of random numbers. Each item selected is then measured and compared with the criterion of acceptability. Based upon the number of items which meet the criterion of acceptability, the entire lot may be accepted, rejected, or subjected to additional testing. The appropriate action is determined by reference to acceptance-rejection tables for the acceptable quality level and number of items tested in the case at hand.

Variable sampling plans are used in essentially the same manner as attribute plans except that the average value and standard deviation, or range, are determined. Unlike attribute plans, which can test several quality characteristics, variable plans can be used to test only one. In addition, this quality characteristic must meet certain requirements, as follows:

1. The quality characteristic being measured must be measurable on a continuous scale, such as grams or inches.
2. The measurements of the quality characteristic must be independent, identically distributed normal random variables.

The condition of normal random variables is essential when a variable sampling plan is used. A badly skewed population would result in a change of the quality protection promised by the variable plan. However, in most cases this does not detract from the usefulness of such plans, since the majority of populations found are normal or near normal in form. A test should be made to determine the distribution before variable sampling is used. The great advantage of variable sampling plans is that they reduce the number of items to be tested compared with attribute plans.

A few important precautions are highlighted below.

(1) It is necessary to clean out all components that handle the material and sample and to equilibrate the system with material to be sampled before a laboratory sample is taken.

(2) Homogenization (to the extent possible) is essential to the production of low variance between samples.

(3) Where volume measurements provide the basis for ascertaining the quantity of the material to which the sample relates, it is essential to consider the effect of temperature change in the sample in relating the analytical results to the material sampled.

(4) If the material to be sampled is hygroscopic or efflorescent, extra precautions must be taken to maintain the water content constant. This

generally dictates that the sample be analyzed immediately after sampling or that it be heremetically sealed.

(5) The random choice of sampling points in containers, ingots, etc. is necessary to ensure the representativeness of the sample.

Sampling plans are very numerous, both in type and in application. The selection of the right plan for the job at hand requires a broad background in statistical sampling theory as well as an understanding of the process to which the sampling is to be applied.

3-2.3. Analytical Quality Control.   Once the number and size of samples to be submitted to the laboratory have been determined, a decision can be made as to the number of analyses to be performed on each sample.   This decision is based on the accuracy and precision required of the analytical method.   There are a number of sources of uncertainty in analytical procedures, e.g. standardization of reagents, calibration of instruments, and precision of readings.   An analytical quality-control program should be established to ascertain the precisions involved as well as to maintain control of the methods.   The analytical method will also vary in precision from operator to operator.   Therefore, it is usually desirable to incorporate in the quality-control program a method for obtaining the contribution of the analyst to the precision of the analytical method.

Basic to the quality-control program is a set of standards by which the analytical methods can be tested.   These standards are analyzed routinely, and the results are evaluated statistically.   Besides a test for accuracy and precision, a test for bias and the significance of the bias can be accomplished with these data.   If the standards are routinely analyzed, control procedures can be set up and control charts can be maintained which demonstrate the experience with the method, indicating when a change occurs in either bias or precision.   Quite frequently it is helpful to institute disguised standard samples so that the operator does not realize he is analyzing a standard.   A significant difference in results can be obtained when the operator recognizes that the sample is a standard.

Without adequate standards little can be done about obtaining accuracy data.   As an alternative, samples frequently have been circulated among a number of laboratories.   The analysis of between-laboratory variances is then used as an indication of relative accuracy.

3-2.4. Combining Measurement Uncertainties.   Each measurement has associated with it (whether calculated or not) some degree of precision, a possible bias, and a sampling variation if a sample is used.   Determination of the limit of error associated with each measurement provides the basis on which a limit of error can be established for a quantity resulting from a number of such measurements.

For example, given a material containing element y and isotope x, find the total element content and isotope content, within probability limits.   This can be accomplished by weighing each batch, sampling each batch, and analyzing each sample for element y and isotope x. The total content of the isotope x, for example, can then be expressed as:

$$X = \sum_{\substack{\text{all} \\ \text{batches}}} (W)(A)(I) \tag{3.2}$$

where X is the number of grams of isotope x present, W is the weight of the batch, A is the percentage of element y, and I is the percentage of isotope x in element y.

The uncertainties in the individual measurements contribute to an uncertainty in the value of X totaled for all batches. These independent errors can be combined by a standard error-propagation method known as the "square root of the sum of squared errors" technique.

If ΔX = total independent random error in isotopic content
ΔW = independent random error of weighing
ΔA = independent random error of element analysis
ΔI = independent random error of isotopic analysis
ΔS = independent random error of sampling

then the total error in isotopic content can be calculated as follows:

$$\Delta X = \sqrt{\sum_{\substack{\text{all} \\ \text{batches}}} \left[\frac{(\delta x)}{\delta W}\Delta W\right]^2 + \sum_{\substack{\text{all} \\ \text{batches}}} \left[\frac{(\delta x)}{\delta A}\Delta A\right]^2 \sum_{\substack{\text{all} \\ \text{batches}}} \left[\frac{(\delta x)}{\delta I}\Delta I\right]^2 + \sum_{\substack{\text{all} \\ \text{batches}}} \left[\frac{(\delta x)}{\delta S}\Delta S\right]^2} \tag{3.3}$$

When the above uncertainties are combined, a value is obtained for each lot sampled. If a number of lots of similar material constitute a shipment, the total uncertainty in the value for the entire shipment can be obtained by the same procedure. This statistical technique can be used to obtain the combined uncertainty due to random independent errors only. Systematic errors (i.e. biases) must be summed algebraically.

There are many circumstances in which knowledge of the total uncertainty is important. For example, measurement of a shipment by the shipper and the receiver will be subject to uncertainties by each, and consequently the measured values will usually not be identical.

The receiver is faced with a decision as to whether the lot is as represented by the supplier. If a value has been determined for each item in the lot, the receiver may judge each item by a comparison of his value with that of the supplier. As an alternative, the receiver may sum the values for all items and compare that summation with the total value of the lot as stated by the supplier.

If the supplier has provided limits of uncertainty and the receiver has computed limits of uncertainty for each container, then a statistical test is available to determine whether the statements of content for each container are significantly different. This test then is applied to determine whether the supplier's stated quantities should be accepted or rejected. Such a test of significance is usually performed by what is known as a "t" test. If the supplier has not provided limits of uncertainty, a test of significance is performed to find whether or not his value falls within the range of uncertainty of the receiver. A similar test can be made for a significant difference in the summation of all items.

3-3. ESTABLISHMENT OF MATERIAL CONTROL

In any processing operation, a system of measurements is installed to ensure that the process is efficient and that the product is meeting specifications. Such process-control measurements can also be used in most cases to establish SS control. Statistical quality control for SS control therefore can also aid control of the process.

One of the most important means of implementing SS control is through provision for measurements around appropriate segments of the process known as material balance areas (Sec. 1-4.2). For each material balance area, all input and output of this area can be measured and recorded. A balance can then be drawn around each segment of the operation to ascertain whether there has been satisfactory material control since the previous balance was drawn. As a minimum, the measurements which must be made for each material balance area include each receipt, each product shipment, all side streams such as waste or recycled scrap, and an inventory at the beginning and end of the balance period.

Because each measurement is recorded as materials flow through the material balance areas, the books can be balanced at the end of a specified time period, and the physical inventory then on hand can be predicted. This inventory is predicted by adding to the beginning inventory all receipts and subtracting from that sum the shipments of products and transfers of side streams. A physical inventory is taken at the end of the period and is compared with the statement of inventory on the books (i.e. book inventory). Any difference between these two is then tested for significance.

Each of the measurements being discussed, whether side streams, products, or inventory, consists of multiple determinations involving weight measurements, volume measurements, chemical measurements, and isotopic measurements, each of which has uncertainties associated with it. The ideal circumstance would be to have limits of uncertainty on each measurement in the material balance statement. These uncertainties could be summed by the standard error-propagation technique already discussed to obtain the total uncertainty of the book inventory. It could then be determined whether the physical inventory agrees with the book inventory within this total uncertainty.

However, this ideal case is seldom obtained in practice. Some of the material flows may not be important enough to measure routinely or, if measured, cannot be assigned limits of uncertainty. In addition, for all but the simplest of processes, the summation is quite time consuming. Therefore, in practice, other techniques are utilized. These involve the comparison of the difference between book inventory and physical inventory with prior history, quantities processed, economic value, etc.

3-3.1. Book-Physical Inventory Difference. A comparison of the physical inventory value with the book inventory value usually results in a difference, termed *book-physical inventory difference* (B-PID). This difference may be due to measurement uncertainties, unrecognized process losses, bookkeeping errors, diversions, thefts, and other causes. The magnitude of this difference is of concern to management. If the difference is significant, a decision must be made as to whether corrective action is to be taken.

Shewhart control charts provide a useful method for evaluating this difference. An index is obtained by dividing the B-PID by the beginning inventory plus receipts or some other parameter such as production, through-put, etc. These indexes are then plotted each inventory period on the control charts. Control limits are computed after sufficient inventories have been obtained to indicate how the B-PID index has fluctuated in the past. Whenever a B-PID index is sufficiently different from the past indexes to exceed the control limits established, it indicates that corrective action should be taken.

Corrective action may take the form of reinventorying to see that items were not missed, rechecking the books to see that bookkeeping errors have not been made, or other investigations. In any case, when the B-PID index exceeds the control limits, it is assured that this particular month is sufficiently different from all previous months to warrant an investigation.

The converse is not necessarily true. When a B-PID is within control limits for a particular month, it cannot be assumed that adequate control is being attained; uncertainties may compensate, or balance may be obtained by some such undesirable mechanism as difference accounting (Sec. 1-4.2).

Shewhart control charts on B-PID will give an indication of the degree of control with a stated probability. With this type information, management can decide if it is worth while to improve the precision and accuracy of measurements, usually for some additional increase in cost. Conversely, if the indication is that the cost of the material control is too great for the value of the material involved, the control factors can be reexamined, and some savings in control costs can be achieved.

3-3.2. Design of Experiments. The time and effort required to establish and maintain a measurement system can be optimized by proper planning. One of the most powerful tools to assist in this planning is the design of statistical experiments.

The general subject of design of experiments is too broad to be included with any degree of completeness here. It comprises, foremost, the planning of experiments with the aim of analyzing and interpreting the results by the use of statistical techniques. The AEC and its contractors have used design-of-experiments techniques to investigate the operation of chemical and manufacturing plants, for routine analysis of product, raw materials, etc., for laboratory investigations into chemical processes, and for many other purposes.

One of the most rewarding uses of experimental design is the determination of the best operating conditions for a process by maximizing some feature such as yield or purity or by minimizing some feature such as cost. An experimental design can reveal the effect each factor, or the interaction of factors, has on the yield, purity, or cost.

A good experimental design is one that will give the required information with a minimum of experimental effort. When a properly designed experiment is conducted, it will enable the main effects of each contributing factor to be estimated independently of any other. It will enable the experimenter to determine the effects of these factors with maximum precision. It will also show the interaction of, or the dependence of the effect of, each factor upon the levels of the others. Finally, it will supply an estimate of the experimental error for the purpose of testing the significance of these effects at chosen confidence levels. The statistical techniques used to accomplish such analyses are referred to as "analysis of variance," "Latin squares," "factorial designs," etc.

The design of experiments that permit a number of variables to be studied simultaneously is a major improvement over the former experimental rule, "Keep all variables constant but one." A well-designed experiment that uses sound statistical methods and takes into account all relevant factors is worth several experiments that study only one factor at a time when measured by the amount of effort required for the information obtained. At times, a properly designed experiment can also generate information obtainable from no other known method. There are frequent bonuses from properly designed experiments, a fact which led one experimenter to declare: "The answer to the main problem is, of course, interesting, but the fringe benefits are fascinating."

This section has given only the barest introduction to the subject of experimental design. The general field of experimental design was first explored thoroughly by R. A. Fisher. His book *Design of Experiments*,[7] originally published in 1935, remains today the most important treatment of the subject. The reader is also referred to References 4 and 8 for further study.

3-4. SUMMARY

The discussion in this chapter has introduced the means of establishing and maintaining quantitative material control. The most important means of establishing material control is by establishing internal material balance areas. Material control can then be maintained by measuring and recording all inputs and outputs of each material balance area. From a history of material balance data, accumulated information indicates the average control achieved and places management in the position of being able to ascertain whether the control should be tightened or relaxed. Generally, improved control can be obtained by additional expenditure of funds to improve measurement methods. However, whether the increase in control is worth the additional expenditure in improved measurement methods is a decision that management must make. Conversely, it is possible frequently to achieve economy in measurement methods. Again, it is for management to decide whether the economy in measurements is warranted, considering the relaxation of control which is usually introduced.

REFERENCES FOR CHAPTER 3

1. A. F. TAGGART, *Handbook of Mineral Dressing*, John Wiley & Sons, Inc., New York, 1947.
2. DIVISION OF NUCLEAR MATERIALS MANAGEMENT and NEW YORK OPERATIONS OFFICE, *Control over Source and Special Nuclear Material; A Symposium Held at New York, March 5-7, 1957*, USAEC Report TID-7537 (Pt. 1), November 1957.
3. M. N. HUDSON, JR., *An Economic Approach to Sample Size*, USAEC Report WASH-183, Division of Production, USAEC, October 1954.
4. OWEN L. DAVIES, *The Design and Analysis of the Industrial Experiments*, Oliver and Boyd, Ltd., Edinburgh and London, and Hafner Publishing Co., Inc., New York, 1954.
5. MIL-STD-414, Military Standard, *Sampling Procedures and Tables for Inspection by Variables for Percent Defective*, Department of Defense, Government Printing Office, 1957.
6. MIL-STD-105A, Military Standard, *Sampling Procedures and Tables for Inspection by Attributes*, Department of Defense, Government Printing Office, 1950.
7. R. A. FISHER, *Design of Experiments*, 4th ed., Oliver and Boyd, Ltd., Edinburgh and London, 1945.
8. FRANK YATES, *Design and Analysis of Factorial Experiments*, Imperial Bureau of Soil Science Technical Communication No. 35, Harpenden, England, 1937.

Part Two

RAW MATERIALS

Chapter 4

PROCUREMENT AND PROCESSING
OF RAW MATERIALS

Uranium is the principal raw material for the nuclear materials utilized by the Atomic Energy Commission. It will be the principal material supporting the peaceful applications of nuclear energy, such as power production, for many years. Therefore attention in this chapter is focused on the steps necessary to procure uranium.

Though uranium is widespread in the earth's crust, workable concentrations are rare. The main sources available to the United States are located in Canada, the Belgian Congo, South Africa, Australia, and the Colorado Plateau. The general geographic region in the southwestern United States known as the Colorado Plateau contributes not only the major portion of our domestic supply but also more than half of all the uranium purchased by the AEC. Consequently, the Commission sponsors an extensive procurement program on the Plateau with headquarters in Grand Junction, Colo.

The AEC has set up ore-buying stations at convenient locations to receive and stockpile uranium ore. Mills have been built for chemically processing and concentrating the ore into a form more amenable to refining processes. These concentrates are stockpiled in Grand Junction for transshipment to refineries.

In the early years of the uranium procurement program, privately owned mills engaged in concentrating vanadium ores adapted their processes to concentrating uranium. As more ore was discovered more private mills were constructed. These mills purchase their ore either from AEC stockpiles or directly from miners. The concentrates produced are purchased by the AEC and stockpiled at Grand Junction.

Lucius Pitkin, Inc., acts as the agent of the Commission in the procurement and stockpiling of uranium ore and concentrates. The Grants, N. Mex., mill of The Anaconda Company, which processes its own and other miners' ore, is typical of private mills on the Colorado Plateau. The activities of these two organizations are described in this chapter to illustrate material-management procedures which have been developed.

ORE PROCUREMENT *

4-1. ORE RECEIVING

Ore-receiving stations are equipped for weighing, sampling, and stockpiling ore. A station usually consists of:

1. A 50-ton-capacity truck scale with a 50- to 60-ft bed.
2. A receiving area, preferably concrete covered, where shippers' ore lots are accumulated prior to sampling.
3. Dump trucks and front-end bucket loaders for handling the ore.
4. A sampling plant for obtaining representative samples of ore lots purchased.
5. Fine-crushing and grinding equipment for producing suitable assay samples.
6. Drying ovens and accurate moisture balances for drying assay samples and obtaining the moisture content of ore lots.
7. A large well-drained ore stockpile area.

In addition, there should be the necessary buildings for an office, scale room, employees' wash and locker rooms, fine-grinding and drying-oven section, garage, and sampling plant. It has been found advantageous to house the first four of the above items in a single building to allow convenience and ease of supervision as well as to provide savings in construction costs.

The major cost item of an ore-receiving station is the sampling plant. Various types of automatic sampling plants have been used at the many ore-receiving stations. In general, they fall into two categories, the permanent type (Fig. 4-1), which is intended for heavy-duty continuous operation over a long period, and the so-called "portable type" (Fig. 4-2), which is considered a temporary installation for only a few years' use.

4-1.1. Permanent Sampling Plant. The sampling plant at Moab, Utah, is an example of the permanent type. Fig. 4-3 is a flow sheet of its operations. Trucks delivering the ore are immediately weighed on a 50-ft-bed platform scale with a type registering beam (direct print-out mechanism). As soon as the gross weight has been taken, the truckload is dumped either into a 100-ton receiving hopper or into a lot pile in a receiving area, according to the type of ore received. Each truck is returned to the scale for tare weighing. All trucks are weighed with the driver off. The weight ticket, in duplicate, is obtained from the type registering beam, and the shipper, date, truck license number, and initials of the driver are written on the weight ticket. The truck driver is given the duplicate, and the original is retained to be attached to

* J. N. Latimer and H. C. Jackson, Lucius Pitkin, Inc., Grand Junction, Colo.

FIG. 4-1 View of permanent type sampling plant, Moab, Utah. Scale room, bucking room, office and locker room one in the right foreground.

FIG. 4-2 Portable type sampling plant, Grants, New Mexico, showing view from primary crusher in right foreground.

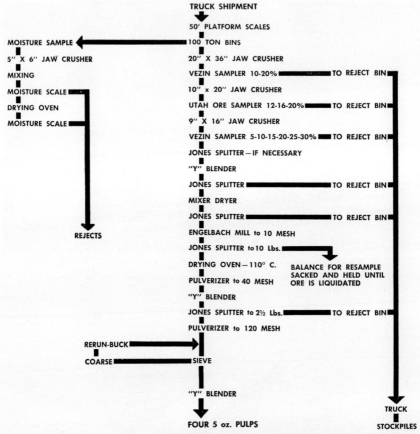

FIG. 4-3 Flow sheet for permanent ore-sampling plant.

the weight and assay certificate on which is listed the wet weight of each truck-load.

Each truckload, at the time it is dumped, is moisture sampled by cutting a total of 10 to 15 lb with a shovel from various parts of the load. This sample is placed in a tightly covered bucket and taken to the moisture room, where it is crushed to minus $\frac{1}{4}$ in. in a 5- by 6-in. jaw crusher and mixed on a steel plate. A 50-oz subsample is weighed on a Toledo moisture balance. This sample is dried at 110°C overnight and then reweighed to determine the percent of moisture content. The result is recorded in the moisture record book and on the weight and assay certificate. The dry weight is then cal-culated for each truckload making up the total ore lot.

Ore lots are accumulated either in 100-ton bins or in a receiving area. If in the latter, the lots are picked up by a power loader, loaded into trucks, and taken to the 100-ton bins. Ore from the 100-ton bins is fed by a plate feeder to conveyor belts, which discharge onto a vibrating grizzly, the coarse ore going into a 20- by 36-in. jaw crusher. The fines from the grizzly fall to the belt conveyor carrying the crusher discharge and then into the receiving hopper of a two-blade 48-in. Vezin sampler. Either a 10 or 20 percent cut is taken at this point. The rejects fall to a conveyor belt and are carried to an 8- by 14-ft steel rejects bin from which ore is loaded into trucks for hauling to stockpiles.

The sample is further crushed to minus $\frac{3}{4}$ in. in a 10- by 20-in. jaw crusher fed by a vibrating grizzly which bypasses the fines. A second sample cut of 12 percent is taken by a Utah Ore Sampler, this cut being further crushed to minus $\frac{1}{2}$ in. by a 9- by 16-in. jaw crusher fed by a vibrating grizzly to bypass the fines. The minus $\frac{1}{2}$-in. sample is fed by a vibrating feeder to a 24-in. four-blade Vezin sampler having two 10 and two 5 percent blades, where a 5, 10, 15, 20, 25, or 30 percent cut can be taken. The sample is accumulated for each lot in a dump-bottom container.

The sample is mixed for 10 to 20 minutes in a twin-shell blender of either 3 or 5-cu-ft capacity depending on the sample size. The sample is then split in a Jones splitter and dried, if necessary, in a mixer dryer. The sample is again split to about 100 lb, ground to minus 10 mesh in an Englebach mill, and split to 10 lb. The rejects from this split are sacked and stored until the lot is liquidated.

The 10-lb sample is dried at 110°C, ground to minus 40 mesh in a Braun pulverizer, and mixed for 5 to 10 minutes in a twin-shell blender. It is then split to $2\frac{1}{2}$ lb with a Jones splitter, ground in a pulverizer, and screened through a 120-mesh screen. Any coarse material on the screen is hand bucked and returned to the screen. The sample is again mixed in a Y blender for 10 minutes, rolled 20 times, and pulped into four 5-oz pulps. Standard wire-closure kraft envelopes are used as sample containers. One pulp is given to the shipper, one to the buyer, and two are held for umpire and reserve.

All bins and all crushing and sampling equipment are thoroughly cleaned after each lot is sampled. Dust equipment consists of a complete dust-collecting system, with exhaust blower and bag house at the sampling plant, and two work hoods, a pulverizer hood, and a crusher hood in the bucking and moisture rooms. Dust respirators and goggles are furnished the workmen. Vacuum cleaners are provided to clean moisture- and bucking-room equipment.

4-1.2. Portable Sampling Plants. The sampling plant at the receiving station in Grants, N. Mex., is an example of the portable type. Fig. 4-4 is a typical flow sheet for its operation. Trucks delivering the ore are immediately weighed on a 50-ft-bed platform scale with a type registering beam. As soon as the gross weight has been taken, the truck is sent to the receiving area, where it is dumped, pending the accumulation of a complete lot of at least 10 tons. The procedures for weighing and moisture sampling are similar to those described for a permanent sampling plant.

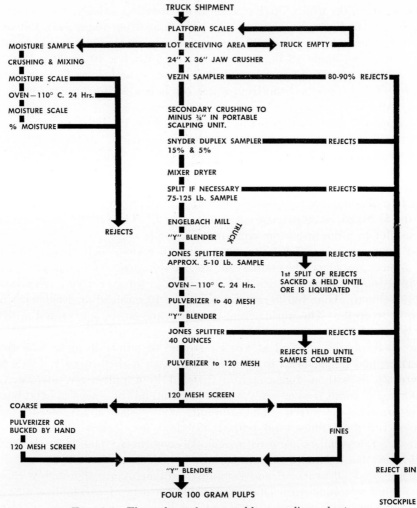

FIG. 4-4 Flow sheet for portable sampling plant.

An ore lot accumulated for sampling is transferred by power loader to trucks that dump into a feed hopper over an apron feeder, which in turn feeds the ore over a stationary grizzly, the coarse ore going into an 18- by 36-in. jaw crusher and the fines being bypassed to the belt conveyor carrying the crusher discharge. Tramp iron is removed by an electromagnet suspended over this belt. The belt conveyor discharges into a two-blade 48-in. Vezin sampler with which either a 10 or 20 percent cut can be taken. Rejects fall to a belt conveyor discharging into a 40-ton-capacity rejects bin, from which the ore is loaded into trucks for hauling to stockpiles.

The sample cut falls on the feeder belt of a portable gravel-crushing machine, consisting of a vibrating screen, a 9- by 16-in. jaw crusher, and a set of rolls that reduces the sample to minus $\frac{3}{4}$-in. size.   The discharge conveyor of the portable gravel crusher feeds a Snyder Duplex Sampler which takes a 15.7 percent cut on the first sampler and a 4.6 or 9.2 percent cut on the second sampler of the unit as desired according to the lot size.   The rejects are carried by belt conveyor to the rejects bin.   The sample falls by gravity to a sample can, where it is collected for the ore lot.

If the sample is wet, it is dried in a mixer-dryer and split if necessary to between 75 and 125 lb.   If the ore sample is dry, it is mixed in a Y blender before splitting.   The sample is then ground to 20 mesh in an Englebach mill, mixed in a Y blender, and split to between 5 and 10 lb with a Jones splitter. The first split is sacked and stored until the lot is liquidated.

The 5- to 10-lb sample is dried for 16 to 24 hours at 110°C in a drying oven, pulverized to 40 mesh in a Braun pulverizer, mixed in a 4-qt Y blender, and split to 40 oz.   This split is then ground to 120 mesh in a Braun pulverizer and screened through a 120-mesh sieve; the coarse portion remaining on the sieve is reground and screened with the sample.   It is then mixed for 10 minutes in a Y blender and packaged into four pulps in standard wire-closure kraft envelopes.   One pulp is given to the seller, one to the buyer, and two are held for reserve and umpire.

All crushing and sampling equipment is thoroughly cleaned with compressed air after each lot is sampled.   Dust equipment in the bucking room consists of two work-table hoods and a pulverizer hood exhausted by an electric blower to the atmosphere.   Dust respirators and goggles are furnished the workmen as needed.

4-1.3. Statistical Evaluation of Sampling Procedures.   Ore-sampling plants and their procedures are evaluated periodically by check-sampling lots of ore and assaying the analytical samples so produced.   The ore lots may be resampled in the same sampling plant or may be taken to another ore-receiving station for resampling.   The latter method is always used to check the sampling results on the start-up of a new sampling plant.

The condensed results of a series of intraplant ore-lot sampling checks may be of interest.   The lots of ore were first sampled for purchase, then resampled for the check.   The data are summarized in Table 4.1.

Although it is not entirely proper to pool the above results owing to differences in types of ores sampled, differences in sampling equipment, etc., if these differences are kept in mind, a pooled result can be indicative of results that may be expected from uranium ore-sampling plants of the types used.

If the variances calculated from the differences between purchase and check results for all the sampling plants are pooled, a pooled 95 percent confidence interval of ±0.027(4) percent U_3O_8 can be calculated.   As a percentage of the average grade of the ore (0.332 percent U_3O_8), this confidence interval then becomes ±8.3 percent of the averaged contained U_3O_8.

TABLE 4.1.   PERCENTAGE DIFFERENCE BY LOTS BETWEEN
PURCHASE AND CHECK SAMPLING[a]

Receiving Station	No. of Lots	Confidence Interval at 95 Percent (Interval Between Purchase Assay and Check Assay, % U_3O_8)
A	2	±0.020(0)
B	6	±0.023(0)
C	9	±0.022(0)
D	4	±0.022(4)
E	23	±0.019(3)
F[b]	23	±0.044(8)
G	10	±0.014(5)
H	17	±0.013(6)

[a] The average grade of all purchase samples for all the above lots was 0.332 percent U_3O_8, and the average grade of all check samples was 0.329 percent U_3O_8.

[b] The sampling plant at receiving station F has a much larger 95 percent confidence interval of the differences between the purchase and check assays than the other stations. This was largely due to the type of ore sampled at this station. The ore was harder than average, and the values in it were segregated, making it a very spotty ore to sample.

If this same calculation is made but receiving station F is eliminated as not being typical, the pooled 95 percent confidence interval between the purchase and check sampling assays is reduced to ±0.018(5) percent U_3O_8. As a percentage of the then average ore grade of all the remaining lots of 0.338 percent U_3O_8, the confidence interval at 95 percent is ±5.5 percent of the average contained U_3O_8. These figures sum over-all sampling and assaying variances.

4-1.4. Assay Samples.   As can be noted from the descriptions of sampling procedures, four identical assay samples are produced for each lot of uranium ore purchased from a shipper. One of these samples is given or mailed to the shipper, one is sent to the receiving plant assay laboratory, and the remaining two samples are held as a possible umpire sample and a reserve sample. A weight and assay certificate is made for each individual ore lot, showing the weights of the various truckloads comprised in the lot, their moisture content, dates received, mileage hauled, total net dry weight, and the assay of the ore. The assays are for U_3O_8 and $CaCO_3$ and may also include V_2O_5 or copper, depending on the type of ore and the shipper's sales contract with the AEC.

Using information from the assay certificate, the buyer calculates a liquidation of the ore lot on the basis of the applicable government ore schedule and pays the shipper. The shipper may wish to have his ore lot sample assayed by an independent laboratory, and if this assay is in disagreement with the buyer's assay, the shipper has the privilege of requesting an umpire assay by written request and the presentation of his independent assay certificate. The buyer then forwards an umpire sample of the lot to an independent umpire laboratory chosen from a list of such laboratories that have received prior approval.

When the umpire assay has been received the ore lot is liquidated on the basis of the middle result of the three assays. The party having the assay farthest from the umpire assay pays the cost of the umpire. If the assays of both parties are equidistant from the umpire result, the cost is split.

4-2. ORE ASSAYING

4-2.1. Analytical Procedures. Accurate laboratory assay work is essential not only for the purchase and sale of uranium ores but also for concentrating-mill control. A search of the literature will show that many uranium

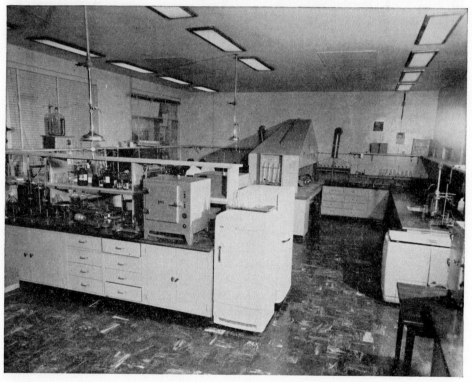

Fig. 4-5 Typical room arrangement for assay laboratory.

analytical procedures for low-grade ores have been developed. The uranium procedure used in the receiving-plant assay laboratory is essentially that described by Sill and Peterson,[1] with some minor changes in equipment and technique. A typical laboratory assay room is shown in Fig. 4-5; the bench

---

[1] Numbered references are to be found at the end of the chapter.

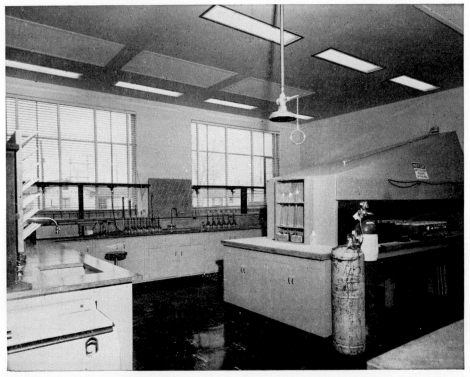

Fig. 4-6 Bench and fume-hood arrangement, assay laboratory.

and fume hood arrangement is shown in Fig. 4-6. The method consists of baking the weighed analytical sample in a Vycor beaker at a dull red heat for 15 to 20 minutes, followed by a mixed acid digestion, separation of the hydrogen sulfide group in perchloric acid by thioacetamide, a cupferron chloroform extraction, removal of organic material by fuming with perchloric acid, and reduction of the uranium in a lead reductor. This is followed by titration with a ceric sulfate solution that has been standardized against pure black uranium oxide.

It is very helpful when large numbers of uranium ore samples are being assayed to first run a radiometric uranium determination on each sample to determine the approximate grade of the ore and to check for possible gross analytical errors. Standard types of scalers, timers, and lead counting chambers with end-window Geiger-Müller tubes are used for this work.

4-2.2. Statistical Evaluation of Assay Program. An Evaluation Group is responsible for checking and evaluating all phases of sampling and assaying work undertaken. Under its supervision a continuous assay control program is carried out in the ore-assaying section by means of specially prepared standard uranium ore samples that are disguised and distributed for assay.

Practically continuous ore-assay comparisons are available between the receiving-plant assay laboratory, the approved umpire laboratories, and the concentrating-mill laboratories, which provide a large volume of check data. The condensed results of a recent statistical study by this group, which involved the uranium assays by the laboratory on 60 uranium ore mill-head composite samples, may be of interest. The results are listed in Table 4.2.

TABLE 4.2.   STATISTICAL RESULTS OF URANIUM
ASSAY DETERMINATIONS[a]

Concentrating Mill	Standard Deviations for a Single Assay Determination (% U_3O_8)	No. of Samples	No. of Individual Assays
A	0.00333	8	29
B	0.00427	9	31
C	0.00269	4	13
D	0.00226	4	12
E	0.00241	4	14
F	0.00252	5	16
G	0.00167	4	13
H	0.00150	2	6
I	0.00230	14	52
J	0.00354	6	28
		Total 60	214

[a] CONDITIONS:
1. A total of eight analysts participated in the determinations.
2. A minimum of three assays was made on each mill-head ore sample.
3. Each assay of a sample was made by a different analyst.
4. The assays were performed during a four-month period.
5. The 60 composite samples represented uranium ore being refined by 10 different concentrating mills and represented nearly all common types of uranium ores occurring in the area.
6. Grade of samples ranged between 0.10 and 0.40 percent U_3O_8.

The standard deviation for all assays for a single determination is 0.00298 percent U_3O_8. Since three U_3O_8 determinations per sample predominate, the standard deviation for the average of three is

$$S_{a3} = \frac{0.00298}{\sqrt{3}} = 0.00173 \text{ percent } U_3O_8 \qquad (4.1)$$

Thus, at the 95 percent confidence level (2 S_{a3}) the average of three determinations can be expected to vary from the true average by no more than ±0.003 percent U_3O_8.

Comparative assays on 48 of the 60 composite mill-head samples were available from 9 of the concentrating-mill laboratories. Assuming that the reported mill laboratory assays are an average of three or more determinations per sample, which is generally true, the standard deviation of the differences between the assay laboratory and the various mill laboratories was calculated. The data are recorded in Table 4.3.

TABLE 4.3. COMPARISON OF ASSAY RESULTS FOR CONCENTRATING MILLS AND ASSAY LABORATORY

Concentrating Mill Laboratory	Standard Deviation of Difference, % U_3O_8	No. of Samples
A	0.0080	8
C	0.0054	4
D	0.0025	4
E	0.0008	4
F	0.0055	4
G	0.0040	4
H	0.0050	2
I	0.0033	14
J	0.0058	4
		48

The contributions by weighing, assaying, etc. must be considered in ascertaining the sampling variance. If it is assumed that the assay variance is the only other significant contribution, the sampling variance can be calculated from the relationship:

$$S_T^2 = S_s^2 + S_a^2 \qquad (4.2)$$

where S_T^2 = total variance
S_s^2 = sampling variance
S_a^2 = assay variance

The 95 percent confidence interval for sampling is, therefore, estimated to be $\pm 0.026(7)$ percent and $\pm 0.017(5)$ percent U_3O_8 for all plants and typical plants respectively.

If the variances for the differences for all laboratories are pooled and the pooled standard deviation $(\sqrt{S_p^2})$ is calculated a value of 0.005 percent U_3O_8 and a 95 percent confidence level of approximately 0.01 percent U_3O_8 are found.

4-3. BASIC ACCOUNTING RECORDS

Uranium ore purchasing consists basically in weighing, sampling, assaying, stockpiling, liquidating (or settling by financial payment for ores purchased), and eventually disposing of accumulated stocks. Certain books of account, common to business generally, must be maintained. These are, in the order discussed:

1. General ledger
2. Cash and voucher record

3. Accounts receivable and accounts payable (subsidiary ledger)
4. Purchase and stock records (liquidation record)
5. Stockpile ledgers or records (warehouse supplies)

These are the basic records; other pertinent records as may be required are discussed in Sec. 4-4.

4-3.1. General Ledger. This is a loose-leaf ledger containing all accounts. The individual *general ledger* sheets or pages provide generous space for a brief description of transactions to be recorded as well as for date and reference columns standard to all ledgers.

4-3.2. Cash-Voucher Record. This may be two separate records whereby cash transactions and memo vouchers or journal entries are completely separated from each other. The combination *cash-voucher record* has often been adopted. This record is a book of original entry and carries a record of all essential transactions in chronological sequence with identifying reference to voucher number and check number when cash is disbursed. By columnar development, provision is made for most frequently used accounts. All infrequently used accounts are entered under a Sundry column, which provides space for account name, as well as debit and credit columns and folio reference columns.

4-3.3. Accounts Receivable and Accounts Payable (Subsidiary Ledgers). These ledgers record the detail charges and credits to individuals, firms, and corporations. In both these ledgers the balances must be in absolute agreement with the *general ledger control account*, and *accounts receivable or accounts payable*, when all entries are posted to a given date.

4-3.4. Purchase and Stock Record (Liquidation Record). This record contains the metallurgical and financial data on all ore purchases, developed from direct posting of cash and memo vouchers as they appear in the *cash-voucher record* referred to above, for the respective stockpile account of the ore buying station. The postings are made from one source only: the certified final liquidation that supports the financial settlement for all ores purchased. The *purchase and stock record* is therefore commonly called the *liquidation record*.

The *liquidation record* reflects the following information:

ORES PURCHASED
 Date received (weighed at ore-buying station)
 Shipper's name
 Liquidation number
 Lot number or numbers
 Percent moisture (two decimals)
 Dry weight of ore received (even pounds)
 Percent and content of essential metals

DETAIL COST ANALYSIS

SPECIAL ALLOWANCES—separately, such as development and haulage allowances

SPECIAL PENALTIES—such as excess lime or impurities, if any

TOTAL COST OF ORES

If the ore is segregated into stockpiles of similar characteristics or within certain predetermined grade ranges later milling or concentrating processes will be facilitated. Therefore, the *liquidation record* carries the liquidated ore purchases segregated into various ore piles. Determination of appropriate stockpile is made on the basis of the shipper's consistent ore type and grade range. When this information is not available, as in the case of new shippers, a piling determination is made on the basis of type and assays, such ores not being placed in stockpiles but held "N.S.P." (not stockpiled) until determination is made at a later date.

The lot liquidations, or financial settlements, are prepared by two settlement clerks working independently; the respective results thereof are compared by a third party. The *liquidation record* contains only lots actually liquidated, i.e., financially settled. The accumulated totals of such financial settlements must be in absolute agreement with the ore purchase accounts recorded in the *cash-voucher record*, which reflect the ore cost of ore purchased in any month.

There will always be a variance or discrepancy in tonnage and assay recorded in this record as to the actual tonnage and contents of ores received at the ore-buying station. This variance must be reconciled in detail to ensure complete and accurate recording.

4-3.5. Stockpile Record. The stockpile record is maintained independently of the liquidation record. The stockpile record reflects the stock position currently as ores are acquired by receipt; whereas the liquidation record deals with the same material only as it becomes a completed financial transaction by the presentation of a final liquidation or financial ore settlement to the seller.

The *stockpile record* shows the ores received and piled in individual ore stockpiles at the ore-receiving station. Postings made from the *weight and assay certificates* (Fig. 4-7) note the following information: name and address of shipper, ore claim name, official government (AEC) license number, type of ore, pile number in which the ore is placed after sampling, scale-ticket number (scale tickets themselves show the gross, tare, and net wet weights, RR car or truck number), assays, and contents.

Since information recorded on the stockpile record will not exactly agree with information recorded on the liquidation record, certain control procedures are required to ensure accuracy. Therefore, a detailed reconciliation is required to establish balance between these two independent records in recorded

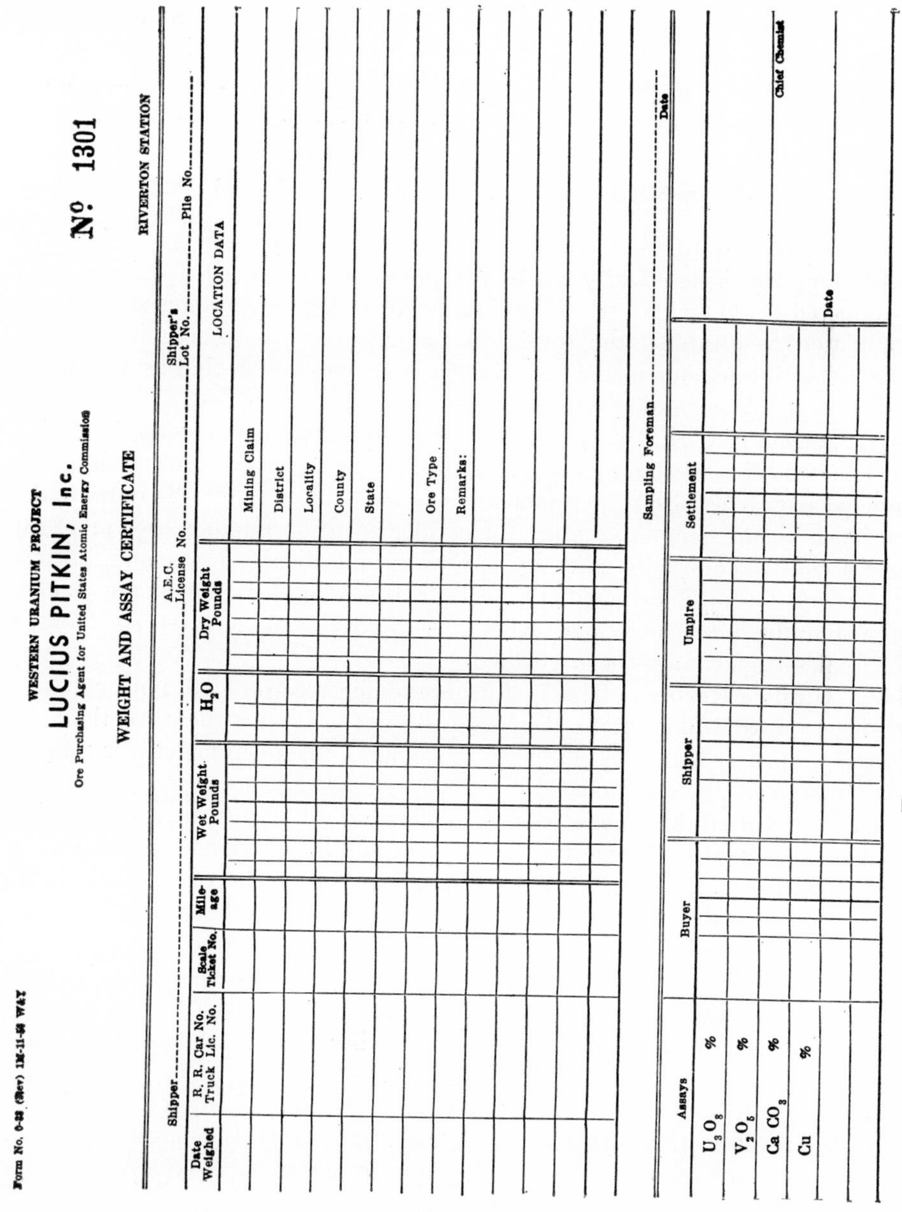
Form No. 0-53 (Rev) 1M-11-56 W&Y

WESTERN URANIUM PROJECT

LUCIUS PITKIN, Inc.

Ore Purchasing Agent for United States Atomic Energy Commission

No. 1301

WEIGHT AND ASSAY CERTIFICATE

RIVERTON STATION

Shipper________ A.E.C. License No.________ Shipper's Lot No.________ Pile No.________

Date Weighed	R. R. Car No. Truck Lic. No.	Scale Ticket No.	Mileage	Wet Weight Pounds	H_2O	Dry Weight Pounds	LOCATION DATA
							Mining Claim
							District
							Locality
							County
							State
							Ore Type
							Remarks:

Sampling Foreman________ Date________

Assays	Buyer	Shipper	Umpire	Settlement	
U_3O_8 %					
V_2O_5 %					
$Ca\ CO_3$ %					Chief Chemist
Cu %					Date

Fig. 4-7 Weight and assay certificate.

tonnage, assay, and contents. Such reconciliations are maintained in the Metallurgical Department files for reference and audit inspection.

If accuracy is to be retained, it is necessary to establish control procedures to cross check and reconcile collective entries with similar information developed from independent sources. Errors are thus brought to light promptly, and the records in error are thereby adjusted. These control procedures have been explained in the discussion of the various records.

4-4. MISCELLANEOUS ACCOUNTING RECORDS

Other records required or desirable in ore buying can be described as follows:

4-4.1. Ore Receipts—Daily Scale Weights. Daily recorded weights from prenumbered scale tickets of all ore received at the ore-buying station are accumulated to establish the total wet tonnage receipts in a given month. These are accounted for in the records of the ore-buying station as well as in the records in the general books of account.

4-4.2. Assay Record. Because this is a vital record, it should be maintained for the life of the company. It should be a bound book (with prenumbered pages) to ensure permanency. It must provide for the date determination is made, sample number, lot or identification number, assays of all required constituents with space for assays of additional constituents, initials of the chemist who determined the assay, and storage location of the sample pulp remaining after assaying. All pulps are retained at least six months after final settlement has been effected.

4-4.3. Umpire Record. This is a memorandum record of all umpire assays resulting from contest by the seller as to assay of any constituents of the ores. Generally, open schedule or purchase agreements make provision for umpire assays under certain conditions.

4-4.4. Individual Shippers Record. This record serves as a cumulative record of the total ores received at any ore-buying station. It contains a control sheet of total ores received and a breakdown thereof to individual shippers of such ore. It is invaluable in determining at any time and for any period the exact tonnage, grade, and metal content of ores received from and payment made to individual shippers. When totaled and checked by month with the total month's purchases as recorded in the liquidation record and the cost of value, which appears in the cash-voucher record account "Ore Purchases," these records should be in agreement.

4-4.5. Cash Advances to Ore Shippers (Subsidiary Ledger). Cash advances to ore shippers are customary in ore buying when the shipper requests and authorizes such cash advances. The percentage of value so advanced depends upon many factors but should always be on a conservative basis, generally not over 75 to 80 percent of the estimated value of ores actually in the possession of the buyer. The most practical basis for the buyer is to restrict cash advances to an agreed percentage of the values determined on previously measured tonnage with actual assays thereon.

This subledger is merely a refinement of natural segregation of accounts which might be carried in an *accounts receivable* subledger, inasmuch as such advances become a charge against the recipient or in fact an account receivable. However, since the purchase of ore is the primary function of the company and considerable funds are expended by way of cash advances against the value thereof, it is most essential that recovery of all such cash advances be made by deduction from the final settlement of ores purchased from the respective shipper. Therefore, to ensure immediate and accurate determination of cash advances to ore shippers, advances are set up in this subledger thus making available to the liquidation or settlement clerks the amount to be withheld from final settlement. This record must always be referred to prior to the determination and payment of any final liquidation.

4-4.6. Shippers Record. For control purposes, the total recorded for all shippers in a given month must be in absolute agreement with the liquidation record insofar as metallurgical information is concerned. Financial records for that particular month double check the cost totals. Any variance is investigated, and adjusting entries are made. Since this record is a memorandum account, such control and reconciliation can be made at convenient times, say each month, second month, or each calendar quarter, but in no case should it be less frequent than every six months.

4-5. INVENTORY PROCEDURES

Uranium ore stocks are recorded on the basis of scale weights taken on scales currently certified by State inspection. Individual lot assays are recorded under a system of metallurgical and financial control. Such ore stocks are of comparatively low economic value, and accurate physical inventory is neither feasible nor warranted. Granted that accurate physical measurement of piles can be made, the prime requisite of a physical inventory is value, and this can only be determined by resampling the entire stock. The cost of such resampling for normal inventory purposes is not justified under the circumstances. Therefore, book values are accepted as inventory values. A visual inventory is taken to discover any gross discrepancies.

4-6. DISPOSITION OF ORE STOCKS

Ores are stockpiled pending the time they are required for processing. As ore stocks so acquired are needed for processing, they are released to the AEC upon written request and are physically moved directly to the process mill specified by the AEC.

Ores transferred from stockpiles to process mills are weighed and grab-sampled to obtain a check against tonnages and contents recorded in the accounts. Weathering, leaching, and weight losses due to movement should be negligible when stockpiles are properly stored, i.e. not subjected to excessive rainfalls, floods, or prolonged storage. As an example of experience, samples taken from 250,000 tons of ore which had been in storage $2\frac{1}{2}$ to 3 years gave an over-all gain of 1 percent in wet weight, 2 percent in dry weight, and a uranium content loss of 0.6 percent. The ore had been crushed to a maximum of 2 in. and stored on soft uncompacted bare ground.

ORE CONCENTRATION*

4-7. INTRODUCTION

Ore receipt and the subsequent concentration in the milling operation, packaging, and delivery of the uranium concentrate to the AEC require a very careful and exact system of metallurgical accounting and record keeping of the mineral content of the material handled, whatever its state or location, as it is moved processwise through the system from receiving pad to shipping van. The various steps to be so accounted for are:

1. Ore receiving.
2. Crushing and sampling.
3. Leaching and precipitation.
4. Packaging and shipping.

Throughout each of these steps material control is maintained by a combination of chemical assay, weight, and other measurement. Strict adherence to these controls prevents errors that might cause costly misrepresentations as to true quantities involved.

4-8. ORE RECEIVING

Material control of ore receipts is by ore lot; each lot is composed of one or more delivered loads, either railroad or truck. The weighed ore is dumped on a receiving pad in an area specifically set aside for the particular lot and shipper. Each lot is strictly separated from other lots and is plainly marked with a stake bearing all data physically identifying the lot and tying it in with the records in the metallurgical office, the laboratory, and the operating divisions.

Before each load of ore is dumped onto the receiving pad, a laboratory representative takes a sample for moisture determination.

* G. L. Hankinson, The Anaconda Company, Grants, New Mexico. The author wishes to acknowledge the assistance of A. K. Veeder, T. R. Beck, and A. J. Fitch in the preparation of this material.

4-9. CRUSHING AND SAMPLING

As ore is required by the mill, individual lots are scooped up from the receiving pad, crushed to the desired size and passed through a mechanical sampling mill. The entire system is carefully cleaned out after passage of each ore lot to avoid any possibility of contamination of a subsequent batch.

The crushed ore is deposited in fine-ore bins and held there for disposition to the concentration mills. A detailed book record is kept of the weights, by lot, of the ores remaining in each individual bin. Individual bin sheets show daily beginning inventories, receipts, transfers to mills, and ending inventories. Data recorded include wet and dry tonnage, percentage of uranium content, and the calculated pounds of uranium content. The receipts are recorded from a *daily crushing-plant report,* which shows the lot numbers of all tonnage crushed daily and deposited in the various bins. The transfers to the mills are recorded on the basis of daily weightometer weights adjusted to weekly and monthly observed and estimated bin inventories. Transfers to the mill are computed on a bin first-in, first-out basis, by lots.

At the close of each month's accounting period, the bins are measured for inventory purposes. Mill material balance is greatly affected by these inventory calculations and every precaution must be taken to ensure the accuracy of these figures. The bin capacities are known, as are also the densities of the various types of ores; bin measurements are of empty space, the difference between bin capacity and the empty space representing ore volume. This calculation of each bin inventory is checked against the book figure as proof against unreasonable discrepancies.

The sample obtained by the mechanical sampling mill is sent to the laboratory where it is divided into four pulps. One of these pulps is analyzed by the laboratory and the others are distributed to the shipper, the AEC, and the umpire (if necessary). The lot number assigned to the ore is the identifying code for handling lot samples in the laboratory.

Upon completion of the chemical assay, results are recorded on the *weight and assay certificate.* The chief chemist signs the certificate and returns it to the metallurgical accounting department. This certificate, on which has been recorded all pertinent information necessary for identification—i.e. wet weight, percentage of moisture, dry weight, and assay percentages of mineral content—is now complete and ready for posting in the various metallurgical ledgers and reports.

4-10. LEACHINGS AND PRECIPITATION

Two distinct chemical processes are used to concentrate the uranium contained in the ore feed to the mill. The particular process used depends upon the nature of the ore to be processed. Each depends upon leaching the uranium from the crushed ore, in one case using carbonate liquor and in the other, acid. The following sections describe each process and the material control procedures adopted for each.

4-10.1. Carbonate-Leach Mill: *Process.* The first step in this process is the leaching of the finely ground ore with carbonates to put the uranium into solution for later filtering separation (see Fig. 4-8). Two types of filters

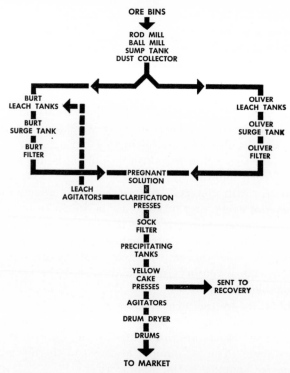

ORE BINS

ROD MILL
BALL MILL
SUMP TANK
DUST COLLECTOR

BURT
LEACH TANKS

OLIVER
LEACH TANKS

BURT
SURGE TANK

OLIVER
SURGE TANK

BURT
FILTER

OLIVER
FILTER

PREGNANT
SOLUTION

LEACH
AGITATORS — CLARIFICATION
PRESSES

SOCK
FILTER

PRECIPITATING
TANKS

YELLOW
CAKE
PRESSES ——→ SENT TO
RECOVERY

AGITATORS

DRUM DRYER

DRUMS

TO MARKET

FIG. 4-8 Carbonate-leach mill flow diagram.

are used, and therefore two sets of leach tanks are used to provide two different feeds for these filters. Neither leaching section has any tails or accountable losses and both are fully contained units.

Two filtering units are used in this process. Burt Filters each work on a batch of leach-ore pulp, filter-washing it with three different wash solutions and finally discharging the repulped ore solids portion to waste ponds. This discharged ore carries very little uranium out with it. Oliver Filters provide a continuous process, separating solids from the uranium solution. Three washes are used, the solids being discharged from the last filter. These solids carry only a small amount of uranium to the tailings or waste ponds.

The pregnant filtrate, which carries the bulk of the uranium from the filters, is sent to the next step in the mill, the precipitating section. Here the pregnant solutions from the two filters are combined, clarified in filter presses, and sent to the precipitating tanks. The sludge (solids) from the clarification presses is returned to the mill entrance point for rerunning. By chemical batch process in these tanks, the uranium is precipitated out of solution as yellow cake (a crude uranate). The entire precipitated load is then filtered through a press, and the resulting cake is ready for drying and barreling for shipment. The solution from the press is almost barren of uranium and is sent back for use in the milling processes.

Material Control. Material control is provided by month-end inventories which establish beginning and ending in-process figures. The necessary sampling and measuring is done at the end of the night shift on the last day of each month or between six and seven A.M. on the first day of the following month. Adjustments, to input figures, are made for dust losses between the ore bins and the rod mills and possible weightometer discrepancies and possible moisture differences.

The determination of inventory quantities in the carbonate-leach mill is outlined below.

1. GRINDING CIRCUIT (quantity fixed): Uranium content based on assays of last lots treated.
2. LEACH TANKS: Solids assay is determined from assays of the last lots put in. Solution assay is determined from assays of pregnant solution samples.
3. SURGE TANKS: Volume is determined by a depth measurement. A density measurement is used to convert volume to weight, and a uranium assay is made on a solution sample.
4. BURT FILTERS (fixed tonnage solids in each, unless filters are discharging or are down): Plant record shows in which stage each filter is operating at inventory time. Each wash solution is measured when put in. The applicable day's tails assay is used on solids, and the applicable day's filtrate assay is used on each solution.
5. OLIVER FILTERS (fixed tonnage solids if operating): The percent solids in the surge tank is used to obtain solution weight. Solids assay is determined by the tails assay and the solution assay is determined by a sample assay.
6. WASH TANKS: Wash and filtrate tanks have gauges on their sides or are measured with a stick. The fixed volume tons per foot of depth, are converted to solution weights with reported densities.
7. SOLUTION TANKS: All solution tanks, except the precipitating tanks, have side gauges and are calculated in the same way as the wash tanks.
8. CLARIFICATION PRESS AND SUMP TANK: The sump tank is measured for depth and is calculated as above for wash tanks. Any inventory in the press is considered to be included in the sump-tank inventory.

9. PRECIPITATING TANKS: If the tank is being filled, the side gauge is used and inventory is calculated as with other tanks. If the tank is riding, the book inventory of solids and solutions which carries actual assays is used. If the tank is being emptied, book inventory is used to include this and the press portion.

When all measurements and assays have been received, the mill superintendent prepares a detailed accounting for all uranium contained in-process. A consolidated report is then turned over to the metallurgical accounting department for a determination of the carbonate mill material balance.

4-10.2. Acid-Leach Mill: *Process.* After passing through a grinding circuit, the ore is leached with sulfuric acid to put the uranium into solution before the classifier section separates the sands from the solution and sends the sand tails to waste (Fig. 4-9). The solution is then mixed with the proper reagents before being run through a series of banks of resin-in-pulp tanks. By the time the solution has gone through these banks, most of the uranium has been deposited on the resin; the resultant stripped solution is sent to tails with the classifier waste before being sent to the waste ponds.

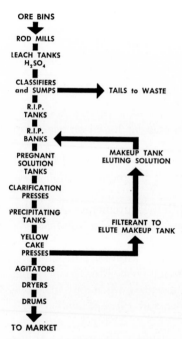

ORE BINS
ROD MILLS
LEACH TANKS H₂SO₄
CLASSIFIERS and SUMPS → TAILS to WASTE
R.I.P. TANKS
R.I.P. BANKS
PREGNANT SOLUTION TANKS   MAKEUP TANK ELUTING SOLUTION
CLARIFICATION PRESSES
PRECIPITATING TANKS   FILTERANT TO ELUTE MAKEUP TANK
YELLOW CAKE PRESSES
AGITATORS
DRYERS
DRUMS
TO MARKET

FIG. 4.9 Acid-leach mill flow diagram. (R.I.P. = Resin-In-Pulp)

The resin in the resin-in-pulp section is in suspended baskets that continually rise and fall slowly in the tanks to present a greater surface to the uranium solution as it circulates. This resin is an ion exchange material similar to that used in commercial water softeners. It scavenges the uranium from the solution, replacing the chloride ions in the resin. After a bank of resin baskets has been loaded with uranium, a chloride solution is run through it to elute or unload the uranium, replacing it on the resin with the stronger chloride ions. The eluted solution is then a pregnant solution ready for precipitation. The unloaded pulp carrying original sulfate ions and replaced chloride ions goes out to tails.

The pregnant solution is clarified in a filter press, the solids being returned to the grinding circuit. The clarified solution is then precipitated in batches with caustic to bring the uranium back to a solid state. The precipitated load is then separated in a filter press, the barren solution returning to the resin-in-pulp section to be used as an eluting solution. The solids (or yellow cake) are dried on a rotating drum and barreled for shipment and sale.

ACID MILL
MONTHLY INVENTORY
SAMPLE CHECK SHEET

Date:

	Mill	Sample Preparation Dept.			Bucking Room		Gen. Lab.
	S=Sample NS=No Sample	Rcvd frm Mill	Delivered To		Rcvd	Del'd	Rcvd
			Buck Rm.	Gen. Lab.			
Classifier Feed -							
Total (% U_3O_8)							
Soluble (% U_3O_8)							
R I P Rinse Soln.							
Washed Solids (% U_3O_8)							
Solution (g/1 U_3O_8)							
I X Resin - cc Resin cc Eluate							
Sample #1							
#2							
R I P Solution -							
Washed Solids (% U_3O_8)							
Solution (g/1 U_3O_8)							
Eluting Solution -							
Washed Solids (% U_3O_8)							
Solution (g/1 U_3O_8)							
Unclarified Preg. Solution -							
Washed Solids (% U_3O_8)							
Solution (g/1 U_3O_8)							
Clarification Press Sludge - % Moisture							
Eluting Makeup Soln - (g/1 U_3O_8)							
Precip. Tk. #1 - (g/1 U_3O_8)							
#2 "							
#3 "							
Y C Press Filtrate Samp #1 (g/1 U_3O_8)							
#2 "							
#3 "							
#4 "							
Dust Collection Tank - (g/1 U_3O_8)							
Barren Filtrate Tank - (g/1 U_3O_8)							

Mill Supt.

Fig. 4-10 Acid-mill monthly inventory—sample check sheet. (IX = ion exchange)

Material Control. As in the carbonate mill, month-end inventory measurements, samples, and calculations of mineral content are necessary to the control of the material introduced to, and processed by, the acid-mill circuit. Here also, inventorying is done just before the end of the last shift of the last day of each month.

MONTHLY INVENTORY

WORK SHEET

Agitator Building   Taken at 6/30 AM, Date:

Bin Inventory:	Bin No.	Wet Tons	Lot No.	To Sect.
	1			
Report visual inventory of Bin content at 6/30 AM.	2			
Indicate the Lot No. of the ore and the Section	3			
to which it is being fed at 6/30 AM.	4			
	5			

Grinding Circuit:		Section	Condition
Indicate whether Rod Mills are operating or not.		West	
		East	

Leach Tanks:		Section	No. of Full Tks.	Avg. % Solids
Take sample of the pulp overflow from each leach tank				
to determine % solids. Report average % solids for all		West		
tanks for each Section.		East		

Classifier Feed: (500 cc/Classifier)		Section	No. in Service	Avg. % Solids
Take sample of feed going to each classifier and composite		West		
in one sample bucket. Report average % solids.		East		

R-I-P Rinse Solution: (100 cc/V.T.)	Section	Volume Ft.	Vol Ton/ Ft.	Total Vol. Tons	Density
To correctly sample each tank; measure	West		3.53		
volume of solution in ft., multiply by V. T/Ft.	East		3.53		
indicated to get total vol. tons, and take					
100 cc of sample per each vol. ton.					

Composite such sample from each tank in one sample bucket. Report density of sample.

R-I-P Solution: (10 cc/V.T.)	Tank	Section	Volume Ft.	Vol.Ton/ Ft.	Total Vol. Ton
Take Duplicate Sample. To correctly sample	RIP Feed	West		3.53	
each tank; measure volume of solution in ft.,		East		3.53	
multiply by V. T/Ft. indicated to get total	RIP Slime	West		3.53	
vol. tons, and take 10 cc of sample per		East		3.53	
each vol. ton. Composite such sample from					
each tank in one sample bucket. (This					

Sample will later be composited with "R-I-P Solution" sample taken in IX Building)

Remarks: _____
_____
_____
_____

Foreman

Fig. 4-11   Monthly inventory—work sheet.

Uranium in process undergoes progressive stages of treatment, starting in its original ore state and terminating in an acceptable yellow cake product. It originates in a solid phase and passes through other physical phases, including pulp phases, solution phases, and a special phase involving resin. When a list of the samples to be taken and storage units to be measured is being made, note must be taken of the particular phase in which the uranium is contained. Each of these phases must be further classified into type and grade.

In a continuous flow process it is imperative that all inventory samplings and measurements be accurately made and executed as rapidly as possible. Hence, consideration must also be given to the manner in which tanks and other storage units are grouped. As will be noted from a study of the acid-mill sampling check list (Fig. 4-10), pulps and solutions of identical types exist in separate sections of the plant. For the sake of a rapid inventory, however, these must be sampled and measured separately.

To ensure that the required number and types of samples from each section are obtained and that they are routed to and from the proper agencies, a sampling check list has been prepared from which the mill superintendent may trace the entire procedure.

It can be noted from the detailed monthly-inventory work sheet (Fig. 4-11) that the total volume of the materials in each tank of pulp or solution determines the volume of sample to be obtained. This method of volume sampling on a unit basis allows for direct compositing of separate samples.

Since assay of solids is on a weight basis and assay of solution is on a volume basis, density measurements are obtained for samples taken from heterogeneous solution-solid content. When the assay is determined for both solid and volume fractions, the total uranium content of the mixture is calculated.

Inventory sampling of plant resin merits special discussion. Although basically a solid, the resin is measured on a volume basis (wet settled resin). For a determination of uranium retained on the resin, a measured volume is taken from the inventory sample, and this is very thoroughly and effectively eluted or "stripped" of its uranium by a standard eluting solution. The amount of uranium removed from this measured resin sample is calculated from the volume and assay of the eluting solution used. Total uranium inventory of the plant resin can then be calculated from the total volume of resin known to be in service at the time of inventory.

The check sheet has been invaluable in safeguarding the delivery of samples through the various departments.

Upon completion of all calculations for the uranium content in each section, a special inventory report sheet is filled out which indicates the net uranium in each section and summarizes the total plant uranium inventory. This report is sent to the metallurgical accounting department. Similar detailed inventory work sheets are provided for the other sections of the plant.

4-11. PACKAGING AND SHIPPING

The precipitated product from both carbonate- and acid-leach mills is separated in filter presses, agitated with water, and then placed on a rotating drying drum.   As the drum revolves, the yellow cake falls off and down into the steel drums in which this product is shipped.

The inventory of material in the presses, agitators, and dryers is obtained from a book record of precipitate loads.   Whatever cleanup there may be is drummed, weighed, and sampled for the same purpose.

Tare weights are stenciled on the shipping drums under the supervision of a representative of the AEC.   Loaded drums are then weighed, and the gross weight is automatically stamped on a prepared ticket showing all information needed by the accounting office to control production and shipment totals. Each drum is sampled for moisture and uranium content and when assayed, an assay and moisture report is given to the office staff.   After careful compilation of dry weights, drum by drum, the drum samples are composited to give a uranium assay for the entire lot being prepared for shipment.

After sampling has been completed, the drums are covered with steel lids which are fastened with steel rings and bolts.   Each ring is then sealed as a precaution against tampering, and the drum is weighed.

Drums comprised in a shipment lot are stenciled with the corresponding lot number and the gross, tare, and net weights.   Shipment is via locked motor trailer, and the loading of lots is done under the supervision of a representative from the metallurgical accounting office.   The truck driver carries with him an advice of the shipment, a carbon copy of which is receipted by the receiving agent and returned to the shipping office.

4-12. SUMMARY

Throughout the entire operation, a close, detailed recording is made of every movement of the material for which an accounting must be made.   Let us now take this material control step by step.

1. ORE RECEIPTS: A scale ticket is prepared for every load received.   Information from scale tickets and sample assays is recorded on a *weight and assay certificate*, which provides the basis for the lots of ore receipts subsequently crushed, sampled, and deposited in the fine ore bins.
2. FINE ORE: A monthly statement is prepared showing, lot by lot, all material crushed, sampled, and made ready for either the acid- or carbonate-leach mill.
3. PLANT OPERATIONS MATERIAL BALANCE: This is a mill material control report and shows, in pounds of uranium content, material received and treated and reflects the Book-Physical Inventory Difference.
4. PLANT OPERATIONS PRODUCTION REPORT: This report shows production for the accounting period.

In the final accounting, there is material control that, location by location, itemizes the amount of uranium for which the mill is accountable.   The final inventory report shows: (1) ore on the receiving pad, (2) ore in the fine-ore bins, (3) material in process in the carbonate-leach mill, (4) material in process in the acid-leach mill, (5) finished product, or yellow cake, at the plant site, and (6) finished product, or yellow cake, in transit to the purchaser.

CONCENTRATE PROCUREMENT *

All uranium concentrates produced west of the Mississippi River are received in Grand Junction by Lucius Pitkin, Inc, for sampling, assaying, and storage. Facilities consist of a concentrate sampling plant (Fig. 4-12) with storage and

FIG. 4-12   Uranium-concentrate sampling plant, Grand Junction, Colo.

railroad-car loading equipment and an assay laboratory.   The purpose of this operation is to produce the lot weights, moistures, samples, and assays neces- sary before payment can be made to the concentrating mills.

Concentrates packed in pretared 55-gal removable-head steel drums are received direct from the mills.   The sampled uranium concentrates are held in storage pending rail shipment to refineries.

4-13. CONCENTRATE RECEIVING AND SAMPLING PROCEDURES

All drums used at the mill for packaging uranium concentrates destined for Lucius Pitkin are tared empty by a Lucius Pitkin representative at the mill.

* J. N. Latimer and H. C. Jackson, Western Uranium Project, Lucius Pitkin, Inc.

The tare weight of the empty drum is painted on the side and lid of the drum. Net wet weight of the contents of these drums runs between 300 and 1300 lb.

Incoming shipments, by truck and rail, are received at the sampling plant unloading dock. Drums are unloaded by lift truck and placed in storage until

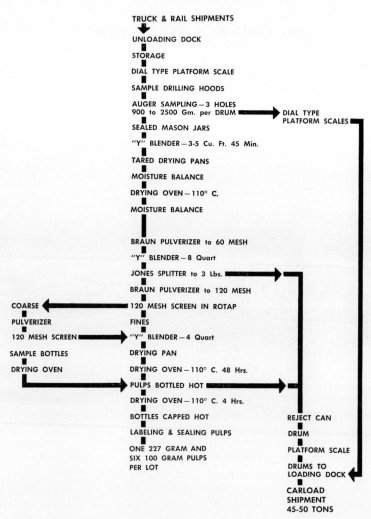

TRUCK & RAIL SHIPMENTS

UNLOADING DOCK

STORAGE

DIAL TYPE PLATFORM SCALE

SAMPLE DRILLING HOODS

AUGER SAMPLING — 3 HOLES
900 to 2500 Gm. per DRUM ━━━▶ DIAL TYPE
PLATFORM SCALES

SEALED MASON JARS

"Y" BLENDER — 3-5 Cu. Ft. 45 Min.

TARED DRYING PANS

MOISTURE BALANCE

DRYING OVEN — 110° C.

MOISTURE BALANCE

BRAUN PULVERIZER to 60 MESH

"Y" BLENDER — 8 Quart

JONES SPLITTER to 3 Lbs.

BRAUN PULVERIZER to 120 MESH

COARSE ◀━━━ 120 MESH SCREEN IN ROTAP

PULVERIZER

120 MESH SCREEN ━━━▶ FINES

SAMPLE BOTTLES   "Y" BLENDER — 4 Quart

DRYING OVEN   DRYING PAN

DRYING OVEN — 110° C. 48 Hrs.

PULPS BOTTLED HOT ━━━▶

DRYING OVEN — 110° C. 4 Hrs.

BOTTLES CAPPED HOT   REJECT CAN

LABELING & SEALING PULPS   DRUM

ONE 227 GRAM AND   PLATFORM SCALE
SIX 100 GRAM PULPS
PER LOT   DRUMS TO
LOADING DOCK

CARLOAD
SHIPMENT
45-50 TONS

Fig. 4-13 Mill products sampling—flow sheet.

sampled. A lot may consist of from 10 to 75 drums and have a wet weight of 4000 to 40,000 lb. The general flow of material is illustrated in Fig. 4-13.

When a lot is sampled, the individual drums are weighed, and the gross and tare weights are recorded. A 2000-lb-capacity dial type platform scale with a 500-lb dial is used for weighing, and the weights are recorded to the nearest one-half pound. The drums are then lined up in front of the sampling hoods (Fig. 4-14), the drum lids are removed, and auger samples are taken from each drum by means of an electric drill with a 36-in. long by 1⅜-in. diameter ship auger attached. Three auger samples from each drum are caught in a specially constructed stainless steel pan and immediately placed in a one-half gallon sealed mason jar. Samples of 900 to 2500 gm are taken from each drum, the quantity varying with the density of the material. After auger sampling of a lot has been completed, the drum heads are replaced, and the drums are again weighed and moved to the outdoor loading dock.

FIG. 4-14 Sample cutting line, uranium-concentrate sampling plant.

The individual drum samples for the lot are quickly emptied into either a 3- or a 5-cu-ft twin-shell blender, the size depending on the total volume of the composite lot sample. Although volume compositing is not a generally acceptable procedure, check-sampling comparisons between the volume compositing and weighted-compositing methods have been carried out in large numbers on every type of uranium-mill concentrate received for over two years. Agreement between the two procedures generally has been within the normal precision of the moisture and assay procedures, except in a few rare cases where the moisture content of the concentrates has been so high as to cause the material to be of a sticky consistency.

The composited sample is then mixed in the blender for 1 hour. A typical mixing room is shown in Fig. 4-15.

After mixing has been completed, the blender is stopped in a vertical position, a large sample bucket is placed under the outlet, and the outlet gate opened. Four blender samples of 2000 to 3000 gm each are taken with a scoop as quickly as possible from the falling stream; the bottom gate of the blender is closed between samplings. These samples are sealed immediately in individual mason jars. The remainder of the composite sample is placed in the lot rejects drum.

The sealed samples are taken to the moisture weighing room, placed in tared stainless steel drying pans, weighed, and dried to a point of minimum weight at 110°C. A view of the drying room is presented in Fig. 4-16. The

Fig. 4-15 Mixing room, uranium-concentrate sampling plant.

percent weight losses shown by the four samples are averaged and used as the lot moisture.

4-13.1. Sample Grinding and Drying Operations. After being dried, the four samples are taken to the bucking room (Fig. 4-17), ground in a Braun pulverizer to about 60 mesh, combined and mixed for 15 minutes in an 8-qt twin-shell blender, split down to about $2\frac{1}{2}$ lb in a Jones splitter, and again ground in a Braun pulverizer to 120 mesh. This sample is then screened through 120-mesh screens in a Rotap, any oversize material being reground and screened; and then the total sample is mixed for 15 minutes in a 4-qt twin-shell blender. The blended sample is placed in a drying pan and dried

FIG. 4-16 Section of drying-oven room, uranium-concentrate sampling plant.

FIG. 4-17 View of bucking room, uranium-concentrate sampling plant.

for 48 hours at 110°C.   Clean ½-pt mason jars are also put in the drying oven and dried for 4 hours at 110°C.   The sample is removed from the oven and six 100-gm samples and one 227-gm sample are weighed into the mason jars as rapidly as possible.   The uncapped jars are immediately replaced in the drying oven for 4 hours at 110°C, then capped hot, sealed, and labeled. Sampling rejects of the lot are put into a tared 30-gal drum, weighed, marked with the lot number, and placed in outdoor storage with the lot from which they came.

All sampling equipment and work areas are kept as clean as possible.   Bucking room equipment is blown out with compressed air and washed.   Work benches and hoods are frequently scoured.   Drying pans and jars are washed and dried after each use.   All work-area floors in the sampling, mixing, and bucking rooms are scrubbed at the end of each shift.

The men working on uranium-concentrate sampling are provided with clean caps, safety shoes, coveralls, and cotton gloves daily.   Leather gloves are also provided for certain jobs.   Regular wash-up and bathing periods are required daily.   Respirators are required at all locations where dusting may occur. Medical examinations are provided every 12 months and frequent urinalyses for uranium are also made.   Radiation hazard has been proved negligible through tests with film badges, dosimeters, and checks with radiation counting equipment.

An extensive dust-collection system is used at all points where dust may be generated.   The bag houses for the systems are cleaned at intervals, the dust being weighed, drummed, and placed in storage for shipment.   The quantity of dust collected is relatively small, averaging about 0.005 percent of the uranium sampled.

4-13.2. Distribution of Samples.   Of the seven samples produced for a lot of concentrates, one sample is sent to the shipper and two samples are sent to the assay laboratory.   One 100-gm and one 227-gm sample accompany the lot to the refinery, and the remaining samples are held for umpire and reserve. A *weight and assay certificate* for the lot originates at the Grand Junction Sampling Plant, is sent to the Assay Laboratory for entry of assay information, is taken to the office for duplication and recording, and then is forwarded to the Grand Junction Operations Office.   Assay comparisons are made with the shipper, and, if they are within the U_3O_8 contract splitting limits, the lot is liquidated.   If comparisons are outside the splitting limits, a lot sample is sent to the National Bureau of Standards (NBS) in Washington, D. C., for umpire.   Specification assays that must be met by the shipper are for U_3O_8, V_2O_5, PO_4, molybdenum, boron, halogens (excluding fluorine), fluorine, copper, arsenic, CO_2, SO_4, and H_2O.   Iron and sodium determinations are also made on the lot samples.

4-14. CONCENTRATE ASSAYING

The assaying of uranium lot samples for U_3O_8 is the most important determination made on these samples. The procedure consists in a mixed acid
digestion of the weighed sample, separation of the hydrogen sulfide group by
thioacetamide, a cupferron chloroform extraction, removal of remaining organic
material, a hydrochloric-hydrobromic acid fuming, dilution and aliquoting for
reduction in an amalgamated zinc reductor, aeration, and titration with standard potassium dichromate solution using sodium diphenylamine sulfonate indicator. A moisture determination is also made on each lot sample, the moisture samples being weighed out at the same time the samples are weighed for
assay. The assay sample weight is later calculated to the dry basis by use
of the result from the corresponding moisture determination.

Duplicate aliquots are prepared from each lot sample and determinations
for U_3O_8 are carried out. Results on the duplicate determinations corrected
for any moisture found in the sample are expected to check within 0.10 percent U_3O_8. If this precision is not obtained, the work is repeated. Sample
grades range from 60 to 90 percent U_3O_8.

Assays for boron, molybdenum, and arsenic are run spectrographically; the
remaining specification assays are run by usual wet methods. A publication
describing analytical procedures used by the Lucius Pitkin assay laboratory
is available from the Office of Technical Services.[2]

4-15. COMPARISON OF SHIPPER AND RECEIVER DATA

Since the assays of all concentrate lots are compared with the shipper's
assays, and, in the case of umpires, with results from NBS, a continuing external check on laboratory work is available. The Evaluation Group, discussed in Sec. 4-2.2, carries out an internal check program for the laboratory
and evaluates new analytical procedures. This group made a study of the
determination of U_3O_8 content in concentrate lot samples and obtained an
estimate of the precision of the determination made in the assay laboratory.
Thirty standard uranium-concentrate samples containing products from seven
mills were assayed by eight chemists, who made a total of 79 individual determinations on the samples. The standard deviation of the results for each
sample was calculated; then the deviations were pooled, and a further calculation was made to determine the 95 percent confidence interval, which was
±0.09 percent U_3O_8 for this series of determinations.

The Evaluation Group carries out studies of all phases of the uranium concentrate sampling procedure, with particular attention to check-sampling complete lots of concentrate from the various mills. The tabulation in Table 4.4
shows results on check-sampling 10 lots of uranium concentrate from the same
mill. The lots were not reweighed before check-sampling, otherwise the com-

plete sampling procedure was followed for both the purchase and check samples.

TABLE 4.4.   DEVIATION OF CHECK-SAMPLING RESULTS
FOR 10 LOTS OF URANIUM CONCENTRATE

Lot No.	Net Wet Weight, lb	Purchase U_3O_8 Contained, lb	Check U_3O_8 Contained, lb	Diff. U_3O_8, lb	Diff. 10,000 lb Wet Lot Weight Basis, lb
1	9,860.00	7,956.95	7,951.36	+5.59	+5.67
2	10,031.50	8,194.70	8,192.20	+2.50	+2.49
3	10,390.00	8,480.70	8,487.70	−7.00	−6.74
4	10,160.50	8,249.54	8,238.18	+11.36	+11.18
5	9,424.00	7,606.25	7,601.69	+4.56	+4.84
6	9,677.00	7,879.23	7,880.28	−1.05	−1.08
7	12,271.50	9,794.60	9,773.17	+21.43	+17.46
8	12,669.50	9,960.23	9,933.28	+26.95	+21.27
9	11,598.50	9,285.23	9,285.18	+0.05	+0.04
10	11,002.50	8,509.60	8,520.95	−11.35	−10.32
Average		8,591.70	8,586.40	9.18	8.11

The standard deviation calculated for the 10,000-lb wet lot basis is 7.4 lb. If a t factor of 2.093 for 19 degrees of freedom at the 95 percent probability level is used, a confidence interval of ±15.5 lb of U_3O_8 per 10,000 lb of net wet concentrate weight is obtained for the sampling.

4-16. ACCOUNTING RECORDS

Accounting for SS material is restricted to quantities only: i.e. no dollar values are carried in these records.

The following records are maintained to account for the receipt, storage, and disposition of all uranium concentrates delivered:

1. Receiving Record
2. Lot Ledger
3. Transfer-Out Record
4. Inventory Record
5. Sample Ledger
6. Assay Record

4-16.1. Receiving Record.   This record is a loose-leaf binder in which are recorded all receipts of concentrates, all essential information as to name of shipper, lot number, weights (gross, tare, and net wet weight), percentage of H_2O, net dry weight, assay, and contents provisionally determined by the shipper and reported on his shipping advice, or manifest.

These advices, or shippers' manifests, are generally received at the same time that the shipment arrives or shortly thereafter. As final weights and assays become available, they are recorded in a space provided opposite the shipper's provisional shipping information with plus or minus adjustments posted in total to the shipper's provisional deliveries in the current month in which the final weights and assays become available.

4-16.2. Lot Ledger. This is a loose-leaf ledger in which are recorded receipts, by shipper and shipper's lot number, and the removal or disposition of such lots in detail.

4-16.3. Transfer-Out Record. This is a loose-leaf record in which all lot removals are recorded. No removals are made except upon written direction signed by a responsible official of the AEC.

Transfers out are usually made prior to the determination of final assays. Such transfers are recorded on a provisional basis; i.e. the producing mill or shipper's weights and assays are used as a provisional basis. These are adjusted to final weights and assays when they become available. If such adjustments are not available within the month, necessary adjustments are made in the month in which they are determined.

4-16.4. Inventory Record. This is a loose-leaf record subdivided into sections for each type of material with a breakdown of amounts on a provisional and/or final basis.

Loose-leaf inventory sheets are used at the point of physical check or inventory. Each sheet is headed with the shipper's name, lot number, and product type. All product is contained in steel drums that bear the shipper's name, lot number, and individual drum number. All drums are physically inspected, and the checker calls the identifying particulars as he encounters each numbered drum. The checker or recorder at that time marks such drum numbers as being on hand. Complete physical inventory of all drums is made during one continuous period, and no movement is permitted in the stockpile area while inventorying is in process. When physical inventory of concentrate lots has been completed, a further physical inventory is made of sample residue, the dust in the collecting system at the sampling plant, ashes, and sweepings, all of which are weighed, assayed, and reported in inventory as material on hand as of June 30 and December 31 of each year. The drum inventory is then converted to pounds of uranium from the book records data. Book records are adjusted by entry to the Book-Physical Inventory Difference account on the basis of physical inventory at that time.

REFERENCES FOR CHAPTER 4

1. C. W. Sill and H. E. Peterson, Volumetric Determination of Milligram Quantities of Uranium, *Anal. Chem.*, 24:1175-1182, July 1952.
2. R. W. Langridge (comp.), *Grand Junction Operations Office Analytical Methods*, USAEC Report RMO-3001, Lucius Pitkin, Inc., 1957.

Part Three

MATERIALS PROCESSING

Chapter 5

FEED MATERIALS PROCESSING *

5-1. INTRODUCTION

After uranium ore is concentrated, it must be treated chemically to sub-stantially reduce its impurities and to produce a chemical form (uranium trioxide, UO_3) suitable for either fluorination to uranium tetrafluoride (UF_4) and reduction to uranium metal or for conversion to uranium hexafluoride (UF_6). Uranium metal is used mainly in reactors, and UF_6 is used as feed in the gaseous diffusion plants (Chapter 6). The purification, formation of UF_4, and reduction steps are commonly called "feed materials processing." The material management aspects of these operations as conducted at the Mallin-ckrodt Chemical Works are discussed in this chapter.

5-2. GENERAL PROCESS DESCRIPTION

5-2.1. Feed Material. Feed material consists of various ore concentrates which come from foreign and domestic sources. The concentrates are in the form of calcined and milled yellow cakes with an assay range of 15 to 70 per-cent uranium.

The foreign and certain domestic concentrates must be weighed, sampled, and analyzed for payment by the Atomic Energy Commission. Vendor's rep-resentatives observe this measuring in their interest. Some domestic materials have been weighed, sampled, and analyzed for payment prior to shipment. However, upon receipt these materials are generally again weighed, sampled, and analyzed. These measurements should be as accurate as those for pay-ment purposes.

5-2.2. Processes. The over-all material flow at Mallinckrodt is shown in Fig. 5-1 and briefly discussed below.

* M. N. Kuehn, Mallinckrodt Chemical Works, St. Louis, Mo. The author wishes to acknowledge the encouragement and assistance of William J. Shelley. His understanding of the problems involved greatly expedited the preparation of this chapter.

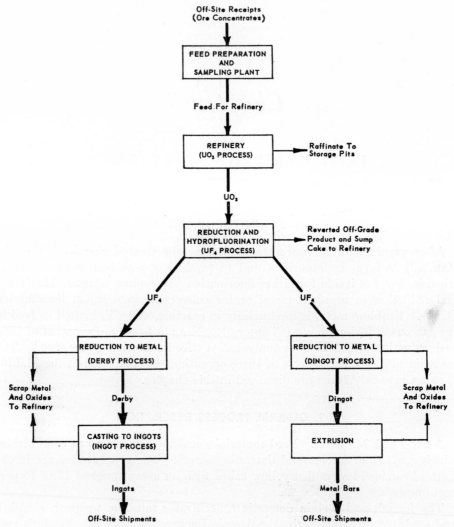

FIG. 5-1   Feed materials processing flow diagram.

Feed Preparation and Sampling.   Foreign and domestic ores and ore concentrates are sampled and prepared as feed for the refinery.

Refinery.   The refinery digests these prepared feeds in nitric acid.   This solution is then adjusted for acid and uranium content and purified by extraction into tributyl phosphate and reextraction into water.   The resultant pure aqueous solution of uranyl nitrate is denitrated to uranium trioxide.

Reducation and Hydrofluorination.   The uranium trioxide is reduced to uranium dioxide with hydrogen and then is hydrofluorinated with anhydrous hydrofluoric acid to uranium tetrafluoride.

Reduction to Derby Metal.   The uranium tetrafluoride is blended with magnesium metal, charged to a refractory-lined shell, capped, and placed in a furnace. The reaction, when appropriate times and temperatures are met, results in a solid piece of metal commonly called a "derby."

Casting. The derbies and other castable recycle metal are loaded into a graphite crucible, placed in a vacuum furnace, melted, and poured into graphite molds. The ingots produced in this fashion are then shipped to another facility for rolling and fabrication into slugs for reactor use.

Reduction to Dingot Metal. The reduction to dingot metal differs from the reduction to derby metal in that a "dingot" is 10 times as large as a derby. This massive piece of metal, commonly called a dingot is scalped to remove surface impurities and defects.

The scalped dingot is heated in an induction furnace and extruded into bars approximately the size of cast ingots. This process eliminates the casting operation and results in a metal of purer quality than that obtained in the cast ingots. The ingot-size bars are shipped to another facility for rolling and slug fabrication.

5-3. FEED PREPARATION AND SAMPLING PLANT

5-3.1. Process Description. The sampling plant (Fig. 5-2) includes facilities for sampling, preparing, and storing feed materials for the UO_3 refinery process.

FIG. 5-2 Mallinckrodt Chemical Works feed preparation and sampling plant.

Feed materials are received in containers of various size, primarily in 55-gal metal drums. The feed materials are grouped into lots, lot size varying

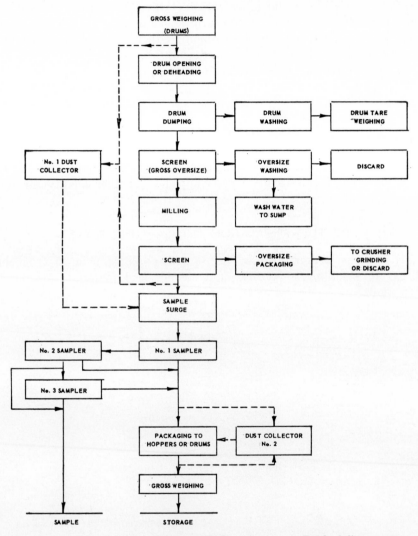

FIG. 5-3 Automatic sampling system flow diagram. Dashed lines represent the dust-collection system.

from a few drums to as many drums as are contained in one or more railroad cars. The vendor or AEC contractor gives a quantity of feed material a lot identity which is maintained through the sampling plant.

The process streams in the sampling plant are:

1. Sampling (automatic or auger).
2. Calcining.
3. Crushing.

Fig. 5-3 is a flow diagram of the automatic sampling system, and Fig. 5-4 is a composite flow diagram showing auger sampling, calcining, crushing, repackaging, and sump recovery systems.

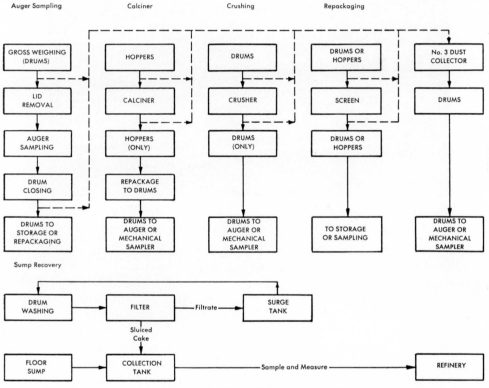

FIG. 5-4   Auger sampling, calcining, crushing, and repackaging systems flow diagram.   Dashed lines represent the dust-collection system.

Sampling. Sampling for payment and refinery-feed adjustment purposes can be done either by automatic (mechanical) sampling or by auger sampling. The automatic sampling system is used primarily for sampling large lots of material, whereas auger samples are taken from small lots or feed material unsuitable for automatic sampling. Automatic sampling is preferred because of its greater efficiency and accuracy.

FIG. 5-5 View of ticket-printing scale and conveyor. Note the drum-opening enclosure on the left.

(*a*) AUTOMATIC SAMPLING. The automatic sampling system consists of a series of three samplers splitting a falling stream of material. Drums of ore concentrates suitable for continuous automatic sampling (as determined from their point of origin, consignees analysis, or lot size) are transferred by fork truck from the storage pad to the feed preparation and sampling plant.

Drums are removed from the pallets individually by fork truck and placed on a conveyor that conveys them to a ticket-printing scale. Fig. 5-5 is an illustration of such a scale; the weight and drum number are printed on a ticket and recorded on a continuous tape by an integral printing mechanism.

After being weighed the drums are conveyed into the drum-opening equipment and then to the drum elevator. The drum elevator lifts the drums to a point where the ore concentrates can be unloaded to flow by gravity through the feed preparation equipment and samplers. When the drums have been emptied, they are conveyed on an enclosed roller conveyor into the drum washing and drying station.

The ore concentrates fall from the drums onto and through a 3-in. scalping screen into the unloading hopper. The oversize material is intermittently raked off the screen into a chute leading to a packaging station for oversize material.

The ore concentrates that pass through the screen flow by gravity to an impact mill which yields a screened product size of $\frac{3}{8}$ in. or less.

The screened ore concentrates fall by gravity directly into a surge hopper. A rotary valve is installed at the discharge end of the surge hopper to prevent sample classification and surging of the concentrate to the vibratory feeder that feeds the samplers. Three Galigher samplers are mounted in series in the duct into which the vibratory feeder discharges. Sampler 1 takes a cut of approximately 10 percent from the main feed stream. Each succeeding sampler cuts approximately 10 percent of the sample extracted by the preceding sampler; so the final sample is approximately 0.1 percent of the main feed stream. Provisions are made for bypassing the third sampler so that a sample of 1 percent for small lots can be obtained.

Samplers are electrically interlocked so that all parts start simultaneously, and if any part stops, all parts stop. The sample is collected in an airtight container to guard against exposure to atmospheric conditions. The main stream of ore concentrates, after passing through the samplers, is fed to a bucket elevator. From the bucket elevator the sampled ore flows by gravity either to a portable hopper filling station or to a drum packaging station (Fig. 5-6),

FIG. 5-6 Drum packaging conveyors and scales.

depending on its ultimate destination. The portable hoppers are double-cone self-standing hoppers. Filled hoppers are transported to a ticket-printing scale, where the weight is recorded on a ticket and continuous tape. After being weighed, the hoppers are transported to the storage pad until transfer to the refinery is requested.

Two dust collectors service the automatic sampling systems. The first collects the dusts generated from the start of the operation up to the first sampler. This dust is discharged to the sample surge hopper, since it represents unsampled material and must therefore be sampled. The second collects the dusts generated after sampling. This dust is discharged to one of the packaging stations.

(b) AUGER SAMPLING. Drums of feed material that are not to be sampled by the automatic sampling system are handled in the auger sampling station. Provision is made for positioning drums in the auger sampling station along the roller conveyor so that a sample can be taken from any part of the drum. When the drum is in position, the auger is lowered into the drum, and a sample is withdrawn and collected in a container. After being sampled the drums are transferred to the storage pad until needed.

The auger sampler is a motor-driven auger enclosed in a sheath. The auger is forced through the material in a drum and is then removed; the sample is discharged to a sample container.

Calcining. Some of the feed materials received contain ammonia and organic material in quantities large enough to interfere with the refinery process. These feeds require calcining before being sent to the refinery.

After the weights of filled hoppers have been recorded, the hoppers are transported to a bucket elevator, and the ore concentrate is fed to the calciner. The calciner, a gas-fired vertical multiple-hearth furnace, drives off the ammonia and organic material within 1 to 2 hours at temperatures between 700 and 1000°F. The calciner discharges the hot ore concentrates to a cooling screw conveyor where they are air-cooled before being discharged to a portable hopper.

Crushing. The crushing station is provided to crush recoverable materials that are too large to pass through the 3-in. scalping screen described above.

Material is crushed from a maximum 10-in. size to a product size of 1 in. Crushed material is discharged directly to 55-gal drums and returned to the sampling operation.

Sump Collection Recovery. The material collected in the sump collection tanks originates from the drum- and lid-washing station and from the washings from gross oversize materials. This wash water is recirculated through a filter. The cake collected on the filter is discharged to a reslurry tank. Periodically the slurry tank is sampled, the volume is measured, and the slurry is pumped to a tank in the refinery.

5-3.2. Measurements. The measurements made in this plant are weighing, sampling, and analyzing for uranium. In addition to the uranium analysis, the samples are also analyzed for other elements and impurities to determine the amenability of the material to the refinery process.

Each container is gross weighed to the nearest 0.5 lb on a ticket-printing scale. After the contents of the container have been emptied to the system, the empty container is washed, dried, and tare weighed to the nearest 0.25 lb on a ticket-printing scale. The net weight of the material received is then determined by subtracting the tare from the gross.

The sample obtained as previously described is delivered to the laboratory for analysis. The uranium analysis is a volumetric determination; this is applied against the weight of the material in computing total uranium received.

Sampled material, packaged in pretared portable hoppers, is gross weighed on a ticket-printing scale. The assay obtained from sampling is applied to the net weight for determination of total uranium contained in each hopper shipped to the refinery.

Many of the feeds to this plant represent materials previously weighed, sampled, and analyzed by other AEC contractors acting as official samplers for the United States. A statistical program has been designed to determine the reliability of the sampling performed by the shippers of materials. When agreement with the shipper is within satisfactory limits, Mallinckrodt will accept the shipper's sample but will reweigh the material and reanalyze the sample. The materials so accepted are repackaged directly from drums to portable hoppers for refinery use.

5-3.3. Statistical Control. The feed preparation and sampling plant is of prime importance to the material control of feed material processing. Here measurements are made of all materials entering the operation; errors in these measurements are reflected in the material balance. It is essential that no bias be allowed in these measurements and that the limits of error of the measurements be known. For this reason a statistical evaluation program was designed for the sampling system to correct any bias that might exist and to determine the limits of error of each measurement method.

Weighing. All scales used in the weighing operations are subjected to a continuous statistical evaluation program. Test weights in the range of the weight of the material normally weighed on the scales are applied at predetermined intervals during all weighing operations. When the difference between the scale reading and the test weights exceeds a statistically determined limit, the scale maintenance mechanic is called to make adjustments or repairs. All units weighed in the period between the time the scale went out of control and the prior check when the scale was in control are reweighed.

Control charts are maintained for each scale, which plot the weight differences between the scale reading and the test weights. In this manner small biases are detected when they occur, and adjustments to the scales can then be made.

Because errors are minimized and the bias in weights is controlled, the over-all effect of weight variances on the variance in uranium evaluation is negligible.

Sampling. Before this plant was operated on a production basis, a statistical evaluation program was designed to evaluate the two sampling systems involved. From past experience, the auger sampler was selected as the base with which the automatic sampler was to be compared.

(*a*) AUGER SAMPLING. Since the validity of samples obtained by auger sampling may be open to question because of possible material classification in the drums and the inability of an auger to remove a representative sample from material containing particle sizes approaching the width of the auger ribbon, an evaluation program was designed to test the auger sampler prior to the start-up of this plant. This program consisted in the following operations:

1. Two drums were randomly selected from each of two or more lots of each type feed.

2. Three auger samples were removed from each drum at prescribed positions in the drum. A template was made from a drum lid with three holes cut in the radius large enough to permit the auger sampler to enter. The samples were numbered one through three, three being in the center of the drum.

3. The contents of each drum were transferred to two empty drums, and the materials were blended by tumbling. The blended material was then transferred to the original containers. Extreme care was taken during these operations to prevent spillage and dust losses.

4. Three auger samples were then taken of the blended material, and the samples were identified by number as mentioned above.

Statistical analysis of the assays obtained from the above sampling yielded the following information:

1. Materials amenable to auger sampling without prior blending.

2. Bias between sampling locations in the drum.

3. Validity of auger sampling of unblended material.

(*b*) AUTOMATIC SAMPLER. The statistical evaluation of the automatic sampler consisted in the following program:

1. Five lots of material of each type found suitable for auger sampling were selected.

2. Two auger samples were removed from each drum from randomly selected positions in the drum. These drum samples were then blended into a lot sample.

3. The lot was then processed through the automatic sampling system, and the material was redrummed.

4. Two auger samples were removed from each drum of the redrummed material and blended into a lot sample.

5. The lot was again processed through the automatic sampling system.

All lot samples were dried to a constant weight under controlled humidity, and the dried samples were analyzed for uranium.

The statistical test made of the data accumulated was the t test for paired variates. It was found that for most materials the automatic sampling system provided excellent reproducibility of results.

From the statistical analysis of all data accumulated during the evaluation program, it was possible to arrive at limits of error in materials received. These limits of error are divided into the following increments:

1. Weighing
2. Sampling
3. Moisture determination
4. Assay determination

Statistically combining the uranium values computed for the above increments permits the establishment of limits of error for each lot processed and subsequently the limits of error for the material balance for this plant.

5-3.4. Collection and Flow of Data. The following are source documents for posting to the books of record:

Receipts. All transfer documents for materials received are supported by a *receiving ticket* and the *printed weight records* obtained in the plant. The *laboratory analytical report* supplies the assay for the computation of uranium contents.

Consumed. A *charge ticket* initiated at the time the material is charged to the sampling plant provides the record of materials consumed and removed from the raw material (or unprocessed material) inventory.

Produced. A printed weight card for each hopper provides a record of the materials produced. The card includes information relevant to the hopper number, lot number, and material type.

Shipments. An *internal move order* listing in detail the materials transferred to the refinery provides the record for shipments. Materials shipped off site are recorded on the official AEC transfer forms.

Postings of the receipt and shipment documents are made in a Transfer Journal, which is summarized at the close of each month for the preparation of the reports.

A ledger provides for posting lot detail of materials received, consumed, produced, shipped, and on inventory. In this operation, lot identity is maintained throughout the system; therefore one line in the detail ledger for each lot received is sufficient to show the required information.

In addition, a *perpetual inventory board* primarily used for process control is maintained in the plant office. One section of this board is restricted to lots of unprocessed materials. Cards representing each lot are prepared at time of receipt of material and are then hung on hooks provided for each type material. As materials are charged, the related cards are removed and placed on another section of the board under the appropriate process title to which the material is charged. As materials are produced, a card is prepared for each hopper and hung on the respective hopper number hook on another section of the board. As materials are shipped, the related hopper card is removed and hung on a hook representing shipments.

The status of the plant operations and inventory can be determined in a minimum of time by reference to this board. Daily *plant activity reports* for management are prepared in approximately 30 minutes by use of the perpetual inventory board.

At the end of each month a physical inventory is taken. Physical inventory is compared with the *perpetual inventory record,* and discrepancies are corrected either to the physical inventory when recounts disclose an error or to the *perpetual inventory record* when the physical inventory is correct.

The physical inventory is posted to the ending inventory for the over-all operation, and the material balance report for the feed preparation and sampling plant is prepared. Table 5.1 outlines the report procedure.

TABLE 5.1. REPORTING FORMAT FOR FEED PREPARATION AND SAMPLING PROCESS

Material	Beginning Inventory	Receipts	Shipments	Ending Inventory	Produced	Consumed
Raw material	A	B	C	D		E
Finished material	A	B	C	D	F	
Total	A	B	C	D	F	E
B-PID				G		G

5-3.5. Material Balance Report. The material balance report for the feed preparation and sampling process is divided into three categories: raw material, finished material, and B-PID (Table 5.1).

Under the raw- and finished-material categories are listed the various types of materials.

$$E = A + B - C - D$$
$$F = D + C - B - A \qquad (5.1)$$

G, ideally zero, can be either positive or negative and is determined by total, $(A + B) - (C + D)$ or by $E - F$.

In general, G does not exceed the limits of error associated with the measurements made of the materials handled in this operation, the principal criterion for satisfactory material control.

5-4. REFINERY

5-4.1. Process Description: *Feed Material.* The feed material used in the refinery process consists primarily of ore concentrates and recycle materials packaged into portable hoppers. The portable hoppers are the product from the feed preparation and sampling plant and have been weighed, sampled, and analyzed prior to movement to the refinery operations, as previously described.

The uranium value so determined is the value charged to the refinery process at the time the portable hoppers are transferred from the sampling plant storage area to the refinery feed-hopper storage area. No other measurements are made of the portable feed hoppers in the refinery, with the exception of a gross weight check when the hoppers are placed on the scales directly over the digestion tanks.

Uranium metal scrap not suitable for recasting is weighed, and an assay factor of 98 percent uranium is applied. A small metal-dissolving unit is included in the refinery operation to dissolve such metal with nitric acid.

Process. The refinery digests feed material in nitric acid and purifies the dissolved feeds through an extraction system. The resultant pure uranyl nitrate solution is then denitrated to UO_3. Fig. 5-7 represents schematically the process flow for UO_3 production.

Portable hoppers containing refinery feeds are transported to the refinery

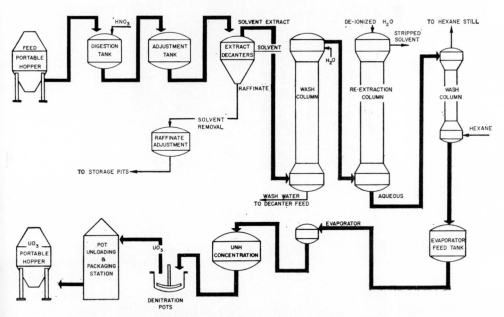

FIG. 5-7   Refinery flow diagram.

from the storage pad in the feed preparation and sampling plant balance area. The hopper is hoisted to a position on a scale over the digest tanks (as illustrated in Fig. 5-8), and a screw feeds the concentrates to the agitated acid. The hopper scale is used to control the rate of feed and the total feed added to the tank.

FIG. 5-8 Portable feed hopper over digest tank.

The digested solution is then pumped to an adjustment tank where acidity is adjusted, reagents are added, and the solution is blended.

A miscellaneous-material dissolving unit is a part of the refinery operation. This unit is designed to handle limited quantities of materials not suited for packaging into hoppers for feed to the digesters, such as wet cake and small quantities of dry material generated within this operation. The solution from the miscellaneous-material dissolving unit can be pumped to the digesters or to the adjustment tanks.

Floor sumps within the refinery collect overflows, leakage, washings, etc. The floor sumps are pumped to sump-liquor concentration tanks, where the solution is concentrated by evaporation of excess water. After concentration, the solution may be pumped to the digesters or to the adjustment tanks. All vessels described above are equipped with agitators to provide a homogeneous solution. Ports are provided on all tanks for volume measurements and sampling for process control and inventory.

Fig. 5-9 Extraction decanters.

The adjusted solution is fed to a series of extraction decanters (Fig. 5-9). The adjusted solution (aqueous feed) is contacted with a solvent flowing countercurrently. The uranium in the aqueous feed is transferred to the solvent, and the aqueous solution remaining is drained from the bottom of the decanters as a raffinate. The raffinate contains the major portion of the impurities from the aqueous feed. A very small percentage of uranium, both in a soluble and an insoluble form, is removed in the raffinate. The raffinate is stripped free of any solvent and is then pumped to the raffinate hold tanks. Uranium is precipitated with lime, after which the raffinate solution is sampled and measured for volume before being pumped to the raffinate storage pits. The assay of the sample for uranium, combined with the volume measurement, is used in accounting for the uranium transferred to the pits.

The solvent (solvent extract) containing the uranium and some impurities from the aqueous feed now enters a pulse column for washing. The washed extract overflows to the reextraction pulse column, and the wash water is drained to the aqueous feed tanks for recycle through the decanters.

The uranyl nitrate in the washed extract is reextracted into water in the reextraction column. This operation is performed by countercurrently contacting the washed extract with water in a reextraction pulse column (Fig. 5-10). The stripped solvent is treated with sodium carbonate and recycled

FIG. 5-10   Reextraction pulse columns.

to the decanters. The carbonate cake formed is drummed, sampled, weighed, and shipped to a scrap-recovery process.

The dilute high-purity uranyl nitrate is pumped to hold tanks that serve as feed tanks to an evaporator which concentrates the uranyl nitrate to about one-half the desired concentration. The product from the evaporator is pumped to tanks for final concentration to uranyl nitrate hexahydrate (UNH).

After final concentration, the UNH is drained to a series of gas-fired denitration pots. The denitrated UNH or UO_3 is removed from the pots by vacuum gulpers that discharge into a packaging system (Fig. 5-11).

The packaging system discharges the UO_3 to pretared portable hoppers through an automatic sample device. The portable hoppers are gross weighed on a print-weigh scale. A sample representing the contents of each hopper is sent to the laboratory for analysis. The hoppers are held in storage until analyses have been completed; then they are moved to the next step in the over-all operation, the UF_4 process, or are repackaged into other types of containers for shipment off site.

All process sewers in the refinery converge into one sewer line. A sampling device is installed in the sewer stream to measure volume of flow and to continuously remove samples.

Losses to the atmosphere through dust-collection stacks and concentration-tank stacks are measured at regular intervals.

FIG. 5-11 Unloading denitration pots.

Product. The refinery product, milled UO_3, orange in color, is a high-purity homogeneous material. It is packaged in portable hoppers after sampling and is then held in a storage area until laboratory analyses have been completed. After laboratory approval has been given, the UO_3 is transferred to the hydrofluorination plant.

5-4.2. Measurements: *Products.* The UO_3 product is sampled by an automatic Galigher sample splitter installed in the system between the packaging hopper and the portable hopper. The sample size is roughly 0.15 percent of the total weight of the material sampled. The gross sample is blended in the laboratory, and aliquots of the blended sample are analyzed for uranium by a gravimetric method. The assay of the sample is applied against the weight of the material to determine the uranium content of the UO_3.

The hopper print-weight scale is tested daily and evaluated as discussed under Weighing, Sec. 5-3.3.

Raffinate. The raffinate is a precipitated slurry containing small quantities of uranium. The slurry is under agitation to provide a homogeneous mixture for sampling. After the mixture is quiescent, volume measurements are made, and the contents of the batch-identified tanks are pumped to outside storage pits.

Carbonate Cake. Carbonate cake resulting from the sodium carbonate treatment of stripped solvent is clarified through a filter and is discharged from the filter to drums. The drums collected within a one-month period are weighed and then grouped as one lot. Each drum is sampled with a slotted pipe, and the drum samples are composited into a lot sample for subsequent colorimetric analysis.

Tank Calibrations. Prior to the start-up of the refinery, all tanks for uranium solutions were calibrated. The tanks may be equipped with a sampling port that can be opened for sampling and measurement or are pressure vessels that are totally enclosed, primarily for safety reasons.

The tanks equipped with ports are calibrated with the top edge of the port acting as a bench mark. A depth gauge designed by the instrument department is used for measuring the distance from the bench mark to the level of the liquor. The depth gauge consists of a small stainless steel cable that is unwound from a small drum equipped with a handle for winding and unwinding. A plumb bob on the cable provides enough weight to lower and hold the cable in a vertical position. A white light indicates plumb bob contact with the liquor, and a red light indicates the submersion of approximately the first half inch of the plumb bob. Therefore, when the red light burns, the cable is slowly rewound until only the white light is lit. The cable drum is geared to direct-reading dials to measure from zero at the top edge of the open port to the level of the liquor.

A very accurate water meter is used for tank-calibration purposes. The meter is checked for accuracy prior to its use and rechecked periodically after a number of uses. The meter check consists in placing a vessel on a scale and then adding water to the vessel through the meter. The volume of water added to the vessel is read from the meter, and the weight is read from the scale. The water temperature is obtained, and the specific gravity of the water is determined from a sample. The weight is then converted to gallons and compared with the meter reading. When the meter accuracy is 99.8 percent or better, the meter is used for calibration, and adjustments to the meter reading are made on the basis of the accuracy check. When the meter accuracy is less than 99.8 percent, the meter is adjusted by the instrument department.

A tank is calibrated by alternately adding a preset number of gallons of water through the meter and plotting the depth-gauge reading against the known volume of water added. Tank conversion tables are prepared from the charts so that readings in inches can be readily converted to gallons.

Tanks referred to as pressure vessels are calibrated in the same manner without the convenience of the depth gauge. Such tanks are, in many cases, provided with a sight glass, and markings are made on the glass. Tanks without sight glasses are provided with panel instrument gauges for measuring the depth of the solution. Corrections to the instrument gauge readings are required, depending on the ratio of the specific gravity of the water and the solution being measured. The error in instrument gauge readings is large when compared with the other two methods.

Inventory. The taking of refinery inventory consists primarily in sampling and measuring solutions contained in tanks and making a physical count and identification of UO_3 and carbonate-cake containers. The sampling and weighing of UO_3 and carbonate cake is performed at the time of production of these materials, and no additional weighings and samplings are made for inventory. Other miscellaneous dry materials such as dust are weighed and sampled.

A predetermined set of conditions must be attained in the refinery process to permit an accurate inventory. Portions of the refinery process are at near standstill condition, and other portions such as the extraction operation must be operating at an optimum rate. Therefore inventories must be carefully planned and organized and well executed to achieve reliable data.

The liquid inventory consists in removing three samples, approximately 250 ml each, from each tank while the solutions are under agitation and measuring the tank volumes after the agitation has been stopped and the solutions are quiescent. Some tanks, such as the uranyl nitrate concentration tanks, contain high concentrations of uranium under high temperatures, and the samples, if taken in the normal manner, would solidify on cooling. Such solutions are sampled with a calibrated sampler, and the sample is then diluted to a known volume. Solutions contained in the various extraction columns are not measured or sampled for inventory because it is not feasible to obtain samples representatives of the solution in the entire column. A standard uranium value, computed by operating engineers, is carried on inventory for the uranium contained in the columns.

Inventory forms are provided to record all inventory measurements, conversions of readings to gallons, temperatures and temperature corrections, laboratory aliquots and dilutions, and uranium assays and total uranium. The inventory forms are preprinted forms containing all tank numbers, and they serve as a check list against the items to be included on inventory. Tank samples representing similar solutions are composited on a weighted basis to reduce the number of samples requiring analyses. Corrections are made to tank volumes for temperature differences between the solutions in the tank and the sample.

Sewers. All effluents from the refinery converge into one sewer flow, which is continuously sampled and measured. The sewer flows through a calibrated flume for a measure of volume. The depth of the flow through the flume is measured with a level indicator, which, in turn, is integrated with a recorder for a reading in gallons. A gross sample is continuously pumped from a sump below the flume and is discharged to an agitating tank. The overflow from the tank passes through a sample splitter, where samples can be collected in a vessel for daily subsampling and analyzing.

The uranium analysis of the sample is applied against the recorded volume for determination of the total daily uranium loss. These losses are permanently recorded for control purposes and for accumulating statistical data for sewage losses.

When daily losses exceed the control limits, an extensive sampling plan within the refinery is put into effect. All sewer feeder lines within the refinery provide for sampling outlets; however, no provisions are made for volume measurements in these instances. Past experience indicates that sources of high loss are readily detected by this method, and corrective measures can be made immediately to reduce the losses to a nominal level.

Process-Control Samples. Various analyses are made of the process-control samples such as gravity, solids, and uranium. These analyses are accomplished by rough, rapid methods and do not always explicitly determine uranium content, although reasonable correlation exists. The process-control samples are not routinely used for uranium accounting purposes. However, when serious trouble is experienced in the refinery material balance, the process-control samples can be used to track down the difficulty.

5-4.3. Statistical Evaluations. The statistical evaluations in the refinery are concerned primarily with the evaluation of the refinery material balance. The limits of error associated with the refinery feeds are computed in the feed preparation and sampling plant.

The limits of error around the product stream are small and are a function of the weight and of the assay. The scales used for product-stream weighings are under statistical control and contribute very little to the product limits of error. The assay determinations in the laboratory are made in duplicate and are also under statistical control. The sampling error is estimated and is based on the sampling error determined for the similar automatic sampling system in the feed preparation and sampling plant.

The material balance consists in a balance between the beginning inventory plus receipts and the ending inventory plus shipments. The refinery inventory presents a complex problem. As mentioned under refinery measurements, a series of three samples is taken from each refinery tank on inventory and tank samples representing similar solutions are composites. The laboratory runs duplicate analyses on the composites prepared from two sets of samples. When the two analyses are within statistical agreement, the average of the two analyses is used as the uranium value when the two analyses are not within statistical agreement, a third set of samples is composited and analyzed, and the average of the two results in statistical agreement is used. From an accumulation of the results of the two duplicate analyses on two sets of composites, the variance in assay can be determined. The statistical procedure followed for computing the variance in assay is taken from *Statistical Methods in Research and Production*.[1]

In this procedure the sources of variation can be separated into: between months, between samples within months, and within samples or analytical. The variation between months is of no interest. The variation between samples within months and analytical can be statistically combined for the total variance of the assay. The variance in volume is estimated by assuming an accuracy of volume reading of ± 1 in. and an accuracy of tank calibration of 99.9 percent. The variance in pounds of uranium for each tank composite sample can then be computed as

$$S_u^2 = (V^2 \times S_a^2) + (A^2 \times S_v^2) \tag{5.2}$$

where S_u^2 = total sample variance in pounds of uranium
  V = volume
  S_a^2 = variance in assay in pounds per gallon
  A = assay
  S_v^2 = variance in volume in gallons

S_u^2 is computed for each composite on inventory and summed for the total variance in uranium of the inventory.

Since both the beginning and ending inventories affect the material balance, the variance in uranium of both inventories and the receipts and shipments are combined to produce the total expected variance in the material balance. The square root of the total variance multiplied by 2 results in the 95 percent limits within which the material balance should lie.

As a check for a bias in the material balance, the variance in the beginning and ending inventories for the period are combined with the variance in the cumulated receipts and shipments for the period; the 95 percent limits of error so computed are then compared with the cumulated material balance for the same period.

The method described above is time consuming and is not used routinely. A much quicker method is employed to check the reasonableness of the monthly material balances. The common practice is to compute the material balance as a percentage of the material consumed. The percentage values are plotted on a control chart with two sigma limits. When values exceed these limits, a check is made using the longer procedure described above. A chart plotting percentage values is also more convenient for checking bias.

[1] Numbered references are listed at the end of the chapter.

5-4.4. Collection and Flow of Data: *Receipts.* Transfer from the feed preparation and sampling plant is recorded on an *internal move order* which bears the signature of the chief clerks of the plants involved in the transfer. The transfer document is posted in total to a Transfer Journal and in detail to the raw-material *lot detail ledger.*

Consumed. As raw materials are charged to process, the date charged as indicated on the plant batch sheet is recorded in the *lot detail ledger.*

Produced. A *printed weight card* for each lot of finished goods serves as a notice of production and is posted to a finished *lot detail ledger.* A *laboratory analytical report* relating the assay to the lot, by a lot number, supplies the basis for computation of the uranium content. A tabulation of batch sheets and assay reports for raffinate transferred to the storage pits provides the record for raffinate. The data for carbonate cake are similar to those for finished goods. Sewer losses are recorded daily for process control and uranium accounting purposes.

Shipments. Shipments can be either internal or off site. The appropriate transfer document is prepared and posted as a total for each shipment to the Transfer Journal and in detail to the lot detail ledger.

Inventory. At the close of the month, a physical inventory is taken and compared with the open items in the lot detail ledger; differences are reconciled. This inventory is posted to the ending inventory for the over-all operation, and finally all ledgers are closed and balanced for the preparation of the material balance for the refinery.

5-4.5. Material Balance Report. The material balance report for the refinery is divided into six categories: raw material, work in process, finished goods, residues, losses, and B-PID (Table 5.2).

TABLE 5.2. REPORTING FORMAT REFINERY OPERATIONS

Material	Beginning Inventory	Receipts	Shipments	Ending Inventory	Produced	Consumed
Raw material	A	B	C	D		E
Work in process	A			D		E
Finished goods	A	B	C	D	F	
Residues	A	B	C	D	F	
Losses			C		F	
Total	A	B	C	D	F	E
B-PID				G	G	

Under raw material and residues are listed the various types of material, and under work in process are listed the areas and associated uranium values necessary for cost-account breakdown.

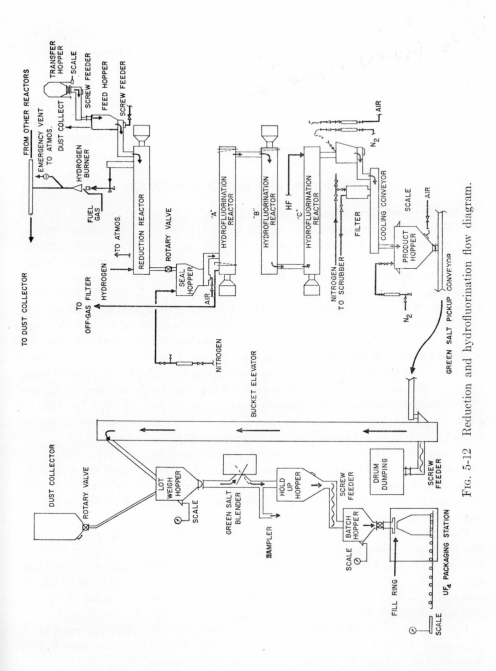

FIG. 5-12 Reduction and hydrofluorination flow diagram.

For raw material and work in process

$$E = A + B - C - D \tag{5.3}$$

E for work in process can be positive or negative and reflects inventory change only.

For finished goods and residues

$$F = D + C - B - A \tag{5.4}$$

The B-PID, G, can be either a plus or minus value. It is determined by total $(A + B) - (C + D)$ and must agree with total $F - E$.

5-5. REDUCTION AND HYDROFLUORINATION

5-5.1. Process Description: *Feed Material.* The feed material to the reduction and hydrofluorination (green salt) process is UO_3 (orange oxide) from the refinery. It is transferred in portable hoppers. Adequate uranium measurements of the UO_3 are made in the refinery, and no additional measurements other than a gross weight check is made in the green-salt plant.

Process. The green-salt plant converts UO_3 to UF_4 in a series of four screw reactors. The first reactor reduces UO_3 to UO_2 with hydrogen, and the remaining three reactors convert the UO_2 to UF_4 by hydrofluorination. A rerun reactor reworks off-grade UF_4 to produce a product within specifications. A reverter included in this plant reverts very impure UF_4 to UO_2 or U_3O_8, which is recycled to the UO_3 process. Also included in this plant is a reactor bank reserved for research and development. This reactor is isolated from the dust collectors servicing the remaining plant areas and, if need be, can be used for processing enriched and depleted material without danger of costly crossover. Figure 5-12 is a diagram of material flow.

Orange oxide (UO_3) enters the main production reactors (Fig. 5-13) from the portable transfer hoppers, which are placed on scales and are manually connected to the feed hoppers. Orange oxide is fed into the reduction reactor by screw feeders. The UO_3 feed rate is manually controlled by adjusting the reactor feeder.

Excess hydrogen and inert nitrogen sweep the water formed from the reactor, the hydrogen being burned at the reactor gas outlet. The products of combustion from this burner are diluted with air and are drawn into a dust-collection system. The UO_2 discharges from the reduction reactor through a rotary valve into a seal hopper and is fed into hydrofluorination reactor A by the seal hopper feeder.

Partially hydrofluorinated UO_2 flows from hydrofluorination reactor A to reactor B, and then to reactor C in series, where it is contacted with vaporized anhydrous hydrofluoric acid and converted to UF_4.

Excess hydrofluoric acid vapor, water vapor, and inert gas, along with entrained solids, leave reactor A and enter the off-gas filter, where the solids are deposited on carbon tubes. Periodically, solids are removed by flushing the filter with nitrogen. The solids are dropped back into reactor A through the off-gas riser.

The UF_4 is discharged from reactor C into the cooling conveyor hopper. The material then flows from the cooling conveyor feeder to the cooling conveyor, where it is contacted and cooled by a stream of nitrogen flowing countercurrently to the material. The nitrogen and entrained solids, with a small amount of hydrofluoric acid picked up in the cooling conveyor, leave through a filter, where the solids are deposited on a single carbon tube. Infrequently, the solids collected on the filter are blown back by means of nitrogen to the cooling conveyor.

The UF_4 then flows to a weigh hopper, which is provided with a scale to determine approximately when a lot has been collected and to give accurate inventory data. The UF_4 is then transferred to the blender. The blender (Fig. 5-14) is designed to receive and blend a complete lot of UF_4 from the lot weigh hopper. After a predetermined blending period, blender contents are discharged into the holdup hopper. A Geary-Jennings sampler is started when

FIG. 5-13 Production reactor bank.

the blended material is dropped, and a representative sample of the batch is taken.

The tare weight of the green-salt transfer hopper is recorded on a card by the Printweigh unit on the weight scale. The UF_4 discharges from the holdup hopper to the portable transfer hopper; the gross weight of the transfer hopper is then recorded on the same card as the tare weight. The hopper is then transferred to a storage area adjacent to the packaging station.

Product. The product of the reduction and hydrofluorination plant is

FIG. 5-14   Uranium tetrafluoride blender.

milled UF_4 (green in color). The green salt is discharged to either portable hoppers or drums. The portable hoppers are filled to a predetermined weight, plus or minus a small allowable weight difference, and are equal to one charge in the dingot process. For use in the derby process the UF_4 is packaged into drums to a predetermined weight, plus or minus a small allowable weight difference, so that two drums equal one charge in the derby process.

The packaged UF_4 is held in a storage area until laboratory analyses have been completed, and it is then transferred to the appropriate derby or dingot process.

Rerun Reactor. The rerun reactor can operate as a normal production reactor. However, when it is operating as a rerun reactor, the off-grade material bypasses the reduction reactor. The operation of the hydrofluorination reactors and product packaging is similar to that of the main production reactors.

Reverter. The reverter is designed to revert impure UF_4 to either UO_2 or U_3O_8 by contact with superheated steam and air. The material is fed to the reverter through a dumping station.

Steam is metered, superheated in an electric superheater, and introduced into the reverter countercurrent to the flow of material. The material is oxidized to U_3O_8 with steam and air or to UO_2 with steam only. Entrained solids enter the reverter off-gas filter, where the solids are deposited on carbon tubes. Solids collected on the off-gas filter, removed from the filter by flushing with nitrogen, drop back into the reverter.

Black oxide (U_3O_8) and UO_2 are discharged from the reverter into the reverter cooling-conveyor hopper and then to the reverter product hopper. This hopper is provided with a scale to determine approximately when a lot has been collected and to give accurate inventory data.

From the hopper the uranium oxide flows to the reverter drum packaging station. A continuous sample of the lot is taken while drums are being filled. After a drum has been filled, it is weighed on a Printweigh scale.

Side Streams: (a) SUMP COLLECTION. Sump-collection and processing facilities are provided to handle wastes and washes accumulated in the various sumps in the green salt plant. From the sumps the wastes are pumped to one of two sump tanks. Two tanks are provided so that the wastes can be collected in one of the tanks while the contents of the other are being prepared for processing in the rest of the system. The washes and wastes are first neutralized with KOH and then pumped to the sump-liquor filter; the filtrate is allowed to flow to the sump-liquor filtrate tank.

On completion of the cycle, cake is washed off the filter leaves, and the resulting slurry is dropped into the sump slurry tank. The slurry is fed to the centrifuge. The liquor from the centrifuge is returned to the sump tank.

The cake from the centrifuge is packaged in drums in the centrifuge packaging station. For material control the drums are weighed on a printweigh scale.

The liquor in the sump-liquor filtrate tank is pumped to the sump liquor clarification filter. This filter acts as a polishing filter to remove any traces of solids that may have passed the first filtration step. The filtrate from this filtration step flows to the out-fall sewer.

Periodically, the cake in the sump-liquor clarification filter is sluiced off into the sump slurry tank and centrifuged in the normal manner.

(b) DUST COLLECTION. There are five dust-collection systems and one exhaust system. Dust collector 1 collects dust from equipment handling UO_3 and UO_2. Periodically, the dust collected is removed by dumping to the UO_3

feed hoppers on production lines. A smoke indicating controller on the exhaust to the atmosphere shuts down the blower if dust comes through the collector.

The other four systems are for mixed UO_2, UO_3, and UF_4 from the reactors; pure UF_4 from the packaging line; rerun materials; and contaminated material. Each has a smoke-indicating controller on the exhaust which shuts down the blower if dust comes through the collector. They discharge into the rerun or reverter systems, whichever is best suited to recovery of the uranium contained.

All packing glands of the reduction and hydrofluorination reactors are vented by an exhaust blower. The packing glands on the reduction reactors are always vented to prevent explosive hazard due to H_2 leakage; whereas the packing glands on the hydrofluorination reactors are vented only if a leak is detected.

(c) RESIDUES. The residual streams are reverted product and wet cake. The reverted product results from converting chemically impure UF_4 to UO_2 or U_3O_8. This product is packaged into drums through a sampling system, where an individual sample is obtained from each drum. The drum samples are composited into a lot sample, and the lot sample is analyzed for uranium and fluorides. Excess fluorides would damage the refinery equipment. The lot size is dependent on the need for feed material in the refinery; however, the lot is closed at the end of each month. The reverter product, after analysis, is transferred to the feed preparation and sampling plant for packaging into hoppers and then to the refinery as feed material.

The wet cake results from filtering and centrifuging of precipitated wastes and washes collected in the various sumps within the plant. Each drum of wet cake is sampled with a slotted thief sampler, and the drum samples are composited into a lot sample for uranium analyses. One month's production of wet cake constitutes a lot. The wet cake is transferred to the refinery and introduced to the refinery process through the miscellaneous-material dissolving facility.

(d) LOSSES. Losses to the atmosphere are possible through the dust collection bags and are measured by sampling the exhaust stack gases at regular intervals. These measurements, made primarily for health purposes, are also used for uranium accounting.

5-5.2. **Measurements:** *Product.* The product UF_4 is a high-purity homogeneous material. The portable hoppers containing the UF_4 are tare weighed and, after being filled, are gross weighed on appropriate scales under statistical control. Such weights are printed on a ticket and recorded on a continuous tape by an integral printing mechanism.

The UF_4 is sampled by a Galigher sampler as the blender discharges to the portable hoppers. Aliquots of the sample are analyzed for uranium by the pyrohydrolysis method. The sample is also analyzed for impurities for process control. The assay of the sample is applied to the weight of the hoppers in the lot for uranium content of the UF_4.

Residues. The reverter product and wet cake are weighed on print-weigh scales. Each drum of reverter product is mechanically sampled as it is being filled. The drum samples are composited into a lot sample and analyzed for uranium using a volumetric method. The wet cake is sampled with a slotted thief sampler and is composited into a lot sample. The lot sample is analyzed for uranium by a colorimetric method, which is less accurate than the volumetric method but is nevertheless adequate for this small volume of material.

Inventory. The inventory of the reduction and hydrofluorination process consists in a drum or hopper count of the UO_3 feed, the UF_4 product, the reverter, and wet-cake residue and a reading of all stationary hopper scales throughout the system. The weighings and sampling of the UO_3, UF_4, and reverter and wet-cake residues were performed at the time of production of these materials; no additional measurements are made for inventory.

The assay applied to the material in the stationary hoppers is an average assay determined for the particular type material contained. The reactor banks contain material for which no direct method of measurement is practicable. The uranium value assigned to these reactors is determined at their start-up. A measured feed is added to a reactor; and after the reactor is in equilibrium, the product is measured, and a by-difference uranium holdup value is determined. The holdup values are subject to considerable variations because of feed rate changes. Since they are carried as a fixed value for the material balance error. By far the greatest influence on the material balance.

5-5.3. Statistical Evaluations. The feed and the product in this operation are high-purity homogeneous materials. The limits of error in the uranium values assigned to these materials are small; they are used as standard factors in the establishment of the limits of error in the material balance. The residues represent a very small percentage of the materials consumed; thus limits of error associated with these materials are negligible contributors to the material-balance error. By far the greatest influence on the material balance for this operation is the variation in the material holdup factor assigned to the reactors.

Periodically, the variance as pounds of uranium in the holdup factor is computed for each reactor, and the most recently computed variances are used in the evaluation of the material balance. The variance as pounds of uranium for each reactor is computed by making a daily material balance around each bank of reactors for a period of a month.

From plant-operation data sheets the input and output for each bank of reactors are obtained. The difference between the input and output values represents the variation in holdup over the 24-hour period. The variance of these differences is computed in the standard manner.

$$S^2 = \frac{[\Sigma\, d^2 - (\Sigma\, d)^2/n]}{n-1} \qquad (5.5)$$

The variance for each reactor is summed for the total variance as pounds of uranium expected in the reactor inventory. It is realized that the input and output values for each reactor are not precise, nor need they be for plant operation. However, such values do provide an excellent means for estimating the variance in the standard holdup values.

The variance associated with materials contained in stationary hoppers is estimated. The variance in weight is based on the accuracy that can be expected in weighings of this nature. The variance in assay is computed by the difference between the standard assay value assigned to these materials and the experienced values for a month's production.

The variance as pounds of uranium is computed for each stationary hopper, or lot, of material as follows:

$$S_u{}^2 = (W^2 \times S_a{}^2) + (A^2 \times S_w{}^2) \tag{5.6}$$

where $S_u{}^2$ = variance in pounds of uranium
W = weight
$S_a{}^2$ = variance in assay
A = assay
$S_w{}^2$ = variance in weight

The variances $S_u{}^2$ for each lot or measured unit of the various materials are summed for the materials involved in the month's activities. To this is added twice the variance of the holdup factor assigned to the reactors since both the beginning and ending inventories of the reactors affect the material balance for the operation. Twice the square root of the total variance represents the 95 percent limit of error within which the material balance should fall if no unusual circumstances affected the balance.

As mentioned previously, the variations in the reactor holdup value have the greatest influence on the material balance for this operation. As a quick check against the reasonableness of the material balance, the 95 percent limits of error around the reactor holdup value are sufficient to detect gross errors.

As in the case of the refinery process, the material balance is computed as a percentage of the material consumed, and the percentage values are plotted on a control chart for bias checks.

5-5.4. Collection and Flow of Data: *Receipts.* The receipts to this process are the products from the refinery. The transfer is recorded on an *internal move order,* which is signed by the chief clerks in the related plants. The document registering the transfer is posted as a total to the *receipt ledger* and in detail to the *lot detail ledger* for raw materials.

Consumed. As the hoppers of UO_3 are charged to the system, an operational data sheet serves as a record for posting to the *lot detail ledger* for raw material.

Produced. A *printed weight card* for each unit packaged and included in a lot provides a record of materials produced. A *lot detail ledger* is maintained for each category of materials produced.

Shipments. An *internal move order* is prepared for movements of material to various destinations. The move order is posted as a total to the Transfer Journal and in detail to the appropriate *lot detail ledger.* Materials shipped off site are recorded on the official AEC transfer documents and are posted to ledgers and records in the same manner as the *internal move orders.*

Inventory. The physical inventory taken at the close of each month is reconciled with the lot detail records. The physical inventory is posted to the ending inventory for the over-all operation.

5-5.5. Material Balance Report. After all detail records have been closed and balanced, the material balance report is prepared. The format of the report is shown in Table 5.3.

TABLE 5.3. REPORTING FORMAT FOR UF_4 PROCESS

Material	Beginning Inventory	Receipts	Shipments	Ending Inventory	Produced	Consumed
Raw material	A	B	C	D		E
Work in process	A			D		E
Finished goods	A	B	C	D	F	
Residues	A	B	C	D	F	
Estimated losses			C		F	
Total	A	B	C	D	F	E
B-PID				G	G	

The work-in-process category is subdivided into categories for cost accounting use.

For raw material

$$E = A + B - C - D \qquad (5.7)$$

For work in process

$$E = A - D \qquad (5.8)$$

and reflects the change in the work-in-process inventory.

For finished goods and residues

$$F = D + C - B - A \qquad (5.9)$$

Estimated losses are reported as removals (shipment) and production.

The B-PID is determined as the total $(A + B) - (C + D)$ and must also be equal to the total $E - F$. This by-difference value can be either positive or negative.

5-6. REDUCTION TO DERBY METAL

5-6.1. Process Description: *Feed Material.* The feed material to the reduction process is the UF_4 product from the green-salt process. Since the drummed UF_4 has been adequately sampled and weighed prior to the transfer from the green-salt process, no other measurements are made on this material.

Process. The reduction process is the reaction of a blend of UF_4 and magnesium metal chips. The metal produced in this reaction is commonly called a "derby." The name derby was given to this metal in the early days under the Manhattan Project because the original metal produced in this

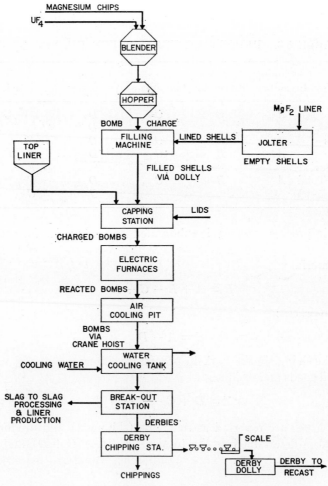

FIG. 5-15   Reduction to derby metal flow diagram.

fashion resembled a derby complete with the brim. Figure 5-15 is a flow diagram of the process.

The blend of UF_4 and magnesium is charged (Fig. 5-16) to a steel shell lined with milled magnesium fluoride (MgF_2). This linear is refractory and serves to contain the heat of reaction and prevent damage to the steel shell. A steel lid is then bolted to the shell flange, and the charge, commonly called a "bomb," is placed in a furnace (Fig. 5-17). The furnaces which are electrically heated, have a capacity of one bomb.

The fired bomb is removed from the furnace and placed in a pit for air cooling. After a period of time in the air-cooling pit, the bomb is placed in a water pit for further cooling. The cooled bomb is then moved to the

FIG. 5-16   Derby filling station. Note the magnesium fluoride liner in the steel shell. The blender will continue down until the lip rests on the flange of the shell, at which time charging will commence.

Fig. 5-17   Loading charged shell to furnace.

Fig. 5-18   Breaking cap on fired charge.

"break-out" station, and the lid is removed. The MgF$_2$ cap is broken (Fig. 5-18), and the shell is inverted over a 3 by 3-in. screen and jolted several times. The massive metal derby and MgF$_2$ slag are discharged. The slag passes through the screen to a jaw crusher and then on to the slag-liner processing building. The derby is moved to a chipping station, where all slag

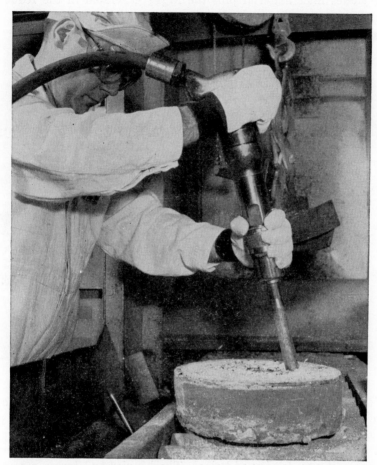

Fig. 5-19 Derby chipping.

adhering to the derby is removed by a pneumatic hammer (Fig. 5-19), and then it is weighed. The derby weight is printed on a card and on a continuous tape by an integral printing mechanism (Fig. 5-20).

Product. Derbies produced by this operation are massive pieces of high-purity metal with some imbedded slag and a magnesium-metal film coating. The derbies are serially numbered for identification and process correlation.

Residues. The residues resulting from this operation are reject slag, dust collection, sump-recovery cake, and scrap metal.

(*a*) REJECT SLAG. The reject slag is the excess slag generated in each reduction reaction, varying in size from dust to pieces approximately 2 in. in diameter. The reject slag is a very heterogeneous material, varying in an assay range of 5 to 10 percent uranium and containing MgF_2, free uranium metal, uranium particles imbedded in the slag, and various oxides. The MgF_2 content includes liner material plus the MgF_2 generated in the reduction of the uranium.

FIG. 5-20   Derby weighing.

The slag, after jaw crushing, is passed over a coarse screen. The oversize from the coarse screen is mainly uranium metal. The material passing through the screen is fed to a ball mill for reduction of particle size. The ball-mill product is passed over a fine-mesh screen and air classified into two streams according to density and size. The heavier and larger particle sizes are chuted to a reject packaging hopper. The lighter and smaller particle sizes are chuted to a product packaging hopper for use in linear formation. Approximately one-half the total of original material plus the new generation of MgF_2 is reject.

(*b*) DUST COLLECTION. The dust-collection system is divided into the slag dust collection and the blending and charging dust collection. The slag dust collection is added to the reject slag stream in the slag liner building. The second category of dust collection, containing UF_4, magnesium, and some MgF_2, is a very heterogeneous material with an assay range of 20 to 50 percent uranium. This material is packaged into drums, sampled, weighed, and shipped off site for uranium recovery.

(c) SUMP-RECOVERY CAKE. The sump system collects washes and wastes from the reduction process. After precipitation and filtration operation, a wet cake is recovered assaying approximately 35 percent uranium. Drums of cake are collected during the month and are then weighed, sampled, and shipped off site for uranium recovery. The fluoride contamination of this cake does not permit recycle to the refinery.

(d) SCRAP METAL. Scrap metal results from the coarse screening of slag in the slag-liner building. Some MgF_2 remains attached to metal of this type. The scrap metal is drummed, weighed, and transferred to the metal dissolver in the refinery.

5-6.2. Measurements: *Product.* The product, derby metal, is a high-purity metal containing some imbedded slag and some magnesium metal. Various methods were tried to determine an assay factor that could be applied to the derby. Representative samples of a derby are not practical to obtain and would be very costly. Density measurements are possible by weighings made of the derby in air and again when suspended in water. This again is a tedious method subject to large errors. The method finally arrived at was to perform a measurement of the impurities in the derby in the next step in the process, the casting operation.

The derbies are placed in a graphite crucible, melted, and poured into graphite molds. Essentially all impurities and some metal remains in the crucible after pouring. The crucible, after use, is inverted over a gas flame, and the metal is converted to oxide. The oxides collected in this manner are weighed and sampled.

Assuming the derbies to be 100 percent uranium, the oxides resulting from crucible burn-outs should be pure U_3O_8 assaying at 84.802 percent uranium. Any deviations from this theoretical assay therefore represent entrained impurities. This measurement is made on a monthly basis.

Residues. The residues are the dust collection, reject slag, sump cake, and scrap metal. All residues are weighed on print-weigh scales accurately controlled through a statistical scale check program. The dust collection represents a very heterogeneous mixture of UF_4, magnesium metal, and MgF_2. Samples from each drum are obtained by use of the auger sampler in the feed preparation and sampling plant. The drum samples are composited into lot samples and analyzed for uranium by a volumetric method.

Reject slag is not amenable to reasonably accurate sampling by presently known methods. The uranium content assigned to the slag residue is determined by difference as follows:

UF₄ charged		xx pounds uranium
Derbies produced	xx	
Dust collection produced	xx	
Sump cake produced	xx	
Scrap metal produced	xx	
Total produced		xx
Difference assigned to slag residues		xx

Then the assay value assigned to the slag residues is computed from the uranium determined by difference and the total weight of slag produced.

Drums of wet sump cake are sampled with a slotted thief sampler, and the drum samples are composited into a lot sample for subsequent colorimetric analysis.

Scrap metal represents a very minor portion of the total material handled in this operation. An arbitrary assay factor of 95 percent uranium is assigned to this scrap.

5-6.3. Statistical Evaluations. Since the uranium content assigned to the slag residues is determined by difference, any errors or losses are included in the uranium content assigned to the slag. The limits of error associated with the slag residues can be estimated by computing the limits of error for each of the materials associated with this process, other than the slag residues, and by statistically combining these limits of error.

The materials measured in this operation are the UF₄ feed, the derby product, and the residues: dust, wet cake, and scrap metal. The quantities of wet cake and scrap metal produced are small and do not warrant an extensive statistical program to determine limits of error. An arbitrary estimate of the limits of error of ±10 percent of the contained uranium is assigned to these materials.

The limits of error associated with the derby assay include the uncertainties in (1) derby weighings, (2) oxide weighings, (3) oxide sampling, and (4) analyses of the oxide sample. From the statistical scale-testing program the uncertainties in weighings are readily available. The uncertainty in sampling is determined by replicate samplings. The statistical program in the laboratory provides limits of error for the analyses. The various uncertainties can then be combined to determine the total uncertainty in the derby assay.

The limits of error associated with UF₄ are small and have been computed in the reduction and hydrofluorination process.

The limits of error associated with the dust collection material are large mainly because of the difficulty in obtaining a representative sample from this heterogeneous material. The dust collection is shipped off site for uranium recovery. Sampling by both the Mallinckrodt and the scrap-recovery facilities provided an excellent opportunity to determine the limits of error in the assay of this material. A series of five lots was selected for an experimental program. Duplicate samples were taken from each lot by both Mallinckrodt and the scrap-recovery unit, and portions of the samples were exchanged. Duplicate analyses were made on all samples, and limits of error were computed for sampling and analyses. These limits of error were then applied to the dust collection materials.

The total limits of error are then determined for the uranium content assigned to the slag residues by statistically combining the individual contributing limits of error.

The measurements made for uranium accounting purposes are also used for process control. Derby yields are computed for each derby and correlated with UF_4 feed lots and processing equipment with the objective of attaining optimum yield.

5-6.4. Collection and Flow of Data: *Receipts.* The receipts to this process are the drums of UF_4 from the reduction and hydrofluorination process. The transfer of the material is recorded on an *internal move order* that is signed by the chief clerks associated with the related plants. The *internal move order* is posted as a total in a Transfer Journal and in detail to a *lot detail ledger* for raw materials.

Consumed. As materials are charged to the blender, an operational data sheet serves as the record for posting the date consumed to the *lot detail ledger* for raw material.

Produced. A *printed weight card* for each derby produced serves as the notice of production. Each derby is sequentially numbered, and no lot mark is assigned to the derbies produced. The derby number and related weight are recorded in a *derby record* with date of production.

The *derby record* serves as a record of production and as a record of shipment. The shipment of the derby is recorded as of the date the derby is charged to the casting crucible. The derby and casting operations are both contained within one building; therefore, since the derbies do not require movement by the warehousing group, an *internal move order* is not required.

The printed weight record for each drum of residues produced is attached to a *tally sheet* or notice of production. The *tally sheet* lists the lot number assigned to the material, followed by container numbers with the related gross, tare, and net weights. The *tally sheet* totals for each lot are recorded in a *lot detail ledger*. A laboratory analytical report relating the assay to the material by lot-number identification provides the basis for uranium determination.

Shipments. Shipments of material internally and off site are effected by the preparation of the appropriate transfer document. These documents are posted as a total to the Transfer Journal and in detail to the *lot detail ledger*.

Inventory. At the close of the month a physical inventory is taken and compared with the *lot detail ledger*. The differences are reconciled, and the

physical inventory is then posted to the ending-inventory detail for the over-
all operation. All ledgers are then closed and balanced for the preparation
of the material-balance report for the metal-reduction process.

5-6.5. Material Balance Report. Table 5.4 is the format of the report.
From processing considerations the following relations must hold:

For raw material

$$E = A + B - C - D \tag{5.10}$$

For work in process

$$E = A - D \tag{5.11}$$

and reflects the change in the work-in-process inventory.

For finished goods and residues

$$F = D + C - B - A \tag{5.12}$$

For slags F is determined as subtotal E minus subtotal F and is applied to
slag D.

Total line: $$(A + B) = (C + D) \tag{5.13}$$
$$E = F \tag{5.14}$$

TABLE 5.4.   REPORTING FORMAT FOR METAL
REDUCTION PROCESS

Material	Beginning Inventory	Receipts	Shipments	Ending Inventory	Produced	Consumed
Raw material	A	B	C	D		E
Work in process	A			D		E
Finished goods	A	B	C	D	F	
Residues						
(measured)	A	B	C	D	F	E
Subtotal	A	B	C	D	F	E
Slags	A	B	C	D	F	
Total	A	B	C	D	F	E

5-7. CASTING

5-7.1. Process Description: *Feed Material.* The feed material to this
process is the metal derby produced in the metal-reduction process and recycle
metal. The recycle metal generally consists of rod ends from ingot-rolling
operations and reject fuel elements.

Process. In the casting process, metal derbies and other recastable metal
are melted in graphite crucibles, and the melt is discharged into graphite molds
for the formation of ingots (see Fig. 5-21 for flow diagram). In general, the
crucible is loaded with four derbies and with enough recycle metal to bring
the total load to the desired weight.

The loaded crucible is then lowered into an induction vacuum casting furnace. The graphite molds are placed in an insulated bottom portion of the furnace and locked in place, as illustrated in Fig. 5-22. When the metal has melted, the crucible plug is removed, and the metal flows into the mold.

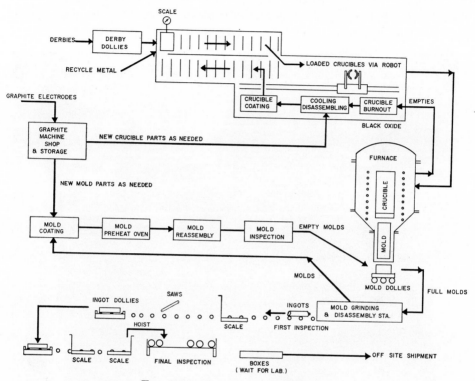

FIG. 5-21 Casting flow diagram.

The furnace is then permitted to cool, and the molten metal solidifies. The crucible is removed from the furnace and conveyed to a crucible burn-out station where it is inverted over a gas flame for removal of metal by oxidation. The furnace bottom containing the mold with the cooled ingot is transferred to a mold-disassembly station. The mold is split away from the ingot and small fins of metal on the ingot resulting from the mold joints are removed with a grinding wheel. The crude ingot is conveyed on roller conveyors over a ticket-printing scale, where the weight of the crude ingot is recorded.

The crude ingot is inspected for surface defects. If the ingot is rejected for surface defects, it is cut into pieces for remelting. The ingots passing the surface inspection are conveyed to a power hack saw, and the top 1 in. of the ingot is removed. A flow of oil over the saw blade cools the blade and reduces the oxidation of the metal. The piece of metal removed is commonly called the "top crop." The top crop contains essentially all the impurities not retained in the crucible.

Additional croppings of the ingot are made to reach a level in the ingot free of pipes and other voids (see Fig. 5-23). A thin slice of metal is taken from the cropped end of the ingot and delivered to the laboratory for analysis. Additional croppings and samplings are made as required to pass density specifications.

FIG. 5-22   Inserting mold into casting furnace.

Crops removed after the top crop are degreased and transferred to the crucible loading station for recycling. The excess of the sample delivered to the laboratory is also returned for recycling.

After laboratory approval, the finished ingots are packaged (Fig. 5-24) and shipped off site to a rolling and slug-fabrication facility.

Product. The product from the casting operation is a high-purity uranium metal ingot with an assay of 100 percent uranium (for all practical purposes) and a density of 19 gm/cm³. Each ingot is sequentially numbered for identification.

Residues. The residual streams are: oxides, grindings, sawdust, top crop, and crushed uranium-contaminated graphite.

The oxides result from the burn-out of the crucibles and are black with a density of approximately 3.2 gm/cm³ and an assay in the 70 to 80 percent uranium range. The oxides are collected in a dust collection system that unloads into drums, and the drums are collected for a one-month period. The drums are then lot marked, sampled, weighed, and transferred to the feed preparation and sampling plant for packaging into portable hoppers for refinery feed.

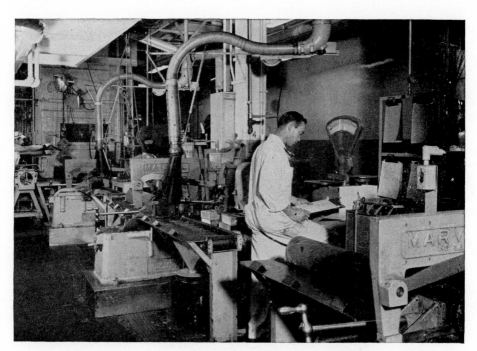

Fig. 5-23 Ingot cutting area. Note the mold disassembly station in the left background, the cropping stations, the dust-collection system, and the weighing station.

The grindings, resulting from grinding metal fins from the ingot, are a mixture of carborundum (from the grinding wheel), uranium oxide, and finely divided metal. The volume of grindings is very small, amounting to one or two drums per month. The drummed grindings from one month's production are sampled and weighed and then transferred to the miscellaneous-material dissolving station in the refinery.

The sawdust generated in the ingot cutting consists of granular metal particles; its density is roughly 18 gm/cm³. The sawdust is collected in drums and covered with oil for shipment off site to a scrap-recovery facility.

Top crops have a density somewhat less than 19 gm/cm³. The top crops are collected in drums for a one-month period, weighed, and transferred to the metal dissolving station in the refinery.

Graphite containing small quantities of uranium in the range of 1 percent of the weight of the graphite is jaw crushed, drummed, weighed, and shipped off site to a scrap recovery facility.

5-7.2. Measurements: *Product.* The product is a high-purity uranium metal ingot to which 100 percent uranium assay factor is applied. Each ingot

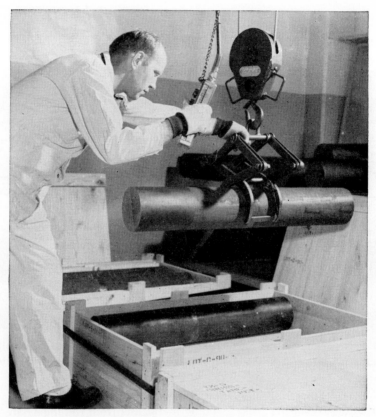

FIG. 5-24 Ingot packaging.

is weighed, and the weight is recorded on continuous tape by the ticket-printing scale. The boxes used for packaging ingots for shipment are tare weighed prior to their use, and boxed ingots are gross weighed prior to shipment for detection of gross errors.

Residues. The auger samples of each drum of oxide are composited into a lot sample for volumetric uranium analysis. The pretared sampled drums are then gross weighed on a Printweigh scale. Grindings are sampled with a slotted thief sampler, composited, and analyzed colorimetrically. Each drum of grindings is weighed on a Printweigh scale.

The weight of the sawdust is determined prior to the addition of an oil covering. After the oil has been added, the drums are gross weighed. The sawdust is not routinely sampled, and a tentative assay factor of 95 percent uranium is applied to the weight of the sawdust. The uranium value for sawdust determined by the scrap recovery facility is used for uranium accounting.

Top crops are drummed in pretared drums and gross weighed. The assay applied to the top-crop weight is a standard assay determined from a series of random samples.

Crushed graphite is also drummed in pretared drums and gross weighed. A tentative assay factor of 1 percent is applied to the weight of the graphite. The uranium value determined for graphite by the scrap recovery facility is used for uranium accounting.

5-7.3. Statistical Evaluations. Statistical evaluations in the casting process are concerned with scale controls, establishment of a standard assay factor for top crops, and the evaluation of the material balance for this operation.

The standard assay factor for top crops was established by randomly selecting a number of top crops and sawing a wedge-shaped section from each as a sample. The samples were totally dissolved and analyzed, and the results were plotted on a standard control chart. Outlying values are rejected, and the average of the remaining values is used as the standard assay factor. Each week a series of five top-crop samples is analyzed, and the values are plotted on the control chart. Revisions to the standard assay factor are made when a shift in the plotted values occurs.

The expected limits of error (as uranium) are computed periodically for the casting material balance. The limits of error are computed for each lot of each type of material involved in the casting process. These limits of error are statistically combined for the total limits of error around the material balance.

This method is time consuming and is only done periodically; the method most generally employed is to compute the B-PID as a percentage of the material consumed. These percentage values are plotted on a control chart with two sigma limits. When the computed value exceeds the control chart limits, all records are audited; when no errors are found in the records, a second inventory is taken.

5-7.4. Collection and Flow of Data: *Receipts.* The *derby record* described in Sec. 5-6.4 serves as a record of derby receipts. The derby is recorded as a receipt in the *derby record* at the time the derby is loaded in the crucible. An *internal move order* is prepared each month from a summation of the derby record and is posted to the Transfer Journal. The document representing off-site receipts of recycle metal is posted to the Transfer Journal and to the *lot detail ledger.*

Consumed. Since derbies are not recorded as receipts until they are charged to the crucible, the receipt and consumed values are identical. The *plant process data sheet* records recycle metal charged to the crucible. The date charged is entered in the *lot detail ledger*.

Produced. A tally sheet is prepared in the plant for each lot of finished goods and residues produced. The printed weight records are attached to the related tally sheets, which are posted to a *lot detail ledger*. The analytical report relating assays of samples to the materials by lot number supplies the basis for uranium determination.

Shipments. Internal move orders for materials recycled internally and appropriate AEC transfer documents for shipments off site are prepared. The documents representing transfers from the casting process are recorded as totals in the Transfer Journal and in detail to the appropriate *lot detail ledger*.

Inventory. The physical inventory taken at the close of each month is reconciled with the *lot detail ledgers* and is posted to the ending inventory for the over-all operations.

5-7.5. Material Balance Report. After all detail records are closed and balanced, the material balance report is prepared in the format of Table 5.5.

TABLE 5.5. REPORTING FORMAT FOR CASTING PROCESS

Material	Beginning Inventory	Receipts	Shipments	Ending Inventory	Produced	Consumed
Raw material	A	B	C	D		E
Work in process	A			D		E
Finished goods	A	B	C	D	F	
Residues	A	B	C	D	F	
Total	A	B	C	D	F	E
B-PID				G	G	

For raw material,
$$E = A + B - C - D \qquad (5.15)$$

For work in process,
$$E = A - D \qquad (5.16)$$

For finished goods and residues,
$$F = D + C - B - A \qquad (5.17)$$

The B-PID can be either a positive or a negative value and is determined as:
$$\text{Total line: } (A + B) - (C + D) \qquad (5.18)$$

and must also equal
$$\text{Total } E - F \qquad (5.19)$$

5-8. DINGOT METAL PRODUCTION

5-8.1. Process Description: *Feed Material.* The feed material to the dingot process is green salt (UF_4), which is packaged in portable hoppers. Adequate measurements of the contained uranium in the UF_4 are made at the time of production and shipment by the reduction and hydrofluorination plant, and no additional measurements are made in the dingot plant.

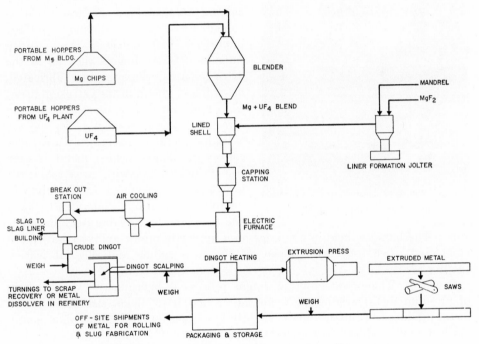

Fig. 5-25   Dingot metal production flow diagram.

Process. The dingot process reduces a blend of UF_4 and magnesium metal chips to a massive piece of metal. The process, as outlined in Fig. 5-25, is similar to the derby process, except that the massive metal produced weighs 10 times more. The massive metal is scalped on a lathe, heated, and extruded into round bars.

The reduction is accomplished in a fashion similar to that described in Sec. 5-6.1. Blended UF_4 and magnesium are charged to a MgF_2-lined steel bomb (Fig. 5-26), and the bomb is placed in a furnace (Fig. 5-27). When the proper temperature is reached, the reaction takes place with the evolution of considerable heat. The bomb is then transferred to cooling pits.

The bomb, after cooling, is moved to a break-out station, where the lid is removed and the bomb is inverted and jolted over an 8 by 8-in. heavy screen to discharge the crude metal dingot and slag. The slag passes through the heavy screen and is conveyed to the liner-processing building.

The crude dingot (Fig. 5-28) is removed from the break-out enclosure and

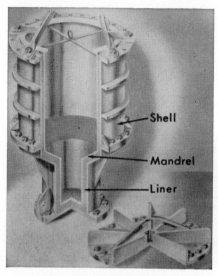

FIG. 5-26   Dingot shell.

weighed. Crude dingots with poor tops are transferred to a power hacksaw, the top is removed, and the dingot is re-weighed.

The dingots are transferred to the machining area, and all surfaces are machined ("scalped") to remove surface impurities and defects. The cleaned smooth-surfaced dingots then go to the extrusion area, where they are lubricated, heated, and placed in the extrusion press. The hydraulically operated ram then forces the dingot through a die, and the extruded metal is discharged to a roller conveyor. The extruded metal is then transferred to a sawing area to be cut into lengths convenient for handling in the rolling operation. Samples are taken and delivered to the laboratory for analysis. The bars are held in a storage area until laboratory analyses have been completed; then they are shipped off site to a rolling and slug fabrication facility.

Product. The product of the dingot process is high-purity extruded bars of uranium metal originating from the reduction to dingot-size metal. The metal produced in this fashion is slightly less impure than cast uranium metal. Each dingot produced is sequentially numbered. The number is assigned at the time the shell is charged with the UF_4-magnesium blend and remains with the dingot throughout the operation.

Residues. The residues resulting from dingot production are the same as the residues generated from the reduction-to-derby process with the addition of solid scrap metal, sawdust, and turnings. Solid scrap metal can be of two types, metal suitable for recycle to the casting operation and metal requiring recycle to the refinery metal dissolver. In general, the crops from extruded bars are suitable for recycle to a casting furnace; whereas crops from crude dingots must be recycled to the refinery. Visual inspection of the metal determines the recycle destination.

Granular metal sawdust, generated when dingots and extruded bars are sawed, is packaged into drums and shipped off site to a scrap-recovery facility for burning to an oxide and eventual recycle to the refinery.

Turnings generated from dingot scalping are packaged into drums and transferred to the metal-dissolving unit in the refinery operations. The turnings may also be burned to an oxide.

The processing of the reject slag, dust collection, and sump-recovery cake residues is described in Sec. 5-6.1. The only exception is the recycling of sump cake having low fluoride content to the refinery.

5-8.2. Measurements: *Product.* The product, extruded metal bars cut to convenient lengths, is placed on a ticket-printing scale, where the weight is recorded on a continuous tape by an integral printing mechanism. Scale accuracy is maintained through a statistical scale-testing procedure. The uranium metal product is 100 percent uranium for all practical purposes; therefore, actual assaying of the metal is not performed. Stringent impurity specifications assure the maintenance of this quality.

Residues. Scrap metal visually approved for recycle to the casting operation is assumed to assay 100 percent uranium. Scrap metal of this nature is packaged into pretared containers and gross weighed. Metal destined for recycle to the refinery is not sampled for uranium but is assigned an arbitrary

FIG. 5-27 Dingot furnace. The furnace door is in the raised position. The furnace bottom can be moved forward on rails. The charged dingot bomb is moved to the furnace by crane and lowered to the furnace bottom. The furnace bottom is returned to the furnace, the furnace door is lowered, and the heating cycle is started.

assay of 98 percent uranium and packaged into pretared containers for gross weighing and storage.

Sawdust is drained free of oil and packaged into pretared containers, gross weighed, covered with oil, and again gross weighed for shipment weights. A tentative assay of 95 percent is applied to the weight of the sawdust for shipment off site to the recovery facility. The assay determined by the recovery facility after processing is accepted for uranium accounting.

Turnings resulting from the machining of a series of dingots are collected separately in a group of drums. The uranium value assigned to a group of drummed turnings is determined by the weight difference of the related dingots before and after machining. Turnings contain the surface impurities from the dingot and would therefore assay somewhat less than 100 percent uranium. Data on experiments conducted on small quantities of turnings resulted in assays of over 99 percent. The turnings are eventually briquetted and recast.

The dust collection containing UF_4, magnesium, and MgF_2 is a very heter-

FIG. 5-28   Crude dingot.

ogeneous material. Auger samples are removed from each drum, and the drum samples are composited into a lot sample for volumetric analysis. The drummed dusts are shipped off site to a scrap-recovery facility for uranium recovery.

The reject slag is a very heterogeneous material and is not amenable to accurate sampling. Its uranium content is assigned by difference as follows:

	kg	kg
UF_4 charged as uranium		xx
Dust produced as uranium	xx	
Crude dingot produced as uranium	xx	
Total produced		xx
Difference assigned to reject slag		xx

The error in the value assigned to the reject slag arises from the use of a 100 percent uranium assay applied to the crude dingot. The true uranium assay of the crude dingot is unknown and is impractical to obtain by a direct method.

The sump cake from the filtration of wash and waste waters is sampled with a slotted thief sampler. The sludge from the settlement tanks is sampled by a slotted thief sampler or a heavy-duty pipet, depending on the composition of the sludge. Drum samples are composited into lot samples and analyzed for uranium colorimetrically. All residues are weighed on a print-weigh scale under a statistically controlled scale-checking program.

5-8.3. Statistical Evaluations. The statistical evaluations are primarily concerned with the limits of error around the assigned uranium value assigned to the reject slag. All measurements on the materials associated with the assignment of the uranium to the reject slag are evaluated, and known or estimated limits of error are computed.

The statistical sum of the individual limits of error is the limit of error assigned to the reject slag.

The material balance for the dingot process is in effect three separate balances: (1) a balance around the reduction operation, (2) a balance around the machining operations, and (3) a balance around the extrusion operation. The first two are balanced to zero since the uranium content of the reject slag and of the turnings is determined by difference. The evaluation of the material balance around the extrusion operation is a function of weight, since the assay of uranium metal is 100 percent uranium. Statistical evaluations of operational data are performed as required. These evaluations are primarily concerned with improvement in yields and more efficient operations.

5-8.4. Collection and Flow of Data: *Receipt.* The receipt to this process is the product from the reduction and hydrofluorination plant. The movement of this product is recorded on an *internal move order* signed by the chief plant clerks. The *internal move order* is posted as a total to the Transfer Journal and in detail to the *lot detail ledger* for raw materials.

Consumed. As hoppers of UF_4 are charged to the blender, an operational data sheet serves as the record for posting date charged to the *lot detail ledger* for raw materials.

Produced. A *tally sheet* (notice of production) is prepared for each lot of finished goods and residues produced. The *printed weight cards* or tapes are attached to the *tally sheet.* When a lot has been completed, the *tally sheet* is posted to the appropriate category in the *lot detail ledger* for production.

Shipments. A transfer document, either the *internal move order* or the appropriate AEC transfer document, is prepared for all materials moved out of the dingot plant. The transfer document is posted to the Transfer Journal as a total and in detail to the appropriate *lot detail ledger.*

Inventories. The physical inventory taken at the close of each month is reconciled with the *lot detail ledger* and is then posted to the ending inventory for the over-all operations. The material balance for the dingot process is in effect three material balances as described previously.

5-8.5. Material Balance Report. The format for the material balance report is the same as the standardized form used for other operations; however, the reporting differs slightly, as shown in Table 5.6.

TABLE 5.6.   REPORTING FORMAT FOR DINGOT PROCESS

Material	Beginning Inventory	Receipts	Shipments	Ending Inventory	Produced	Consumed
UF$_4$	A	B		D		E
Dust	A		C	D	F	
Crude dingot	A		C	D	F	
Subtotal (1)	A	B	C	D	F	E
Reject slag	A		C	D	F	
Total (1)	A	B	C	D	F	E
Crude dingot	A	B		D		E
Sawdust	A		C	D	F	
Crop	A		C	D	F	
Machined dingot	A		C	D	F	
Subtotal (2)	A	B	C	D	F	E
Turnings	A		C	D	F	
Total (2)	A	B	C	D	F	E
Machined dingot	A	B		D		E
Crop	A		C	D	F	
Sawdust	A		C	D	F	
Metal bars	A		C	D	F	
Subtotal (3)	A	B	C	D	F	E
B-PID				D	F	E
Grand total	A	B	C	D	F	E

(1) For UF$_4$ consumed, $E = A + B - D$
    For dust and crude ingot produced, $F = D + C - A$
    For slag produced, $F =$ subtotal (1) $E - F$
    For ending inventory of reject slag, $D = A + F - C$
    In the total (1), $A + B = C + D$ and $F = E$
(2) For crude dingot consumed in the scalping operation, $E = A + B - D$
    Crude dingot B in (2) must equal crude dingot C in (1), provided no crude dingots were transferred to other destinations
    For sawdust, machined dingot, and crop produced, $F = D + C - A$
    Turnings produced, F must equal subtotal (2) $E - F$
    For turnings ending inventory, $D = A + F - C$
(3) For machined dingots consumed in the extrusion process, $E = A + B - D$
    Machined dingot B in (3) must equal machined dingot C in (2), provided no machined dingots were transferred to other destinations
    For crop, sawdust, and metal bars produced, $F = D + C - A$
    B-PID is obtained by the difference, $E - F$, and can be positive or negative
In the grand total the beginning inventory and receipts $(A + B)$ must equal shipments and ending inventory $(C + D)$.   Also, that which is produced (F) must equal that which is consumed (E).

5-9. MATERIAL BALANCE EVALUATIONS

Material balance evaluations serve the prime purpose of evaluating the B-PID. The reasonableness of the B-PID must be established with full consideration given to all pertinent factors to detect and correct serious losses and errors.

The evaluations of the material balance are divided into two distinct categories: (1) the material balances for each operating unit and (2) the material balance for the over-all operation. The effect of errors made, for instance, on UO_3 transferred from the refinery to reduction and hydrofluorination would be a negative error in one material balance area and a positive error in the other, with a zero effect on the over-all balance. These errors would cause a bias or large variations in the respective balance areas and would indicate poor internal control, but would in no way affect the material balance for the over-all operations.

5-9.1. Balance Areas. As described previously in the material balance report sections, the B-PID for the balance areas is arrived at by taking the difference between the consumed and the produced values. The uncertainties attached only to these values affect the B-PID. It must be remembered that the change in the work-in-process inventory is a part of the consumed value; therefore, the uncertainties in the beginning and ending work-in-process inventories, in addition to uncertainties in the raw materials consumed and the materials produced, must be determined to arrive at the uncertainty in the B-PID.

In a determination of the uranium content of a given material (U) the weight (W) (or volume) is obtained and then multiplied by the appropriate assay (A), i.e.

$$U = WA \tag{5.20}$$

The variance in U then arises from the variance in W and the variance in A. From the statistical scale-testing program the variance $S_w{}^2$ in weight is readily available for all materials.

Sampling evaluation programs provide the variance $S_a{}^2$ in the assays, are available for most materials, and can be estimated for similar materials not included in the evaluation programs. The variance $S_a{}^2$ includes the sampling, compositing, and analytical errors. These errors have in many instances been determined separately and have been combined for the total uncertainty in assay.

The variance in uranium can then be computed for any given lot or batch of material as follows:

$$S_u{}^2 = (S_a{}^2 \times W^2) + (S_w{}^2 \times A^2) \tag{5.21}$$

where $S_u{}^2$ = the variance in units of uranium

$S_a{}^2$ = the variance in the assay

W = the weight or volume

$S_w{}^2$ = the variance in weight

A = the assay of the material

The 95 percent limits of error can be found for a given lot by extracting the square root of $S_u{}^2$ and multiplying by 2. This is done only as a matter of information and is not necessary for the evaluation of the material balance.

When $S_u{}^2$ has been determined for each lot or unit consumed and produced and on work-in-process inventories, the total variance of the material balance can be found as follows:

$$S_u{}^2 - \text{B-PID} = S_u{}^2R + S_u{}^2P + (S_u{}^2 - B) + (S_u{}^2 - E) \qquad (5.22)$$

where $S_u{}^2 - \text{B-PID}$ = the variance in measurements expected in the B-PID

$S_u{}^2R$ = the sum of the individual lot variances for raw materials consumed

$S_u{}^2P$ = the sum of the individual lot variances for materials produced

$S_u{}^2 - B$ = the variance in the beginning work-in-process inventory

$S_u{}^2 - E$ = the variance in the ending work-in-process inventories

The square root of $S_u{}^2 - \text{B-PID}$ multiplied by 2 would then give the 95 percent limits of error in the material balance for the plant. $S_u{}^2$ can be subtotaled for each category of materials to determine the sources of greatest error.

The sum of the $S_u{}^2 - \text{B-PID}$ for each of the balance areas is not the variance in the over-all B-PID because positive errors in one balance area could be negative errors in another and would in no manner affect the over-all material balance.

5-9.2. Over-All Material Balance. The factors affecting the over-all B-PID are the applicable receipts, shipments, and measured inventories. Materials on static inventories affect the B-PID only in the month the materials were transferred to the static inventory.

Likewise, materials received and not consumed do not affect the current month's B-PID, and materials shipped from prior months' production and inventories do not affect the B-PID for the current month. The variance $S_u{}^2$ can be computed for each shipment, receipt, and inventory item as described previously

$$S_u{}^2 = (S_a{}^2 \times W^2) + (S_w{}^2 \times A^2) \qquad (5.23)$$

However, the sorting of the applicable variances for inclusion in the grand total of the variance in the B-PID is a rather lengthy operation and must be done as outlined in Table 5.7.

TABLE 5.7. TABLE OF APPLICABLE-NONAPPLICABLE VARIANCES
IN B-PID

Variance	Applicable	Not Applicable
RECEIPTS:		
Received and consumed in same month	X	
Received and on ending inventory in same month		X
Received in prior months, consumed in current month	X	
SHIPMENTS:		
Produced and shipped in same month	X	
Shipped from prior production and inventory		X
INVENTORIES:		
Produced and on inventory in same month	X	
Beginning and ending work-in-process inventories	X	
Static inventories		X
All other inventory values		X

The total variance of the over-all station B-PID can then be determined as follows:

$$S_u^2 - \text{B-PID} = S_u^2R + S_u^2S + S_u^2I \tag{5.24}$$

where $S_u^2 - \text{B-PID}$ = the total variance in measurements expected in the over-all B-PID

S_u^2R = the total applicable variance in receipts
S_u^2S = the total applicable variance in shipments
S_u^2I = the total applicable variance in inventories

The total variance can then be converted to 95 percent limits of error associated with measurements in the over-all material balance.

The computation of the measurement errors is tedious and time consuming and is not done on a routine basis. However, the errors are determined for several months to obtain the breakdown of the total variation in the material balances. The measurement errors so determined indicate where effort should be expended to obtain better material balance control through improved measurement procedures.

As explained above, for a simpler and more readily applied evaluation the B-PID is computed as a percentage of the materials consumed for the balance areas and for the over-all balance. These percentage values are plotted on a control chart. The average and two sigma (95 percent) limits are computed. Note that the average is seldom found to be zero. The deviation of the average from zero, measured over a large number of observations, is a measure of unmeasured process losses and bias in measurements.

A positive value for the average percentage indicates that a small loss occurred or that a bias exists. A negative value indicates that a negative bias exists which is large enough to exceed the losses, if any.

The two sigma limits of the percentage values represent the total variation that can be expected in the material balances. This total variation can be divided into the following increments:

(1) Measurement uncertainties obtainable as explained previously.
(2) Uncertainties in losses and bias measured as the deviation of the average from zero.
(3) Intangible uncertainties such as clerical errors and inventory errors.

Assume a hypothetical example for an average month: $\bar{X}$, average percentage value, is $+0.10$ percent; two sigma limits are ±0.50 percent; the 95 percent limits of error of measurements computed as a percentage of an average month's consumed material equals 0.30 percent. Then $0.50 - (0.30 + 0.10) = 0.10$ percent of the materials consumed represents the error in intangibles.

It must then be decided whether the 0.10 percent error can be tolerated considering the cost of the materials involved.

5-10. INVENTORY PROCEDURES

5-10.1. Physical Inventory Procedure. At the end of each month a physical inventory is taken of all uranium materials. All operating units are notified of the inventory date approximately one week in advance so that adequate preparations and consolidations of materials can be made. The inventories of all units are taken simultaneously to avoid omissions or duplications of inventories which can be caused by the movement of materials between units during inventory.

Standard procedures for inventory preparations have been prepared by operating engineers. These procedures provide for the most favorable conditions for accurate inventories and a minimum of interference with production activities. The procedures outline specific actions such as emptying all dust collectors and packaging, sampling, and weighing the material discharged; cleaning out certain systems for which no measurement or reasonable estimate can be made; and emptying floor sumps.

Standard preprinted forms for inventory are provided so that the inventories will be recorded in an orderly fashion. The forms also serve as a check list against the items to be included on inventory. A sample copy of a form in use for a part of the refinery work-in-process inventory is included (Fig. 5-29).

The physical inventory is taken by production control personnel. Plant-operating personnel assist with the inventory only in moving the materials as

Form 6537-2
Rev. 1-21-58
Page 2

Month _____ Year _____
Day _____
Inv. By _____

MALLINCKRODT CHEMICAL WORKS, URANIUM DIVISION
WELDON SPRING REFINERY (105)
WIP INVENTORY FORM

TANK CONV. BY: _____ OK BY: _____
MI in COMP. OF BY: _____

AREA	B.K. TANK NO.	TANK TITLE	BY	GAUGE USED	GAUGE READ	A	B	A+B	S.G.	°F	°C	THERMAL CORR. GAL.	CORR'D GAL.	MI in COMP. GAL.
PRIMARY EXTRACTION AND WASHING AND RE-EXTRACTION	3361-1	EXTRACTION DECANTER												
		EXTRACTION DECANTER												
	3361-2	EXTRACTION DECANTER												
	3361-3	EXTRACTION DECANTER												
	3362	EXTRACTION DECANTER												
	3363	EXTRACTION DECANTER												
	3398	TBP EXT. PUMP TK.												
	3399	WASHED EXTRACT PUMP TANK												
	3436	DECANTER PUMP TK.												
	3360-1	AQUEOUS FEED TANK												
	3360-2	AQUEOUS FEED TANK												
		TOTAL												

COMP. BY _____ OBS. BY _____
DIL'N _____ OBS. BY _____
COMP. 1 (A) _____ (B) _____
COMP. 2 (A) _____ (B) _____
COMP. 3 (A) _____ (B) _____
AVG. g/1 _____ LBS. U _____

AREA	B.K. TANK NO.	TANK TITLE
SOLVENT	3364-1	SOLVENT ADJ. TK.
	3364-2	SOLVENT ADJ. TK.
	3401	STRIPPED SOLVENT PUMP TANK
	3400	RE-EXTRACTION ORGANIC PUMP TK.
	3386	TREATED SOLVENT HOLD TANK
	3417	PUMP OUT TANK
		TOTAL

COMP. BY _____ OBS. BY _____
DIL'N _____ OBS. BY _____
COMP. 1 (A) _____ (B) _____
COMP. 2 (A) _____ (B) _____
COMP. 3 (A) _____ (B) _____
AVG. g/1 _____ LBS. U _____

AREA	B.K. TANK NO.	TANK TITLE
MISCELLANEOUS (105-TBP)	3374	SUMP LIQUOR STRIPPING TANK
	3438	SODIUM CARBONATE TREATING TANK
	3416	SUMP LIQUOR COLLECTION TANK
		TOTAL

COMP. BY _____ OBS. BY _____
DIL'N _____ OBS. BY _____
COMP. 1 (A) _____ (B) _____
COMP. 2 (A) _____ (B) _____
COMP. 3 (A) _____ (B) _____
AVG. g/1 _____ LBS. U _____

Fig. 5-29 Sample work-in-process inventory form.

needed for inventory. The production-control personnel are divided into inventory crews, and each crew is assigned to specific plant areas. Complete lots of feed material, finished goods, and residues are counted and tabulated. The weights and assays of these materials as reported on receiving reports and production notices are used for assignment of uranium values. All other materials fall under the category of work in process and are physically measured. The use of standard assay and holdup factors is kept at a minimum.

5-10.2. Accumulation of Data. Immediately following the physical inventory, the physical counts of complete lots of feed material, finished goods, and residues are checked and reconciled with the book inventories for these materials.

The book inventory of the work in process in each of the balance areas is the beginning work-in-process inventory plus the materials charged minus the materials produced. The book inventory so obtained is compared with the physical inventory, and the difference is reported as the B-PID. After all laboratory analyses have been made available for materials on inventory, the uranium values are computed.

5-10.3. Reporting of Inventories. The physical inventories for each balance area are posted to the related material balance report for the balance area, the materials having been consolidated by material type. The material type coincides with the material type designated on the ending inventory report form prescribed by the AEC.

As the reports for the balance areas are completed, the ending inventory for each balance area is transcribed to a spread sheet. This sheet has the material type listed in the left-hand column; the appropriate balance areas listed across the top of the page, with a column for each balance area; and a line total column on the extreme right. All columns are totaled and the balance area columns are crosscast to equal the total of the line total column.

The values in the total column are now transcribed to the AEC prescribed ending-inventory form. The grand total of the ending inventory is reported as the ending inventory on the over-all material balance report.

5-10.4. Statistical Evaluation of Inventories. The statistical evaluation of the inventories is primarily concerned with the limits of error around the uranium contents assigned to the inventory items. The method for computing limits of error for the various materials has been described in preceding portions of this chapter.

The limit of error in the over-all material balance is determined by combining the limits of error for the applicable inventory items with the limits of error for the applicable receipts and shipments. As discussed in Sec. 5-9, the limits of error so determined are associated with measurements only.

On two occasions, duplicate inventories have been taken of the refinery work in process. The duplicate inventories when compared with each other were within the limits of the measurement error computed for both inventories.

Duplicating inventories is costly, but it provides confidence in the inventories and their reported limits of error.

5-11. STATISTICS

Modern statistical methods are employed to evaluate plant operational data and much of the detail related to uranium material accounting. Control charts are maintained within operating plants to record data such as daily uranium losses to sewers, product quality, and product yields. These charts are a valuable aid to plant superintendents since trends are readily detectable and provide a basis for appropriate action.

Student's t test is widely used to determine the significance of the difference between various operating data. Simple two-factor as well as multiple-factor, correlations are made between various measured stages in the over-all operation to determine effects on yields and product quality.

One of the largest uses made of statistics is in the evaluation of the difference in the uranium values determined by the shipper and the receiver of uranium materials. In this evaluation, should the differences between the shipper and receiver be unbiased, reduced measurements are possible and result in reduced costs. For those materials routinely shipped, control charts are maintained for the shipper-receiver differences. The t test is made to check for bias; should no bias be found, the measurements are reduced to a random selection of items or shipments. These randomly selected differences are plotted on the control chart, and as long as they remain unbiased and within the control chart limits, the measurements continue on a random selection basis. If a bias is found, a more detailed evaluation is made to determine the source or sources causing the bias such as weights, samples, analyses, or any combination of these measurements.

Many of the control charts and some of the evaluations have been reduced to a clerical function and are reviewed periodically by the plant statistician. A work sheet for the t tests has been designed, and the t test can be a routine clerical function for many of the evaluations made. The statistician is consulted only for the design of experimental evaluation and the analyses of the results.

REFERENCES FOR CHAPTER 5

1. O. L. Davies, *Statistical Methods in Research and Production,* 3rd ed., p. 112, Hafner Publishing Company, New York, 1957.

Chapter 6

URANIUM-235 ISOTOPIC ENRICHMENT*

6-1. THE GASEOUS DIFFUSION PROCESS

Since the late 1940's the primary method of increasing the U^{235} content of uranium has been the gaseous diffusion process. In this process, normal uranium in the form of uranium hexafluoride gas is fed into the system near the bottom of gaseous diffusion process equipment, which, through a series of separating stages, enriches the material in the isotope U^{235}. At the top, uranium hexafluoride with a high concentration of U^{235} is collected; at the bottom, uranium hexafluoride depleted in that isotope is discharged. The term "depleted" means that the U^{235} isotope content is less than the U^{235} content of the feed material.

Separation by gaseous diffusion depends upon the fact that the velocities of molecules of different mass differ. When a gas is confined in or moved through a containing vessel, the molecules of the gas exert a continuous pressure on the vessel's walls. This pressure is a function of the number of molecules striking the walls and the kinetic energy of each. If the gas is a mixture of molecules of different molecular weights, the lighter molecules, which have higher velocities, strike the container walls more frequently than the heavier molecules. In the gaseous diffusion process the gas is confined by a porous membrane with pores of such small dimensions that gross flow is minimized. The lighter molecules diffuse preferentially through the pores of this membrane, which is called a "barrier."

Uranium hexafluoride has been selected as the process material because it is easily maintained in the gas phase at moderate temperatures and because the associated fluorine has only one stable isotope. When uranium hexafluoride is derived from ores (i.e. includes no enriched or depleted uranium), approximately 99.3 percent of the hexafluoride contains U^{238} and has a molecular weight of 352, and 0.7 percent contains U^{235} and has a molecular weight of 349. Since the enrichment achieved by a single separation in the diffusion

* James A. Parsons, Union Carbide Nuclear Co., The Gaseous Diffusion Plant, Oak Ridge, Tenn. The author acknowledges the contributions and assistance of R. R. Frazier, J. F. Hudson, and W. D. McCluen in the preparation of this material.

plant is very slight, a large number of separations are necessary for substantial enrichment. Equipment for a series of interconnecting separations is called a "cascade" and the plant itself is often known as a "gaseous diffusion cascade."

Fig. 6-1 is an aerial view of an Oak Ridge gaseous diffusion plant.

The basic unit of a diffusion cascade is called a "stage." It consists of a container to enclose the barrier, compressors to move the uranium hexafluoride, and associated heat-exchange equipment and controllers to maintain the required process conditions. Fig. 6-2 illustrates a representative stage arrangement. The entering gas is brought to the proper pressure by the com-

Fig. 6-1 Aerial view of an Oak Ridge gaseous diffusion plant.

pressor; the heat exchanger controls the gas temperature. The gas flows against the barrier material, and approximately half the gas diffuses through the barrier to the lower pressure region. This gas (slightly enriched in U^{235}) is passed to the next higher stage for a repetition of the cycle. The part that does not penetrate the barrier, now slightly depleted in U^{235}, reenters the next lower stage. Thus, the diffusion cascade can be visualized as a long succession of connected separating stages, each passing on to the next higher stage uranium hexafluoride gas enriched in U^{235}.

Uranium hexafluoride feed is introduced into the plant at the point where the U^{235} concentration of the cascade stream equals that of the feed material. The enriched product material is withdrawn at one end of the cascade; the tails, or depleted materials, are withdrawn at the other end. Side products can be withdrawn at any intervening U^{235} concentration.

The uranium hexafluoride feed for the cascade is manufactured at the plant site. The starting material for feed manufacture is uranium trioxide, which is reduced to dioxide by exposure to hydrogen at an elevated temperature. Uranium dioxide, in turn, is reacted to uranium tetrafluoride (green salt) by exposure to hydrogen fluoride, also at an elevated temperature. Green salt is converted to uranium hexafluoride by reaction with fluorine. The resultant product, together with any unused fluorine, is pumped through specially constructed equipment commonly referred to as "cold traps." The low-temperature portion of the cycle condenses uranium hexafluoride and permits any fluorine present to pass through. This method of product removal also serves

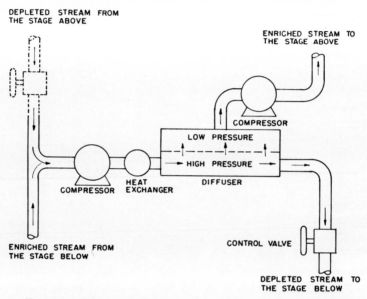

FIG. 6-2 Schematic diagram of a gaseous diffusion stage.

as a purification step, removing noncondensable contaminants. As a cold trap is filled, it is isolated and heated to liquefy the hexafluoride, which is then drained to a shipping container.

Extensive repair facilities are maintained because most of the plant equipment that has been in contact with the process material contains deposits of uranium materials formed by reaction of the metal surfaces with the highly corrosive uranium hexafluoride. Fairly sizable installations are required to remove these uranium deposits from the equipment and to recover the uranium in a form that can be returned to the major process stream. These installations include cleaning facilities for the chemical scrubbing of all sizes of equipment (generally acid treatment). The recovery facilities consist of evaporators, extraction columns, drum driers, and calciners to recover uranium from the cleaning solutions. Fig. 6-3 is a typical flow diagram illustrating the flow of material to the recovery facilities. The system illustrated recovers uranium from recycled cleaning solutions and miscellaneous waste solutions generated during normal plant operations. The recovered uranium is converted to uranium oxide for subsequent fluorination to uranium hexafluoride, which is then returned to the diffusion cascade.

The mixer-settler system, shown in Fig. 6-4, rapidly extracts uranium from a nitric acid solution by the action of an organic solvent. Recycle solutions are fed at a rate of approximately 100 gal/hr to a vertical mixer, where they

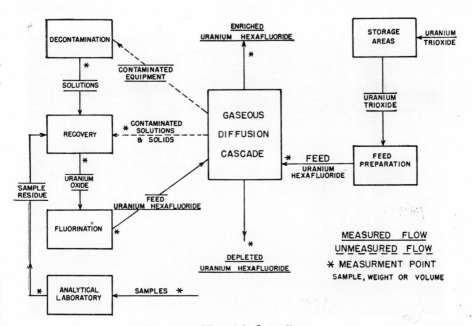

FIG. 6-3 Material flow diagram.

are mixed with tributyl phosphate and Varsol. The organic phase is fed to the mixer at a rate of about 26 gal/hr.

The acid-solvent mixture flows by gravity to a horizontal settler, where the phases separate by density difference. The raffinate (waste aqueous phase) from the settler, containing a reduced amount of uranium, is returned to the cleaning facility to be used as rinse solution.

The organic solution is pumped to a pulse-agitated stripper column, where the organic solvent is washed free of the uranium by a countercurrent water flow. The uranyl nitrate solution in the aqueous phase is then concentrated by evaporation and drum dried to uranyl nitrate hexahydrate. The drum-dried product is fed to an indirectly fired rotary kiln calciner, which thermally decomposes it to uranium trioxide and urano-uranic oxide.

The general recovery system, shown schematically with the mixer-settler system in Fig. 6-5, is designed to extract uranium exhaustively from concentrated, acidified miscellaneous waste solutions. This system comprises a pre-evapora-tor, a mixer-agitated extraction column, a mixer-agitated stripper column, and (in conjunction with the mixer-settler system) a post-evaporator, a drum drier, and a calciner. The extraction column, through countercurrent flow, is designed to effect the mass transfer of uranium from the nitric acid feed solution to an organic solvent. The stripper column effects the mass transfer of the uranium from the organic to the aqueous phase through agitated coun-tercurrent flow. The stripper column product is pumped to the post-evaporator

Fig. 6-4   Mixer-settler system. Shown here are two vertical mixers on the left and two horizontal settlers on the right.

for concentration and from there to the drum drier and calciner, where ura-nium trioxide and urano-uranic oxide are produced.

The oxide fluorination system consists of a 5-in. tower reactor, where dried uranium oxide is treated with fluorine gas in a flame-type reaction. This treatment yields uranium hexafluoride, waste gases, and unreacted ash prod-ucts. The yield gases are piped to a condensing system, a series of chilled cylinders, where the uranium hexafluoride is collected as a solid. Waste gases pass through the system and are vented to the atmosphere.

6-2. SS CONTROL

During the initial years of gaseous diffusion plant operation, SS control was influenced significantly by the wartime strategic value of the material being

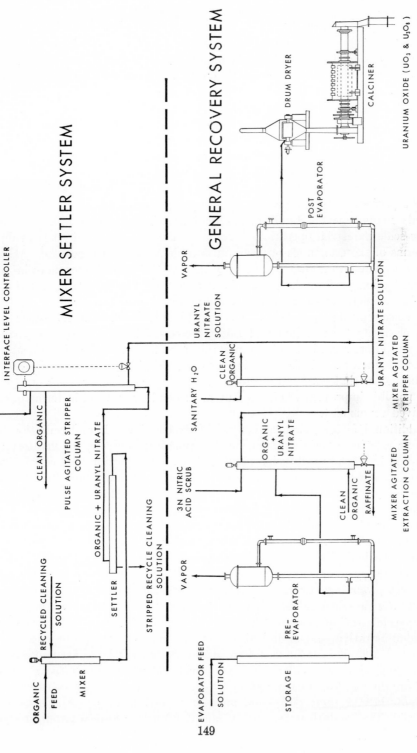

Fig. 6-5 Schematic diagram of mixer-settler and general recovery systems.

149

processed. The control during this period was to a large degree a security measure, designed to guard against unauthorized and undetected diversions of SS material which could disclose that uranium isotopes were being separated and could indicate the degree of success achieved. Strategic value in the above sense is no longer a governing consideration, and therefore the emphasis has shifted to material and inventory control comparable to the general industrial practice of conserving valuable materials. The resulting materials-control program has brought about economic and efficient utilization of organization, communications, and information-generating facilities.

The huge size of the diffusion facilities and the extremely high unit value of the process materials present an exceptional challenge in the field of materials management. Small errors or biases considered tolerable in most large-scale industrial operations become startlingly significant when evaluated in terms of the economics of uranium isotopic separation processes. Material balances, which to a large degree form the basis of control over material losses or production performance, must be accurate to minute tolerances; the economic considerations are such that the material accounting requirements call for measurements approaching an unattainable level. On the other hand, measurements for uranium and isotopic composition are very costly, and a constant effort must be made to maintain a realistic balance of the competing economic factors. This situation has led to widespread use of statistical evaluation so that potential errors can be evaluated in terms of material value, and possible improvements in measurement can be expressed in terms of value received versus cost.

Additional factors, such as control of nuclear hazards and radiation, play a large role in materials management economics; however, the greatest complication in a gaseous diffusion plant is that a large portion of a very valuable inventory must be measured as highly corrosive uranium hexafluoride gas in an extremely large, dynamic system (i.e. the gaseous diffusion cascade). The system requires the maintenance of very large inventories, large even in relation to the plant throughput. The economic factors associated with the cost of equipment shutdown make it inconceivable to consider removing this inventory periodically for convenient direct measurement. Therefore, it has been necessary to develop approaches permitting continuous productive operation, yet providing extremely precise and accurate inventory determinations.

6-2.1 Organizational Structure. Responsibility for SS control is delegated to a special staff of personnel appropriately trained to handle the wide range of administrative and technical aspects of control which are encountered. The staff is composed of chemists, engineers, statisticians, accountants, and supporting operating and clerical personnel. Complementing the SS control staff are the plant operational groups, which are responsible for conservation of SS materials in their possession and for reporting all relevant data to SS control. The analytical laboratory and the Nuclear Safety Group, although not integral parts of the SS control organization, are vital components of the control function.

SS Control Group. The SS Control Group is a part of the Process Engineering Division. As such, it is directly associated with an organization that deals closely with the interpretation of plant performance. The SS Control Group is divided into two major sections: one is concerned with the technical aspects of control; the other, with records and data-processing systems. The technical section is staffed with engineers and statisticians responsible for the continual development and evaluation of data-producing mechanisms and operations. The records and data-processing section is staffed with accountants and material-control clerks responsible for the processing, reporting, and evaluation of SS control.

Materials Handling Group. The Materials Handling Group, also part of the Process Engineering Division, provides for transporting and storing all SS material. This specially trained organization makes most of the gross measurements of all material receipts or shipments. A special control sampling facility is also maintained to effect the best attainable control of the field sampling operation for many materials processed. Many special studies on sampling techniques are made possible through the use of the central sampling facility.

This group also maintains, inspects, and supervises the thousands of containers necessary for the efficient operation of the gaseous diffusion and auxiliary facilities. Specifically, the group procures, inspects, and conducts leak and pressure tests of cylinders and cylinder valves used in transporting uranium. No less important than the proper handling of uranium is the establishment and maintenance of systems of identification for the various container classifications.

Laboratory Group. Serving the analytical needs of the SS control function and the plant is a well-equipped analytical laboratory, a part of the Technical Division. At peak periods as many as 5000 uranium samples per month are analyzed in the laboratory for both uranium and U^{235}. Very high levels of accuracy and precision are attained.

In addition to the research and development portions, the laboratory is divided into the Sample Preparation Section, the Uranium Analysis Section, and the Spectrometer Section.

The Sample Preparation Section prepares field samples for the analyst. Responsibilities include the homogenization by liquefaction or blending, as in the case of powdered solids, of the larger field samples to permit the removal of a representative subsample. This section also maintains facilities for the direct fluorination of materials such as oxides to the hexafluoride for spectrometer analyses. Freeze-point depression analyses for uranium hexafluoride are also performed. A very important additional function is the maintenance of the supply of standard material. Closely associated with this activity is the preparation of disguised samples. These are of predetermined uranium and U^{235} content and are used to implement the program for precision and accuracy control of the analytical procedures.

The Uranium Analysis Section performs all uranium analyses for SS-control purposes with the exceptions noted for the Sample Preparation Section. Methods of analysis range from the very precise potassium dichromate titration used for pure materials through the gravimetric, fluorometric, and colorimetric methods. Samples processed range from very pure materials that can be directly ignited and analyzed gravimetrically to very impure samples that require extensive extraction and purification steps before analysis. The section also makes isotopic analyses by the fission-counting method.

The Spectrometer Section maintains a group of mass spectrometers for the isotopic analysis of plant SS-control samples. These instruments are capable of measuring samples with U^{235} concentrations covering the entire range encountered in a diffusion plant. This section also performs extensive analytical work for the research and development sections.

Nuclear Safety Group. The Nuclear Safety Group, a section of the Industrial Relations Division, assists in furnishing criticality data and in formulating regulations for handling various quantities of uranium materials of varying isotopic enrichments, such as setting maximum safe assay (U^{235} concentrations) limitations for different container sizes and material characteristics. A major problem in the handling of fissionable material is the prevention of the assembly of a critical mass, i.e. that quantity of material in the proper geometrical configuration which will support or create a chain reaction.

6-2.2. Processing Accounting Data. The plant is divided into major functional areas of material control. These areas are further subdivided into the basic accounts that localize the responsibility for materials received and processed. Flowing into and out of these areas are materials of many different types, i.e. materials ranging in assay from cascade tails to product, numerous chemical compositions, and many types of production residues.

These materials are classified for accounting purposes into approximately 75 different types to assure adequate coverage for all material. A code is used for this purpose. An additional classification is made to prevent the mixing of isotopic assays. This consists of a second code that divides the U^{235} concentration range into 31 increments.

The reporting unit for SS materials is the gram, regardless of material, that is, material of depleted, normal, or enriched U^{235} content. This standardization of reporting unit simplifies the accounting procedures.

The accounting system has been adapted to the use of punched-card calculating equipment for handling the large volume of records and computations required. However, some hand computing is still done. The function of the Accounting Group is therefore largely to audit and to ascertain that papers flowing to and from the calculating equipment are correct. The material accounting office records approximately 12,000 material movements each month; this total includes containers moving in process into, within, and from the plant area and their related sample transfers. Information regarding these movements is forwarded to the office on standard prenumbered material-transfer forms.

Upon receipt, the prenumbered forms are registered or logged into the office and then distributed to material-control clerks on the basis of the processing account involved. Each material-control clerk is responsible for processing transaction and inventory data of one or more internal accounts. Each has a knowledge of the particular process—for example, conversion from oxide to uranium hexafluoride, decontamination systems, or laboratory procedures. It is possible, through a working acquaintance with the various systems, for the clerks to ascertain whether the material transfers to and from accounts are reasonable as to type and quantity and whether the laboratory results supplied are in the range expected. The clerks also assure that a proper inventory cutoff takes place.

Contact between the material-control clerks and the operating personnel is encouraged so that clerical errors that may occur in the field can be corrected on a current basis. The material-control clerks preaudit each transfer document before it is passed on for further processing; this is considered a significant factor of internal control over book-physical inventory differences.

A punched card is prepared for each container transferred after preaudit. The basic accounting data are placed on the card, verified, and extended through the use of a calculator punch. The card contains all pertinent information regarding the container transferred in the following order: (1) the unit of measure, (2) subaccounts to and from, (3) reference to the transfer authorization, including number and date, (4) sample references, (5) material type, (6) gross, tare, and net weights, (7) weight percent uranium and U^{235}, and (8) grams of uranium and U^{235}.

Perpetual-inventory card decks with a card for each container transferred into the account are maintained for all storage areas. Since no processing is involved in a storage account, the eventual movement of the container to a processing account or off site requires no punching or calculation. The operator reproduces from the storage-deck card another that contains the proper information for the next movement. The new card becomes a part of the transfer record, and the storage-deck card is filed for possible future use.

Samples flowing to the laboratory make up approximately one-third of the 12,000 monthly transfers. The cards prepared for each sample movement are summarized by account from, account to, and assay range at the close of the accounting period. Approximately 50 cards represent the total quantities charged to the laboratory by the processing accounts.

Cards representing containers of material are also summarized as often as practical, usually every third work day. Process transfers are passed through the accounting machine and the detail cards are listed and totaled on the back of each transfer form. At the same time, through connection with the reproducing punch, one card is produced which is equivalent in grams uranium and U^{235} to the total contained in each classification of material transferred by that paper. Following this summary punch, the forms are returned to the proper material-control clerk for postaudit and filing authorization. In this manner, detail decks are reduced on a current basis to a more easily handled deck of approximately 1500 cards.

The material movements thus represented retain identity as to accounts, transfer paper number, and material type and assay increment. At the close of the accounting period, the intermediate deck is again summarized. A deck of approximately 400 cards is prepared, equal to the total of each material type by assay moving to and from each account. This deck, with the addition of the summarized sample cards, is utilized for posting to the ledger accounts and eventually for preparing the material control reports.

6-2.3. Material Control. The working of the material-control system can best be seen by following a specific production stream. Uranium trioxide is received from off site in containers holding approximately 5 tons. When the material is received, it is weighed, tally-in forms are completed and transmitted to the accounting offices, and the containers are stored until the material is required for processing. At the time of receipt, a verification of the uranium and U^{235} content is required at the receiving installation. In most instances involving routine flows, the shipper supplies a sample of the material constituting the shipment together with all pertinent measurement data for uranium content. The validity of the samples and data is determined through the application of a statistical acceptance sampling plan for shipper-provided data.

If the receiver is to accept the shipper's data, he has to be assured that the accounting data supplied by the shipper reasonably represents the material received. To obtain this assurance, the receiver may sample the material and test the sample for comparison with shipping data. The plan used for such a comparison determines the amount of sampling required and indicates the chances of accepting material that does not agree with shipping data. A routine acceptance sampling plan is described in Sec. 3-2.2.

Under the acceptance sampling plan a product is alleged to have an average content or lot average specified by the shipper. A sample of the lot is taken, and if the average of the sample does not fall above or below predetermined upper and lower averages for the sample, the lot of material is accepted. The receiving measurement is set as the criterion of acceptability; thus if the shipping measurement conforms to this measurement, it is acceptable as an entry to the control records. This requires that the receiving measurement facilities be carefully evaluated. When the facilities have been shown to be acceptable, specifications can be set for the agreement between the measurements of the shipper and the receiver. A cooperative effort must be maintained, since the shipper must afford the receiver an opportunity to determine the variability of the shipping measurement methods. In addition, the shipper must maintain control of his methods and inform the receiver of any change in variability.

Normally the shipper will forward to the receiver one-half the sample on

FIG. 6-6 Top view of five-ton uranium oxide container being sampled with a vacuum thief sampler.

which the shipping analysis was determined. When this is received, the receiver will sample it (see Fig. 6-6) and compare the analyses of the shipping sample and the receiving sample. In accepting the shipper-supplied analytical measurements as a basis for material responsibility, the receiver is, in effect, agreeing that the shipper is providing a representative sample and analysis. However, if the analytical results of the shipper do not meet receiving standards, the receiver's analysis of the shipper-supplied sample may form the basis for the statement of quantity. When sufficient experience indicates that the reliability of the shipper's analytical data and sample is acceptable, receiver sampling and analysis is discontinued, except for a minimum control program to provide assurance that shipper reliability has not changed.

When the material is needed for processing, it is transferred to the uranium hexafluoride feed manufacturing area. Appropriate charges and credits are made to the accounting records for the storage area and for the feed-manufacturing account. New measurement data are not obtained for this transaction. When the oxide has been converted to uranium hexafluoride, the material is drained into cylinders. When the cylinders have been filled, the material is weighed, sampled, and shipped to storage areas before being fed to the diffusion cascade.

Feed Material Sampling and Analysis. A large parent sample of uranium hexafluoride feed material is taken to ensure a representative sample of the container. Too large to be accommodated by laboratory methods of analysis,

FIG. 6-7   Five-inch cylinder for enriched material.

this sample is subsampled to obtain a quantity that can be handled by laboratory methods. The quantity obtained is then sent to the Uranium Analysis Section.

At the same time that the subsample is taken for the uranium analysis, another subsample is taken for mass assay.

A gravimetric analysis is performed normally to determine total uranium. After the laboratory subsample has been weighed, the tube containing the subsample is entirely submerged in distilled water and the uranium hexafluoride is hydrolyzed. The solution is evaporated and then taken up in nitric acid and heated until the nitric acid evaporates. The residue is ignited to uranouranic oxide (U_3O_8), allowed to cool, and weighed. The percentage of uranium in the sample can be computed from the weight of the sample, the weight of the solution, and the gravimetric factor for uranium in U_3O_8.

In the Spectrometer Section the subsample that was obtained for the U^{235} analysis is directly connected to the mass spectrometer and fed into it. The U^{235} content of the sample is determined by comparing it with that of a standard having a known U^{235} content. When the uranium and U^{235} analyses have been completed, they are reported to the accounting office, where the uranium and U^{235} involved in the transfer are computed. Appropriate entries are then made to the accounting records.

Product-Sample Analysis. As stated above, the gaseous diffusion plant

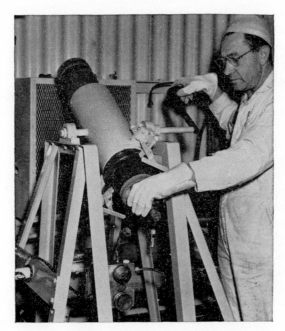

FIG. 6-8   Five-inch cylinder being homogenized.

produces a U^{235}-enriched stream from the top of the plant and a depleted tails stream. Depleted material withdrawn at the bottom of the plant is normally placed in commercial chlorine-type cylinders. Enriched material withdrawn at the top of the plant is placed in special individually safe cylinders 5 in. in diameter. Fig. 6-7 exhibits the 5-in. cylinder in which the top product of the plant is withdrawn. When materials are withdrawn from the diffusion cascade, they are weighed, sampled, and analyzed for uranium and U^{235}. Sampling procedures used for cascade tails are comparable to those used for feed manufacture, and therefore do not require additional discussion. Enriched uranium hexafluoride, however, requires slightly different techniques, principally because of its high unit value.

The enriched product material is sampled by melting, homogenizing the material, and transferring a portion of the container contents to a sample container. Homogenizing the cylinder for sampling requires at least five rotations for adequate mixing. The procedure is illustrated in Fig. 6-8. When the cylinder of material is thoroughly mixed, the cylinder is inverted and connected to a sampling manifold.

Side Stream Sample Analysis. Not all the material remains in the major production streams. A small portion of the material leaves the gaseous diffusion plant in a large variety of streams. Some of these are in the form of corrosion products on equipment removed for maintenance; others are in the form of contaminated materials, such as oils and cleaning solutions, which are quite difficult to sample.

Equipment removed from cascade service for maintenance is transported to the cleaning facility before any attempt is made to ascertain directly the quantity of contained material. At this point, the statement of uranium content is an engineering estimate based on the known history of the equipment and the characteristics of the materials involved. At the cleaning facility, the equipment is dismantled and scrubbed or sprayed with nitric acid solution. The cleaned equipment is then water-rinsed, air-dried, and removed from the cleaning facility for maintenance work or storage. The nitric acid cleaning solution is recycled through the spray booth or scrub tables for approximately one-half hour, and a 1-liter sample is removed. Then the solution is pumped to calibrated storage columns to await transfer to the recovery facility.

The acid sample is transferred to the analytical laboratory for uranium and U^{235} analysis. The uranium is determined gravimetrically, a pentaether-water extraction being used to separate the uranium from impurities. The uranium is precipitated in the aqueous phase, and ignited to U_3O_8 for gravimetric determination. The U^{235}-content analysis is made on a portion of the oxide produced in the chemical analysis. The purified oxide is weighed, dissolved, and electroplated on an electropolished nickel disk. The disk is then counted on a fission counter, and the counting rate is compared with that of a known standard to obtain the percentage of U^{235}.

When scheduled for recovery, the acid solution is pumped to the recovery system, and appropriate charges and credits are made to the cleaning and recovery accounts on the basis of the analysis of the acid sample and the volume of acid transferred.

The recovery system extracts the uranium from the acid solution by contacting it with organic solvents in mixer-settlers: it strips the uranium from the organic into the aqueous phase; and then it concentrates, drum dries, and calcines it to UO_3. The acid is again measured for volume, sampled for residual uranium and U^{235} analyses, and transferred back to the cleaning facility for re-use. The necessary charges and credits are made to the concerned accounts on the basis of this analysis and the volume of acid transferred.

The oxide produced in this operation is homogenized by rod milling, and a 50-gm sample is obtained by quartering. The sample is transferred to the analytical laboratory for uranium and U^{235} analysis.

These oxide samples are weighed, dissolved in nitric acid, and purified through a pentaether aqueous extraction. The purified solution is precipitated and ignited to U_3O_8 for the gravimetric determination. The U^{235} content is determined by fission counting.

The oxide is weighed and either transferred from the recovery accounts to storage to await further processing or moved directly to the fluorination account for processing to uranium hexafluoride. Appropriate entries, based on the results of the analysis and the oxide weight, are made to the concerned account ledgers.

If economically feasible, contaminated materials generated from normal plant operation are recovered as oxide and converted to uranium hexafluoride for return to production streams. Economic justification for recovery is based upon the value of the uranium as determined by the U^{235} content.

Recovery Operations. Enumeration of each type of material encountered and its specific measurement problem is beyond the scope of this chapter. However, a few examples of the material types encountered can be noted together with the factors that present unusual problems of measurement. Generally encountered are large quantities of 4-mesh activated alumina with stratified layers of uranium deposits; uranyl nitrate solutions with partially crystallized uranium salts; oil and aqueous mixtures having different uranium concentrations within each phase; and incinerator ash and vacuum cleanings with stratified layers or isolated pockets of uranium compounds. Such materials present significant measurement problems. Knowledge of the uranium and U^{235} concentrations is necessary not only for adequate material control but to allow the material to be properly evaluated in relation to economic recovery criteria and to allow an assessment of the criticality problem.

When scheduled for processing, these materials are transferred directly to the recovery operation. No new measurement is required if the materials are moved from a storage area unless individual containers have been batched for economic recovery.

The materials are charged to a recovery dissolving and solution preparation area. Here the solids are dissolved, and solutions are chemically adjusted for recovery with nitric acid. A sample is obtained after one-half hour of recycling the solution through the preparation tanks. The materials can be transferred to the general recovery operation, depending on the laboratory analysis of this sample (pentaether extractions, gravimetric analysis for uranium and the fission count for U^{235}) and the calibrated volume of acid in the tanks.

The uranium-acid solution is fed into the top of the 20-ft 5-in.-diameter Pyrex extraction column, where a countercurrent of organic solution under agitation effects the transfer of uranium from the acid phase. The raffinate stream from this column is monitored by periodic check samples when the equipment is operating and is discarded if economically not recoverable.

The uranium-organic solution is pumped from the extraction column to a stripper column of identical design to the extraction column, where the organic is washed free of the uranium with a countercurrent flow of water. The resulting uranyl nitrate from the stripper column is evaporated to concentrate the solution; then it is drum dried and calcined to UO_3 and U_3O_8.

6-2.4. Cascade Inventory. The preceding discussion dealt primarily with material flows between the different processing facilities. Inventories are also needed to complete a material balance. In general, these are divided into two categories: dynamic and static. This terminology should not be confused with the frequently used terms "active" and "inactive" inventory, meaning in process or in storage, respectively. A dynamic inventory is a statement of material holdup in a continuous process at a precise instant; a static inventory is the comparable measurement of a batch or non-continuous process. This means that dynamic inventories are taken in systems where physical equipment shutdown is impractical and static inventories are taken where equipment shutdown does not appreciably alter production efficiency.

Examples of static inventories are those in the decontamination and recovery balance areas. Here the equipment is calibrated before use so that a liquid level can be quickly converted to volume. The inventory can be determined easily by withdrawing a sample for analytical measurement. The shutdown lasts long enough to obtain a correct liquid level and to withdraw a sample. If containers of material are at these locations in an *as-received* condition, their presence is verified and reported. This eliminates duplicating previous measurement.

The dynamic inventory of major concern is for the gaseous diffusion plant or cascade. Physical inventory of this plant is an unusual problem, complicated by the fact that the in-process material is in constant flow and cannot be interrupted for any direct measurement such as weighing. It is also impractical to shut down the cascade for inventory. This would take too long, with very high production loss. Thus this facility is inventoried while on-stream through the application of the universal gas law.

The estimate of cascade holdup must be made on the basis of thousands of pressure and temperature measurements together with laboratory analyses of samples withdrawn at many points. Material balance estimates must also include consideration of the solid uranium compounds held on equipment surface as a result of reactions in uranium hexafluoride. These deposits are composed of two different types of material, inactive consumption and active chemisorption.

Inactive consumption refers to the hydrolysis of uranium hexafluoride to form uranyl fluoride, a solid compound. The term "inactive" as used here means that the reaction is irreversible, i.e. the uranyl fluoride will not return to nor exchange with the uranium hexafluoride to which it is exposed. Once the deposit is formed, it will not change under normal operating conditions.

Active chemisorption results from the loss of an atom of fluorine from a molecule of uranium hexafluoride to produce uranium pentafluoride. This reaction, unlike the hydrolysis, is readily reversible. This means that the uranium in active chemisorption may exchange places with the uranium in the gas-phase material, affecting the material balance as the assay level varies during operation. As the isotopic level rises in a particular stage so will the apparent loss of U^{235}; conversely, as the isotopic level decreases, there will be an apparent gain of U^{235} in the gas phase.

Although not a chemical reaction, a third phenomenon is closely related. This is referred to as "physical adsorption" and involves the deposit of uranium hexafluoride on the surface of the containing equipment without a chemical change. It varies directly with pressure and inversely with temperature, affecting the material balance in the same fashion as active chemisorption.

Although the effect of these phenomena per square foot of containing surface area is quite small, the total real surface exposed to uranium hexafluoride is measured in square miles. Therefore, the aggregate effect on the material balance is significant during periods of changing cascade isotopic level.

If the inventory of the gaseous diffusion cascades could be considered as a static inventory, a simple application of the gas law equation could be applied to calculate it. The equation is usually expressed as

$$U = \frac{(P)(V)(N)}{(T)(R)}$$

where P = pressure
$\quad\quad V$ = volume
$\quad\quad N$ = mole fraction of uranium
$\quad\quad R$ = gas constant

$\quad\quad T$ = temperature
$\quad\quad U$ = uranium

In addition to the fact that uranium hexafluoride is not an ideal gas, the determination of the uranium inventory within a gaseous diffusion cascade is complicated because the gas is not in a static state; pressures and temperatures vary throughout the equipment. There are usually six to eight pressure and temperature regions in each stage, but only one temperature and two pressure measurements are actually made during normal operation. With these pressure and temperature data and the known relationship between gas flow and compressor characteristics, an iterative calculation process can be employed to determine the temperatures and pressures of the remaining regions. Once this information has been obtained, the gas law can be applied to each region to determine the inventory.

The gas-phase inventory as determined is not the required uranium hexafluoride inventory, but that of a gas mixture containing appreciable amounts of nitrogen and oxygen in addition to the uranium hexafluoride. It is therefore necessary to correct the gas-mixture inventory for mole percent of uranium hexafluoride present in the gas stream. This is accomplished by obtaining from continuous mass-spectrometric monitors the gaseous inventory of on-stream materials other than uranium hexafluoride. In addition, a correction is necessary for the nonideality of uranium hexafluoride gas.

The magnitude of the task of measuring the inventory can be grasped by considering the thousands of stages, each with many pressure regions and miles of connecting pipeline throughout the cascade. Fortunately, electronic computing equipment is available to aid in calculating the inventory. Associated with the determination of the uranium inventory is the determination of the U^{235} inventory. This is done by means of the U^{235} gradient (as a percentage of uranium content) across the cascade calculated from samples taken at specified intervals from tails to product. Once the U^{235} gradient has been ascertained, the U^{235} inventory for representative stages can be calculated by multiplying the percentage of U^{235} by the uranium inventory and summing for the entire cascade.

Accurate inventory of a gaseous diffusion plant is the end accomplishment of many years of engineering effort. Extensive studies on the characteristics of compressors and the flow characteristics of gases through valves, barriers, and the various configurations of confining equipment are necessary. These studies are carried on primarily to evaluate plant performance and improve production.

Cascade installations are simulated by test loops of production equipment operated over extensive ranges of pressure, temperature, and valve-setting conditions. Data accumulated from these studies are used to determine the cascade on-stream inventories.

All plant internal volumes must be calculated and verified by engineering test data. From construction blueprints, engineers calculate the internal volumes of the cascade. Verifications are made by the nitrogen calibration test. An isolated section of equipment is charged with a known weight of nitrogen gas, and the pressure rise and the temperature are observed; the correct volume can be readily calculated by applying the standard gas law equation corrected for the nonideality of the gas. Agreement between the calculated volume and the nitrogen calibrated volume must be within the limits of error for the measurements.

Allied to the problem of determining equipment characteristics for inventory calculation is the engineering work needed to verify the dynamic inventory and the inventory of consumed uranium. A method used in verifying these inventories, particularly dynamic inventories, involves an isotopic dilution technique.

This technique was originally designed to permit an accurate determination of material consumption in the gaseous diffusion plant process equipment.

Later it was used for verification of in-process inventory. Since each separative component contains many different gas pressures and temperatures and since regional volumes are not mechanically defined but must be calculated from engineering drawings, it can be seen that the inventory may be biased. During periods of stable operation, material balances would be acceptable because the bias, occurring in both the beginning and ending inventories, would be canceling. However, as operating conditions change, the material balance would reflect nonexistent gains or losses.

This technique can be used only on material that can be made isotopically homogeneous. With this technique a quantity of inventory is isolated from the continuous process without altering the distribution of material among the regional volumes, in a selected portion of the equipment. This is the material to be verified; its amount is estimated by engineering calculations based on equipment pressure and temperature instrumentation. Recirculation is allowed to continue until the required isotopic homogeneity is attained. Since facilities for recirculation are part of the equipment, this poses no problem. When isotopic homogeneity has been attained, no further change in U^{235} content occurs.

As equilibrium is approached, control samples are withdrawn for U^{235} measurements. After equilibrium has been reached, a diluent charge of accurately determined weight and isotopic assay is added. This consists of a known amount of uranium hexafluoride having a significantly different assay. After the diluent charge has been added, the mixture is again allowed to reach isotopic equilibrium. Through the change in isotopic assay, the original or unknown inventory can be determined.

The basic material balance equation is utilized to determine the result of the isotopic dilution test. This equation is

$$I x_1 + C x_c = (I + C) x_2 \qquad (6.1)$$

where I = system inventory to be measured
x_1 = measured initial isotopic assay of the system
C = measured weight of diluent charge
x_c = measured isotopic assay of diluent charge
x_2 = measured terminal isotopic assay of the system

The unknown system inventory is determined by rearranging Eq. 6.1.

$$I = C \left(\frac{x_2 - x_c}{x_1 - x_2} \right) \qquad (6.2)$$

The precision of the inventory is based upon the simple propagation of the component measurements. For this reason all isotopic measurements must be made to the best attainable precision in the laboratory. When this technique is used, care must be taken to correct for the effect of active chemisorption and physical adsorption. Since the method is based upon isotopic change and since these two items also participate in that change, failure to recognize the effect would result in biased test data.

6-3. STATISTICAL APPLICATIONS

The accuracy and precision of the cascade material balance is dependent upon the accuracy of the measurements of cascade streams as well as upon the accuracy and precision of the cascade inventory. Although the three major flows (product, tails, and feed) of materials from and to the gaseous diffusion cascade are all uranium hexafluoride, characteristics peculiar to each flow require that their measurement problems be considered separately. Cascade tails are chemically pure uranium hexafluoride, but the isotopic value fluctuates; whereas cascade product is characteristically stable in the isotopic component but relatively unstable in the uranium component. Therefore, in the sampling of cascade tails, emphasis is on the isotopic component rather than on the purity of the uranium compound. Conversely, in the sampling of product, particular attention is placed on obtaining a representative chemical sample.

In like manner the analytical techniques for a very pure material are different from those employed for material with relatively high contamination. Only in the weighing of these materials are the statistical techniques relatively consistent. This is illustrated by the following description of scale types, their maintenance and calibration, and statistical concepts used to evaluate their reliability.

6-3.1. Weighing Quality-Control Program. For most large material flows a nominal 5-ton capacity scale is used. The scale is equipped with a weight-printing attachment, actuated from the dial head and recording on a card form. The size and number of drop weights are such that the required weight range, minimum to maximum, can be covered without the use of the tare beam counterpoises. A possible source of error has been eliminated by making the counterpoises on the tare beams inoperable at zero position.

Nearly all scale manufacturers warrant their product to be accurate to the smallest dial graduation. This generally establishes a tolerance interval upon which weight acceptability is based within the mechanical limitations of the scale.

The primary avoirdupois weight standard is a two-piece chrome plated 50-lb Gurley weight certified by the National Bureau of Standards to be accurate to within less than 2 grains. This is within the weight tolerance for class A standards. Working standards for the plant are calibrated with the primary standard by the substitution method. These working standards are used to check and calibrate the scales through the complete operating range at least once per week.

Utilizing the working standard weights for calibration is expensive and cumbersome, and they are not considered suitable for a quality control program. Therefore, two cylinders for each scale, one full and one empty, are removed from regular service and assigned as operational standards. These cylinders represent the weight levels for which the scale is utilized. Each is weighed a minimum of 10 times on two scales. Both scales are calibrated immediately before and after the cylinders are weighed. Between successive weighings, the scales are checked for zero drift. The true weight for each standard cylinder is then taken to be the mean of the 20 observations. Since the precision of these data has been observed to be extremely high for practical purposes, the mean can be assumed to be the exact weight of the cylinder.

The weight control program has been designed to maintain, with a predictable degree of assurance, the accuracy of the reported weights of materials transferred. In this may be seen the similarity to the control of quality in a manufactured item. The scale, as the production device, is producing weights each day on an around-the-clock basis. It is imperative that its accuracy be maintained at all times and that any malfunction be detected immediately.

Each standard cylinder is weighed six times per day (twice on each of the three daily shifts—once at the beginning of the shift and once near the middle of the shift). Since the daily weighing activity on a scale is likely to occur at any time, it is a reasonable assumption that fixing the time of weighing the standard results in a fairly random sample of the sequence of daily weighing operations on the scale. The weight differences between each of the observed weights and the standard weight, expressed as observed minus standard, are collected in subgroups of six which constitute the variables of control. The average of the six differences is plotted on a control chart. If the plotted daily average exhibits characteristics of noncontrol, the scale is judged to be out of calibration and is corrected.

Data from the daily weighing of the standard cylinders are collected, and daily checks are made on the maintenance of scale calibration using the working standards. Inherent variation and the prevailing level of quality of a scale in calibration and in producing weights under routine operating conditions are determined. These data are collected for approximately two months with trial control limits for the daily subgroup means calculated after the first week of operation and revised each week. At the end of this period, enough data are available to serve as a standard against which subsequent samples can be compared to detect significant variation. Working control limits are computed and plotted about the central line. For the $\overline{X}$ chart an average of zero as the central line is used, since this is the average performance level desired for the scale. After placing the charts in use, a routine schedule is established to review the standards of control.

6-3.2. Sampling and Analysis. The next step toward representative stream measurements is that of obtaining adequate samples. A definite interrelationship exists between sampling and analytical measurements; for this reason, they are discussed together.   The approach is to isolate each material flow within the plant, giving particular attention to the sampling and analytical procedures in use.   Statistical tests are designed to analyze the variance of the respective errors.   These analyses of variance can then be utilized to evaluate and distinguish between the sampling and analytical errors.

Analysis of Variance Experiment.   The variance due to sampling and laboratory analysis is found through the use of multiple laboratory determinations on several samples from the same lot of material.   It is assumed that if the material is properly homogenized, one sample should not differ from another.   By the same logic, if the laboratory analysis is properly carried out, one determination on a sample should not differ from another.   However, random factors are inherent in all measurements; therefore the technique of analysis of variance is used to determine whether the differences noted in the samples are too large to have been caused by chance.

The main purpose of this experiment is to determine variation in the quality of material between samples, which would indicate the effectiveness of the sampling method.   Specifically, it is assumed that if the between-sample variation is significant or excessively large, either the material is not properly homogenized before sampling or stratified samples representing heterogeneous materials were not properly taken.   The statistical analyses, shown diagrammatically, are as follows:

SAMPLE	1	2	$\ldots, n$
REPLICATION	$1, 2, 3, \ldots, r$	$1, 2, 3, \ldots, r$	$1, 2, 3, \ldots, r$

The analysis of variance table for this design is as follows:

Source of Variation	Sum of Squares	Degrees of Freedom	Mean Square or Variance
Between samples	—	$n - 1$	$r\sigma_1^2 + \sigma_0^2$
Within samples	—	$n(r - 1)$	σ_0^2
Total	—	$nr - 1$	

where n = number of samples
    r = number of replicates
    σ_0^2 = variance within samples (analytical error)
    σ_1^2 = variance between samples

When the variability associated with sampling is evaluated, it is necessary to consider the hypothetical universe of all samples of the material from which the n samples are a random selection.   Let the variance of this universe with respect to quality be σ_1^2.   This variance is hypothetical for two reasons: first, it refers to an infinite universe, and since only a finite number of samples can be examined, it cannot be exactly determined; second, the quality of a sample can be determined only by means of a test which is in itself subject to experimental error and, therefore, cannot be exactly determined. Let σ_0^2 denote the variance of the experimental error which will measure the within-sample, or analytical, error since it measures the variance between r determinations on the same sample. These variances are additive, and the true variance of the quality of the universe of samples determined on the basis of one determination on each sample is $\sigma_1^2 + \sigma_0^2$. This means that the analytical error increases the apparent variation between the quality of samples.

The quality of each sample of material is obtained as a mean of r determinations. The effect of this is to increase the accuracy of the determination of the quality and to reduce the variance due to the within-sample error to σ_0^2/r. If σ_t^2 denotes the variance of the universe of material samples with respect to quality which has been determined as a mean of r determinations on each sample, the following expression is obtained

$$\sigma_t^2 = \sigma_1^2 + \sigma_0^2/r \tag{6.3}$$

or

$$r\sigma_t^2 = r\sigma_1^2 + \sigma_0^2 \tag{6.4}$$

The terms σ_t^2, σ_1^2, and σ_0^2 cannot be determined exactly but can be estimated from the experimental data. For an estimate of σ_t^2, i.e. the total variance of a single sample mean, n means are available from the data. The variance between these n means will give an estimate of σ_t^2 based on n-1 degrees of freedom.

The mean square within samples and the mean square between samples are estimates based, respectively, on $n(r$-1$)$ and $(n$-1$)$ degrees of freedom and are subject to random error. Differences between these two mean squares may arise as a result of chance variation; it is necessary, therefore, to test whether the estimate of σ_1^2 obtained in this manner may be so explained.

The best method of testing whether the difference between samples and the difference within samples is due to chance error is to postulate the null hypothesis that all the results are from the same universe. In effect, this assumes that there is no real difference between the samples, i.e. $\sigma_1^2 = 0$. The mean square between samples and within samples becomes two independent estimates of σ_0^2. It is important to recognize the inaccuracies of these two estimates in testing whether they differ significantly, i.e. more than could reasonably be explained on the basis of errors in the estimates.

If the mean square between samples is significantly greater than the mean square within samples, the difference cannot logically be explained on the theory of chance and the null hypothesis cannot be accepted. Therefore, the conclusion to be reached is that the quantity $(r\sigma_t^2 + \sigma_0^2)$ is greater than σ_0^2 because σ_1^2 is appreciable. Therefore, it is concluded that variation due to sampling is not negligible. This is tested by the F test, using the appropriate degrees of freedom. If the variance between samples is significantly less than the variance within samples, the difference cannot reasonably be due to chance. Neither can it be explained by sampling variance $\sigma_1{}^2$ since $\sigma_1{}^2$ is essentially positive and must make the between-sample variance greater than the within-sample variance. A suggested reason for this situation is a systematic variation or trend in sample results.

Because of the effect of such an experimental design on specific types of material with respect to adequacy in producing useful results, care must be

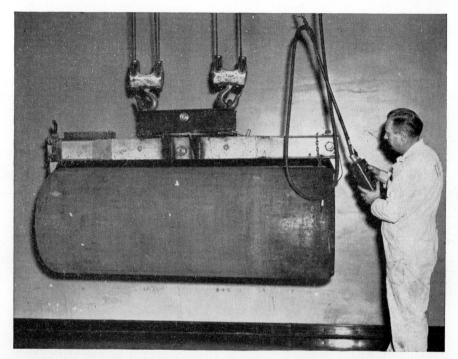

Fig. 6-9 Commercial chlorine type (2.5-ton) cylinder for handling uranium hexafluoride.

taken to ensure that unusual or unanticipated data will not lead to misinterpretations. The discussion will be confined to one type of material, uranium hexafluoride; but equally careful considerations should be given to all applications of this theory for any material type.

Sampling. In a determination of the variability of sampling, consideration must be given to the variability of the material itself with respect to the component being measured. In a general sense, the uranium content in uranium hexafluoride is being measured. In a specific sense, this is complicated by the presence of impurities such as oxygen, nitrogen, helium, hydrogen fluoride, and some organics.

Multiple samples are taken from a quantity of uranium hexafluoride. In the lower isotopic ranges, uranium hexafluoride outside plant facilities is frequently handled in commercial chlorine cylinders (Fig. 6-9) with a capacity of approximately $2\frac{1}{2}$ tons of material and a gross weight of approximately 6500 lb, or in larger cylinders (Fig. 6-10) commonly referred to as "10-ton" cylinders. Sampling such containers requires sufficient heating to liquefy the contents.

Some of the properties of uranium hexafluoride should be noted for a better understanding of the problem. At room temperature the material is solid; it melts at about 147°F under a pressure of 22 psia. The cylinders of material

FIG. 6-10 Ten-ton cylinder for handling uranium hexafluoride.

are placed in hot-air furnaces or steam baths until liquefied. This process, in the case of the chlorine cylinder, takes approximately 12 hours; and for the 10-ton cylinder, 18 to 24 hours, depending upon the source of heat.

Adequate homogenization of the cylinder contents in the liquid state is attained by shaking. This involves oscillating the container enough to mix uranium hexafluoride and any contaminants that may be present. The contaminants may be either lighter or heavier than the uranium hexafluoride. Light contaminants tend to volatilize into the cylinder void volume, i.e. the volume above the liquid level; whereas heavy contaminants may stratify after a period of time. Obviously, the condition for best sampling is when the cylinder is filled to or near its safe limit. Shaking the cylinder tends to re-create the binary phase equilibrium and to mix the less-volatile heavy impurity with the uranium hexafluoride.

A second reason for homogenization is the method by which the cylinder is filled. Material entering a cylinder may be different from one interval of time to another, and since cylinders during filling are not kept hot, the material may solidify in strata. Homogenization is especially important if isotopic variation occurs during filling. Homogenization of the cylinder can be accomplished by rocking it from end to end for several minutes between test samples. Tests have indicated that, in the case of different isotopic concentra-

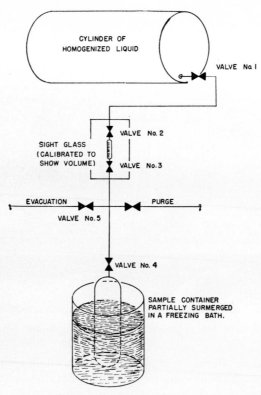

Fig. 6-11 Schematic diagram of cylinder sampling equipment.

tions, a minimum of five complete inversions of the cylinder from end to end were necessary to attain agreeable sample results when the samples were pulled in duplicate from opposite ends of the cylinder. For homogeneity of purity, experience has shown this type of shaking to be entirely adequate. A diagram illustrating the sampling equipment is shown in Fig. 6-11.

The sampling equipment, except for the sample container, is heated and evacuated. Then all valves are closed, except valve 2. Valve 1 is opened, and the material is allowed to flow into the calibrated volume. When sufficient material is in the calibrated volume, valves 1 and 2 are closed and valves 3 and 4 are opened, allowing the material to flow into the sample container. Valves 3 and 4 are then closed.

Fractional distillation, also known as "flash purification," may occur at this time. When the valves are opened, the measured quantity of material is pulled into the cold evacuated sample container. This greatly reduces pressure and results in partial purification of the sample material through the release of volatile impurities. The transfers should be made under pressure while a liquid head is maintained above the sample block to minimize the flash purification phenomenon. This ensures that any volatiles left by a given aliquot will be swept into the sample container by the succeeding aliquot. Therefore, a series of aliquots will tend to minimize any sample bias occurring through flash purification.

Analytical Quality-Control Program. Closely associated with the problem of ascertaining the uncertainty in sampling and analytical techniques, as illustrated above, is the mechanism of maintaining assurance that the uncertainties as determined do not change. For laboratory analytical techniques this is accomplished by applying typical statistical quality control techniques.

The mechanics of such a quality-control system include processing disguised samples with a known analysis through each analytical section of the laboratory. The analyst processes this as he would any other plant sample and reports the analytical results in the routine manner. These data are assembled by the laboratory statistician who, with the aid of quality control charts, ascertains the level of precision and accuracy of the analytical method.

Materials of many chemical compositions with known analyses are channeled through the laboratory for comprehensive coverage of all chemical analytical techniques in use. Such materials as pure uranium hexafluoride, uranium hexafluoride spiked with known concentrations of impurities, uranium oxides both pure and impure, and various concentrations of water-media uranium solutions are employed as disguised samples. The spectrometer section of the laboratory implements its control program by processing disguised samples for isotopic analysis, covering incrementally the range of possible isotopic concentrations that are routinely analyzed.

6-3.3. Measurement Uncertainty in Cascade Inventory. Appropriate to this discussion is consideration of the measurement uncertainty of inventories. The cascade-inventory uncertainty has been approached by two methods, but only one has proved successful. An attempt was made to apply statistical error-propagation techniques to the cascade inventory equations. It was found that correlation between the different variables entering into the cascade inventory equations obscured the estimates of variability; therefore this approach was abandoned.

The present technique involves the taking of three complete inventories at 8-hour intervals. No operational changes are permitted during the total time required for these inventories. Flow in and out of the cascade is restricted to the major feed, tails, and production streams.

Considering these inventories as final inventories, material balances are made using the most recent inventory as the beginning inventory. Since the material flows in the 16-hour test period can be measured accurately and precisely, it is reasonable to suppose that the variation seen in the three material balances is due to the final inventory uncertainty.

The above discussion considers only uncertainties due to random errors in measuring the cascade inventory. In this system, probably more than in any other, consideration must also be given to systematic error in determination of the cascade inventory. Operating changes resulting in shifts in the U^{235} inventory, but not necessarily in the total uranium inventory, over a material-balance interval are reflected as large apparent losses or gains in the U^{235} inventory. Simultaneously, the total uranium balance shows no loss or gain, since the bias affects both beginning and ending inventories equally. The source of error is usually either (1) drift of the instrument with time or (2) error in the calibration of the equipment inventory holdup.

The previously discussed isotopic dilution test can be successfully used to determine the magnitude of the bias and the locations in which corrections should be made to the data entering into the cascade inventory calculation.

Inventory-measurement uncertainty of other systems is much simpler to determine than the uncertainty of the diffusion cascade, since as a rule only sampling, laboratory analysis, and container-volume measurement uncertainties need be considered. Estimates of variation attributable to the measurement components, noted above, are determined by appropriate tests; and through straightforward applications of statistical error-propagation techniques, the uncertainty of the inventory can be determined readily.

The measurement uncertainties of the individual components of a material balance are combined to yield the uncertainty calculated for the balance's book-physical inventory difference. The technique by which this is accomplished is the error-propagation method of mathematical statistics.

Error Propagation: Application to Material Control. As an example of the use of error-propagation methods to SS control, consider the functional relations for uranium and U^{235} as employed in the material balance.

Let the functional relationship for a single container of a particular uranium compound be

$$U = WP \qquad (6.5)$$

where U = uranium in grams
   W = weight or volume of a uranium compound
   P = analysis of the compound in uranium content

Under the assumption that the errors in W and P vary independently and randomly, an estimate of the variance of U is given by the equation

$$\sigma_U^2 = P^2\sigma_W^2 + W^2\sigma_P^2 \tag{6.6}$$

where σ_U^2 = variance in the derived quantity U
σ_W^2 = variance attributed to weight or volume
σ_P^2 = variance attributed to purity

It is also known that the σ^2 of independent variates may be added; therefore, assuming n containers, the relation can be written

$$\sum_{i=1}^{n} \sigma_{U_i}^2 = \sum_{i=1}^{n} (P_i^2\sigma_W^2 + W_i^2\sigma_P^2), \quad i = 1, 2, \ldots, n \tag{6.7}$$

Similarly, for U^{235} the functional relationship for a container of a particular uranium compound is

$$U^{235} = WPX \tag{6.8}$$

where X = assay, percentage of uranium that is U^{235}.

From the method of error propagation, an estimate of the variance of U^{235} is obtained by the equation

$$\sigma_{U^{235}}^2 = P^2X^2\sigma_W^2 + W^2X^2\sigma_P^2 + W^2P^2\sigma_X^2 \tag{6.9}$$

where σ_X^2 = estimate of variance of the isotopic measurement.

For n containers, then, the relation is

$$\sum_{i=1}^{n} \sigma_{U^{235}_i}^2 = \sum_{i=1}^{n} (P_i^2X_i^2\sigma_W^2 + W_i^2X_i^2\sigma_P^2 + W_i^2P_i^2\sigma_X^2), \quad i = 1, 2, \ldots, n \tag{6.10}$$

It can be readily seen that there is wide and useful application of the above methods of propagation technique to problems of SS control. In particular, this study is concerned with applications to material balance deficiencies of balance areas.

The material balance for a specified accounting period can be expressed by a mathematical equation thus:

$$D = (I_B + R) - (I_E + S) \tag{6.11}$$

where I_B = beginning inventory
I_E = ending inventory
R = receipts during the period
S = shipments during the period
D = B-PID (D may be either plus or minus in practice; a negative D would signify a gain of material)

The functional relationship for uranium or U^{235} for each component Eq. 6.11 is of the form

$$\sum_{i=1}^{n} U_i = \sum_{i=1}^{n} W_i P_i, \quad i = 1, 2, \ldots, n \tag{6.12}$$

or

$$\sum_{i=1}^{n} U_i^{235} = \sum_{i=1}^{n} W_i P_i X_i, \quad i = 1, 2, \ldots, n \tag{6.13}$$

When the methods of propagation are applied to the material-balance equation, it is shown that

$$\sigma_D^2 = \sigma_{I_B}^2 + \sigma_R^2 + \sigma_{I_E}^2 + \sigma_S^2 \tag{6.14}$$

provided each item in the balance enters the above equation once and only once.*

There remains the problem of combining the results, as shown in Eqs. 6.6, 6.7, and 6.14, to derive a relation between each σ_U^2 or σ_{U235}^2 and $\sigma_{D_U}^2$ or $\sigma_{D_{U235}}^2$.

This is accomplished by deriving a method for obtaining σ_F^2 where F is a function of the form

$$F(X, Y, Z) = X + Y + Z \tag{6.15}$$

From Eq. 6.11 observe each I_B, R, I_E, and S is of the form $F(X,Y,Z)$ above, where any one, for example, R, may be expressed

$$R = \sum_{1}^{n} U = U_1 + U_2 + U_3 + \cdots + U_n \tag{6.16}$$

The σ_R^2 becomes the sum of those σ_U^2 that are receipts. Every σ_U^2, whether an inventory item, a receipt, or a shipment, can be computed by Eq. 6.6. Similarly, $\sigma_{I_E}^2$, $\sigma_{I_B}^2$, and σ_S^2 are sums of σ_U^2, which are, respectively, ending inventory materials, beginning inventory materials, and materials shipped. It follows that

$$\sigma_{D_U}^2 = \sum_{i=1}^{n} \sigma_{U_i}^2, \quad i = 1, 2, 3, \ldots, n \tag{6.17}$$

From these equations variances are determined for D_U or D_U^{235} attributable to random error.

When $\sigma_{D_U}^2$ for a balance is known, the limit of error due to measurement uncertainty, can be computed directly. The equation for the limit of error is

$$\text{LE (balance area)} = t\sqrt{\sigma_{D_U}^2} \tag{6.18}$$

---

*In the calculation of σ_D^2, care should be taken that only one measurement variance estimate be counted for an unprocessed container of material in any account. In the accounting records, materials on beginning inventories may occur identically as a shipment or on ending inventory. In like manner, a receipt may occur identically as a shipment or on ending inventory. An artificially large and erroneous σ_D^2 may result from the inclusion of such items more than once in the calculation of σ_D^2. It will be necessary, prior to calculating the σ_D^2, to eliminate one of these duplicates.

Interpreting Material Balance Data. Material balance data can give reliable estimates of plant performance when reviewed in the proper perspective. The term "proper perspective" implies that certain inherent qualities of diffusion plant operation must be considered. It has been pointed out that the process is one which does not lend itself to inventorying by static methods. This means that all statements concerning material in process are the result of engineering evaluation and depend upon the accuracy of thousands of instrument readings. It becomes obvious, therefore, that stated inventory quantities in material balances are not to be considered absolute values but rather they indicate changes relative to a preceding inventory.

A second qualifying consideration concerns the chemical characteristics of the process material, uranium hexafluoride. Because of its corrosive nature, every processing step is subject to apparent loss through adsorption and chemisorption on the wall of the containing equipment. As material is transformed by chemical or physical changes from the gas phase in which it is inventoried to a solid phase, production will be less than the total amount of material fed to the process in a given time interval. To be sure, these apparent losses will be compensated for by equipment decontamination as the need arises, but there is need for considering this seemingly minor detail in interpreting material balance data.

The adequacy of control against even small biases in measuring material debits and credits is a major qualifying consideration. Throughputs in a gaseous diffusion plant are normally quite high. Hence, a measurement bias of insignificant magnitude when considered for a single container can become an overwhelming factor when multiplied thousands of times. Measurement bias may result in apparent processing losses or gains when, in fact, none exist. This usually results in extensive equipment inspection or shutdown which is expensive from a production point of view. On the other hand, the bias may be such that it obscures an actual loss that is quite significant when the economic value of the material is considered.

In these qualifying considerations for interpreting a material balance for the gaseous diffusion plant proper, the intent has been to show that a statistical evaluation is necessary. Merely to develop a set of numbers is not enough. These numbers must be accepted only with knowledge of their uncertainty. In final analysis the evaluation must be based upon a judgment born of experience, a close knowledge of plant operations, a capability for statistical evaluation, and a "feel" for the process that cannot be reduced to finite numbers. Of these, probably the most important is the last named, for, in fact, it encompasses all.

Linked to the gaseous diffusion process are the auxiliary functions of decontamination and recovery, discussed earlier in the chapter. From an accounting viewpoint, their material balance behavior is important. Because activity in the decontamination operation consists of returning uranium material to a measurable form from processing equipment, apparent gains emanate from these accounts. However, the material actually is the same as that which disappeared as hidden inventory during the service life of the equipment. Therefore, compensation for prior balance-interval deficiencies results. In practice, this material is credited to the proper point of origin when this is clearly known. Contaminated solutions originating from process areas pass through recovery. Similar to decontamination solutions, these quantities are compensatory for prior balance-interval deficiencies in processing accounts. Recovering uranium to oxide from solutions is frequently a high unit cost operation. It is important to know that the value of the recovered material is at least as great as the cost of recovery. At frequent intervals this is reviewed both for changes in recovery costs and changes in material value.

Part Four

REACTOR FUEL FABRICATION

Chapter 7

PRINCIPLES OF FUEL ELEMENT FABRICATION *

7-1. INTRODUCTION

The term "atomic pile" was used to describe early natural-uranium graphite reactors because their bulk consisted of thousands of pieces of graphite and fissionable fuel carefully piled into huge cubes. This nomenclature misleads those not familiar with the field of atomic energy to think that the fissionable fuel is piled into a reactor much as coal is shoveled into the firebox of a boiler. It would be better to call a modern reactor an "atomic stack" because the fuel material is very carefully fabricated into predetermined shapes, called fuel elements, which are fitted or stacked together in a reactor to form a cluster or core.

A core must be of a size and shape to achieve a critical mass, i.e. that quantity of fissionable material which in a given environment will produce and sustain a fission reaction. A nuclear reactor is a chain-reacting system much like an atomic bomb, except that the energy is released at a predetermined and controlled rate over a long period of time. The core containing the fuel is the heart of the system; here the fission takes place and the radiation, heat, and fission products are produced.

Most reactors have been fueled with uranium. The first two sections of this chapter describe the different types of uranium fuel elements and their fabrication. The rest of the chapter is devoted to methods of controlling the nuclear materials involved in the fabrication operations. Plutonium fuel elements are discussed in Chapter 10.

* R. G. Cardwell, Union Carbide Nuclear Company, Oak Ridge National Laboratory, Oak Ridge, Tennessee. The author wishes to acknowledge the technical advice and assistance of J. E. Cunningham, Assistant Director, Metallurgy Division, Oak Ridge National Laboratory, without whose valuable help the writing of this chapter would not have been possible. Acknowledgment is also given to J. C. Gower and E. P. Griggs, Photographic Section, Metallurgy Division, and W. C. Colwell, Oak Ridge National Laboratory Graphic Arts Department, for the photographs and illustrations in the chapter.

7-2. TYPES OF FUEL ELEMENTS

Fuel elements can be classified in a variety of ways. For instance, they can be described in terms of geometrical shape, such as rod, tube, or plate. Sometimes a distinction is made according to the nature and grade of fuel used, e.g. uranium fuel elements in the natural, slightly enriched, or highly enriched form, or plutonium fuel elements. At other times the element is typed according to the cladding or canning material employed, and the term aluminum, zirconium, or stainless steel is incorporated into the title. In addition, fuel elements are referred to as "gas cooled" or "water cooled" to specify the environment in which the component will be utilized. More often than not, more than one or two terms are used to describe or classify an element.

Fuel elements can further be classified according to the use of the reactor in which they are inserted. A materials-testing reactor (MTR) type fuel element, for example, designates an assembly of aluminum-clad enriched-uranium-aluminum alloy fuel plates for service in a low-temperature water-cooled and water-moderated reactor designed for research and radiation damage studies. In other instances, the reactor name connotes a breeder or converter, a nuclear power plant, or a radioisotope producer. It sometimes designates the neutron-energy spectrum of the reactor and carries such descriptive terms as fast, intermediate, or thermal—terms that refer to the velocity of the neutrons producing the greatest percentage of fission in the reacting system.

For the purposes of this chapter, uranium fuel elements will be classified according to type of fuel-bearing material. On this basis they fall into four general categories:

1. Pure and slightly alloyed uranium metal, i.e. natural or partially enriched uranium in the pure form or in uranium-base alloys containing small percentages of chromium, zirconium, molybdenum, niobium, and silicon or combinations of these.
2. Highly alloyed uranium metal, i.e. uranium-aluminum and uranium-zirconium alloys containing a few atomic percent of uranium.
3. Dispersion elements, i.e. refractory compounds such as UO_2, UN, and U_3O_8 dispersed in metallic matrixes of aluminum, zirconium, or stainless steel.
4. Bulk-oxide elements, i.e. bulk compounds, such as UO_2, or mixtures of refractory compounds, such as UO_2-ThO_2, UO_2-BeO, UO_2-C, or Si-SiC-UO_2.

Fig. 7-1 illustrates the physical form and material make-up of four representative types of fuel elements.

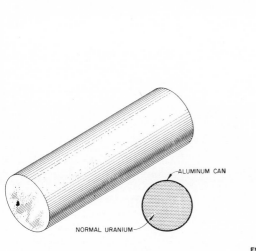

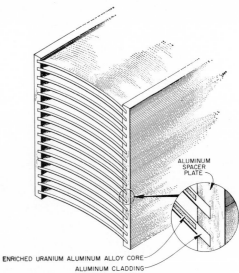

(a) Metallic Fuel Slug — X-10 Reactor.

(b) Alloy Fuel Plate Element — MTR Reactor.

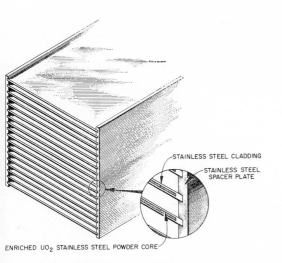

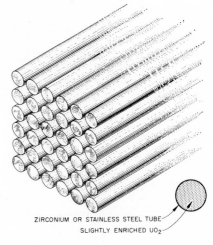

(c) Dispersion Fuel Plate Element — APPR Reactor.

(d) Bulk Oxide Rod Element — Power Reactor.

Fig. 7-1   Representative fuel element types.   These types are representative of: (a) pure and slightly alloyed uranium metal, (b) highly alloyed uranium metal, (c) dispersion and (d) bulk-oxide categories.

TABLE 7.1.   COMBINATIONS OF MATERIALS IN SOME
FUEL ELEMENTS

Enrichment and Fuel	Fuel-Bearing Material	Cladding (or Canning) Material	Reactor
0.7% U^{235}	Uranium metal	Aluminum	Oak Ridge Graphite Reactor (X-10)
90% U^{235}	uranium-aluminum alloy	Aluminum	Low-Intensity Test Reactor Bulk Shielding Reactor Materials Testing Reactor (MTR) Argonne Research Reactor Pennsylvania State University Omega West Reactor University of Michigan Battelle Memorial Institute Engineering Test Reactor Brookhaven Medical Reactor Oak Ridge Research Reactor
20% U^{235}	UO_2 dispersed in aluminum	Ni-Al alloy Aluminum	Army Low Power Reactor Geneva Conference Reactor (1955)
90% U^{235}	UO_2 dispersed in stainless steel	Stainless steel	Army Package Power Reactor Vallecitos Boiling Water Reactor
20% U^{235}	U_3O_8 dispersed in aluminum	Aluminum	Puerto Rican Reactor
2.78% U^{235}	Uranium metal	Stainless steel with NaK bond	Sodium Reactor Experiment
90% U^{235}	U-Zr alloy	Zircaloy-2	Shippingport Pressurized Water Reactor (seed elements)
0.7% U^{235}	UO_2 pellets	Zircaloy-2	Shippingport Pressurized Water Reactor (blanket elements)
90% U^{235}	U-Zr alloy	Stainless steel with NaK bond	Experimental Breeder Reactor No. 1 (Core 2)
Plutonium	Pu-Al alloy	Stainless steel with NaK bond	(Core 3)
0.7% U^{235}	Uranium metal	Zircaloy-2	(Blanket)
1.5% U^{235}	UO_2 pellets	Zircaloy-2	Dresden Nuclear Power Station
90% U^{235}	UO_2-ThO_2 mixture	Stainless steel	Consolidated Edison Thorium Reactor
3.0% U^{235}	UO_2 pellets	Stainless steel	Yankee Pressurized Water Power Plant
25% U^{235}	U-Mo alloy	Zircaloy-2	Enrico Fermi Atomic Power Plant (Core)
Depleted uranium	U-Mo alloy	Stainless steel	(Blanket)

Fuel materials can be incorporated into solid fuel elements in a variety of ways. Some combinations of materials which are either already in service in reactors or under extensive investigation are listed in Table 7.1. Only three basic materials have been widely employed for cladding or canning in the manufacture of solid fuel components. These are aluminum, stainless steel, and hafnium-free zirconium. The most commonly used form of zirconium is Zircaloy-2, an alloy prepared from sponge zirconium containing nominally 1.5 wt. % tin, 0.1 wt. % iron, 0.1 wt. % chromium, and 0.05 wt. % niobium. It exhibits corrosion resistance in pressurized water comparable to that of its predecessor, crystal-bar zirconium, and is cheaper.

7-2.1. Metallic Fuel Slug. The metallic fuel slug is a cylindrical rod of short length to facilitate recovery of plutonium during chemical reprocessing. Though usually made of natural uranium, slugs sometimes consist of partially enriched uranium and uranium-base alloys with a small percentage of additives. Variations in shape include long cylindrical rods and short and long tubes.

The natural uranium fuel slugs for the ORNL graphite reactor, for example (Fig. 7-1a), are 1.1 in. in diameter by 4 in. long and are contained in 0.025-in.-thick aluminum cans bonded to the uranium by aluminum-silicon eutectic alloy. The aluminum-silicon bonding layer retards interdiffusion of uranium and aluminum and promotes heat transfer.

7-2.2. Alloy Fuel Plate Elements. Alloy fuel plate elements, containing highly enriched fuel, are designed for use in compact-core reactors (which produce a large amount of heat in a core of small volume). The fuel is in the form of a dilute alloy and is clad with a suitable material to yield a composite plate of thin cross section. The cladding affords corrosion protection and prevents the highly radioactive fission products from contaminating the coolant. In the case of the MTR element (Fig. 7-1b), clad uranium-aluminum alloy fuel plates are assembled into a unit by brazing. Plate type fuel elements are characterized by a high surface to volume ratio, which facilitates removal of heat. The plates are spaced to permit water to flow freely between them.

7-2.3. Dispersion Fuel Plate Elements. Dispersion fuel plate elements are characterized by discrete particles of fuel material, usually refractory, dispersed in a continuous matrix of diluent. Fuel particles must be large enough to retain most of the fission products; the matrix provides the desired physical and mechanical properties. The element's core, matrix mixed with fuel, is metallurgically bonded with the cladding, which is normally of the same material as the matrix. The Army Package Power Reactor (APPR) is fueled with an element of this general type. It consists of an assembly of fuel plates (Fig. 7-1c) similar in design to that of the MTR. The cores of the plates are composed of a uniform mixture of enriched UO_2 and stainless steel powder and their cladding is of wrought stainless steel.

7-2.4. Bulk-Oxide Rod Element. The bulk oxide rod element consists of a container loaded with high-density compacts of partially enriched UO_2. There is no metallurgical bond between fuel and container. Instead of bonding, the space between the fuel and the container is filled with a material (air, helium, or liquid metal) to improve heat transfer.

The blanket element for the Shippingport Pressurized Water Reactor (PWR), illustrated in Fig. 7-1d, is an example of this type fuel element. The blanket is composed of a cluster or bundle of many Zircaloy tubes of long length and small diameter, each filled with high-density UO_2 pellets and sealed at the ends with metal plugs.

7-3. PRODUCTION METHODS

The fuel element is the central and most important component in the heterogeneous reactor system and, as such, demands the utmost attention in its manufacture. Although the requirements of an element will vary greatly, depending on the reactor system in which it is to be used, all fuel elements for solid-fuel reactors must

1. Physically locate the fuel and fission products in the reactor
2. Transfer fission heat to the coolant at the desired temperature
3. Isolate fuel and fission products from the coolant
4. Be compatible with environmental constituents
5. Provide their own mechanical and dimensional stability
6. Possess good nuclear characteristics
7. Be amenable to inexpensive fabrication and chemical reprocessing and be simple to install and remove.

A premium is placed on the integrity or reliability of the manufacturing process because maintenance is usually impractical after the component has been placed in service. The basic methods of manufacture are outlined in the following paragraphs.

7-3.1. Pure and Slightly Alloyed Uranium Method. Natural uranium is melted and cast in vacuum-induction furnaces. The melt is prepared in graphite crucibles coated with MgO to minimize carbon pickup, and is cast in similarly coated graphite molds. The temperature cycle involves rapid heating to the liquid state, further heating at a slower rate to 1425°C to expel volatile matter, and holding at this temperature prior to pouring to effect separation from insoluble compounds.

Most of the uranium processed for fueling reactors is normal uranium that is made into fuel slugs. The simplified flow diagram of Fig. 7-2a depicts the major operations in the production of metallic uranium fuel slugs. The performance of these components depends to a large extent on the metallurgical history of the uranium; therefore considerable care must be exercised during

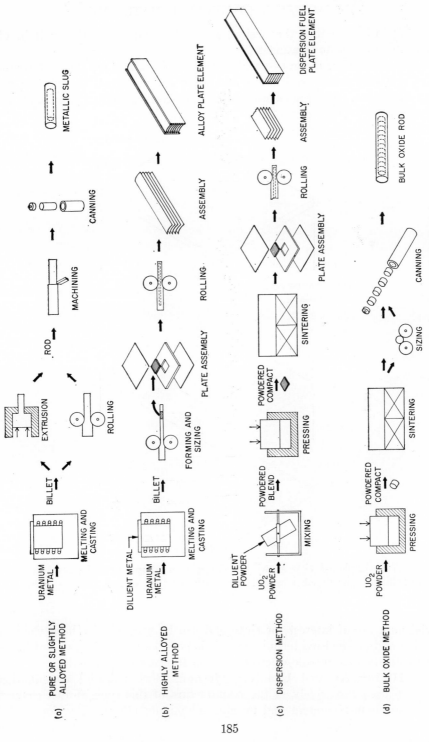

Fig. 7-2 Methods of processing representative fuel element types.

(a) PURE OR SLIGHTLY ALLOYED METHOD

URANIUM METAL → MELTING AND CASTING → BILLET → EXTRUSION / ROLLING → ROD → MACHINING → CANNING → METALLIC SLUG

(b) HIGHLY ALLOYED METHOD

DILUENT METAL, URANIUM METAL → MELTING AND CASTING → BILLET → FORMING AND SIZING → PLATE ASSEMBLY → ROLLING → ASSEMBLY → ALLOY PLATE ELEMENT

(c) DISPERSION METHOD

DILUENT POWDER, UO₂ POWDER → MIXING → POWDERED BLEND → PRESSING → POWDERED COMPACT → SINTERING → PLATE ASSEMBLY → ROLLING → ASSEMBLY → DISPERSION FUEL PLATE ELEMENT

(d) BULK OXIDE METHOD

UO₂ POWDER → PRESSING → POWDERED COMPACT → SINTERING → SIZING → CANNING → BULK OXIDE ROD

185

processing to ensure that the desired grain size and orientation will be obtained after final heat treatment.

Alloy additions are made to uranium primarily to improve the performance of the material under irradiation and, to a lesser extent, to enhance corrosion resistance. Uranium-base alloys containing zirconium, niobium, and

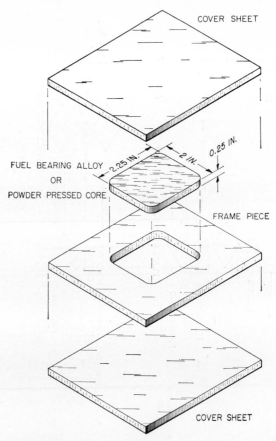

COVER SHEET

FUEL BEARING ALLOY
OR
POWDER PRESSED CORE

2.25 IN.   2 IN.   0.25 IN.

FRAME PIECE

COVER SHEET

FIG. 7-3 Exploded view showing make-up of a composite fuel plate prior to rolling. The dimensions will vary with the type of fuel element being processed.

molybdenum are of interest for slugs and can be prepared by both vacuum-induction and arc-melting techniques. It is possible to obtain melts of higher purity with the consumable-electrode, arc-melting technique.

7-3.2. Highly Alloyed Uranium Method. Two material combinations have been used extensively in the manufacture of this type of fuel element, namely, uranium-zirconium and uranium-aluminum alloys. The former has been employed chiefly for fueling nuclear-powered vessels; the latter for research reactors.   The basic concept of processing the two components is essentially the same.   The major steps involved in the process are illustrated in the flow diagram shown in Fig. 7-2b.

Enriched uranium-aluminum alloys containing 10 to 20 wt. % uranium are prepared in a graphite crucible in the open atmosphere by induction heating.

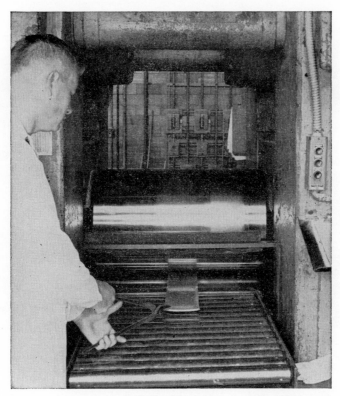

FIG. 7-4   View of typical hot-rolling process to reduce the sandwich to the desired thickness.

The melt size is limited by critical mass considerations.   After the constituents have been dissolved and degassing has been completed, the molten alloy is poured into graphite molds to produce slabs for rolling.   Careful attention must be given to casting conditions because of the large density difference in the melt constituents and the resultant problem of segregation.

The cast alloy slab is heated and then hot-worked by rolling to produce strip stock of desired thickness.   Alloy blanks or fuel-plate cores, 2 in. by 2.25 in. by 0.25 in., are punched from the strip stock with a conventional punch and die set.

Each alloy core is completely jacketed by the picture-frame technique. The jacket consists of a frame piece for enclosing the four lateral sides and two cover sheets. An exploded view of the component parts is shown in Fig. 7-3.

The fuel plate is hot-rolled (the procedure is shown in Fig. 7-4) so as to produce a sound metallurgical bond between clad and core material; then it is flux annealed to prevent the formation of objectionable blisters during subsequent processing.

FIG. 7-5　Placing steel template over fuel element to locate core by X-ray fluoroscopy. When cover is closed over element, operator views fluoroscopic screen through lead glass.

The fuel plates are reduced cold in several passes to final thickness and then are stress annealed. They are examined visually and then under a fluoroscopic X-ray screen (Fig. 7-5) to locate possible internal defects, determine core straightness, and delineate the fuel-bearing core section. After being marked and rough sheared to size, the fuel plates are stacked and batch machined to final length and width, as illustrated in Fig. 7-6.

Prior to assembly the fuel plates are curved to the desired radius of curvature. The curved plates are joined into a single fuel assembly by brazing. Fig. 7-7 illustrates the device for measuring the water-gap spacing. This device has an eccentric cam located on the end of the probe.

7-3.3. Dispersion Type Method. A fuel element with a refractory compound in a metallic matrix offers several advantages over an all-metal element.   The chief advantages are (1) greater freedom in the selection of fuel and matrix material to attain better nuclear, thermal, chemical, physical, and mechanical properties and (2) confinement of the fission-product damage to the compound, which leaves a large portion of the matrix material relatively free of damage to carry the structural load of the fuel element.   Hence, such objectives as good neutron economy, improved corrosion resistance, operation

FIG. 7-6   Gang milling sheared plates to finish dimensions.   Dimensions of core as determined by fluoroscopy (see Fig. 7-5) ensure that outer edge of cover plate is not removed, exposing fuel material.

at higher power density, and increased reactivity lifetime are more easily obtained with dispersion type elements.

An example of this type of element is the stainless steel–uranium dioxide component for fueling the APPR.   The fuel is dispersed in stainless steel by powder-metallurgy techniques that involve blending the component powders, cold pressing them into a green compact, sintering, and coining.   Such processing offers the advantages of (1) excellent distribution of the fuel and (2) extremely accurate accounting for these critical ingredients.   The fuel-bearing compact is contained in a wrought stainless steel protective cladding that prevents leakage of fission products.   The cladding is metallurgically bonded to the compact to maximize heat transfer. A simplified flow diagram for the manufacture of stainless steel–uranium dioxide fuel elements is given in Fig. 7-2c.

7-3.4. Bulk-Oxide Method. Most cost analyses show that the area for greatest savings in the generation of nuclear power lies in the field of fuel costs. Further examination indicates that fuel costs can be substantially reduced by increasing the lifetime of fuel elements in an operating reactor. In an effort to get longer fuel element life, or burn-up, emphasis has shifted from metallic to refractory or ceramic type fuel because the latter is not subject

FIG. 7-7   Measuring plate spacings of the element. An eccentric cam is on the end of the probe between the plates of the element. Maximum rotation of the cam in left and right directions is measured on the front of the instrument. The average limit of the two rotations denotes the amount of spacing between the plates at any selected point.

to deformation at low temperature under conditions of high fuel burn-up. If properly designed, ceramic fuels also permit operation at higher temperatures and exhibit better thermal efficiency.

A simplified flow diagram for the manufacture of bulk-oxide rod components is shown in Fig. 7-2d. The oxide best suited for subsequent forming and sintering into pellets, tubes, or plates is made from uranium compounds precipitated from a uranyl salt solution and subsequently reduced to UO_2 by firing. The product has a large surface to volume ratio, low bulk and packing density, and a moderate to high oxygen to uranium ratio. The UO_2 is compacted at low pressures in a steel die, and the briquet is broken through a screen to produce granulated powder. The granulated powder is cold pressed and sintered in hydrogen. This process produces a slug, or pellet, with a sintered density in excess of 94 percent of theoretical. The pellets are assembled in tubes and the tubes closed by welding end caps.

7-4. FUEL-MATERIALS CONTROL

The successful manufacture of fuel elements depends to a large extent on the exercise of proper controls around the various fabrication operations. These controls fall into two major categories: process controls and nuclear-materials controls.

Since fuel-element fabrication utilizes standard metallurgical processes and equipment, the process controls are similar to those found in any metals industry. There are specifications regarding dimensions, fuel content, spacing between components, internal core size and position, cladding thickness, and time at high temperature during processing. These and other factors must be controlled within close tolerances to achieve maximum quality. Methods for producing elements of such quality include not only mechanical measurements but also statistical procedures for evaluating variances.

However, in the area of materials control, there are few similarities between conventional and nuclear operations. The nature of nuclear fuel materials presents unique control problems in handling and processing.

7-4.1. Methods. Although fabricating certain fuel elements sometimes generates problems peculiar to those elements above, fuel-materials control can be generalized into six basic areas: (1) control of the beginning material in the form received by the fabricator, (2) control during the processing of these materials into component products, (3) control of the component products, (4) control of accumulated scrap resulting from the processing, (5) a consolidation of all control results into an internal master control summary, and (6) preparation of management reports.

Earlier in this chapter the four representative types of uranium fuel materials and their fabrication into fuel elements were discussed; this section deals with methods of controlling operations with these different material types in each of the six basic areas. The discussion is intended to be informative rather than specifically instructive because, as previously mentioned, individual controls will vary with local conditions.

7-4.2. Control of Beginning Material. For material control purposes, fuel element manufacture begins with receipt of the uranium materials. These fall into two general categories: solid metals and powdered materials.

Solid metals include both pure uranium metal and uranium alloys, since the fabricator will often eliminate the melting and casting step in his process by purchasing his beginning materials in the prealloyed state. Powdered materials include the oxides and other compounds of uranium, which are mechanically mixed rather than alloyed with other materials to form the necessary fuel materials combinations.

Receipt and Verification. A shipment of material is always accompanied by a document on which the shipper has listed the weight of the uranium-bearing material (net weight), the total uranium* in the material, and the

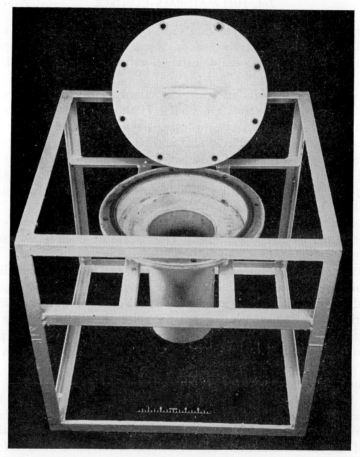

FIG. 7-8 Bird cage shipping container for pure U^{235} materials. An inner container in which the materials are first packaged is placed inside the center opening. Note that here again criticality safety is achieved by enforced spacing between containers.

amount of contained U^{235} based on the level to which the total uranium has been enriched. Verification of all three figures is extremely important to the fabricator not only because the materials are expensive but also because an improper relationship could cause intolerable fuel element content. Net-weight verification is a prime requirement and is accomplished by the use

* This figure is significant, particularly where uranium compounds are received. For instance, UO_2 is only about 88 percent uranium.

of good balances.   Total uranium can be chemically verified by potentiometric titration analysis.   Verification of isotopic enrichment is accomplished by spectrometric means.   If discrepancies occur, they must be resolved with the shipper.

In some instances the fabricator receives his material in the form of an alloy of uranium and another metal.   Here it is important to verify the relation of the total alloy (net weight) to the total uranium.   This can also

Fig. 7-9   Check weighing highly enriched uranium metal.   Container in foreground is typical metal batch container with batch card.   Tare on container permits rapid check of batch at any time.

be done chemically, but for this analysis it is quite important to establish good sampling techniques because of the dispersion of the uranium within the alloy.

Handling and Storage.   Fig. 7-8 shows a "bird cage" container such as is commonly used for shipping pure undiluted U^{235} materials.   The center section is the container proper where the materials are packed.   The frame serves only to keep quantities of the material separated during shipment and temporary storage to avoid a criticality accident.

The materials are removed from their containers and are check weighed on suitable scales.   If the material is in the form of metal, it may be placed directly on the balance (Fig. 7-9).   If it is in the form of powder, however, the tare weight of the inner container must be known; otherwise the material must be check weighed remotely to protect the operator from toxicity and contamination. It is often advantageous for the fabricator to supply the materials vendor with pretared inner containers. In this case a check weighing

Fig. 7-10 Safe used for storage of fuel materials and components. The number of shelves and amount of material on each shelf are controlled by criticality regulations.

consists simply of placing the entire container on the balance and subtracting the tare from the total weight to arrive at the materials net. If this method is utilized, the container weight should be engraved or otherwise permanently placed on the container. Such containers should always be well protected from damage and spillage and should have safety and criticality approval.

After receipt and verification the material should be properly stored in a suitable metal cabinet that conforms to both safety and criticality regulations. The cabinet itself, if not placed within a vault or approved barricade, should generally be a security type safe (Fig. 7-10).

Control Records. Materials are usually processed by the fabricator in smaller quantities than received. The control problem with regard to the beginning materials is one of knowing how much material has been received, how much has been assigned to process, and how much is on hand.

The most desirable beginning control is the simple in-out balance perpetual inventory, which, if it is to facilitate immediate materials tracing, should include references for the particular quantity received as well as the process batch to which the smaller quantities were assigned.

The extent of such a control can be varied to suit the needs of the individual fabricator. Where the operation is small, a single balance sheet would probably suffice. If the operation is large and the enrichments are widely varied, the system must be extensive enough to provide a complete and thorough accounting.

7-4.3. Control of Alloy Process. *Primary Fabrication.* This includes all fabrication stages in which fuel materials are being formed into the proper shape for containment in nonfuel metals. In alloy fabrication work, for example, the U^{235} metal is alloyed with aluminum into an ingot, which is hot rolled into a plate. Cores punched from this plate are then pressed into an aluminum frame and covered with aluminum plates to form a "sandwich." At this point the primary step ends, since the materials are in the beginning form of the component product or composite plate and cannot be altered in weight or content except by destruction of the component.

In nearly every instance, particularly where the uranium is to be alloyed or dispersed, the fabricator will perform developmental work on new or altered products. Since the control of U^{235} content is both a process- and materials-control objective, it is usually advantageous for a control investigation to be made along with the process investigation to determine and establish the methods necessary to ensure proper component content.

Alloy Materials Control. It is necessary to predetermine the proper weight percent uranium in the alloy which will yield the desired U^{235} content in the final component. Given information on the design of the component and the amount of uranium to be contained within it, Aronin and Klein[1] have shown that in the uranium-aluminum system the density method is the most satisfactory for determining the proper weight percent alloy composition. It has been shown that the calculated weight percent correlates with analytical results within ±0.19 percent in alloys up to 35 wt. % uranium.

It is very important that the uranium content of this predetermined alloy be verified. One common method of verification is a potentiometric titration analysis (wet chemical) of random dip samples taken from each melt before casting. Experience has shown the samples to be very representative, and measurement at this early stage of fabrication permits adjustment of uranium content more readily than at a later stage. Other techniques include drill or section sampling of the material during its processing and the sampling of scrap material located adjacent to the component sections cut from the alloy.

The results of such analyses must be evaluated to determine whether the uranium content is acceptable. The establishment of standards by which this determination can be made depends upon a predetermination of the variables involved and the evaluation of resulting uncertainties. Basically, there are two variables in an alloy-content determination: (1) the variation of the chemically determined percent uranium from the intended percent and (2) the recognized limits of error in the sampling and analysis. By examining the two collectively, the fabricator can determine whether a required unit portion of the sampled alloy meets specifications.

Just as important as a single specific measurement and evaluation are the long-run variations between chemical analysis and intended content. The trends of this comparison will often reveal fabrication factors that affect content control. In one specific long-run comparison, for example, it was noted that, when scrap uranium-aluminum fuel plates were remelted as a part of a new heat, the uranium analysis generally ran higher than expected. Investigation showed that the outer clad of the plates contained small amounts of copper, which were titrated with the uranium during the analysis. The addition of an analysis for copper properly adjusted the chemical results, and the situation was corrected.

In the processing of the alloy after analysis, dependence is generally placed on the average analytical result rather than the intended composition. The reasoning for this is that the former would tend to correct for the several human and mechanical errors that might possibly occur during the preparation of the alloy.

A determination of the amount of U^{235} in the cast alloy ingot is not the final content-control step; the fabricator must also determine the content of each component fabricated from the alloy. If, for instance, several plate cores are punched from the rolled ingot, the content of each of these must be known before they can be further processed into fuel elements for which a definite element content has been established.

Where components are identical in dimension and are fabricated from a single ingot, experience has shown that the average component weight method for determining individual component content is very reliable within tolerable limits of error. In this method the entire batch of components from a single heat are weighed, and their total weight is divided by their number. If an extremely close tolerance is desired, a density measurement of each component is taken, and the content is determined from this measurement. For general fabrication purposes, however, the average-weight method is very satisfactory.

The U^{235} homogeneity of the alloy depends to a great extent on the integrity of the fabrication process. In using the average-weight method of determining alloy component content, the fabricator assumes a homogeneous spread of the U^{235} throughout the alloy. Such an assumption is usually based on developmental work that has proved that homogeneity will always exist in the particular alloy within reasonable limits of error. Once integrity has been established for a particular process, the fabricator can ensure good U^{235} homogeneity by means of close process control during fabrication of the alloy billet.

   Control Records. The record forms utilized for the material control of U^{235} in alloy fabrication differ from fabricator to fabricator even more widely than the fabricated shapes that they represent. In every case, however, they must answer three basic control questions: (1) Where is the material located? (2) What is its physical shape? and (3) What is its quantity in relation to the matrix materials in which it is dispersed?

   Individual forms must be created, depending on the shape to be fabricated and the various processes that make up the fabrication effort. Let us take as an example the fabrication of uranium-aluminum alloy cores for composite fuel plates. The particular steps in the process are (1) combining the materials into an alloy ingot, (2) rolling the alloy into a plate, (3) punching out the cores, (4) collecting the remelt scrap, and (5) collecting the heat dross for recovery. The control records for this operation must give us the following facts:

1. The composition of the melt and the amount of each material in the charge
2. The alloy net weights of each of the products of the melt, i.e. ingot, dip samples, and dross
3. The total weight of the charge balanced against the total weight of the alloy products and the process difference
4. The number and total weight of the cores punched from the reduced ingot and their average weight
5. The total weight of the alloy products balanced against the total weight of the component materials and the process difference
6. The weight of the scrap remaining in the punched-out plate
7. The analytical results of the dip samples compared with the intended composition of the melt

   Fig. 7-11 illustrates a practical alloy heat log that permanently records the desired information in all seven categories. (This form could also be applied to other alloy component fabrication steps such as the casting and extrusion of rods and slugs, since the required facts are the same.) Note that the weight percent uranium figure applied to the net alloy weights is an average of the analytical results of the dip samples. Note also that a great deal of information has been condensed into a single control record. This was done to show that such condensation is possible as well as to show the relation of the categories.

7-4.4. Control of Powder Process: *Powder Material Control.* The problems of controlling U^{235} that is fabricated into component products by the powder-dispersion method are identical with those of the alloy work; i.e. the

ALLOY HEAT LOG

Heat No.	Type Material	Intended wt % U	wt % U by Avg. Chem. Analysis		Fabrication Order No.
E-514	U al alloy	15.95	15.97		1124 RJB

BEGINNING MATERIALS					
Type Material		Identification	Net Weight	Total U	U^{235}
Uranium Metal		IC - 842	720.14	720.14	648.13
Alloy Scrap		E - 497	1654.12	239.02	215.12
Scrap Components 3 Plates		E - 492	591.22	25.17	22.65
Scrap Components 2 Plates		E - 494	393.68	16.74	15.07
Scrap Components 2 Plates		E - 500	397.10	20.13	18.12
Other Matrix High Purity Al Metal			2646.22	—	—
Other Material					
Total Materials			6402.48	1021.20	919.09

ALLOY PRODUCTS					
Alloy Billets (1)		E - 514	6096.28	973.58	876.22
Alloy Samples		#1 AR 15.99	6.62	1.06	0.95
		#2 AR 15.96	6.40	1.02	0.92
		#3 AR 15.95	4.57	0.73	0.66
Waste Products		Heat Dross	315.80	50.43	45.39
Total Alloy Products			6429.67	1026.82	924.14
Beginning Materials – Alloy Product Difference			+27.19	+5.62	+5.06

COMPONENT PRODUCTS					
No. Acceptable Pieces		76 Cores	4482.91	715.92	644.33
Average Weight Piece			(58.98)	(9.42)	(8.48)
Scrap Materials		After Punching	1611.24	257.32	231.58
Waste Materials					
Total Products			6094.15	973.24	875.91
Alloy – Component Difference			-2.13	-0.34	-0.31

AR – Analytical Result

FIG. 7-11   Sample of an alloy heat log.

desired amount of homogeneously dispersed fuel material must be contained in the component and must be accounted for properly.

Component Specifications. As with the alloy, a determination must be made of the proper weight percent uranium that will yield the desired U^{235} content in the final component. This becomes more difficult when the dispersion technique is utilized because of the additional variables involved. These variables, which have a direct effect on the density of the compact, include such factors as the amount of uranium per weight unit of its compound and the particle size, shape, and density of both the uranium and matrix powdered materials.

Homogeneity is also a problem in dispersion fabrication. Although it is a relatively simple matter to initially mix the powders into a homogeneous blend, process handling can cause classification within the blend, which could result in considerable uranium-content variation in the fabricated components.

The fabricator can precalculate with only a fair degree of certainty the proper quantity relation of the fuel and matrix materials for a given dispersion component. The best assurance can be obtained from a development effort on the particular component desired. Calculations are proved or corrected from results obtained in actual fabrication of trial components, and handling methods that assure a consistent product are developed.

Because it is extremely difficult to verify the uranium content of a fabricated dispersion component without destroying it, the fabricator must find other means of assuring himself that the fabricated piece is within content tolerance. Although there are a few nondestructive testing methods, the most commonly chosen alternative is to verify that the process itself will produce the desired result. In this case, verification becomes a part of the development effort. A series of shapes are processed in the selected manner, dissolved, and analyzed for uranium content. If the analytical results are satisfactory, quality components are reasonably assured by strict control of the process. Randomly selected control samples should be routinely analyzed to ensure that the process is being so controlled.

One important determination that must be made during development is whether or not the materials for several identical components can be mixed in a single batch. If it is determined that classification will occur, an alternative method of weighing and mixing the materials separately for each component must be utilized.

Control Records. The type of control record utilized for dispersed fuel materials fabrication is almost identical with the type utilized in the fabrication of the alloy. Since there are fewer steps in fabricating components by the dispersion method than by the alloy method, the record is somewhat simpler in form. It does, however, answer the three basic control questions of location, physical status, and quantity relation of the fuel materials.

In the fabrication of a dispersed uranium compact from powdered materials, there are only three general steps: (1) combining the fuel and matrix powders into a blend, (2) pressing the shapes, and (3) collecting any scrap residues that occur. Fig. 7-12 illustrates a type of record which reflects complete information relative to the three process steps. Note that it is very similar in form to the previously illustrated alloy heat log.

7-4.5. Control of Unalloyed Metals and Bulk Oxides Process. The problems of controlling single unalloyed metals and bulk oxides during in-process fabrication are relatively simple when compared with the problems of alloying and dispersion. Although it is still necessary to control the amount of fuel material in the component, no weight percent relations are involved, and homogeneity is not a consideration.

Component Specifications. If the component is to be fabricated from unalloyed metal, the fabricator need determine only the proper isotopic enrichment necessary to achieve the desired U^{235} content for a given finished dimension. If it is to be fabricated by powder metallurgy techniques from uranium compounds, the additional factors of final density and percent uranium in the compound must be considered.

BLENDED MATERIALS BATCH LOG

Blend No.	Type Material	wt % Uranium	Fabrication Order No.	
EB-284	UO_2-*Aluminum*	*48.00*	*1127*	*RJB*

BEGINNING MATERIALS				
Type Material	Identification	Net Weight	Total U	U^{235}
Uranium UO_2 *Powder*	*IC-927*	*1011.63*	*890.23*	*178.05*
Residue from Previous Blend	*EB-283*	*12.21*	*5.86*	*1.17*
Matrix Material *Al Powder*		*843.01*	–	–
Other Material				
Total Blend		*1866.85*	*896.09*	*179.22*

COMPONENT PRODUCTS				
No. Acceptable Pressed Comp.	*19*	*1759.42*	*844.52*	*168.90*
Average weight Acceptable Comp.	–	*(92.60)*	*(44.45)*	*(8.89)*
Rejected Components	*1*	*92.60*	*44.45*	*8.89*
Unused Blend Residue		*10.61*	*5.09*	*1.02*
Total Component Products		*1862.63*	*894.06*	*178.81*
Blend-Component Difference		*4.22*	*2.03*	*0.41*

Fig. 7-12　Sample of a blended batch log.

Since homogeneity is not a problem in fabricating unalloyed or undispersed materials, verification of U^{235} content can be achieved by closely weighing the finished component. It is important, however, that high-quality weighing methods be established and good equipment be used, since the potential variation of uranium content in a pure component is greater than that of one in which the material is alloyed or dispersed with other metals or metallic powders.

Control Records. The records used in controlling the unalloyed or bulk materials during fabrication are very similar to those previously illustrated for control of alloyed and dispersed materials, the basic difference being that no second materials are involved. In fabricating bulk uranium oxide powders into pressed shapes, for example, it would be perfectly logical to use the Blended Materials Batch Log illustrated in Fig. 7-12 and to ignore the Matrix Material section. By the same token, the Alloy Heat Log illustrated in Fig.

7-11 could be utilized as a record for controlling the melting, casting, and further fabrication of unalloyed metals into desired pure components, although slight modifications might be necessary to fit particular processes.

7-4.6. Control During Secondary Fabrication: *Material Control.* When the U^{235} materials reach the beginning form of the component product, i.e. where they are completely contained within their protective coverings, material control becomes relatively simplified. As previously discussed, changes in the uranium content of product components are impossible without their

FIG. 7-13 Batch control container. Inspector has finished examining plates for mechanical imperfections and is replacing them in batch control container for movement to next stage. Note plates in upper section which were rejected in earlier stage.

destruction; therefore, only a piece identification and referral to a previous recording are necessary to maintain control.

The most difficult part of contained materials control is to maintain identification of small individual components until they can be permanently marked. The best method is to assemble small components containing like amounts of U^{235} into groups or batches and to maintain an identification of each batch. In composite plate fabrication of alloys, for example, the average weight method is generally utilized for assigning a U^{235} value to each punched core from a particular heat. Since all the cores of this heat will theoretically contain equal amounts of U^{235}, it is not necessary to maintain an individual identification, and the cores can be worked as a single batch. This batch, however, should be carefully segregated from other similar batches to prevent components from being erroneously identified.

The use of batch containers (Fig. 7-13) is recommended as a good method for maintaining such identification during the early stages of the process. Components are transported from stage to stage by means of the marked container, which is always in close proximity to the materials for use as a quick and positive identifying reference.

BATCH CONTROL CARD

Batch No. *E-514*

Number Components _76_   Type _U al alloy Plates_

Stage	Processed By	Rejections and Reason	Inspected By
1. Frame	GHC	OK	HJW
2. Cover	GHC	OK	HJW
3. Can	—	—	—
4. Weld	aW	OK	aK
5. Hot Roll	CWH	OK	HJW
6. Cold Roll	CWH	1-0.057	HJW
7. Anneal	JNH	2-Blisters	WWP
8. Fluoroscopy	JWB	3-Core of Tol.	JWB
9. Shear	JWB	OK	JWB
10. Machine	CRR	OK	aK
11. Anneal	JNH	1-Blisters	WWP
12. Inspect	WWP	1-Thin Edge	WWP

Total Accepted Components to Storage   68

Total Scrapped Components   8

FIG. 7-14   Sample batch control card.

Since the components are metallic, they are usually permanently identified at some practical point during the process. One method of identification is a coded mark scribed on the cladding. Unless the cladding is relatively thick, however, it is weakened at the scribing point by such a mark. On a composite plate, for example, the mark is never made over the core but always at the end of the plate near the edge.

Another method of marking components consists in drilling tiny holes in the outer protective material. By spacing these holes in a particular manner, the marker is able to indicate the batch in which the plates belong. However, such a method must never be used where the outer cladding over the uranium materials would be weakened or punctured.

Once the components have been permanently marked, the portable batch container becomes less important in identification and can be diverted to new batches. Like components, however, should remain together through the latter stages of the process for ease of location during inventory and, when applicable, during the selection of several components for assembly into an element.

Components from more than one batch will often be used in reaching proper U^{235} content within close tolerance. At this point, control shifts from batch identification to element identification. The shift is accomplished by pulling the selected plates from their batch and grouping them in a temporary manner, e.g. by tying or taping, until they can be permanently assembled into a fuel element. For purposes of U^{235} materials control, as will be explained later, the element is considered to have been assembled when the plates are selected.

Control Records. Secondary fabrication records fall into three general categories: (1) component-processing records, (2) component-disposition records, and (3) assembled-component records.

(*a*) COMPONENT-PROCESSING RECORDS. The logical type of record for controlling uranium materials during component processing is illustrated in Fig. 7-14. This Batch Control Card accompanies the batch through its various stages of processing until the components are finished. On this record is the outline of the entire process of containment; space is provided for the initials of the responsible employee at each stage to signify that the batch has completed that particular part of the process. The card also provides space for a listing of rejected components.

When individual components have been rejected, as can occur at almost any stage of the process, they should be immediately separated from the batch, recorded as rejected on the card, and eventually returned to the salvage point, where they will be either recycled into the process or recovered with other U^{235} scrap. It is recommended that one compartment of the batch container be used for collecting rejected components so that the entire batch may be kept together until its processing is completed.

The batch, after its processing has been completed, is returned along with its control card to the materials-control storage point. The card is completed and attached to the heat or batch log, and the two records are placed in a permanent file. Note that the two records now serve as a single master record showing disposition of the entire beginning quantity of U^{235}. Again, both records shown here are illustrative examples and can be altered to suit individual needs.

(*b*) COMPONENT-DISPOSITION RECORDS. At this point the fuel components may be finished products or may require further assembly into multicomponent units. In either case, an additional record must be prepared to indicate the disposition of the finished, accepted components. One example of such a record (Fig. 7-15) provides for initially recording the temporary storage of the finished components. Their shipment or further processing into assembled units is indicated as it occurs, and a permanent record of their disposition is established.

If the components are to be shipped, a notation is made on the record as to the number of components in the shipment and their shipping order number.

COMPLETED COMPONENT DISPOSITION RECORD

Heat or Batch No. _E- 514_   Average Total U Each Component _9. 42_ U235 _8. 48_

Disposition	Date	Number Components			Balance on Hand	
		In	Out	Bal	Total U	U235
Received for Storage	6-12-58	68		68	640.56	576.64
Element I-109	6-14-58		12	56	527.52	474.88
Shipment 1142-1	6-15-58		27	29	273.18	245.92
Element I-121	6-24-58		16	13	122.46	110.24
Element I-123	6-25-58		9	4	37.68	33.92
Element I-127	6-27-58		4	0	-0-	-0-

Fig. 7-15 Sample component disposition record.

If they are diverted for assembly into an element, the notation includes the number of components for each particular assembled unit and the number of that unit. When all dispositions have been completed, the record is filed for reference and the batch control ends, since all components have either been shipped or have been reidentified as fuel elements.

(c) ASSEMBLED COMPONENT RECORDS. Materials control in component assembly is very much like batch control. A record card is issued on each selected group of components which is to be assembled, and this card, like the Batch Control Card, follows the components through their complete processing into a finished unit ready for shipment. This type of record is illustrated and described more fully in the final section of this chapter.

7-4.7. Scrap Accumulation. Scrap materials can occur at any time during the fabrication process and must be disposed of by one of two methods: (1) recycle to the process by combining with new batches of like materials or

(2) chemical recovery for reprocessing of the uranium into its original form. More recently, economic feasibility has become a prime consideration in the decision as to whether the material should be recovered or discarded.

Some materials offer themselves ideally for combination with new batches. Alloy residues of good quality can be remelted with additional uranium and aluminum to form a new ingot and should never be offered for recovery unless a process is closed. Rejected solid-metal component products can often be put back into the process by direct remelting of the entire component or of the contained material from which the cladding has been removed. Left-over powder residues are often usable in other blends.

Others must be taken out of the process. Heat dross contains such a wide variety of impurities that it would never be recycle melted. Pressed powder shapes are no longer usable as beginning material. Metal particles clinging to process equipment can often be collected only by scraping or dissolving, which destroys their recycle utility.

The uranium contained within these scrap materials makes them strictly accountable and nearly always recoverable. Since they occur in rather small amounts in relation to the size of the melt or worked batch, the most inexpensive recovery method is to accumulate the single quantities into a large batch for one recovery operation. The size of such a batch is, of course, subject to criticality regulations, but the fabricator should remember that the larger the quantity to recover, the lower the recovery cost per gram of the uranium material.

7-4.8. Summary. Although the combining of the materials-controls records covering the fabrication process into a single composite record is an internal function, the results of such a summary must be reported externally. For that reason, the internal record and the external report are closely allied, and a discussion of one necessarily ties in with a discussion of the other.

In the final analysis, the total amount of fuel material which has entered the fabrication plant must be compared with the total amount on hand after processing, and a determination must be made of process differences. These differences, in turn, must be properly explained to those in authority according to materials-control regulations that apply.

Materials-Control Cycle. Since all fabrication processes are designed around the preparation of uranium for reactor use, the material can be looked upon as having passed through a cycle in which its basic quantity and quality have remained the same but its form has been altered.

Control mechanics necessarily follow the material through its cycle until final disposition is made and it leaves the fabrication site. This is graphically illustrated by Fig. 7-16, which reflects the general fabrication stages and their related controls from the receipt of the U^{235} to the shipment of the finished elements.

Note that the storage unit serves as the channel through which the uranium materials are both introduced into the process and removed from it. The function of this unit makes it easily adaptable as a central control point for the entire process and closely allies it with the SS material control section.

The illustration also locates each already described functional control record with the process it represents and shows its relation to the other records in

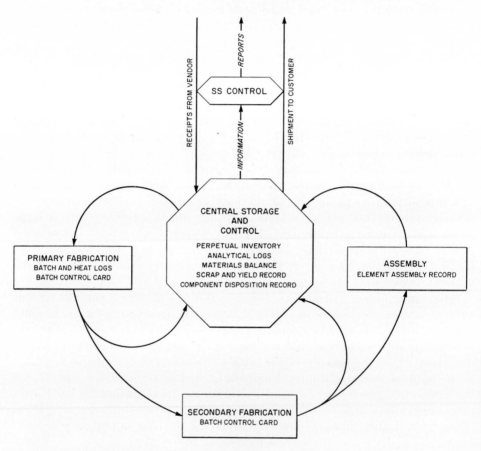

The Fuel Materials Control Cycle.

Fɪɢ. 7-16 Schematic diagram of materials and control records flow.

the control system. A reexamination of each individual record will reveal that it serves the additional purpose of establishing beginning control data for the record it precedes as well as the purpose of recording and balancing its own fabrication stage.

Material Balance. The most practical method for comparison of the materials before and after processing is to establish a material balance. In this method the process is theoretically cut off at some selected point, and a physical inventory is taken of all materials in storage and process. Pure and unclad materials are weighed and counted, and their uranium content is computed from the readings. Piece counts are taken of the clad materials, and uranium content is established from fabrication records on the basis of their

URANIUM MATERIALS BALANCE

Period: July 1 - 31, 1958 Type Material: 90% Enriched Uranium Alloy		Total Uranium Grams	U-235 Grams
Balance on Hand, June 30, 1958		17,037	15,333
Total Receipts - July		25,274	22,747
Total Previous Balance and Receipts		42,311	38,080
Less Total Shipments - July		16,426	14,783
Balance on Hand, July 31, 1958		25,885	23,297
Materials Inventory			
Beginning Materials: Metal		3,421	3,079
Materials in Process:			
Billets		2,652	2,387
Rods		1,381	1,243
Cores		1,829	1,646
Remelt Alloy from Punchings		1,545	1,391
Product Materials:			
Plates		6,737	6,063
Assembled Element		7,347	6,612
Scrap Materials for Recovery: Heat Dross			
By Weight and % Uranium	998		
By Difference	973		
Recovered	924	924	832
TOTAL INVENTORY		25,836	23,253
Process Difference (Loss)		49	44

FIG. 7-17 Sample material balance and inventory statement. The difference between the Balance on Hand, July 31, 1958 and Total Inventory is the Process Difference, which may be either a loss or a gain.

identification. In some fabrication plants production is actually shut down, and employees assist in taking the inventory to expedite its completion.

The materials control records now serve a very important purpose in that each unit of material can be checked against them to determine whether any misplacements have occurred during the process or whether there are any errors in number or amount. If the records and inventory are correct and no misplacements have occurred, the first step in the material balance has been completed.

The second step of the balance involves the comparison of the total amount of uranium shown in the materials-control record with the total amount in the balance area. Significant differences must be resolved by further checks on the materials-control records, but differences within the process limits of error are to be expected.

Fig. 7-17 illustrates a material balance drawn around a uranium-aluminum alloy operation in which uranium of 90 percent enrichment has been processed. Note that the dross content is stated in three quantities: (1) the quantity based on the weight percent uranium in the alloy, (2) the quantity based on what the dross should theoretically contain by difference, and (3) the actual recovered scrap content.

The first and second are useful only as temporary media to determine a balance within reasonable limits until the scrap materials can be recovered. Coupled with a confirmed weight and piece inventory of the usable materials in process, this reasonable limit balance permits the fabricator to continue operations until scrap recovery has been completed with a sound assumption that his U^{235} materials are accounted for properly. The latter recovery figure is, of course, used as the basis for fine determination of process differences.

The material balance is important not only as a materials control tool but also as a means of confirming the content of the finished products. A difference within operating limits of error is a good indication that the U^{235} content of the materials is as intended. This, of course, is a general indication of the process in total and does nothing to confirm the individual content of the components; however, it does indicate that no general abnormalities have occurred.

Process Differences. The question now arises as to what variations in the final balance constitute a reasonable process difference. There are no concrete figures that can be quoted because of the many variations in processes. Certainly, if the final difference falls within the collective analytical and weight limits of error of the operation it is a reasonable one. Since this is not always the case, however, individual process circumstances must be considered. The fabricator must refer to all process records affecting the particular balance in an effort to determine where the difference occurred. The individual records of the cycle are designed to aid in isolating the source of the difference, which must be determined before proper action can be taken.

7-5. CENTRALIZED UNIT OPERATION

Experience has indicated that if the operation and control of the process and materials are centralized, closer and more complete controls can be maintained with a minimum of effort. This centralization includes not only the combining of process and materials-control records but also a centralized plant layout in which the operation is contained in a single compact unit.

7-5.1. Centralized Materials and Process Control. The value of the U^{235} material, coupled with the extreme measurement tolerances required in fuel element fabrication, makes many examination, inspection, and recording steps necessary to maintain general control. The process is a step-by-step change in the physical form of the U^{235}. Each step in the process is dependent on the ones that precede it, and errors in one step can cause additional errors in the following steps.

It is desirable, therefore, that both materials and process control records be combined into single simplified record forms. Such forms present a complete picture of all measurement results in a particular stage and can save much time and effort in checking conformance to specifications.

If the operation is of such magnitude that it requires mechanical quality inspection of components by persons other than those performing the fabrication steps, the inspections should be combined with the materials control function into a Product Control Department under an individual whose sole responsibility is to ensure quality of product and proper handling of the U^{235}. Even if mechanical inspections are performed as a routine function by the fabricating personnel, the establishment of such a department to perform the materials control function and to audit inspection records is desirable.

7-5.2. Control Records. In a product control system the form records tend to fall into six categories. Four of these are combined records, and two, because of their nature and application, must remain as single materials-control data accumulations.

Perpetual Inventory. The first of the single type records is the perpetual U^{235} inventory. This record is the same as described in an earlier section, i.e. a simple in-out balance record of the U^{235} materials on hand. Such a record is very useful in any U^{235} work because it serves as a quick inventory reference for procurement purposes and as a check against all physical inventories of the material.

Heat-Analysis Log. In alloy work the second single type record, which provides chemical analysis information for the process, is utilized. This form, also already discussed, chronologically accumulates analytical results of each heat sample along with extended figures based on the weight of the materials alloyed. Its purpose is to provide quick reference information in scrap remelting, general information, and a basis for statistical comparison for limits of error determinations.

Batch Process Record. The first of the combined forms is a Batch Process Record, which reflects a complete picture of the fabrication from the initial use of the beginning uranium materials through the first containment of the single component parts.

Fig. 7-18 illustrates a suggested form for such a record. Note that the

BATCH PROCESS RECORD

Heat or Batch No.	Type Material	Intended wt % U	wt % U by Chem. Analysis	Fabrication Order No.
E-514	U al alloy	15.95	15.97	1124 RJB

Instructions: Charge Furnace and Bring to 1130°C Melt. Take 3 Dip Samples. Pour at 825°C into Two Type "A" Graphite Molds

BEGINNING MATERIALS

Type Material	Identification	Net Weight	Total U	U²³⁵
Uranium Metal	IC-842	720.14	720.14	648.12
Scrap Alloy	E-497	1654.12	239.02	215.12
Scrap Plates (3)	E-492	591.22	25.17	22.65
Scrap Plates (1)	E-494	393.68	16.74	15.07
Scrap Plates (1)	E-500	397.10	20.13	18.12
Aluminum Metal	High Purity	2646.22	—	—
Total Materials		6402.48	1021.20	919.08

INTERMEDIATE PRODUCTS

Samples	#1 AR 15.99	6.62	1.06	0.95
	#2 AR 15.96	6.40	1.02	0.92
	#3 AR 15.95	4.57	0.73	0.66
Cast Billets (2)	E-514	6096.28	973.58	876.22
Waste Materials	Heat Dross	315.80	50.43	45.39
Total Products		6429.67	1026.82	924.14
Materials – Product Difference		+27.19	+5.62	+5.06

COMPONENT PRODUCTS

Instructions: Anneal Billets at 600°C for 4 hrs. Hot Roll to 0.280 per Schedule. Cold Roll at 0.258. Punch out 2¼ × 2¼ in. Cores.

No. Acceptable Components	76 Cores	4482.91	715.92	644.33
Average Weight Component		(58.99)	(9.42)	(8.48)
Scrap Materials	After Punching	1611.24	257.32	231.58
Waste Materials				
Total Component Products		6094.15	973.24	875.91
Intermediate – Component Difference		-2.13	-0.34	-0.31

BATCH CONTROL CARD

Batch No. E-514   No. Components 76   Type U al alloy   Fabrication Order No. 1124

Batch No.	Instructions	Processed By	Rejections and Reason	Inspected By
1. Frame	Press ft into ¼" double al Frames	BHC	OK	AJW
2. Cover	2-⅝₁₆" Cover Plates	BHC	OK	AJW
3. Can				
4. Weld	Tack Weld Sandwich Edges	AW	OK	AK
5. Hot Roll	at 600°C to 0.065 - 10% Redct.	CWH	OK	AJW
6. Cold Roll	to 0.060	CWH	1 - 0.057	AJW
7. Anneal	Flux Anneal at 600°C 45 min.	JNH	2 - Blisters	WWP
8. Fluoroscopy	Mark Cores with Template "B"	JWB	3 - Core off Tol.	JWB
9. Shear	To Markings – 3" width	JWB	OK	JWB
10. Machine	Plate Width 2.845 ± 0.05 Empl 28	CRR	OK	AK
11. Anneal	45 min. at 600°C	JNH	1 - Blister	WWP
12. Inspect	Gen. Conditions and Core Tol.	—	1 - Thin Edge	WWP

Total Accepted Components to Storage   68

Total Scrap Components for Recycle   9   Recovery

Fig. 7-18   Sample batch process record and batch control card.

X-790 (Rev. 11-55)

Y-26697

Heat No.	Plate Length	No. Plates	Total U Per Plate	U-235 Per Plate	Total U	Total U-235
E-501	Long	2	8.697	7.795	17.394	15.590
	Long					
E-504	Reg.	1	8.683	7.783	8.683	7.783
E-505	Reg.	4	8.707	7.804	34.828	31.216
E-508	Reg.	11	8.738	7.832	96.118	86.152
	Reg.					
Grand Total		18			Total U-235 in Assembly	140.741

PLATE SPACING, MILS

Space No.	Location, Inches			
	2½	12	16	26⅜
1-2	118	122	121	120
2-3	116	113	112	119
3-4	119	115	116	115
4-5	117	117	117	116
5-6	118	112	113	117
6-7	117	123	121	119
7-8	118	117	122	117
8-9	116	116	111	118
9-10	117	118	120	119
10-11	118	119	121	118
11-12	118	119	122	117
12-13	116	114	108	116
13-14	119	119	120	118
14-15	117	118	112	119
15-16	117	115	120	117
16-17	118	126	119	120
17-18	122	113	120	123
18-19	-	-	-	-

CRITICAL DIMENSIONS, INCHES

Pt.	A	B	C	VCH	Sagitta
2½	2.991	2.988	2.991	3.070	0.241
7	2.993	2.990	2.994	3.068	0.240
12	2.995	2.990	2.994	3.068	0.244
16	2.995	2.990	2.992	3.065	0.246
21	2.995	2.991	2.993	3.065	0.248
26⅜	2.992	2.988	2.990	3.073	0.240

Plate Spacing _117_ Mils ± _12_

Plate Thickness: Side Plates _3/16_ inch
Center Plates _0.060_ inch
Outer Plates _0.060_ inch

Side Plates: □ Braze Clad ☒ Braze Metal

Remarks: 18 Curved plate assembly. Long top and bottom plates. Plate content based on average analysis of die sample taken from heat.

SPECIAL ELEMENT PLATE POSITIONING

☑ POSITIONED AS CHECKED
□ NOT APPLICABLE
T = TOP OF ASSEMBLY
B = BOTTOM OF ASSEMBLY

FUEL UNIT FABRICATION RECORD

Type Unit _U-Al alloy_ Destination _____ Shipped _____ On Tr No. _____ Fuel Unit Number _UM-17_

FIG. 7-19 Sample fuel unit fabrication record.

Batch or Heat Log and the Batch Control Card previously discussed have been combined and expanded to record the process instructions. Because the U^{235} content is both a materials and process control function during this fabrication stage, the two records can be combined with the necessary measurement and process specification recordings for the satisfaction of both controls. The resulting form reflects a complete control picture through this rather critical, complex stage.

Note also that the container control section has been separated from the remainder of the record by a perforation. This enables it to be detached and sent as a flow sheet with the batch through the remainder of the processing, after which it is attached again and filed with the original record.

SCRAP, WASTE, AND YIELD RECORD

Uranium Aluminum Alloy   For Period *July 1, 1958* to *July 8, 1958*   *90% U^{235}*

Batch No.	No. Comp. Fab.	*Rejections For						Total	No. Re-cycled	For Recovery – Calculated Value				Actual Recovery		Process Difference	
		1	2	3	4	5	6			No.	Net Weight	Total U	U235	Total U	U235	Total U	U235
E-514	76	3	1		3	1		8	8								
E-514										HB	315.80	50.43	45.39				
E-515	76	2		1		4		7	7								
E-515										HB	289.79	62.07	55.86				
E-516	74	1		3		1	4	9	9								
E-516										HB	326.51	50.45	45.41				
E-517	76	2			1			3	3								
E-517										HB	297.45	54.76	49.28				
E-518	76		1			2		3	3								
E-518										HB	342.81	63.11	56.80				
Totals	378	8	2	4	4	8	4	30	30	-	1572.36	280.82	251.74	252.73	227.46	-28.09	25.28

*Number denotes type of rejection.

FIG. 7-20 Sample scrap, waste, and yield record.

Element Assembly Record. When fuel components are to be permanently assembled into a complex fuel element, their single identity is usually dropped in favor of the identity of an assembled element. The second combined form, called the Element Assembly Record, acts as a collection reference for the individual component numbers so that if future needs require, the components of an element can be traced to the individual batch from which they were fabricated. The record also reflects a complete process and inspection report.

For purposes of illustration, such a record now in current use at a fabrication plant is shown in Fig. 7-19. This particular form is used for recording the assembly of a uranium-aluminum fuel element; hence the curved plate cross-sectional diagram. Note that the position of each plate in the element is indicated by its number and that all dimensional measurements are recorded. Note also that individual plate contents are shown and totaled. The plates are selected and this latter step is performed before the element is processed to ensure content specifications.

Scrap and Yield Record. One of the most important aspects of fabrication is the maintenance of a good ratio of product yield to materials processed. It is important, therefore, that the fabricator have available current figures on the number of rejected components and the reasons for their rejection. On the other hand, the disposition of U^{235} scrap is an integral part of the materials-control cycle. Since the two factors are directly related, records

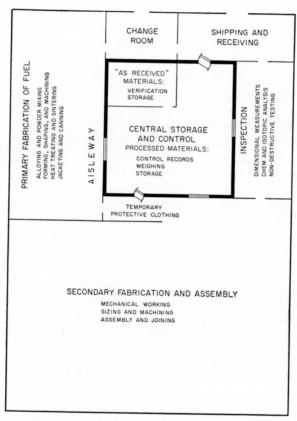

FIG. 7-21   Suggested plant layout for fuel element manufacture.

for the two are logically combined by the use of the third dual-purpose form called the Scrap, Waste, and Yield Record.

Fig. 7-20 illustrates such a form designed to record all rejected components and the reasons for their rejections. In addition, the content of all scrap is calculated, recorded, and its recycle or recovery disposition noted. Where material is recycled, U^{235} content is not noted, since it will appear on the new Batch Process Record. The U^{235} content of material for recovery is noted, however, since it will be removed from the process at this point. Totals of the material are drawn at the time that each material balance inventory is made. The actual recovery figures and differences are noted later upon recovery of the material.

Material Balance Inventory. The last of the dual-purpose forms expands the previously discussed material balance (Fig. 7-17) to include a detailed breakdown of the materials into their particular stage of the process. In addition to the primary purpose of establishing process differences and confirming general U^{235} content of the material, the record also serves as a parts inventory. Each type and amount of processed material is listed on the inventory, which provides a complete reference for the accounting department in making the cost statement for the period. In this respect, it is well to time the material balance to coincide with both the regular cost statement and the required materials-control reports. These are usually compiled at the end of each month.

7-5.3. Centralized Plant Layout. The degree of effort required for successfully controlling U^{235} materials during their fabrication into fuel elements depends to a great extent on the layout of the production plant. A fabricator can alleviate many of his control problems if the U^{235} materials are centrally stored and controlled and if the remaining plant layout is such that duplication of health, safety security, and production, as well as SS-material controls, is minimized.

Fig. 7-21 is a very general illustration of a centralized fabrication plant layout. Note that the primary and secondary fabrication areas and the service areas are segregated but have the necessary controlled access to each other. Note also that the central storage and control section, a vault-type room, is designed to be openly accessible to all other sections during work hours. During off hours the structure is closed and serves as a security vault for the U^{235} materials.

REFERENCES FOR CHAPTER 7

1. L. R. ARONIN and J. L. KLEIN, *Use of Density Method as a Sensitive Absolute Measure of Alloy Composition and Its Application to the Aluminum-Uranium System,* USAEC Report NMI-1118, Nuclear Metals, Inc., Oct. 29, 1954.

SUGGESTED READING

C. ALLARDICE and E. R. TRAPNELL, *The First Pile,* USAEC Report TID-292, Nov. 17, 1949.

ATOMIC ENERGY COMMISSION, *Physical Security Standards,* in *AEC Manual,* Vol. 2000, Chap. 2401, Aug. 16, 1956.

W. H. RAY, *The Design and Operation of Radiochemical Laboratories,* USAEC Report AECU-566, Oak Ridge National Laboratory.

J. E. CUNNINGHAM et al., OAK RIDGE NATIONAL LABORATORY, Fuel Dispersions in Stainless-Steel Components for Power Reactors, in *Fuel Elements Conference, Paris, November 18-23, 1957,* USAEC Report TID-7546 (Bk. 1), pp. 243-268, 1958.

J. E. CUNNINGHAM et al., Fuel Dispersions in Aluminum-Base Elements for Research Reactors, in *Fuel Elements Conference, Paris, November 18-23, 1957*, USAEC Report TID-7546 (Bk. 1), pp. 269-298, 1958.

W. C. THURBER and R. J. BEAVER, *Segregation in Uranium-Aluminum Alloys and Its Effect on the Fuel Loading of Aluminum-Base Fuel Elements*, USAEC Report ORNL-2476, Oak Ridge National Laboratory, Sept. 19, 1958.

J. E. CUNNINGHAM and R. E. ADAMS, Techniques for Canning and Bonding Metallic Uranium with Aluminum, in *Fuel Elements Conference, Paris, November 18-23, 1957*, USAEC Report TID-7546 (Bk. 1), pp. 102-119, 1958.

Chapter 8

NATURAL AND SLIGHTLY ENRICHED
URANIUM FUEL ELEMENTS *

8-1. INTRODUCTION

The Feed Materials Production Center (FMPC), located at Fernald, Ohio, converts raw uranium ore or concentrates into a high-purity uranium metal which, in turn, is fabricated into reactor fuel elements. This latter phase of the operation is discussed in this chapter.

The techniques used in the fabrication process are common to both natural and slightly enriched uranium, and unless it is specifically stated otherwise. this discussion is applicable to the fabrication of either. Although the quantities of enriched metal that can be handled as a batch are somewhat smaller than the quantities of natural uranium, the process is essentially the same. Specific differences will be discussed toward the end of this chapter.

The system of materials control at the FMPC is based on identifying each lot of uranium-bearing material by a multicode number and debiting and crediting at least two material accounts each time a lot is involved in a transaction. The system is described here only briefly; it is described in detail in Chapter 15.

The lot number consists of a three-digit code which fixes the origin of the material, a letter code for the year of production, a three-digit material type code, and a four-digit lot sequence number. If appropriate, an additional number is used to identify an impurity or alloying constituent.

Materials account categories are identified as raw material, material in process, finished material, and scrap. Material in any balance area must fall into one of these four categories.

Transactions are defined as being of eight classes: external receipts, internal receipts, production (category change from in-process to finished or scrap), external shipments, internal shipments, consumption (category change from raw material to in-process), and two memo transfers to reflect changes in cost-

* P. N. McCreery, Feed Materials Production Center (FMPC) operated by the National Lead Co. of Ohio (NLO), Cincinnati, Ohio.

accounting codes or changes in lot markings which are not the result of an actual activity. These transactions are identified, respectively, by code numbers 2 through 9; code 1 is used for items on inventory. Codes 1 through 4 and 8 represent debit transactions, and codes 5 through 7 and 9 represent credits. These codes are punched into automatic tabulating punch cards. The cards also contain complete identification of each lot in existence, and the transaction codes enable the machines to debit and credit each account as required. Detailed instructions for processing these cards are given in Chapter 15.

Although this system is still in a state of evolution, it does serve to illustrate the services available through the use of automatic tabulating equipment which would be economically prohibitive if the work were attempted manually.

8-2. METAL-CASTING PROCESS

8-2.1. Process Description. The feed material for the metal-casting step, depicted schematically in Fig. 8-1, consists of virgin metal in the form of derbies, solid remeltable scrap from any of the fabrication steps, and briquetted machine turnings. The proportion of each type of metal being charged is carefully controlled so that the ingot will fall within impurity specifications and be of optimum size. Reduction slag adhering to a derby is a minor problem in introducing impurities and can cause a below-weight charge. Metal-fabrication scrap may be high in impurities, e.g. scrap from reject ingots or scrap contaminated by salt in the rolling mill. In addition, if the scrap has a large surface-to-volume ratio, it may not make a charge of sufficient density. Both impurities and densities must be considered when briquettes are used.

The loaded crucible is transferred from the charging station to an induction-heated vacuum furnace. A typical furnace is shown in Fig. 8-2. The lower portion of this furnace contains the graphite mold into which the molten charge is poured from the bottom of the crucible after it has reached the desired temperature.

The metal is allowed to solidify in the mold under vacuum. Internal furnace pressure is returned to atmospheric, by the introduction of first an inert gas and then air. The mold tank is then removed, and the mold is stripped from the ingot. Mold flashings and imperfections are ground away, and the top of the ingot is cropped by a power saw to remove impurities and pipe. A thin slice is cut from the ingot for density and chemical analysis, and if this is found to be within specifications, the ingot is ready to be rolled.

8-2.2. Data Collection. Data that reflect the activities of the fabrication processes are originated by production personnel. For example, as a crucible is charged with remeltable metal, the operator notes the reading of the scale on which the crucible rests and identifies on his charge sheet the type of metal

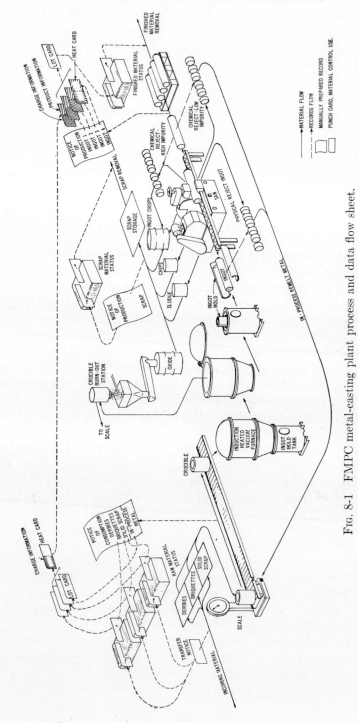

Fig. 8-1 FMPC metal-casting plant process and data flow sheet.

associated with each weight increment. The completed charge sheet then becomes the source document for material control in recording the consumption of raw material. It also serves as a guide in yield studies for various feeds and feed combinations. Should an ingot be out of specification for some impurity, this record will identify all feed material that went into the ingot so that the source of trouble can be determined. This information is punched

FIG. 8-2 Induction furnace used in metal casting process.

into automatic tabulating cards, together with the following data: heat number, furnace number, finished ingot weight, impurity analyses (with a code punch for items out of specification), date poured, and date shipped. The source of this information is shown by the shaded portions of the punch cards in Fig. 8-1. When these cards are sorted by various codes, it becomes possible to look at the activity of a given period as a function of many relationships—e.g. yield for various feed blends, furnace performance, impurity-control evaluation, and rejection data.

At the time of inventory all heats poured but not shipped or remelted should reconcile with the physical inventory. In the event of an inventory discrep-

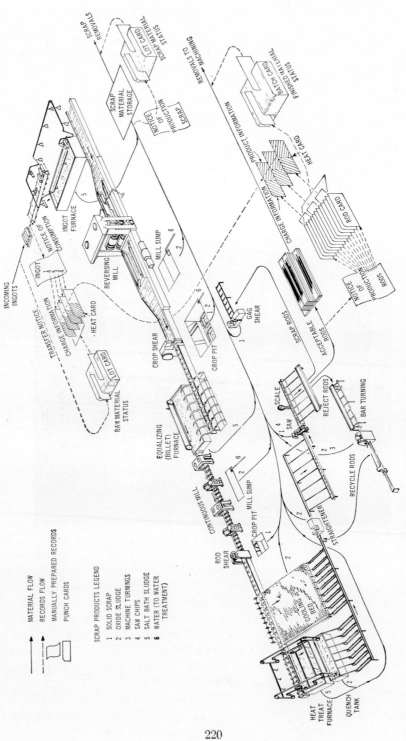

MATERIAL FLOW
RECORDS FLOW
MANUALLY PREPARED RECORDS
PUNCH CARDS

SCRAP PRODUCTS LEGEND

1 SOLID SCRAP
2 OXIDE SLUDGE
3 MACHINE TURNINGS
4 SAW CHIPS
5 SALT BATH SLUDGE
6 WATER (TO WATER TREATMENT)

INCOMING INGOTS

RAW MATERIAL STATUS

LOT CARD

TRANSFER NOTICE

CHARGE INFORMATION

HEAT CARD

INGOT

NOTICE OF CONSUMPTION

INGOT FURNACE

REVERSING MILL

MILL SUMP

CROP SHEAR

CROP PIT

EQUALIZING (BILLET) FURNACE

CONTINUOUS MILL

CROP PIT

MILL SUMP

ROD SHEAR

GAG SHEAR

SCRAP RODS

ACCEPTABLE RODS

SCALE

SAW

REJECT RODS

BAR TURNING

RECYCLE RODS

STRAIGHTENER

COOLING BED

HEAT TREAT FURNACE

QUENCH TANK

NOTICE OF PRODUCTION RODS

ROD CARD

HEAT CARD

CHARGE INFORMATION

PRODUCT INFORMATION

REMOVALS TO MACHINING

BATCH CARD

FINISHED MATERIAL STATUS

SCRAP REMOVALS

SCRAP MATERIAL STORAGE

LOT CARD

SCRAP MATERIAL STATUS

NOTICE OF PRODUCTION SCRAP

Fig. 8-3 FMPC rolling mill process and data flow sheet.

ancy, these cards are valuable in ascertaining the disposition of every ingot in the plant from the previous inventory to date. Once the ingot inventory has been reconciled, one can be certain that if the discrepancy still exists, it does not represent a missing ingot and must be associated with other factors such as feed materials or scrap resulting from the process.

8-3. ROLLING PROCESS

8-3.1. Process Description. A flow diagram of the rolling process is shown in Fig. 8-3. The ingots are heated by electrical immersion heaters in a eutectic

Fig. 8-4 Two-high reversing mill. The many grooves of diminishing size used to reduce the diameter of the billet are readily seen on the top roller.

mixture of lithium carbonate and potassium carbonate. A 7-in.-diameter ingot will require about 1 hour to heat throughout. Feeding the furnace is an automatic conveyor, which picks up ingots from the loading table and places them in one end of the bath as another ingot is removed from the opposite end to be rolled. The bath is so constructed that a given ingot will have heated by the time it completes the in-out cycle. The hot ingots are conveyed to the two-high reversing mill shown in Fig. 8-4 (otherwise known as the roughing mill, blooming mill, etc.), where a series of passes through ever diminishing grooves in the rolls reduces the cross section to a somewhat elliptical pattern.

The ends of the rolled ingot, or billet, are cropped to remove splits and fishtails that might foul in the rolls of the finishing mill, and the billet is cut into two or more sections for more convenient handling in the next steps. The billet sections are reheated in an equalizing furnace bath of the same molten salt described above. When the proper temperature has once again been reached, the billets are mechanically fed into the finishing mill, which consists of three horizontal and three vertical stands. In this operation the cross section of the piece is reduced to a round slightly larger than the desired outside diameter of the finished fuel element. The billet is then cut to lengths of about 20 ft. Rods, as rolled, have a crystalline structure of the alpha phase. The more desirable beta structure can be obtained by heating the rods in a third bath, similar to the first two, for about 15 minutes, then quickly quenching the min water.

Regardless of the heat-treating option, the rods must be straight prior to machining, and this is done with an inclined-roll type straightener. The rods are then inspected for physical defects. The ends are cropped, if necessary, to eliminate machining difficulties, and acceptable rods are batched into "tote pans" to await machining. Some rods with surface defects can be salvaged by cutting away the surface in a bar turning lathe. These rods make a second pass through the straighteners and inspection line and are then classed as either acceptable or reject.

8-3.2. Data Collection. As each ingot is rolled, it is assigned a rolling sequence number. This number, as well as the ingot number, weight, and lot number, is punched into a tabulating card. At any given inventory period, when the cards for ingots transferred are matched with the cards for ingots assigned a rolling sequence number, the former cards, representing the raw material inventory in the rolling mill, should be discarded. Another card showing lot number and lot weight is summary punched from the individual ingot cards and is used to credit the rolling-mill raw-material inventory for material balance purposes.

As each rod is produced, a record is made of the rod weight, the ingot from which it came, and the batch to which it is assigned. An ingot may yield as many as six rods; the number of rods in a batch will be multiples of the number of spindles in the automatic screw machine magazine. Here again a summary card is punched, this time of individual rod cards, showing the weight, type, quality, and batch number of the rods in each given batch. The summary cards are then used to debit the finished material inventory of the rolling mill. If the quality of the rods is acceptable for machining, a code X is punched into the card. Rejected but salvable rods are identified by code R; those scrapped are identified by code G. The salvable rods are machined to remove surface imperfections, are once again inspected, and are categorized as parts of new batches. The batch number will identify them as having been rejected once.

A comparison of individual ingot-consumption and rod-production (by ingot number) cards can be used for ingot yield data broken down into acceptable,

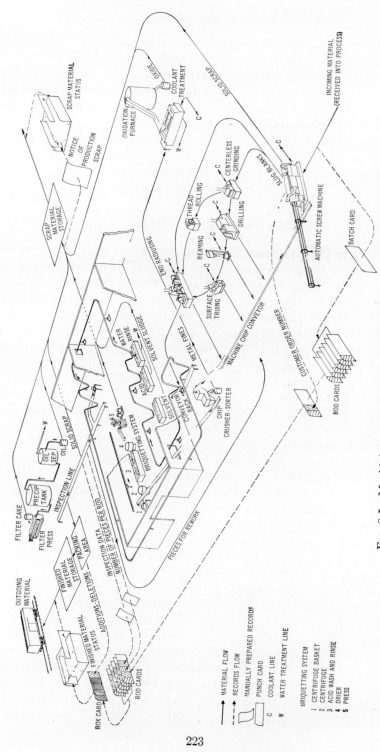

FIG. 8-5 Machining and inspection process and data flow sheet.

223

reject, and scrap categories, detection of special operations in the plant (production other than rods or the fabrication of rods from some external source of metal), and total scrap production (billet crops, etc.). The in-process inventory at any given time can also be deduced from this information if proper cognizance is given to previous inventory values and material transfers. A comparison of reject rod production (R cards) and reject rods processed will inform the investigator of salvage yields and can be used in calculating the inventory of reject rods to be processed. The number of reject rods machined can also be extended by a factor to verify the quantity of machine chips and sludge transferred to the machining area for processing.

8-4. MACHINING PROCESS

8-4.1. Process Description. Slug* blanks are cut from the rods on six-spindle automatic screw machines. With one rod in each spindle, up to six machining operations can be carried out at one time. The spindle then rotates 60°, and identical cuts are made on each successive rod. As can be seen in Fig. 8-5, slug blanks may or may not require further surface conditioning, depending upon customer specifications. Length dimensioning and end finishing (including edge radiusing) are accomplished on specially designed lathes. If the slugs are to be made hollow, the boring and reaming is done on automatic screw machines and reamers adapted for single unit feed rather than feed from rod spindles.

Finished slugs are placed on stainless steel heavy wire racks. They, in turn, are attached to an overhead conveyor, which carries them through an atmosphere of trichloroethylene vapors to degrease the slugs. The rack of slugs, still on the conveyor, is next dipped into nitric acid for surface conditioning prior to inspection. From the acid bath the slugs are conveyed through a water rinse and an air dryer and are finally deposited in the inspection area.

8-4.2. Data Collection. Rod consumption and slug blank production are reported by batch, and the information is punched into cards. Also included in the punched information is slug type and customer order number. From these cards are reproduced cards for material balance data, which include crediting the finished material inventory of the rolling mill and debiting and crediting the raw material inventory of the machining area.

Statistical analyses are used in the machining area to observe trends in yields of a given fabrication step that might indicate the breakdown of either the operation or of the data which are supposed to represent the operation. Corrective action can usually be taken in time to prevent serious consequences. Weight factor control charts are also kept on each type of fuel element in each step of fabrication to expedite the frequent inventories. A piece count by type and location extended by the appropriate weight factor will result in a precise,

---

* The term "slug" is a common expression for a small cylindrical fuel element.

quick inventory. Only a very small percentage of samples, with respect to the over-all population of items, is required for adequate over-all evaluation.

8-5. INSPECTION, PACKAGING, AND SHIPPING

8-5.1. Process Description. As slugs are received from the overhead conveyor, which can be seen near the rear wall in Fig. 8-6, they are placed on belt conveyors, which carry them through dimensional and visual inspection stations. Dimensional inspection is very well suited to a statistical sampling control program, and this has been found to be very effective. Fully auto-

Fig. 8-6 View of inspection and packing area.

matic dimensional inspection equipment is available if a 100 percent inspection program is desired. One hundred percent inspection is required for physical defects in surfaces. Use is made of ultrasonic testing equipment in examinations for defects.

The high degree of uniformity of the finished piece makes possible the use of statistically evaluated average weights for each slug type being produced. When this system is used, the weight of the slugs being transferred is simply the piece count extended by the average weight, or weight factor. Not only does this eliminate considerable physical handling of the material, but it also reduces the consequence of an individual weighing mistake. An incorrect box weight could possibly go undetected through an inventory period, resulting in uncertainties over and above those attributable to inherent errors. ("Error" here is used in the statistical connotation of differences due to imprecision of measurements as opposed to mistakes due to carelessness or ignorance.) On the other hand, mistakes in sample weighings, applying the theory of propagation of errors, are continually weighed against all previous measurements and become less influential as the quantity increases.

The unacceptable slugs detected by the inspection procedures can be divided into two categories: namely, salvable and reject. The former are returned to the machining area for rework; the latter are sent to the casting area for remelting. These, too, are transferred using weight factors determined on random samples of each category.

8-5.2. Data Collection. From data originating at the inspection stations a card is punched for the fuel elements produced from each rod that has been machined. This card contains information as to the total number of slug blanks cut from the rod, the quantities scrapped, the quantities used for samples, the disposition in the inspection area, and the number of the box into which it is packed. A comparison of the quantities shown on this card with the number of blanks produced by batch on a card previously mentioned, with due consideration for previous and present inventories, should predict the number of pieces, by type, in process at any given period. From this comparison are also obtained yields from rods to various stages of slug completions. (For simplicity these record flow lines are not shown in Fig. 8-5.) A card is also punched with the information that appears on the shipping label of each box. This card can be used to credit the inspection area in-process quantity and to debit the finished material inventory. It may later be reproduced as a shipment card to credit the finished material inventory.

8-6. PROCESS RESIDUES

8-6.1. Metal-Casting Residues. There are many forms of residues produced in the ingot-forming process. Slag and uranium oxide adhere to the crucible and must be burned out. This material is collected in a drumming station from conveyors beneath the burn-out station and from dust collectors servicing the burn-out station. Crucibles eventually become unusable and must be sent to the uranium recovery facility.

Broken molds are scraped to remove contamination from their inner surface, then discarded. Grindings from the dressing booths are sent to recovery, along with saw chips. Turnings from the radial cut-off saw are sent to the briquetting process. Top crops from ingots are dissolved in the refinery and returned to the stream in the digestion step. Secondary crops are remelted as described above. Floor sweepings are collected by vacuum and sent to the recovery facility.

The solid metal that is suitable for remelting is presumed, for material control purposes, to contain 100 percent uranium. The top crops are net weighed, and this weight is extended by a factor of 99.3 percent to allow for the oxide, slag, and impurities that migrate to the top of the ingot. A factor that allows for the weight of the adhering machine coolant is applied to briquettable turnings that are transferred from the machining area. Metallic dust and chips are oxidized in the recovery plant so that they can be sampled and evaluated.

Broken graphite parts can be burned and then sampled; but the uranium content is so small that a factor is applied here, too, and the pieces are crushed and recovered along with the reduction slag.

8-6.2. Rolling-Mill Residue. Residue side streams in the rolling mill come into being as soon as the ingot is placed in the first salt bath. The heat shock to the surface of the ingot apparently frees much of the coating of oxide that has accumulated since its production, and this falls to the bottom of the bath. This sloughing off continues throughout the trip through the furnace and is accentuated in the drippings of salt from the ingot as it is lifted from the bath. Approximately 0.1 percent of the ingot is diverted to this salt sludge, and its accumulation creates a problem.* Periodically the superstructure of the furnace is set aside, and the majority of the sludge is removed with a clam shell. The same conditions exist in the other two furnaces (equalizing and heat-treating). The deposition rate of uranium to the baths increases proportionately with surface-to-volume ratios of the pieces; approximately 0.25 percent of the billet is lost to the equalizing furnace, and about 0.30 percent of the rod is lost to the heat-treating bath.

Oxide is deposited along with salt throughout the remainder of its course through the mill. This is usually picked up in the vacuum cleaning system or is washed down through the mill sumps to the water-treatment system. These sludges, sweepings, and water-treatment filter cakes are delegated to the residue recovery facility for conversion to refinery feed. The croppings from billets and rods, along with cut up cobbled pieces or rejected rods, can be recycled to the remelt step of the casting plant. The machine turnings from the bar turning lathe are suitable for briquetting.

8-6.3. Machining Residues. The principal side stream from the machining operation is in the form of machine turnings. These pieces cannot be remelted in their as-generated form because their bulk density is not great enough to permit a full-weight charge to be placed within a crucible and because rapid oxidation of the pieces would result in poor ingot quality. This situation is alleviated by cleaning the turnings and then pressing them into briquettes.

Prior to cleaning, the turnings are crushed to break up the coil geometry and to permit closer packing. The crushed pieces are screened; the very fine particles are not used since they would quickly dissolve in the wash acid and result in high acid consumption.

The screen oversize is washed first in a solution of water and household detergent and then dried in a centrifuge. Oxidation is removed from the surface in a nitric acid wash, the acid being removed in a water rinse; the chips are then dried and are ready for briquetting. The briquette is about 5 in. in

---

* The quantity of accumulated sludge becomes a serious criticality consideration when enriched uranium is being passed through the furnace baths. The conditions in this respect are regarded, pending reliable experimental data to approximate a solution in water with an optimum hydrogen-to-uranium ratio.

diameter and 2 to 3 in. thick. Those that have a bulk density greater than 11.5 gm/cm^3 are remelted along with derbies and solid scrap in the metal-casting facility. A uranium content factor of 99.8 wt. % has been determined for material control use.

Solid uranium scrap generated as rod ends, reject slug blanks, etc., is returned to the casting plant for remelting. If the scrap is contaminated, it is charged to the metal-dissolving tank, and the resulting solution is processed in the refinery.

Because of the highly pyrophoric nature of the sludge from the grinding wheels, an oxidation furnace has been installed in the plant to accomplish controlled burning as soon as the material is generated (this is ordinarily a recovery-plant operation). This furnace is also used to oxidize metallic sawdust, machining fines, and sludges. This system is advantageous from a material-control point of view because the oxide product of this furnace is easily sampled and can be accurately evaluated, whereas these side streams, as generated, are not amenable to conventional sampling and would have to be evaluated by estimation until the recovery plant completed its processing of them.

A variety of liquids containing dissolved or suspended uranium, such as coolant and wash liquors, are also generated in the machining process. These are converted in the treatment system to a material suitable for recycle to the refinery.

The water-treatment system consists of the following steps. Oil emulsions are broken down in a separator tank and the hydrocarbon content is decanted for processing in the recovery plant. The aqueous phase containing suspended or soluble uranium is acidified with nitric acid from the slug pickling tanks. The solution is neutralized with lime, which precipitates the uranium. This slurry is passed through a plate and frame filter; the filtrate is discarded or recycled through the system, depending upon the amount of uranium contained. The filter cake is suitable for refinery feed after being roasted in the recovery plant.

8-7. INVENTORY

Inventory procedures in all the material balance areas are carried out in three phases, namely, preparation, execution, and recapitulation. The preparation phase includes area clean-up, spotting of feed materials in the correct area prior to inventory so that that area can resume production after inventory without interfering with other areas, and identification and weighing of process material. The "recap" phase includes relating sample identification numbers with material identification, checking book quantities against inventoried quantities, and checking areas for completion of inventory steps prior to giving release for their return to production activities. There are, however, some special measurements or calculations that must be made in each area to complete the inventory. These will be discussed in the following paragraphs along with points of preparation or recapitulation that are peculiar to a given area.

8-7.1. Metal Casting. Metal spills sometime occur during the pouring of an ingot. The spilled metal will collect at the bottom of the mold tank and present an evaluation problem unless cleaned out prior to inventory. If not cleaned out the metal content must be calculated "by difference" or must be estimated by experienced personnel. Also, the enclosure in which used crucibles are burned free of adhering slag and oxide will hold up relatively large quantities of oxide on burn-out stands, chutes, etc. Estimates of burn-out holdup must be made by rough calculations of the volume of holdup extended by the bulk density of the burn-out product.

The casting sheets must be available so that inventory personnel can record the quantity of metal in any furnace. Any ingot not broken out at inventory time is carried at the charged weight. Crude ingots (not yet cropped) will be inventoried at their break-out weight. Machine turnings, saw chips, and sludges are drained free of excess coolant and weighed, with a factor analysis applied to determine the actual uranium content.

In the recap, if inventory tags have been used, all tags must be accounted for. A listing of derbies and ingots, by number, is checked against inventory, consumption, and transfer records for errors of omission or duplication. Inventory check-off lists, by units and areas, are verified to be complete, and the area is released for processing.

Most residues produced in the casting operation are not amenable to conventional sampling techniques. They are, therefore, evaluated at tentative analyses for inventory purposes and later adjusted to reflect the true value. Each ingot must be sampled and analyzed for purposes of quality control, but for inventory purposes they are generally considered to be finished material.

In each of the fabrication areas a system of controls set up primarily for yield and quality control studies supplies a great deal of information that is useful in recapping the final inventory.

8-7.2. Rolling. The preinventory cleaning of the rolling mill is rather time consuming because rolls, pits, and sumps must be reasonably free of oxides and metal to ensure minimum inventory uncertainty. It is usual practice to have all metal processed to the rod or residue stage; therefore, in-process metal weights are seldom required. Most residues and metal scrap can be weighed, with a uranium factor being applied for material balance purposes and adjustments made later to reflect actual evaluation. A very large amount of residue, however, is sloughed to the molten-salt heating baths, and this residue can be accurately evaluated only by removing the entire content of the bath, the economics of which is prohibitive. Therefore, a bath holdup factor to be applied against throughput has been calculated for each furnace. The deposition rates vary between furnaces, being proportional to the surface-to volume ratio and depending on the history of the pieces immediately prior to their being submerged in the bath (the amount of oxidation which might have occurred). Until a suitable factor has been determined by actual cleanout, and this happens only when the furnace pot needs to be changed or repaired, the factor can be calculated from estimated holdup.

Two methods are presented for estimating holdup. First, if the inside dimensions of the bath are known and the surface of the sludge at several points can be determined with a stainless steel rod, an average depth of sludge can be calculated from the surface contour. The bulk density and analysis of the sludge can be found in the laboratory and applied to this volume. The deposition rate required to slough off this amount can be computed for the recorded throughput. An alternative method requires several months' experience and suitable provisions for removing some of the sludge from the bath. Here an estimate of the deposit rate is made and the periodic removals are evaluated. If the holdup can be assumed to be constant following each removal, the slope of the line representing the inventory of holdup determined by the estimated factor can be adjusted to zero, and a new factor can be determined on the basis of the amount of the adjustment. The method of least squares for computing the slope of this line is probably the most simple. Large quench tanks for heat-treated metal and decant tanks for mill water can be treated in the same manner.

8-7.3. Machining. Uranium rods that are to be machined into fuel element blanks are recorded in batches of 12 or 18 units. Immediately prior to inventory, all partially used batches should be identified, and the unused portion should be reweighed. Special care should be taken to account for partially consumed rods still in the screw-machine magazines, where they are not readily discernible. All sumps containing coolants should be drained to preclude omission of submerged chips and sludges. The slug conveyor should be allowed to run a sufficient length of time to move any tray to a drop-off station.

As soon as a reasonable determination can be made of what types of fuel elements will be in process at inventory time, a small random sample is taken of units at each stage of completion. An average weight is then determined for these pieces. At inventory time only the number of slugs, by type and by stage of completion, is recorded. The weights are determined by applying the proper weight factor to each category.

The acid tank and rinse tank, in which the slugs are pickled and rinsed, are evaluated by extending the measured volume by the analysis of a sample of each. The same holds true for the chip pickling tanks of the briquette system.

The water treatment system is usually scheduled so that, at the time of inventory, the precipitate tank contains all water in process and the separators and filters are empty. Thus, one volume determination and one sample evaluation are sufficient to evaluate this system.

The oxidation furnace used to burn the grinding-wheel sludges, fine chips, and other pyrophoric residues is rabbled to an irreducible holdup prior to inventory.   The dead bed is assumed to be of the average analysis and bulk density of the product, and the volume is calculated from the geometry of the furnace, i.e. bed area multiplied by rabble clearance.   No samples are taken specifically for inventory purposes.   The current production lot is terminated as of the inventory, and the routine sample analysis is used.

8-7.4. Inspection Area.   The tag inventory system is always used in the inspection area.   Each container is identified as to the type of fuel element and classification, if inspected.   For each item there is a standard weight that has been determined by statistical analysis.   The summation of evaluations by types represents the inventory.   The analysis of weight factors is designed for routine shipping control, not specifically for inventory purposes, even though the resultant information is quite useful in determining inventories.

It is necessary to weigh a carefully selected sample of each type of product in order to collect data to be used in slug factor weight calculations.   From a knowledge of the process variability and the degree of precision desired, it has been possible to determine the routine sample size required to determine and maintain valid factor weights.   Since it has also been noted that the variability (with respect to slug volume) experienced for material produced from different machines is larger than the variability experienced within material produced on any one machine, maximum sampling efficiency is obtained by use of a stratified sampling plan (providing equal representation from each processing lot).

The sample slugs are selected routinely from the inspection line, allowed to accumulate for a one-day period, and weighed on an individual basis the following day.   Since sample weighing must be carried out as a continuing production operation to ensure that data are representative, the scales or balances used must possess both ruggedness and ease of operation, while providing sensitivity within approximately 0.1 percent.   Three different weighing instruments have been provided, their utilization depending upon which fits the particular operating conditions at hand:

1. An electronic specialty scale, which accumulates weight deviations of 0.005 lb or more of the test object from a standard and at the same time charts individual differences by means of an automatic pen recorder.   This scale is well suited to factor weight purposes when production of more or less standard material continues for an extended period of time.   It is not practical for brief campaigns or special orders, since fabrication of standards and relatively elaborate set-up requirements are time consuming and expensive.

2. A 10-lb-capacity double-pan scale sensitive to the nearest 0.005 lb.   This scale has the flexibility needed to handle the wide variety of slug types produced by the FMPC.

3. A 75-lb-capacity print-weigh scale, which records weights to the nearest

ounce. Several slugs at a time can be weighed on this scale, providing rapid checks. It is also used as a primary scale for scrap slugs where accuracy requirements can be somewhat relaxed.

The sample is moved to the weighing booth, which houses the first two scales described above, and is weighed by personnel assigned to the packing and shipping of the material. The fuel elements are weighed either individually or in pairs, as required, to ensure near maximum deflection of the scale indicator. The weighing data are recorded and transmitted to the Technical Control Group.

All weighings for factor weights are made at near-maximum capacity in order to simplify scale control. In this range the scale is sufficiently precise, but it is subject to small biases which, if left uncorrected, could lead to significant discrepancies, especially if several shipments are considered. Bias of an order of magnitude less than the smallest scale division is not detectable by the use of standard test weights; therefore, for check weighing, an instrument must be used that is capable of accurate determinations to at least one more significant digit than the scale. An instrument satisfying these conditions of precision and accuracy is a 5-kg-capacity analytical balance.

A bias correction then is obtained each day for all weighing made on that day by having:

1. All scale weighings for a particular day made by one operator.
2. One slug weighed by this operator in the usual manner selected and weighed on the analytical balance.
3. The difference between the scale weight and balance weight calculated and applied as a correction factor for all weighings made that day.

The use of this daily correction procedure reduces the bias uncertainty of a factor weight from about ±0.005 lb to about ±0.001 lb. It can also be shown that, if the bias uncertainty of the analytical balance is small, the uncertainty of the factor weight attributable to this correction procedure is also small.

Several safeguards have been established against an undetected shift in the process mean. These include:

1. Control charts that are maintained on (a) slug volume, i.e. dimensions, (b) ingot density, and (c) daily average weight per slug correction for scale bias.

2. A sequential test for a significant change in the factor weight, applied on a monthly basis to the computed quantity $F - f$, where F is the factor and f is the average weight based on all weighings since F was established.

The control charts often allow the detection of trends that may affect the factor weight even before any shipments are actually made on erroneous factors. Should some change occur that escapes detection by the control charts, the sequential test will still remain and should indicate a shift within a month or so of its occurrence. An assignable cause for any change detected by one of the aforementioned methods must be found before a factor weight change is justified. If the control charts for density, volume, or daily average weight offer no explanation, then an investigation of weighing procedures is indicated. It can be seen that the inventory factor weights are based on evaluations made for purposes requiring far greater precision than would be necessary for inventory evaluation only.

8-7.5. **Inventory Evaluation.** For practical purposes the evaluation of the inventory is an evaluation of the difference between the book balance and the physical inventory. At the FMPC the variance from an average, based on past experience, is statistically related to 2σ and 3σ control limits. Within $\pm 2\sigma$, the process data and the inventory are felt to be reliable. Between 2σ and 3σ, the process and the inventory are examined for extenuating circumstances. Beyond 3σ, the inventory or the process data are not felt to be representative, and action is taken to determine the source of error with appropriate corrective measures following. It is possible that offsetting errors can exist in such a way as to erroneously indicate good control. This possibility is minimized by utilizing control charts on yield data, physical surveillance of inventory procedures by staff personnel, and cross checking of inventory recaps by two people.

It is essential that every economically feasible effort be expended to (1) eliminate the bias of the uncertainty and (2) reduce the range of the control limits. The former is indicative of a bias in the measurement methods (analytical, sampling, and weighing) or of the existence of an unmeasured flow of materials. There are several relatively simple methods for evaluating measurement biases; however, the detection of an unmeasured flow of materials will require an intimate knowledge and continuous surveillance of plant operations. A vacuum cleaning hose from a given collector can be lengthened to reach into another area; a floor sump in an area adjacent to his own may seem more convenient to an operator for disposing of liquid residues, and so on. A wide spread of control limits usually indicates poor inventory procedures. This may include nonrepresentative sampling of process material, unreliable volume determinations, or omissions or duplications of items on inventory. Sampling and measurements can be improved by statistical evaluation programs. Errors in inventory listing can be reduced by the use of check-off lists for each area and by inventorying in a definite geometric pattern. It is, of course, the desire of production personnel to lose as little time as possible while taking inventory. An optimum relationship between down time and inventory uncertainty can usually be determined by experience; however, a static condition is almost imperative for a high degree of certainty.

8-8. SLIGHTLY ENRICHED URANIUM

The processing of uranium slightly enriched in the isotope U^{235} presents a possible high-intensity radiation hazard that must be avoided at all costs. The physics of a radiation release are not of functional concern to the SS Representative, but the restrictions imposed to prevent this release are of concern. Material movements involve the use of special containers or some means of maintaining a specific configuration. Paper work is increased per unit weight of product because of the small batch sizes, and additional material handling is required to maintain optimum storage and process-area utilization. In addition to the restrictions imposed by the hazardous nature of the material, the substantially increased monetary value dictates a greater effort toward more precise material control.

Additional control is especially warranted to provide substantial confidence in the book-physical inventory difference. When an apparent loss approaches the quantity of uranium required to go critical (this quantity varies with enrichment, form, and other factors), plant operations are stopped until the condition is corrected. With a low degree of confidence such a shutdown would accumulate many unnecessary hours of down time.

The analytical work load for the enriched operation is increased only in proportion to the increase in number of batches. The techniques for sampling and chemically analyzing enriched uranium are identical with the techniques employed for natural uranium. For a complete evaluation, however, an isotopic assay is required. For materials sampled for chemical analysis, it is sufficient to remove an aliquot of that sample for isotopic assay.

Two methods are employed for determining the isotopic assay. One is the mass spectrometer, the most common instrument for such measurements. The other is a fission-product radiation counter, which is rapidly replacing the mass spectrometers in all but the most precise work. This unit consists basically of a gamma-counting and -scaling instrument, a fairly strong radium-beryllium neutron source, and an electronically controlled conveyor and timing device.

The sample must be in the form of rather pure oxide (or metal). A small solvent extraction system is used to remove impurities from the original sample, if necessary. A carefully measured aliquot equal in weight to prepared standards is taken and is tamped into the base of a glass container of cross-sectional area equal to that of the standard. A background count is made. The sample is then placed on a conveyor, and the automatic timer takes over. The sample is exposed to neutrons for a predetermined time and is then removed to a point of access by the technician, who replaces it in the counter. The timing system actuates the counter following a predetermined time lapse. The sample is counted for a period of time equal to that used to determine the background count. The ratio of the counts from the two periods is then interpreted in terms of isotopic assay. Single determinations are accurate to ± 0.003 percent U^{235} in the range of natural uranium. Increased precision is obtained by replicate tests. Approximately 5 minutes is required for one determination, but successive samples can be processed $2\frac{1}{2}$ minutes apart. The cost per sample is about 15 percent of that for a similar determination (accurate to ± 0.0007 percent) on a mass spectrometer.

8-9. COMPARISON OF SLIGHTLY ENRICHED URANIUM PROCESSES WITH NATURAL URANIUM PROCESSES

It is appropriate at this point to review the slightly enriched uranium metal processing steps, this time elaborating upon the ways in which the slightly enriched uranium process differs from the natural uranium process already described.

The slightly enriched uranium feed material has been uranium hexafluoride (UF_6) from the cascades. This is reduced to UF_4 and then processed by the same methods as for natural uranium. Smaller quantities of enriched material are processed, however, because of the danger of a fission reaction; and stricter material control is applied both because of the increased value of the material and because of the criticality danger.

8-9.1. UF_4 Production: *Process.* Slightly enriched UF_6 is shipped from the cascade sites in steel cylinders, the size of which varies inversely with the enrichment. The cylinder is heated by steam to a temperature of approximately 200°F to produce a gaseous feed pressure of approximately 50 psi.

The reaction to produce UF_4 occurs in a vertical Monel tube. Hydrogen supplied from dissociated ammonia is mixed with the gaseous UF_6 as it is introduced into the reactor. The mixed gas entering the heated portion of the reactor tube immediately forms fine particles of UF_4 in the so-called "flame" zone of the reactor. Most of the product falls to the bottom of the reactor tube, but approximately 20 percent collects on the walls of the reactor as a hard slaglike coating. Vibrators mounted on the reactor tube assist in removing this slag as it is formed; however, it is sometimes necessary to cool the tube and utilize contraction and expansion to break the slag free.

An off-gas mixture of hydrogen fluoride, nitrogen, excess hydrogen, and fine UF_4 particles passes through a special cyclone-baffle dust collector and then through a high-speed cyclone collector. The trace of green salt remaining in the off-gas from these two cyclones is finally removed by steel-wool filters. The hydrogen fluoride content of the off-gas is removed by scrubbing with a potassium hydroxide solution.

The hot UF_4 from the reactor passes through a horizontal screw cooling conveyor. From the screw conveyor it is discharged through an automatically regulated seal leg into small transfer hoppers or cans. This product (along with the green salt gathered in the cyclone collectors) is conveyed to a pulverizer. The pulverized UF_4 discharges directly into a rotary blender, from which it is sampled and packaged into cans of a convenient size for use in the next phase of the operation.

A dust-collecting hood is mounted on the blender frame to carry fumes and dust away from the blender discharge. A similar arrangement is provided at the weighing station, where small amounts of UF_4 are added or removed from each product can to obtain the desired weight. The dust collected by this ventilating system is discharged into cans and returned to the pulverizer. Steel-wool filters, contaminated green salt, and floor sweepings are drummed for subsequent recovery of the contained uranium.

Measurements. In this UF_6 to UF_4 process the amount of feed material consumed is taken as the difference between the gross weight of the cylinder put on stream and the gross weight as removed. Uranium hexafluoride, to date, has not been sampled at the FMPC for the following reasons: (1) a representative sample can be readily obtained in the liquid form when this material is withdrawn from the cascade and (2) the uranium content of UF_6, as determined by assay, does not vary appreciably from the theoretical value. Experience to date has subsantiated this decision. Material balances obtained in the UF_6 to UF_4 operation, which are based upon the shipper's analysis of the UF_6, have been extremely good.

Product green salt is pulverized and blended prior to sampling. A composite sample from each lot is obtained by blending samples taken from the top of each drum. This sample is submitted to the analytical laboratory for a gravimetric uranium determination. The product is weighed in cans, each can being gross weighed and tare weighed to the nearest tenth of a pound. This material is then check weighed before transfer to metal reduction.

Loss of material to the atmosphere through the dust collector exhaust is measured by taking air samples* from the exhaust line. Each sample is analyzed, and the total loss of uranium is calculated by relating the quantity of sample obtained to the total quantity of air exhausted. The waste KF solution from the off-gas scrubber is also sampled and analyzed. The analysis is then applied to the volume discarded to determine the amount of uranium involved. Physical losses from this material balance area are very small.

Inventory. The in-process inventory of the unit is essentially UF_4, and this can be reduced to almost zero by a relatively simple cleanout procedure, after which all material recovered is processed on through the packaging station. Filter media, dust bags and steel wool are weighed before being put into place and again after removal. The gain in weight is assumed to be UF_4. The KOH scrubber system is of constant volume and is in continuous circulation; therefore, the fluorometric analysis of a grab sample applied to a known volume is readily interpreted as the uranium content of the scrubber system.

---

* Stack sampling techniques are described in Sec. 15-4.3.

8-9.2. Reduction Casting and Fabrication. The UF_4 to metal reduction step is as described for the natural-uranium operation in Chapter 5. The retort sizes and charge quantities may be smaller, depending again on the extent of enrichment.

The reduction residue is difficult to evaluate directly because of the heterogeneity of the uranium; therefore, a tentative uranium content is assigned, based on the difference in the metal quantity of the UF_4 charged and the weight of the uranium reguli produced. This by-difference quantity must, of course, include all floor sweepings, spills, etc. from the area. As long as metal yields are fairly good, the uncertainty of the residue measurement is not important from a nuclear safety point of view because the mass density of the U^{235} dispersed throughout the MgF_2 is sufficiently low (for *low enrichments* only) to prevent criticality. Reguli are placed side by side on a pallet for handling; they are never stacked. Pallets are spaced only during transportation.

In the metal-casting operation the procedures are identical for enriched and natural uranium with, again, the reduction in batch sizes. Even this may not be pronounced because the geometric configurations of the mold and crucible are conducive to safe operations, within limits. One possible variation might be the cooling of the induction coils with air or a low-neutron moderating liquid rather than water. This is done to eliminate the possibility of moderating a spill by a rupture of the heating coils.

When slightly enriched uranium is rolled, additional spacing is maintained between ingots, billets, and rods in the respective salt baths. Cleanup operations are conducted more frequently, and residues are packaged in limited amounts. Sumps and water-quench tanks must be periodically surveyed to ascertain that the sludge build-up does not approach the danger point.

The machining of rods to fuel elements is conducted in much the same manner with slightly enriched uranium as with natural uranium, and practically no special equipment is used. Lathe beds must be emptied of accumulated chips and sludge more frequently or, for higher enrichments, might have special design features which limit the geometry of accumulated residues to safe configurations. Slug pickling, briquetting, water treatment, etc. must be batch limited to safe quantities.

8-9.3. Packing and Shipping. The prime consideration in packaging finished slugs is the shipping technique to be used. Since most shipping configurations depend upon a safe slab geometry, the containers are designed so that the vertical dimension cannot exceed the specified maximum for a given enrichment. The skids, ordinarily used to facilitate handling by fork truck, are omitted so that the bottom of the box will be supported by the floor over its entire area. The use of the bird-cage type of shoring is not practical for the lower enrichments because of the masses handled. It is customary to fabricate a rigid framework to hold the containers in a safe geometry. This framework may, in turn, be made an integral part of the vehicle so that it utilizes a part of the strength of the vehicle, or it may be made so that it will shear its way free of the vehicle in the event of an accident and still retain its geometry.

8-9.4. Inventory. The inventory of slightly enriched uranium is perhaps simpler than comparable inventories of natural uranium because of the batch type and limited-quantity operational techniques used. The inventory should, however, be more exacting in weights and measurements and thus may be more time consuming.

8-9.5. Reports. Reports prepared for enriched material are basically the same as those prepared for the natural uranium processes. These reports do, however, show a balance of the U^{235} content as well as the total uranium. This is done to detect isotopic crossover and as a verification of the isotopic content of shipments and receipts. Reports are also screened by nuclear safety personnel to detect abnormal amounts of unaccounted for material that might be potentially hazardous.

Two types of reports are submitted to the AEC: one with information of shipments, receipts, and inventory uncertainties and another showing production rates and quantities. The latter is used for scheduling purposes. These reports have extensive distribution and serve a wide variety of purposes.

SUGGESTED READING

A. TANNENBAUM (Ed.), *Toxicology of Uranium—Survey and Collected Papers,* National Nuclear Energy Series, Division IV, Volume 23, McGraw-Hill Book Company, Inc., New York, 1951.

A. D. CALLIHAN, W. J. OZEROFF, H. C. PAXTON, and C. L. SCHUSKE, *Nuclear Safety Guide,* USAEC Report TID-2016.

Chapter 9

ENRICHED URANIUM FUEL ELEMENTS *

The Bettis Atomic Power Laboratory, under contracts with the U. S. Atomic Energy Commission and the Navy, conducts research, development, design, and testing activities to produce atomic power plants and their components. Examples are the plants of the submarines *Nautilus* and *Skate* and the Shippingport Atomic Power Station of the Duquesne Light Company located near Pittsburgh, Pa.

Research and development work in the fields of physics, metallurgy, chemistry, and metal processing is performed in connection with the design of a reactor core. This work usually makes use of uranium in various forms. The core is made up of thousands of enriched fuel bearing parts which are manufactured on a production basis. The amount of uranium required for a project ranges from very minute quantities used in analyses to hundreds of kilograms in critical assemblies.

The variety of activities using uranium and the research and developmental nature of the work dictate that the SS-material control system be flexible and adaptable to rapid changes in the technical program.

Design and operation of the SS-material control system used in the manufacture of enriched fuel elements are assigned to a small central group of specialists, the SS Group, headed by the SS Representative. The SS Representative reports to the Assistant Division Manager and has staff responsibility for all the SS material at the plant.

Portions of the plant using SS material are designated as substations, and the responsibility for the material in each is delegated to a Substation Custodian. The custodians report to their activity managers; however, their SS-material control activity is under the general direction of the SS Representative.

Each substation is a material balance area in that it maintains records that must always balance with material on hand. Transfers of material between

* F. P. Baggerman, P. K. Morrow, W. A. Stanko, and W. B. Thomas, Bettis Atomic Power Laboratory, operated by the Westinghouse Electric Corp., Pittsburgh, Pa. The authors wish to acknowledge the assistance of John Fleming in the preparation of this chapter.

substations are made at the discretion of the Custodians, and the SS Representative is notified of the transactions. Receipts of material from external sources or off-site shipments of material are controlled by procedures established by the SS Representative. All such transactions must have prior clearance from the SS Representative.

One substation is operated by the SS Group. The chief function of this substation is the receipt of highly enriched SS material in the form of metal pellets and the subsequent disbursement of the material to the shop. Unusual situations involving the temporary storage of SS materials are also handled by this substation.

9-1. FUNCTION AND ORGANIZATION OF THE SS GROUP

The SS Group designs and operates the SS system. Its personnel are divided according to two main functions: procurement and control. Responsibility for those functions is assigned to a Procurement Administrator and a Control Administrator.

9-1.1. Procurement. For effective procurement control in a multiproject organization, the establishment of a regular source of procurement information is important. For this purpose each project or activity using SS materials has appointed an SS Material Procurement Coordinator. The coordinators are responsible for keeping up to date with the SS material needs of their activity and for transmitting this information to the Procurement Administrator.

The procurement function starts with the approval of a core design and determination of the amount of SS material required to manufacture the core. A forecast of the amounts and dates of uranium requirements, along with justification information, is forwarded to the Procurement Administrator.

The forecast of uranium requirements must be made at least six months prior to the beginning of core manufacture. These forecasts for all cores are coordinated by the Procurement Administrator and are passed on to the Division of Nuclear Materials Management, AEC, which establishes allotments for the amount of SS material for each core. An identification number is assigned to each allotment, and the material issued under an allotment is identified by the allotment number until its return to a reclamation facility.

At no time during operations is the total amount of SS material issued to a particular project allowed to exceed the allotment. This is enforced by the following procedure. All virgin SS material is received, verified, and stored by the SS Group in a specially designed storage vault (Fig. 9-1). Disbursement is made to the shop upon written request (Fig. 9-2). The form requires the signature of the Substation Custodian of the requesting substation and approval signatures which vary according to the intended use of the material. When the Procurement Administrator signs the form signifying final approval, the Control Administrator orders the issuance of the requested material. The Procurement Administrator maintains a record of the amounts disbursed under each particular project number for comparison to project allotments.

Withdrawals are usually made in small increments owing to production schedule and criticality considerations in the shop. If re-usable material is transferred to a project from another project, this transfer of material must also be reported utilizing the same procedure as outlined above with an addi-

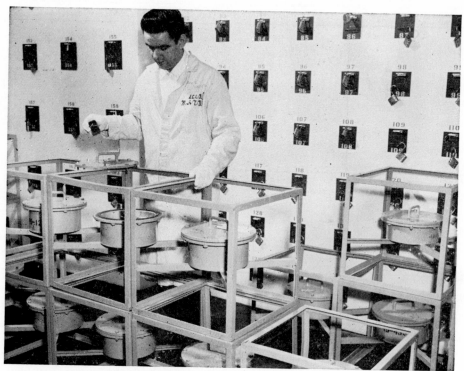

FIG. 9-1 Photograph of the interior of an enriched uranium vault.

tional requirement. Written approval of the local Chief of the Special Materials Branch, AEC, must be obtained before transfer if an allotment will be exceeded or a net increase in virgin material will result. The maximum utilization of SS material is considered of utmost importance for economic reasons. Since the reprocessing of scrap material is costly and time consuming, all material that can be recycled is carefully maintained and recorded so that maximum utilization of the alloyed material can be accomplished.

9-1.2. Control. The Control Group has two major responsibilities: the direction of physical control and the administrative control of all SS material. The group is under the Control Administrator.

REQUEST FOR APPROVAL - SS MATERIAL APPLICATION
FORM APD 395

REQUEST NO.

☐ A. WITHDRAW SS MATERIALS FROM SUBSTATION NO. 1 VAULT	

REQUEST FOR APPROVAL TO:
(CHECK APPROPRIATE BLOCK/S)

☐ B. TRANSFER SS MATERIAL BETWEEN QUOTAS.

☐ C. DILUTE SS MATERIALS

THIS NO. IS TO BE ASSIGNED BY
PROCUREMENT ADMINISTRATION

Instructions:
1. This form is to be initiated by Substation Custodians to obtain approval for above actions.
2. Forward completed form (in triplicate) to SS Procurement Administrator.
3. Approved copy of form will be returned to Substation Custodian as authorization to proceed in accordance with request.

QUANTITY	MATERIAL DESCRIPTION (SPECIFY CATEGORY, FORM, FOR DILUTIONS SHOW CALCULATIONS)

ANTICIPATED USE OF MATERIAL (IF DILUTION - SHOW ALL NECESSARY WEIGHTS AND PERCENT)

EXPERIMENT NO./TEST NO. - IF ANY. SUBSTATION NO.	QUOTA DESIGNATION	CHARGE NO.	DATE MATERIAL IS NEEDED (IF A.)	REFERENCE
SIGNATURE - SUBSTATION CUSTODIAN		DATE	COORDINATOR APPROVAL	DATE
NAME OF COGNIZANT ENGINEER			LOCATION	PHONE

MISCELLANEOUS INFORMATION

APPROVALS		
PROCUREMENT ADMINISTRATOR APPROVAL	CONTROL ADMINISTRATOR APPROVAL (IF A.)	AEC APPROVAL (IF REQUIRED)

FIG. 9-2 Request for Approval—SS Material Application.

Physical control is aimed at the prevention of avoidable loss of SS materials. This is accomplished through the establishment of adequate sampling, weighing, analyzing, and measuring practices and through the establishment of adequate SS material handling practices. Receipt and shipment methods and the manner of disposing of scrap are important areas of physical control.

Administrative control involves the maintenance of accurate records to ensure adequate inventory control. Accuracy is a requisite in both the Central Control records and records kept by the substations. Interpretation of AEC requirements, establishment and enforcement of materials control procedures, and the preparation of the monthly balance report are some of the other important administrative responsibilities discharged by the Control Group.

9-2. CONTROL PROCEDURES FOR VERIFYING RECEIPTS OF ENRICHED URANIUM

The enriched uranium used in the manufacture of enriched fuel elements is received in the form of pellets. The pellets are cylindrical and weigh approximately 0.5 gm apiece. They are contained in plastic screw-cap bottles, each containing approximately 500 gm.

The shipper's data include the gross, tare, and net weight of each bottle to the nearest gram. The bottles are identified by a serial number assigned and affixed to the bottle by the shipper. The batch from which each bottle was taken and the isotopic composition of each bottle is also given. The shipment totals of SS weight, U^{235} weight, and the plus or minus uncertainty of the U^{235} total are given in summary.

Each bottle of pellets is weighed by emptying the contents into a tared container. A 2-kg-capacity balance is used to weigh the material to a thousandth of a gram, and the weight is recorded to the nearest hundredth of a gram.

The size of the samples required for chemical analysis is approximately 5 gm. The pellets required to make a sample are taken at random from bottles in one or more batches, if the percentages of U^{235} reported by the shipper are identical. Both total uranium and isotopic compositions are run on the samples by the Analytical Chemistry Department.

The results of the analysis are reported to the SS Group along with the uncertainties of the analysis. With these data and the results of the weighing, the total SS and U^{235} weights are determined along with their uncertainties. If the results fall within the shipper's determination plus or minus the stated uncertainties, the shipment is considered to be verified.

At least once a week an isotopic determination is made on an established standard that was obtained from Oak Ridge. The results of the standard runs are reported to the SS Group and are plotted on a statistical control chart.

The total uranium analysis is kept in control by reference to a standard established by the Bureau of Standards.

9-3. MANUFACTURING PROCESSES

Manufacturing activities leading to the production of a reactor core are grouped under the Nuclear Core Manufacturing Department. Although each core differs somewhat in its components and method of manufacture, a representative process follows these four main steps:

1. Fuel-alloy and filler-plate production
2. Fuel-plate manufacture
3. Assembly of fuel plates into components
4. Assembly of components into cores

The term "fuel elements" applies to a variety of physical shapes and fuel elements differ from one type of core to another. In this chapter fuel element is restricted to mean a fuel plate of highly enriched uranium alloy clad with a non-SS metal. The manufacture of enriched fuel elements includes the first two of the four main steps listed above. The material-control procedures for these steps are considered in detail.

The manufacturing operations comprise one material balance area substation designated as the Core Manufacturing Substation. The substation custodian serves as a staff assistant and has other responsibilities within the Manufacturing Department. There are several persons on his staff who work full time on material control and several who work part time. Additional personnel are recruited from manufacturing activities to perform temporary functions such as assisting in surveys, inventories, and other special efforts as required.

9-4. FUEL-ALLOY AND FILLER-PLATE PRODUCTION

The first of the main steps in the manufacture of the fuel elements is the production of fuel alloy and filler plates. Material control is stringent during this step because of the opportunities for losses.

Since all the melting, rolling, machining, and pickling operations occur during the manufacture of the filler plates, it is necessary that these operations be performed in an area well segregated from other operations. Security, health, safety, and process control factors also contribute to this need for segregation. Complete separation from the remainder of the plant is maintained, and access is limited to personnel necessary for operation.

This segregated area may be considered a closed system. Enriched uranium is the feed material for the area, and only enriched filler plates or the various materials for reclamation are removed. Only enriched uranium is permitted in the area, thus preventing the possibility of isotopic dilution.

The floor, shower, and sink drainage is reclaimed if high enough in uranium content; if not, it is dumped at sea. The ventilation system serves only the segregated area. Filters from the system are evaluated, and the uranium from them is reclaimed.

9-4.1. Transfer of Enriched Pellets. The SS raw material used in the manufacture of enriched fuel plates is received at the SS Group Substation in the form of highly enriched uranium metal pellets in 500-gm bottles. After the shipment has been verified, a pellet log is set up and maintained by the substation, which shows the net SS and U^{235} values for each bottle. All removals and remaining balances for each bottle are recorded in this log. The material is issued to the Core Manufacturing Substation as described below.

Upon receipt of a written request for metal pellets approved by the Procurement Administrator, the Control Administrator orders the pellets issued. A member of the SS Group Substation removes from the storage vaults the required amount (usually in 10-kg lots) and issues it to the manufacturing department. At the time of issue the book or log value for each bottle is verified by taking a gross weight to the nearest gram and subtracting an average bottle tare.

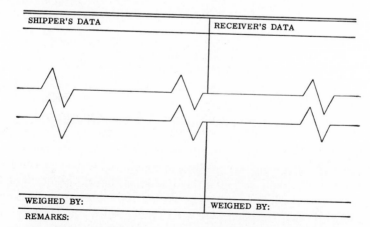

S. S. MATERIAL TRANSFER

HAND RECEIPT

Fig. 9-3   SS Material Transfer Hand Receipt.

A hand receipt (Fig. 9-3) is initiated, and the rough net just obtained, as well as the book or log net, SS, and U^{235} values for each bottle, is listed in the shipper's portion of the hand receipt. The material is given to the fuel alloy and filler plate manufacturing area material courier, who transports the

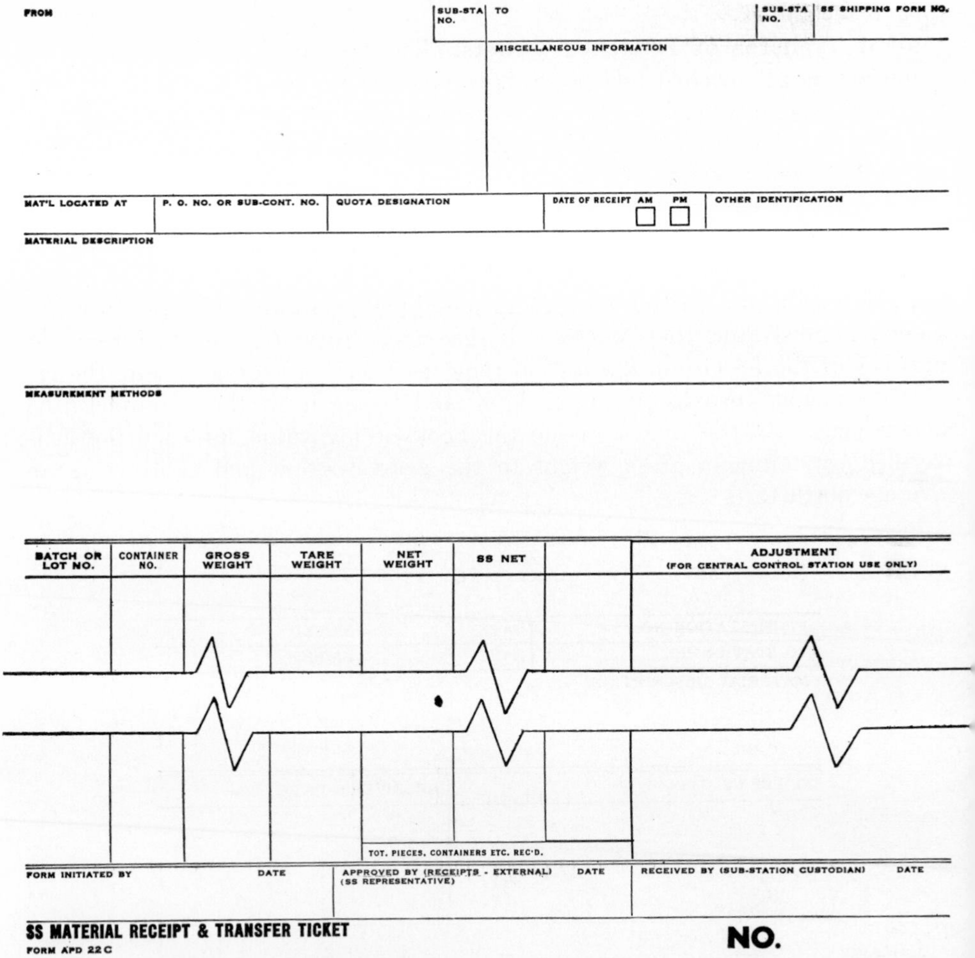

FROM			SUB-STA NO.	TO		SUB-STA NO.	SS SHIPPING FORM NO.
				MISCELLANEOUS INFORMATION			
MAT'L LOCATED AT	P. O. NO. OR SUB-CONT. NO.	QUOTA DESIGNATION		DATE OF RECEIPT AM □ PM □	OTHER IDENTIFICATION		
MATERIAL DESCRIPTION							
MEASUREMENT METHODS							

BATCH OR LOT NO.	CONTAINER NO.	GROSS WEIGHT	TARE WEIGHT	NET WEIGHT	SS NET		ADJUSTMENT (FOR CENTRAL CONTROL STATION USE ONLY)
				TOT. PIECES, CONTAINERS ETC. REC'D.			
FORM INITIATED BY		DATE	APPROVED BY (RECEIPTS - EXTERNAL) (SS REPRESENTATIVE)		DATE	RECEIVED BY (SUB-STATION CUSTODIAN)	DATE

SS MATERIAL RECEIPT & TRANSFER TICKET
FORM APD 22 C
NO.

FIG. 9-4 SS Material Receipt and Transfer Ticket.

material into the alloy manufacturing area and immediately net weighs each bottle to the nearest 0.1 gm, recording the weights obtained in the Receiver's Data portion of the hand receipt accompanying the material. The receiver of the pellets signs the hand receipt, accepting the material if the weights obtained agree with those supplied by the SS Group Substation.

A formal transfer of SS material is executed between the two substations at the earliest convenient time after the completion of the hand receipt. This is accomplished by the use of an SS Material Receipt and Transfer Ticket (Fig. 9-4). The net SS and U^{235} values are indicated on this transfer document to the nearest 0.01 gm by the SS Group Substation (the originating sub-

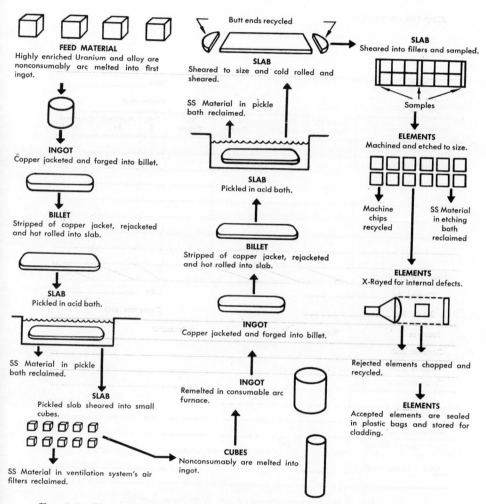

FIG. 9-5   Flow chart for the manufacture of enriched uranium fuel fillers.

station), and the values are recorded in both substation records and also in the central records maintained by the Control Administrator.

The pellets are stored in a vault within the alloy- and filler-manufacturing area until used. The vault custodian is responsible for the material transfer and criticality control in the alloy-manufacture area. All transfers of SS material within the manufacturing area are made only after concurrence of the vault custodian.

9-4.2. Manufacture of Fuel-Bearing Alloy. Records kept during the manufacturing operation may fill as many as five functions, i.e. material con-

Alloy Lab.-F-Building

CHARGE PREPARATION

WEIGHING RECORD

Charge No. _____   Date _____

Batch No. _____   Virgin Melt

Material	Desired Weight	Tare Weight	Total Weight	Net Weight	Cal. %	Weighed By	Checked By
SS Pellets							
Alloying Pellets							
X-Bar Zirconium							
Master Alloy							
Total Charge Weight							

Charge No. _____   Date _____

Batch No. _____   Electrode Melt

Material	Weight	Cal. %	Remarks
Chopped Slab			
Chopped Trim			
Chopped Cores			
Electrode Stub			
Machine Chips			
Total Charge Weight			

Additional Information: _____

FIG. 9-6 Charge Preparation Weighing Record.

trol, criticality control, process control, quality control, and production control. The detail required for the several functions varies, but sufficient detail is available as a result of normal manufacturing operations. The SS system is designed to permit ready accumulation of information, from the basic data, for all the purposes to be served.

The manufacture of enriched fuel fillers involves alloying by melting, homogenizing by remelting, and rolling into slabs. Filler plates are sheared and machined from the slabs. A typical flow chart is shown in Fig. 9-5.

An initial step in the manufacture of fuel elements is the preparation of the fuel alloy. Uranium and the various alloying metals are charged into a

ROUTING CARD

FOR

ALLOY LABORATORY

Ingot No. _____   Date Initiated _____

Part of Batch No. _____   Type Melt _____

Operations	Date	Time	Operator
Materials weighed by			
Checked by			
(1) SS			
(2) Master Alloy			
(3) Zr			
(4) Pellets			
Charge began			
Prepared by			
Charge Completed			

Operations	Date	Time	Operator
Melting Area			
Charge received			
Furnace checked Furnace No.			
Charge installed in furnace			
Melting started			
Melting completed			
Furnace dismantled			
Ingot removed			
Furnace checked			
Ingot removed from area			
REMARKS:			

FIG. 9-7   Routing Card for Alloy Laboratory.

furnace for an alloying melt in predetermined amounts. The enriched uranium metal pellets are issued to the charge preparation area in requested amounts and are weighed on a Gram-atic balance to the nearest 0.01 gm. Upon receipt in the charge preparation area, the uranium pellets are reweighed, and the weights are recorded on a Charge Preparation Weighing Record (Fig. 9-6).

Chopped alloying metal is combined with the uranium. These weights are also recorded on the Charge Preparation Weighing Record. This form also provides space for information on recycle material, if used, for the melt.

The charge mixture is nonconsumably arc melted into an ingot. Records of ingot weights are kept in the furnace area as the ingots are removed from the furnace molds. Each ingot is stamped with a serial number, and subsequent remelts of this material in the alloy area bear the same serial number.

A Routing Card for Alloy Laboratory (Fig. 9-7) is initiated for each ingot and, although it is intended as a processing record, it furnishes a backup document for material control purposes.

The fuel-bearing alloy is jacketed during several of the hot-forming steps. All jacketing material, when removed from the alloy, is collected and weighed. Even though experience indicates that very little uranium is lost to jacket material, all residual jacketing materials are checked with a radiation counter. If the contamination level is within the tolerances specified by the AEC, the scrap jackets are sold as metal scrap. The amount of uranium lost on the jackets is calculated by applying counting techniques. This amount is then written off the books.

After the jacketing material has been stripped off, the slabs are weighed and pickled in acid. The slab is then reweighed to determine the weight of alloy lost in the pickling operation. Ledger records of the weight loss are kept at the pickling vats. Spent pickle liquor is accumulated in polyethylene bottles, and eventually the uranium is reclaimed from the liquor. Considerable difficulty has been encountered in obtaining a representative sample of the pickle liquors, and even though chemical analyses are obtained, they are used only to substantiate the values obtained from the accumulated weight losses of the alloy during pickling.

After the pickling operation, the slabs are sheared into cubes and weighed. Any material weight difference in the shearing operations is accounted for either in the filters in the ventilating system over the shearing machines or in shearing fines. The filters are evaluated and held for the eventual recovery of the contained uranium. The shearing fines are weighed and recycled through the process if believed free from contaminants.

The sheared cubes are nonconsumably arc melted into an ingot; the ingot is then weighed and identified with the number assigned to the original ingot prepared with this material. This ingot is then installed in a furnace as an electrode and consumably arc melted into an ingot similar in size to the original ingot produced. This ingot is weighed and numbered. During the consumable arc melt step a certain amount of splattering takes place. This splatter loss is evaluated by noting the weight loss during the melt; the splattered material is collected and held for the eventual recovery of its uranium content.

A jacket is then placed on the ingot, and it is forged into a billet. The jacket is stripped from the billet and collected with the scrap jackets to be handled in the manner described above.

The billet is rejacketed and hot rolled into a slab. The jackets are again

ALLOY LAB PROCESS SUMMARY SHEET

| Ingot No. _____ | Date _____ |
| Calc. Comp _____ | Act. Comp. _____ |

Weights of Material in Process		Individual Filler Summary					
		Filler No.	ACC.	Release	Rejection		
					Cause	Date Chopped	Ing.
1. Charge Weight	_____	1.					
2. Ingot Wt. (1st Melt)	_____	2.					
3. Fines _____		3.					
4. Pickled Strip Wt.	_____	4.					
5. Pickle Loss	_____	5.					
6. Chop Strip Wt.	_____	6.					
7. Fines _____		7.					
8. Charge Wt. (2nd Melt)	_____	8.					
9. Cons. Ingot Wt.	_____	9.					
10. Fines _____		10.					
11. Pickle Strip	_____	11.					
12. Pickle Loss	_____	12.					
13. Blank Wt. (B.E.)	_____	13.					
14. Blank Wt. (A.E.)	_____	14.					
15. Etch Loss	_____	15.					
16. Filler Wt.	_____	16.					
17. Chip Wt. _____		Chemical Samples					
18. Fines _____		Machined					
19. Chem. Sample	_____	Released					
20. Retainer Sample	_____	Analysis					
21. Chop Trim	_____						
22. Shear Loss	_____						

Trim Usage		Chip Usage		Summary: _____
Ingot No.	Wt.	Ingot No.	Wt.	

FIG. 9-8   Alloy Lab Process Summary Sheet.

stripped off, and the slab is pickled in an acid bath. The same pickling vats used in previous pickling operations are used for this operation. The slab weights before and after pickling are determined to the nearest whole gram. The weights are recorded in the ledger records maintained at the pickling vats.

9-4.3. Manufacture of Filler Plates. After the pickling operation, the slab is sheared to size and cold rolled to a predetermined thickness. The material sheared from the slab and the slab itself are weighed, and these weights are recorded. The rolled slab is sheared into filler plates, and sample strips are sheared from several positions along the length of the slab.

The butt ends and shearing scrap are collected, weighed, and chopped for recycling through the process. The samples removed from the slab consist of a retainer sample and samples that are submitted to the Chemistry Department for uranium assay. The Chemistry Department is another material balance area or substation; the internal transfer of responsibility for the assay samples of SS material is accomplished with an SS Material Receipt and Transfer Ticket. Excess sample after analysis is returned to the manufacturing area, the material responsibility again being transferred by use of this transfer form.

The alloy filler plates are machined to size. The machine chips are carefully collected and degreased with an organic solvent, removed in a centrifuge, dried under infrared lamps, weighed, and recycled through the process. The machine fines are collected in 5-gal containers and immersed in mineral oil as a precaution against spontaneous combustion. The uranium content of the fines is evaluated, and the fines are held for the eventual recovery of their uranium content. The machined alloy fillers are carefully weighed. They are then inspected by X rays to assure freedom from internal defects. The defective fillers are rejected, chopped, weighed, and recycled through the process. The accepted fuel fillers are sealed in polyethylene bags to protect them from surface scratches and other physical damage.

9-4.4. Control Records. The Alloy Lab Process Summary Sheet (Fig. 9-8) serves as a basic control document in the fuel-alloy and filler-plate manufacturing area. One of these sheets is prepared for each ingot. Charge weights, ingot weights, weights of material at various stages in the process, losses in the form of nonrecyclable material, pickling losses, chemistry and retainer sample weights, recyclable material such as chopped trim, weight of chips produced in machining, and an individual summary of the fillers produced from each ingot are shown. In general, this sheet serves as a consolidated work sheet, and it is filled out while the alloy is being processed. This permits a running balance to be maintained between measured quantities of material and losses.

A similar summary sheet is maintained on a daily basis for the fuel alloy and filler plate manufacturing area. The sheet is 22 in. by 34 in. and is entitled SS Material Inventory Summary Sheet. The sheet is maintained by the substation clerk. Information for the sheet is obtained from the other records maintained in the area, some of which have already been described. At inventory time the balances of material in the different stages of process are obtained from these summary sheets for comparison with the net weights obtained in the inventory.

9-5. FUEL-PLATE MANUFACTURE

Fuel-plate manufacture is essentially a cladding of the fuel filler plate with a corrosion-resistant material, usually one of the zirconium alloys, and the final sizing and shaping of the fuel element to the required dimensions. These operations are performed in an area separated from the one in which the filler plates were produced. The filler plates are transferred between areas by the use of a Substation Material Transfer Certificate on which the fillers are listed by serial numbers.

Considerable care is taken before the cladding operation is begun to ensure that the serial numbers of the fillers are accurately recorded on the outside of each cladding bundle. After being clad, the uranium is sealed from any further direct testing except by destructive means. In all subsequent forming of the plate or machining of the cladding, the meat is untouched except by accident, which is extremely rare. Therefore, since the uranium content remains unchanged, material control becomes one of piece count and serial-number verification.

The last step in the manufacture of the enriched fuel element is the thorough inspection of the finished plate. This includes a visual inspection, a dimensional check, and an X-ray inspection to check for internal flaws and location of the meat. The plate may also be evaluated in a test facility, where it is checked radiometrically and compared with a standard plate.

Plates that are rejected by inspection are usually returned to the fuel-alloy and filler-plate production department for recycle of the contained uranium.

9-6. METHODS OF CONTROL

9-6.1. General Control Procedures. The core-manufacturing process previously described as consisting of four main steps, starting with the melting of the uranium-bearing alloy and ending with the completed core, is carried out in three separate buildings within a perimeter fence. The entrances and exits to the plant area are guarded 24 hours a day. The manufacturing areas do not, however, include the entire buildings in which they are located. Each of the three buildings is a restricted area apart from the rest of the buildings. Registration or special identification badges are required for admittance.

Material control for the core-manufacturing process is maintained by a single material-control substation which comprises three internal areas, each corresponding to one of the three buildings housing the separate manufacturing areas. Within the substation, the Material Transfer Receipt is used for transfers of uranium between the manufacturing areas.   Combining these related activities within a single substation minimizes paper work between the substation and the SS Group, without sacrifice of material control.

The basic control record for all areas other than alloy manufacturing is a peg board.   A board is established in or near the SS material vault serving the manufacturing area.   This board lists the main manufacturing steps that it controls.   For example, the board for the area in which the fuel plates are assembled would list the following steps:

1. Assembly
2. Welding
3. Boring mill
4. Bridge mill
5. Jig boring

6. Annealing
7. Corrosion testing
8. Straightening
9. Grinding
10. Inspection

At each step a peg is provided on which are hung cards (approximately $2\frac{3}{4}$ in. by $2\frac{3}{4}$ in.).   On these cards are listed plate or component serial numbers. The vault custodian is part of the material-control organization within the manufacturing department.   Material can only be moved between the operations listed on the peg board by material handlers and with the vault custodian's permission.   The vault custodian is responsible for the board's reflecting accurately the location of the plates and components within a manufacturing area.

Each vault is designed to store specific types of SS material and usually consists of numbered ports or receptacles in which only a specified amount of material can be stored.   As an adjunct to the production process peg board, a vault peg board (or in some cases a log) is maintained by the vault custodian indicating the serial numbers of the plates or components in each of the ports or receptacles.

The area representing each of the production steps listed on a peg board is clearly defined and known by the production men, foreman, and operators. There may be six or more machines, or autoclaves, etc., in any one designated area, and the movement of SS material within the area is the responsibility of a designated group leader.   Inventories of the plates are taken at least once a month.   This is done by the vault custodian and material handlers, with whatever assistance they require.   The inventory is usually accomplished in 4 to 8 hours.   Lists of plates, identified by serial number, are prepared and turned over to the substation custodian for checking and for translation into uranium quantities.

9-6.2. Off-Stream Transfers.   The Quality Control inspection areas are located within the manufacturing areas.   When parts or assemblies are withdrawn from the production process for more detailed inspection than can be given at their production location, the Quality Control engineer executes a hand receipt form for the vault custodian and secures his permission prior to moving the parts to be inspected. Quality Control does not have a separate substation; therefore, no formal transfer of the material to its possession is required.

Written requests for chemical or isotopic analysis are submitted to the Chemistry Department along with the samples. Measurement methods by analysis will be discussed later in this chapter. Various production, research, or development engineers may also remove and transfer material outside the regular production processing flow. Control is maintained by issuing the material to individuals within a building area on a hand-receipt basis. Material can be removed from the building or internal manufacturing area on a hand receipt only if it is to be returned within 24 hours or less. For longer periods of time the material is transferred to other buildings or areas on a Material Transfer Receipt or, if the transfer is into another plant substation, on an SS Material Receipt and Transfer Ticket. Once in the new substation, the material is issued to the individuals there on a hand receipt. By this method the material is transferred to, and becomes the responsibility of, the custodian of the substation in which the material is physically located. If for any reason a fabricated plate or component is rejected, it can be declared scrap and returned to the alloy manufacturing area for removal of the cladding, chopping, and reinjecting into the process. This is accomplished by the use of one of the transfer documents already discussed.

9-6.3. Reclamation Material. One of the more difficult control problems is related to material that cannot be recycled in the process. This nonrecyclable scrap is usually in a physical or chemical form that makes its uranium content difficult to determine. After being evaluated by the best means available, it is prepared for shipment to a recovery plant for the reclamation of uranium. Practically all material of this type is generated in the fuel-alloy manufacturing area, and it is usually found in four forms. The largest proportion of reclamation material is generated in the form of acid etching (pickling) solution. The pickling solution is used until the amount of uranium dissolved reaches a level, determined by a calculation of the uranium content based on the accumulated weight loss of the alloy plates and slabs during the etching operation, permitted for criticality control. As previously mentioned, records are kept on a pickling ledger maintained at the vat area. The spent pickling liquors are transferred to 30-gal polyethylene bottles. Chemistry samples are removed, and the results of analysis are used to substantiate the calculated values. The bottles are packed for shipment in 55-gal steel drums. They are packed one bottle to a drum, with sufficient absorbent packing material to retain all the liquid in the event of bottle rupture. After the drums have been labeled and tagged, they are ready for removal to a collection area.

Hoods attached to exhaust systems are provided over all machines in areas where hazard due to air contamination exists. The systems pass the air through filters which remove the uranium contamination. At predetermined intervals, usually based on the time in use, the filters are removed and placed in tight-lid cans and, after being labeled, are ready for removal from the area. The uranium content of the filters is estimated.

Machining fines and material splattered in the furnace are examples of another type of material returned for uranium recovery. The machining fines are collected in cans under mineral oil. The uranium content of the fines is estimated from weight differences of the alloy before and after machining not accounted for by the weighed chips that are recycled through the process. Splatter losses during melting are determined by the weight difference before and after the melt. As already mentioned, all the floor, shower, and sink drainage is evaporated, and the resulting slurry is evaluated for its uranium content by a radiation counting technique. If, after consideration, it is determined that the slurry is to be recovered, it is packed and prepared for shipment to the recovery site; if it is decided that it is uneconomical to recover its uranium content, this material may be prepared for discard or burial using the procedure outlined in Sec. 9-6.11.

The amount of material collected for reclamation is generally large enough to warrant a special substation established for this purpose. The reclamation substation is operated by personnel of the regular plant Shipping and Receiving Department. By regular schedule, on a weekly basis, a truck picks up material from all over the plant and takes it to a storage area. The necessary paper work is prepared and transmitted to the SS Group to coordinate and make all necessary arrangements, other than transportation, for the shipment of the material from the plant. After this is accomplished, the reclamation substation personnel physically load the material on trucks for shipment to a reclamation site.

9-6.4. Criticality Control. A criticality engineer of the Industrial Hygiene Department has the plant-wide responsibility for the proper handling of material to prevent a hazard due to the accidental collection of a critical mass of material. The alloy-manufacturing area is divided into small physical areas, each having a limit or maximum amount of SS material that can be in the area at any time. The foreman is responsible for the enforcement of this restriction.

Material is physically transferred into, and out of, these areas by material handlers who have been thoroughly briefed on the criticality hazards involved. In the other manufacturing areas, the peg board is an aid to criticality control, but here, as well as in the alloy-manufacturing area, the prime responsibility for keeping amounts of material below the critical limits falls on the foreman. In any case a well-defined limit exists for each machine or area. Constant awareness of the criticality hazard is required by all who work with SS material.

9-6.5. Measurement Methods. The adequacy of material control depends to a large part on the method of measuring the uranium content of any material. Improved techniques and the uncertainties of existing methods are constantly being evaluated. Methods for improving the physical weighing of material are constantly being studied. Balances used are regularly tested, cleaned, and checked with standard weights.

The following is a summary of some of the analytical methods used for SS material:

1. The total uranium content of enriched uranium metal (raw material in pellet form) is determined as follows. Two representative samples of the submitted material are dissolved in hydrochloric acid. Uranium is oxidized to the hexavalent state with hydrogen peroxide, and the solutions fumed with sulfuric acid. The solutions are then transferred to 100-ml volumetric flasks and diluted to volume with distilled water. Aliquots removed with a calibrated pipet are reduced to a mixture of the tri- and tetravalent states, aerated to the tetravalent state, and titrated with standard dichromate solution using diphenylamine sulfonate as indicator. The dichromate solution is prepared by accurate weighing of Bureau of Standards potassium dichromate. Accuracy is ±0.2 percent of the amount of uranium present.

2. The total uranium content of the spent pickling solutions is determined by taking a representative sample of approximately 100 gm of solution and weighing to ±0.5 gm. The sample is taken to fumes of sulfur trioxide, cooled, diluted with water, and digested on a hot plate. Interfering metals (tin, iron, chromium, nickel, and copper) are removed by mercury cathode electrolysis. The volume of solution is evaporated to less than 60 ml, and the uranium is reduced to the trivalent and the tetravalent states with amalgamated zinc. The uranium is aerated to the tetravalent state, ferric chloride is added, and the uranium is titrated with standard ceric sulfate solution, using orthophenanthroline ferrous complex as an indicator. The ceric sulfate is standardized against Bureau of Standards arsenious oxide. Accuracy is ±3 percent of the amount of uranium present.

3. Two methods, chemical and X-ray fluorescence, are used for the analysis of uranium in enriched uranium zirconium base fuel alloys. The former is used primarily for standardization and checking purposes while the latter is used for routine analysis. All values reported are in reference to the chemical method.

    a. CHEMICAL METHOD—Weighed samples are dissolved in hydrofluoric acid with the addition of hydrogen peroxide. Interfering elements (iron, chromium, nickel, and copper) are removed by mercury cathode electrolysis. The solutions are then fumed with sulfuric acid, water and hydrochloric acid are added, and the uranium is reduced to the tri- and tetravalent state with amalgamated zinc. Tin is removed quantitatively at this step by reduction to the metal by the zinc. The uranium is aerated to the tetravalent state, ferric chloride is added, and the uranium is titrated with standard ceric sulfate solution, using the orthophenanthro-line-ferrous complex as indicator. The ceric sulfate is standardized against Bureau of Standards arsenious oxide. Accuracy, ±0.85 percent of amount of uranium present in the normal range.

b. X-RAY FLUORESCENCE METHOD—Samples are received as metal strips with a 32-rms machined surface. Each sample is placed in the fluorescent X-ray instrument, which exposes the specimen to a primary source of X-radiation. To obtain the uranium concentration in the sample, the integrated intensity of the characteristic L radiation emitted by this element is measured and referred to an analytical curve prepared from known standards. The integration time is externally standardized by measuring the fluorescent yield from a copper strip adjacent to the sample. The accuracy of the method for routine analysis is ±1.2 percent of the amount present.

4. Isotopic analyses of uranium in samples of metal pellets, alloys, and solutions of uranium are performed on a 13.5-in.-radius 60° mass spectrometer fitted with a surface ionization source and a vacuum lock for routine introduction of samples. The solid samples are dissolved, and the alloying elements, if any, are separated. A uranyl nitrate solution is prepared by the addition of an excess of nitric acid. The solution is heated to volatilize the excess nitric acid, and the resulting salt is redissolved in water. A neutral or slightly acidic uranyl nitrate solution is deposited on a tantalum filament that is heated by applying an electrical current of several amperes until the salt is dry. The filament is fastened into the ion source of the mass spectrometer and introduced into the instrument through the vacuum lock. Compounds or elements more volatile than uranium oxide are generally removed by preheating the filament in the second stage of the vacuum lock for several minutes. In the final stage, the pressures of the source lock and analyzer tube are allowed to reach 1×10^{-6} mm Hg and 5×10^{-7} mm Hg, respectively, and filament current and accelerating voltage are applied. The ion source is adjusted to obtain maximum intensity of the UO_2^+ ion beam. The magnetic field strength is varied to sweep the mass spectra across the exit slit of the collector and onto a final collector plate.

Twelve to twenty pairs of mass spectra are recorded by successively sweeping toward the higher mass uranium isotope and then toward the lower mass uranium isotope. Ion beam intensities of various isotopes of interest are determined by graphically averaging six to ten pairs of mass spectra. The average values of the peak heights with their associated instrument factors are recorded on input data sheets for computation on an IBM model 650 computer. The computer is programed to correct for unwanted contributions, to determine the weight ratios of individual uranium isotopes present, and to compute the average value of the individual isotopic ratios calculated and the standard deviation of this average, as well as a weight ratio of the uranium to the sample if so desired.

9-6.6. Method of Taking Inventory. In general, there are two approaches to a physical inventory. The first approach eliminates the variable of human judgment as far as possible. This approach dictates that all quantities of material will be remeasured at the time of inventory. There is, of course, some judgment required in specifying the method of measurement to be used. For instance, to really determine the amount of SS material in an alloy ingot would require that a sample be taken from the ingot and the uranium percentage be determined by analysis. If the ingot was not homogeneous, more than one sample would have to be analyzed. The ingot would also have to be weighed. The contained uranium could then be calculated. Also, in a physical inventory by measurement, just reweighing the ingot and determining the SS content by applying an accepted percent uranium content might be considered adequate.

In contrast, the second approach to a physical inventory is that of measurement only to the extent necessary to convince the person directing the inventory that the actual quantities of material are in accord with the recorded quantities. Referring to the example of the ingot, if the serial number of the ingot checked with the serial number of the record and if it was apparent that the ingot was in fact a whole ingot, the recorded SS and U^{235} values for the ingot might be accepted.

A factor that has considerable bearing on the matter of how an inventory should be taken and, in fact, how material received from an outside source is verified is that of ease of measurement for SS materials. It is obviously not desirable to spend more time and money for measurements of SS materials than the material might be worth if the measurement is taken solely for the prevention of loss of the SS material.

The method employed in taking a physical inventory will determine how the uncertainty of the inventory totals are obtained. In the first method the uncertainties inherent in the method of measurement employed in the inventorying of the different quantities of material are applied to measurement results and are totaled. In the second method the uncertainties of the recorded data on the verified material are totaled and become the inventory uncertainty. There is an exception, however, in the second method. If it is necessary to remeasure a quantity of material, for example, an accumulation of chips or fines, to satisfy the director of the inventory, it may well be that the uncertainty of the remeasurement is less than that of the record. This might be true when the recorded total is made up of numerous increments. In this case the uncertainty of the remeasurement would be recorded for that portion of the inventory rather than the uncertainty of the record.

An example of the application of this reasoning is the inventorying of highly enriched uranium pellets. The inventory method employed is to rapidly reweigh each bottle of pellets (pellets are not removed from the bottles) on a two-pan scale. Because of variations in the tare weights of the bottles and the comparative inaccuracy of the scale, there is an increased uncertainty in this measurement over that obtained in the verification of receipt of the material. The above method of performing the inventory does, however, permit the substation custodian to compare the weights obtained on each bottle and to decide whether the recorded content of the bottle has been verified.

The method used in arriving at the inventory uncertainty for a substation is to establish an acceptable method of performing the inventory on the material in the custody of the substation and to provide the substation with charts of uncertainties versus amount of material. The uncertainty associated with an inventoried quantity of a particular form of material is read from the charts. Space is provided on the substation monthly report form for the reporting of uncertainties related to each inventory item.

A physical inventory of the enriched uranium in the entire manufacturing area is made each month for the preparation of the monthly inventory report. The Substation Custodian decides when the inventory will be taken and advises production personnel in advance so that there will be a minimum of disruption to regular processing activities. It is desirable to conduct the inventory as close to the end of the month as possible so that the paper-work adjustments necessary to reflect an accurate end of the month inventory will be held to a minimum. The size of the Core Manufacturing Department's inventory and the time needed for reconciliation necessitates that this inventory be started by the twenty-first day of each month.

Since production is not stopped during the inventory period, the substation clerks designate in advance at what processing stage certain types of material will be inventoried so that no recording duplications will result. Once these borderline cases have been resolved, the inventory can be completed during an 8-hour shift using approximately ten men for the entire manufacturing area.

In the fuel-alloy and filler-plate production area, a substation clerk, the vault custodian, the material courier, and several of the production personnel conduct the inventory. Two factors concerning this area help to ensure an accurate accounting of material. Since this is a restricted area and since all material movements into and out of this area can be made only through the material courier, he will be cognizant of any receipts or transfers of material and can make adjustments to the inventory accordingly. Then too, since this area involves only one portion of the entire manufacturing area, the number of forms in which the fuel can exist is reduced.

Inventory procedure provides that as soon as a particular item or distinguishable quantity of inventory is verified, a 3 by 6-in. inventory tag is affixed immediately. One side of the tag provides spaces where the following information can be noted, if applicable: account or project number, shop location, material identification, material description, number of pieces, and weight in grams. Fourteen spaces are used for each of the last three items to allow for group inventorying. The reverse side of the tag is used to record notations or any reductions or additions to the recorded weight once the inventory has been taken.

The production records normally maintained for the fuel alloy and filler plate production area have been described in a previous section. It was noted that, as a quantity of material progresses through the various manufacturing steps, it is generally weighed before and after each operation. These weights are recorded on the route card and, where applicable, the actual material weight, project number, and identification number are also recorded on a special adhesive tape label, which is attached to the material. For inventory purposes, no material in a form that discourages any partial removal of its weight (ingots, bars, fillers, etc.) is reweighed. The weight appearing on the label is copied on the inventory tag.

9-6.7. Material Types Inventoried. Virgin material, in the form of enriched metal pellets, is received into the substation in plastic bottles whose net weights approximate 500 gm. This material is weighed and verified to the nearest 0.01 gm, and a running inventory of material is kept as it is issued to production. At inventory time, each bottle is gross weighed to the nearest whole gram. An average tare is used, and the net weight difference is compared to pellet inventory records. If this net weight is within a gram of the recorded weight, the recorded weight is considered verified and is used for inventory purposes. For those cases where the difference between whole gram inventory figures and recorded figures exceeds 1 gm, the pellet material is removed from the bottle and weighed to the nearest 0.01 gm. If a difference still exists, the new inventory weight is used, and an inventory adjustment is made if the difference cannot be reconciled.

The weights of the ingots, slabs, and blanks, as noted on the material, are recorded on the tags. Occasional check weighings are made for verification purposes only. Any material not weighed and recorded prior to inventory time is weighed during that time. However, each production filler is weighed to the nearest 0.01 gm. For inventory purposes, the weight that appears on the label of each filler is used. Batches of fillers are weighed to the nearest gram as verification.

As retainer samples are produced, they are weighed to the nearest whole gram; their weight and other pertinent information are recorded on sample bags, and they are stored in a sample cabinet. The recorded weights of these samples are used for inventory purposes. Chemistry samples, both solid and chips, are weighed as produced. Their recorded weights are used for inventory purposes. The Chemistry Department's weights on returned samples are accepted. These weights are checked only when the samples are being prepared for reclamation, and an inventory adjustment is made if any differences result.

During operations machining chips are collected, dried, weighed, and stored in pails with the recorded weight of material in each pail recorded on the tape-on-label. These recorded weights are used for inventory purposes. However, if the chips are being dried during an inventory period, the difference between the weight of the material before and after machining is used; any subsquent inventory adjustment is made during that period when the chips are weighed.

Furnace fines are weighed as produced and stored in a pretared container. The gross weight is obtained, and the net weight difference is recorded on the label. This recorded weight is used for inventorying. If there are any partially filled unweighed pails of fines during an inventory period, they are weighed at that time.

Recyclable trim material, produced as a result of chopping and shearing, is weighed as produced to the nearest 0.1 gm and its weight is recorded on a storage-container tag each time new material is added. At inventory time these individual weights are totaled and recorded on the label attached to the storage container.

Pickling solutions are collected in pretared $6\frac{1}{2}$- and 13-gal capacity polyethylene containers. Once the containers are filled, they are weighed, and the gross and net weights are also recorded on the label of each container. Batch samples are submitted to the Chemistry Department for analysis to substantiate cumulative uranium content. During inventory the weights of these containers are recorded on the inventory tag along with the present uranium concentration based on the cumulative uranium content.

9-6.8. Materials of Estimated Uranium Content. During the production process contaminated jacketing material is produced as a result of rolling operations. The best estimate of the uranium content in these jackets is obtained by taking random 1-in.-square samples from a large number of typical production jackets. Radiation counts are obtained and converted to grams, and this figure is applied to the inside area of the jacket. For inventory purposes the amount of uranium in these scrap jackets is obtained by applying an average grams of uranium per jacket figure to the number of jackets used since the last inventory.

Uranium trapped by the exhaust filters that are attached to some of the production machines is estimated both for reclamation and inventory purposes. Production records show the weight of material before and after each operation and also the weight of the scrap produced. Any differences that result between the weight of the original material and the sum of the finished material weight plus scrap is applied to filters.

All uranium-contaminated wash water from floor, machine, and personnel cleanup is emptied into a special drainage system that serves only the fuel alloy and filler plate production area. This wash water is collected in tanks, and Industrial Hygiene personnel take daily samples. On the basis of counting techniques and the volume of water collected, the amount of uranium collected each month is calculated by the Industrial Hygiene personnel, who submit this report to the Substation Custodian. The SS weight thus reported is prorated to the project accounts active during the month.

9-6.9. Accumulating Data. After all inventory weights have been recorded on inventory tags and collected, the inventory is summarized and broken down by project and material type. This summary sheet gives the following information: project, identification, material description, net weight, uranium composition, SS weight, and U^{235} weight. All but the last two columns are completed by shop personnel. Completed summary forms are sent to the Substation Control Group for SS and U^{253} weight calculation and final reconciliation. The detailed explanation listed above completes the inventory process for the fuel-alloy and filler-plate production area.

For all other enriched-uranium fabricating areas, inventorying is limited to piece count and item identification. The underlying theory is that, once the fillers with their exact weights leave the fuel alloy and filler plate production area, the SS weight is not altered in any manner and, therefore, only item inventory is necessary. In each of the remaining areas, the vault custodian submits to the Substation Control Group a listing, by project, of the plates, subassemblies, and clusters located in his vault or area. Completed cores charged to his area are also listed. The numbers of fuel plates contained in each subassembly, cluster, and core are also specified. This fuel plate count is the basis upon which the Substation Control Group authenticates the inventory reports for the area.

9-6.10. Analyzing Data. Once the Substation Control Group receives the summary and backup sheets from the various manufacturing areas, it must begin immediately to evaluate each area's inventory and to compare the results with its paper-work charge figures.

For the fuel-alloy and filler-plate production area, SS and U^{235} weight calculations by project are performed first. Each project total is checked against its respective control record. The control record shows a beginning inventory, receipts, transfers, and an ending inventory by project. This record is based upon figures obtained from the substation internal transfer certificates or from the SS material transfer tickets. The transfer tickets record receipts and transfers into and out of the Core Manufacturing Department. The internal transfer certificates are used to transfer fillers to one of the other areas or to receive rejected materials from other areas. Static project account inventories should readily balance. However, there may be variation between the physical and paper inventories of active accounts, mainly as the result of the use of nominal uranium percentages in some instances. As previously stated, nominal values are used in some phases of the manufacturing process until results based on analyzed samples become available. At that time the new uranium percentages are applied. Application of corrected percentages to the net weight inventory creates differences that are explained as either positive or negative account differences on the inventory evaluation.

In the other manufacturing areas, however, there can be no weight discrepancy whatsoever. Fillers leave the fuel-alloy and filler-plate production area with analyzed uranium values. These values are submitted only to the Substation Control Group; acceptance of these fillers in other areas is on the basis of piece count and identification number alone. As already stated, transfers of fillers to these other manufacturing areas are made on internal transfer certificates. As part of the inventory reconciliation prior to SS and U^{235} weight evaluation, a comparison is made of the piece count of the filler plates in the manufacturing areas with the total recorded as transferred to these areas.

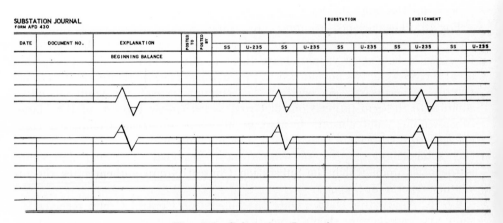

FIG. 9-9   Substation Journal.

The inventories from each individual manufacturing area are submitted to the Substation Control Group in the form of a summary sheet and subsequent detail sheets. The summary sheet shows, by project, the number of items as fillers or fuel plates and also the number of fillers in subassembly or cluster form. The detail sheets denote, by project, the identification of each filler, plate, subassembly, and cluster and give the number of plates in each identified subassembly and cluster.

As a supplement to this inventory check, a daily log is kept of fuel element transfers between manufacturing areas by project. This information is obtained from the hand receipts that accompany transfers of fuel elements between manufacturing areas (excluding the fuel-alloy and filler-plate production area). Any discrepancies in the master log account can be specifically traced to a particular manufacturing area by cross checking the daily log record. Once the total plate count has been verified, the control group completes its evaluation by calculating SS and U^{235} values for the plates, subassemblies, and clusters based on analyzed uranium values of the original fillers. At this point the Substation Control Group has all the information needed for the monthly inventory report. However, before that report is discussed, a closer look into the over-all substation records will be made.

9-6.11. Substation Records. Most of the records mentioned as part of the inventory and evaluations program have dealt with intrastation records and transfers. These records act only as a supplement to the Substation Control Group's principal material-control records. A journal (Fig. 9-9) and supplemental ledger cards (Fig. 9-10) are the main records. Intrastation transfers do not affect the journal.

Four records are used exclusively as posting documents for this form. They are the Request for Shipment of SS Material (Fig. 9-11), the SS Material Receipt and Transfer Ticket, the Material Discard Application (Fig. 9-12), and the SS Material Expendability Report (Fig. 9-13).

Request for Shipment of SS Material. Five copies of the Request for Shipment of SS Material form are initiated by the Substation Control Group each time there is a request to make a shipment of SS material from the plant. All the data needed to make the shipment are recorded on this form. From a records standpoint it is a posting document from which the Substation Control Group can credit a journal project account for each shipment. The Central SS Group uses this information as shipper's data on its AEC-101 shipping form.

The SS Material Receipt and Transfer Ticket. This is a dual-purpose form filled out in quadruplicate. As a material-receipt form, it is used to inform the Central SS Group of the direct receipt of SS material into the substation. Fillers and plates fabricated by subcontractors are received in this manner. In all cases the substation provides all the information concerning the receipt except the SS and U^{235} weights. This latter information is supplied by the Central SS Group after verification and after comparison with the shipper's AEC-101 form. The completed document serves as a substation posting document to debit a receipt of material into a specific project, and it also supplies information to the Central SS Group concerning the receiver's data on the AEC-101 form. As a transfer ticket this form records transactions between substations.

Material Discard Application. This form is initiated by the Substation Control Group for materials whose SS concentration is so slight as to be considered economically unrecoverable. In the Core Manufacturing Substation this form is especially applicable to the drain water and the contaminated jacket material. In the majority of cases the concentration of SS and U^{235} is low, and the AEC Operations Office is requested to approve discard. If this permission is granted, the signed form is used by the substation to credit its project account by the applicable material discard weights.

SS Material Expendability Report. The SS Material Expendability Report

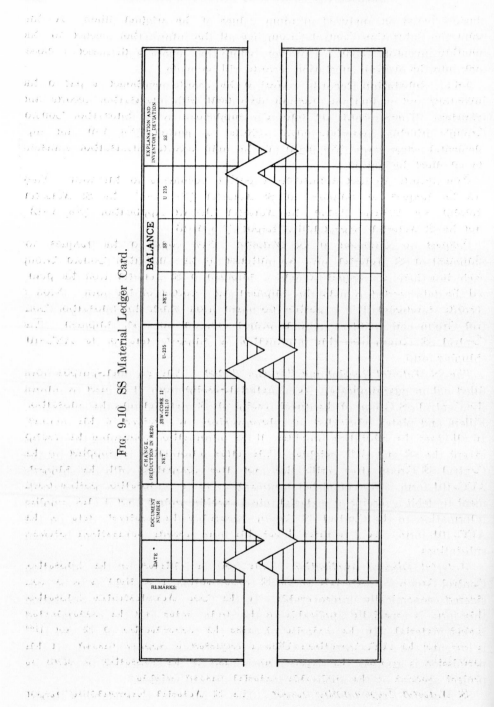

Fig. 9-10. SS Material Ledger Card.

SS MATERIAL LEDGER CARD FORM APD-103B

	PELLETS	OTHER METALS	IN PROCESS	STORAGE	FUEL PLATES	FILLERS	SUB ASSEMBLIES	CLUSTERS	IN REACTORS	CRITICAL ASSEMBLIES	STANDARDS	ACCEPTABLE ACTIVE USE	IN WASTE TANKS	POWDER	PLATES	TAPES	SAMPLES	BUNDLES	SLUDGE AND SLURRY	SCRAP	IRRADIATED	COOLING	PIECE COUNT	ESTIMATED	ANALYZED	
																										BASIC 4000.4
																										PWR-EXP 4101.0
																										PWR-FA 4101.1
																										PWR C1S1 4101.2
																										PWR C2S2 4101.3
																										PWR C1S2 4101.4
																										PWR FA2 4101.6
																										PCT F 4300.0
																										STR-1 4300.1
																										SPCA 4300.2
																										STR-3 4300.3
																										STR-FA 4300.4
																										STR-3A 4300.5
																										STR-3B 4300.6
																										STR-4 4300.7
																										PTF 4300.8
																										A1W-FA 4307.0
																										A1W-MU 4307.1
																										A1W-FA2 4307.2
																										A1W-MU2 4307.3
																										A1W-CORE 1 4307.4
																										A1W-CORE 2 4307.5
																										S3W-FA 1 4311.0
																										S3W-CORE 1 4311.1
																										S3W-CORE 1B 4311.2
																										S3W-CORE 1B 4311.3
																										S3W-CORE 1C 4311.4
																										S3W-CORE 1D 4311.5
																										S3W-CORE 1E 4311.6
																										S5W-FA 4312.0
																										S5W-CORE 1 4312.1
																										S5W-CORE 1A 4312.2
																										S5W-CORE 1B 4312.3
																										S5W-CORE 1C 4312.4
																										S5W-CORE 1D 4312.5
																										S5W-CORE 1E 4312.6
																										S5W-CORE 1F 4312.7
																										S5W-CORE 1G 4312.8
																										S5W-CORE 1H 4312.9

Left-side label column (NUMBER / NO.):

EXPLANATION AND INVENTORY DEVIATION

BALANCE — U-235, SS, NET, U-235, SS, NET

CHANGE (REDUCTION IN RED)

DOCUMENT NUMBER

DATE

Left-margin value ranges:

- 00.0 TO 0.29
- 0.30 TO 0.38
- 0.39 TO 0.41
- 0.42 TO 0.49
- 0.50 TO 0.59
- 0.60 TO .7114
- NORMAL
- .7115 TO .99
- 1.00 TO 1.49
- 1.50 TO 1.99
- 1.99
- 2.00 TO 2.99
- 3.00 TO 4.99
- 5.00 TO 14.99
- 15.00 TO 29.99
- 30.00 TO 74.99
- UNDER 75%
- 75.00 TO 100.00
- THORIUM
- PLUTONIUM
- U-233
- METAL
- ALLOY
- SOLUTION
- OXIDE
- WASTE
- MISC.

REMARKS:

HTTF 4300.12   REACTOR DEVELOPMENT 4000.10   F1W-2A 4213.1   S5W-CORE 11 4312.10

is initiated at the end of the month; it is used to explain book-physical inventory differences (B-PID). All differences and write-offs must be reported to and approved by the Central SS Group. Differences can be either adjusted or not adjusted. Normal manufacturing losses and account differences re-

SHIP TO

CLASSIFICATION

SS SHIPPING FORM NO.

| DATE REQUIRED AT DESTINATION | DEADLINE SHIPPING DATE | DATE SHIPMENT AM PM READY | MAT'L. LOCATED AT |

| CONTACT (NAME & PHONE EX.) | SIZE OF CONTAINER/S |

| SUB-STA. NO | IND. HYG. SURV. NO. | BUDGET | SIGNATURE | SUB-STATION CUSTODIAN | DATE |

| FORM OF MAT'L | METAL | ALLOY | OXIDE | WASTE | SOLUTION | OTHER |

MATERIAL FOR:

| MATERIAL DESCRIPTION | P. O. NO. OR SUB-CONT. NO. | MATERIAL CATEGORY & QUOTA DESIGNATION |

ANTICIPATED USE OF MATERIAL (& EXPERIMENT NO., IF ANY)

| SHIP BY | TRUCK | RWY. EXP. | COURIER | REGISTERED AIR MAIL | AIR FREIGHT | AIR EXPRESS | SPECIAL INST. | BAND | CLASS "D" POISON | LABEL |

MISCELLANEOUS INSTRUCTIONS

MEASUREMENT METHODS

| TRANSFER AUTHORITY | SHIP | PREPAID | COLLECT | | | DATE SHIPPED | SIGNATURE | CENTRAL SS GROUP | DATE |

| BILL/LADING NO. | CARRIER | | ROUTING | CAR NO. INITIALS | SEAL NO. | SIGNATURE | SHIPPING AGENCY | DATE |

FOR USE BY AEC ONLY	SAFETY FACTORS	CATEGORY (CIRCLE ONE) I II III IV	I.C.C. EXEMPTION REQUIRED
			MOTOR VEHICLES REQUIRED
	SAFETY EQUIPMENT REQUIRED	SECURITY CLASSIFICATION	R.R. EQUIPMENT REQUIRED
			OTHER
			INITIAL SIGNATURE AEC APPROVAL DATE

| CONT. NO. | QUANTITY | TYPE OF CONTAINER | GROSS WEIGHT | TARE WEIGHT | NET WEIGHT | SS NET | INDUSTRIAL HYGIENE SURVEY READING |

REQUEST FOR SHIPMENT OF SS MATERIAL
FORM APD 228A

SS REPREPSENTATIVE

FIG. 9-11 Request for Shipment of SS Material.

sulting from the use of nominal rather than analyzed percentages are usually approved for write-off. Differences within the uncertainty of the measurement method are usually not adjusted. Further explanation of the expendability report will be given in Sec. 9-7.

The Journal. The journal is used to record, by project, all transfers into and out of the substation. Each time material is received into the substation from outside contractors or from other substations, each time material is sent off site for reclamation, to the Chemistry Department for analysis, or to other substations in the plant, or each time a B-PID entry must be made, the ap-

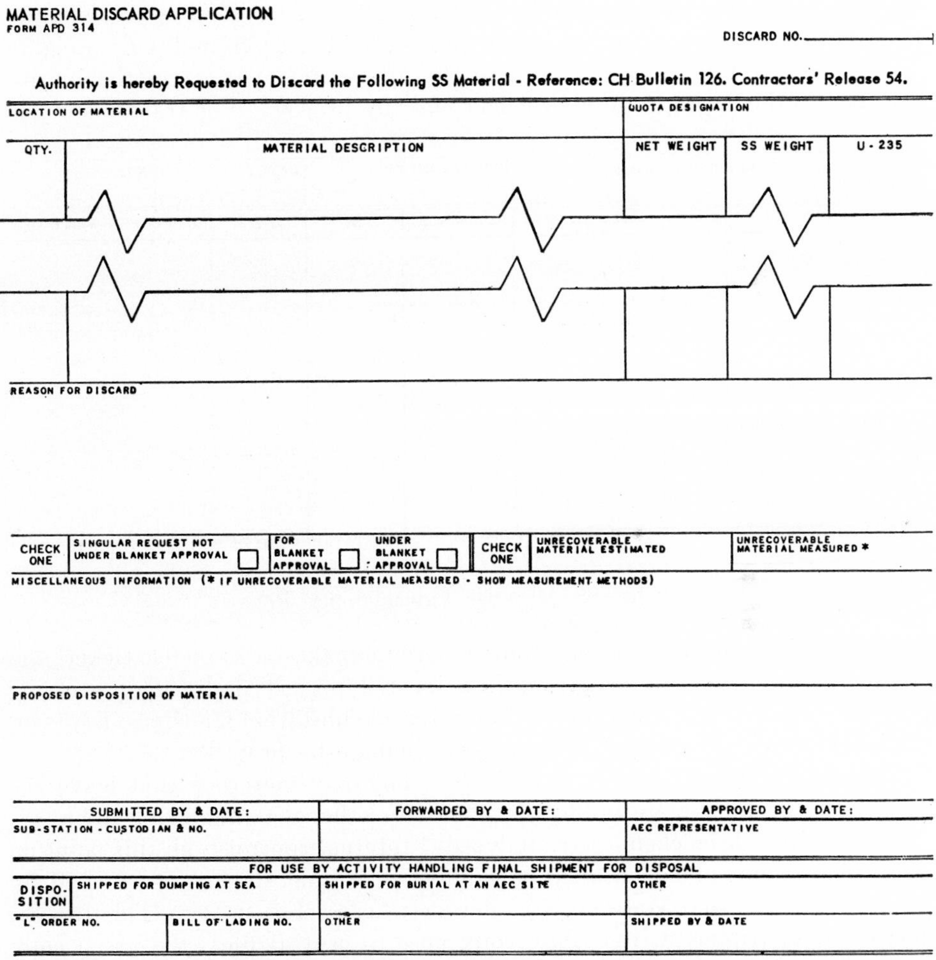

MATERIAL DISCARD APPLICATION
FORM APD 314

DISCARD NO._____

Authority is hereby Requested to Discard the Following SS Material - Reference: CH Bulletin 126. Contractors' Release 54.

LOCATION OF MATERIAL		QUOTA DESIGNATION		
QTY.	MATERIAL DESCRIPTION	NET WEIGHT	SS WEIGHT	U - 235

REASON FOR DISCARD

| CHECK ONE | SINGULAR REQUEST NOT UNDER BLANKET APPROVAL ☐ | FOR BLANKET APPROVAL ☐ | UNDER BLANKET APPROVAL ☐ | CHECK ONE | UNRECOVERABLE MATERIAL ESTIMATED | UNRECOVERABLE MATERIAL MEASURED ✶ |

MISCELLANEOUS INFORMATION (✶ IF UNRECOVERABLE MATERIAL MEASURED - SHOW MEASUREMENT METHODS)

PROPOSED DISPOSITION OF MATERIAL

SUBMITTED BY & DATE:	FORWARDED BY & DATE:	APPROVED BY & DATE:
SUB-STATION - CUSTODIAN & NO.		AEC REPRESENTATIVE

FOR USE BY ACTIVITY HANDLING FINAL SHIPMENT FOR DISPOSAL		
DISPO-SITION	SHIPPED FOR DUMPING AT SEA	SHIPPED FOR BURIAL AT AN AEC SITE	OTHER
"L" ORDER NO.	BILL OF LADING NO.	OTHER	SHIPPED BY & DATE

FIG. 9-12   Material Discard Application.

plicable project is debited or credited accordingly. At the end of the month a balance is struck for each project.

Ledger Card. The edge-punch ledger cards act as a double check for the over-all journal entries. For each project listed in the journal, two ledger cards are kept. On one card is recorded each entry into, and transfer out of, the fuel-alloy and filler-plate production area, and on the other is recorded each entry into, or transfer out of, the other manufacturing areas as a whole. (A close examination of the ledger card shows that each entry could possibly be broken down not only by project but also by material form and type. Although this fine breakdown is maintained by other substations, it is not particularly applicable to the manufacturing substation, since material is constantly changing form.)   As material enters the manufacturing substation, it is accompanied by a transfer ticket which lists the project and the SS and U^{235} weights. These verified weights are debited to the appropriate project in the journal and also to the appropriate area ledger card by project.   For transfers out of

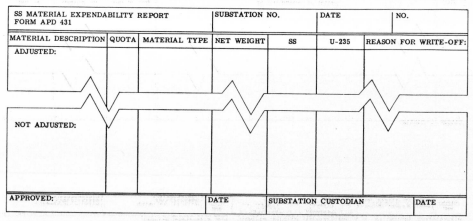

SS MATERIAL EXPENDABILITY REPORT FORM APD 431			SUBSTATION NO.		DATE		NO.	
MATERIAL DESCRIPTION	QUOTA	MATERIAL TYPE	NET WEIGHT	SS	U-235	REASON FOR WRITE-OFF:		
ADJUSTED:								
NOT ADJUSTED:								
APPROVED:			DATE		SUBSTATION CUSTODIAN		DATE	

FIG. 9-13 SS Material Expendability Report.

the substation, the Substation Control Group makes a transfer ticket and credits the weights to the appropriate journal project and ledger area by project.   The journal is not affected by internal substation transfers; however, the ledger cards reflect these internal area changes by project.

Internal Material Transfer Certificate.   The only materials that leave the fuel-alloy and filler-plate production areas for other manufacturing areas are fillers that have been chemically analyzed.   Internal control from this point on is by piece count and identification number only, and transfer is effected by means of the Internal Material Transfer Certificate (Fig. 9-14).   This form is completed in triplicate; the white copy goes to central files; the green copy is for the receiver; and the yellow copy is for the originator.   However, since the Substation Control Group is responsible for maintaining accurate SS and U^{235} values for these internal transfers, all filler values must be known.   This information is obtained from a Fuel Plate Loading Record.

Fuel Plate Loading Record.   As fillers are manufactured, they are numbered consecutively.   Their analyzed SS and U^{235} values are listed on Fuel Plate Loading Record cards (Fig. 9-15).   The Substation Control Group receives a copy of these cards.   Whenever the Substation Control Group receives its

FORM WAPD 2 - A

INTERNAL
MATERIAL TRANSFER CERTIFICATE
STATION #2

NO. _____
DATE _____
TIME _____

FROM _____

TO _____

PROJECT _____

FILLERS	TOTAL NO. OF PIECES
FUEL PLATES	
SUB ASSEMBLIES	_____
CLUSTERS	

PURPOSE:

REMARKS:

PCS.	IDENTIFICATION	PCS.	IDENTIFICATION	PCS.	IDENTIFICATION	PCS.	IDENTIFICATION

WHITE COPY - CENTRAL FILES
GREEN COPY - RECEIVER
YELLOW COPY - ORIGINATOR

ORIGINATOR _____

RECEIVER _____

FIG. 9-14 Internal Material Transfer Certificate.

BAPD - NCM - (A) - 56

FUEL PLATE LOADING RECORD
PROJECT _____ ENRICHMENT

INGOT NO.	WEIGHT	% BORON	TOTAL BORON	% U	SS	U235	SUB ASSY NO.	INGOT NO.	WEIGHT	% BORON	TOTAL BORON	% U	SS	U235	SUB ASSY NO.

CALCULATED BY: DATE: CHECKED BY: DATE:

INFORMATION CATEGORY

_____

AUTHORIZED CLASSIFIER   DATE

FIG. 9-15 Fuel Plate Loading Record.

white copy of the internal transfer certificate, it refers to the Fuel Plate Loading Record for the appropriate SS and U^{235} values and then credits the fuel-alloy and filler-plate production area's ledger account and debits the other manufacturing area's ledger account for the total amount of each transfer.

As mentioned in the inventory evaluation and reconciliation sections, transfers between the manufacturing areas (excluding the fuel-alloy and filler-plate production area) are controlled by the Substation Control Group by piece count and identification number only. As long as piece-count and number-identification verification can be maintained by those areas, over-all SS and U^{235} values can be evaluated by the control group from its records.

The Substation Control Group also keeps records of subassembly and cluster make-up. The Quality Control Department releases a report listing the plates that will be used for each subassembly and the subassemblies that will be used in each cluster. Their own SS and U^{235} values are also listed on this report, a copy of which is forwarded to the Substation Control Group. Separate subassembly and cluster record cards are made up using this report. These cards are useful for applying appropriate SS and U^{235} values to piece-count inventories.

SS MATERIAL ENDING INVENTORY
FORM APD 24 E - 2
SUBSTATION   MONTH

OVER 75 %	ANALYZED				ESTIMATED				QUOTA	TOTAL	
	SS	UNCER-TAINTY	U-235	UNCER-TAINTY	SS	UNCER-TAINTY	U-235	UNCER-TAINTY		SS	U-235
METAL (TOTAL)											
PELLETS											
OTHER											
ALLOY (TOTAL)											
IN PROCESS											
IN CORES											
FUEL PLATES											
SUBASSEMBLIES											
CLUSTERS											
SCRAP											
MISCELLANEOUS											
SOLUTIONS (TOTAL)											
(a)											
(b)											
(c)											
OXIDE (TOTAL)											
POWDER											
PLATES											
TAPES											
MISCELLANEOUS											
SCRAP (TOTAL)											
(a)											
(b)											
(c)											
IRRADIATED (TOTAL)											
(a)											
(b)											
TOTALS											

FIG. 9-16 SS Material Ending Inventory.

In summary, the manufacturing substation maintains material control in three principal ways: (1) by maintaining records of all SS and U^{235} weight transactions into and out of the substation (journal); (2) by maintaining SS and U^{235} weight records of transactions between internal areas (ledger); and

COMPOSITION OF ENDING INVENTORY
FORM APD 409

AS OF: STATION NO.

> 75% ENRICHED URANIUM	U - GRAMS - U-235		DEPLETED URANIUM	U - KILOGRAMS - U-235	
39 IN REACTORS (IRRADIATED)			IRRADIATED MATERIAL		
40 COOLING (IRRADIATED)			39 IN REACTORS		
42 ACCEPTABLE METAL - ACTIVE USE			40 IN COOLING		
43 SCRAP METAL			41 IN SEPARATIONS & RECOVERY		
45 ACCEPTABLE COMPOUNDS - ACTIVE USE			42 IN WASTE TANKS		
46 SCRAP COMPOUNDS			43		
48 ACCEPTABLE SOLUTIONS - ACTIVE USE			44		
49 SCRAP SOLUTIONS			45 TOTAL - IRRADIATED MATERIAL		
50 ALLOYS			UNIRRADIATED MATERIAL		
51 STANDARDS			48 ACCEPTABLE METAL - ACTIVE USE		
52 CRITICAL ASSEMBLIES (ZERO POWER)			49 SCRAP METAL		
53 WASTE			51 ACCEPTABLE COMPOUNDS		
54 ALLOY - IRRADIATED			52 SCRAP COMPOUNDS		
55 OXIDE - IRRADIATED			54 ACCEPTABLE SOLUTIONS - ACTIVE USE		
56			55 SCRAP SOLUTIONS		
57			56 ALLOYS		
58			57 STANDARDS		
59 TOTAL - RESEARCH & DEVELOPMENT			58		
< 75% ENRICHED URANIUM	U - GRAMS - U-235		59		
41 ACCEPTABLE METAL-ACTIVE USE			60 TOTAL - UNIRRADIATED MATERIAL		
42 SCRAP METAL			PLUTONIUM		GRAMS
44 ACCEPTABLE COMPOUNDS - ACTIVE USE			36 IN REACTORS		
45 SCRAP COMPOUNDS			37 COOLING		
47 ACCEPTABLE SOLUTIONS - ACTIVE USE			39 ACCEPTABLE METAL - ACTIVE USE		
48 SCRAP SOLUTIONS			40 SCRAP METAL		
49 ALLOYS			42 ACCEPTABLE COMPOUNDS - ACTIVE USE		
50 STANDARDS			43 SCRAP COMPOUNDS		
51 CRITICAL ASSEMBLIES (ZERO POWER)			45 ACCEPTABLE SOLUTIONS - ACTIVE USE		
52 IRRADIATED - ALLOY			46 SCRAP SOLUTIONS		
53 SCRAP ALLOYS			47 ALLOYS		
53-1 WASTE			48 STANDARDS		
53-2			49		
53-3			50		
54 TOTAL - MISC. RESEARCH & DEVELOPMENT			51		
NORMAL URANIUM		KILOGRAMS	52 TOTAL - RESEARCH & DEVELOPMENT		
75 IN REACTORS			THORIUM		KILOGRAMS
76 COOLING			RESEARCH AND DEVELOPMENT		
78 ACCEPTABLE METAL - ACTIVE USE			50 ACCEPTABLE METAL - ACTIVE USE		
79 SCRAP METAL			53 ACCEPTABLE COMPOUNDS - ACTIVE USE		
81 ACCEPTABLE COMPOUNDS - ACTIVE USE			54 SCRAP COMPOUNDS		
82 SCRAP COMPOUNDS			56 ACCEPTABLE SOLUTIONS - ACTIVE USE		
84 ACCEPTABLE SOLUTIONS - ACTIVE USE			57 SCRAP SOLUTIONS		
85 SCRAP SOLUTIONS			58 ALLOYS		
86 ALLOYS			59 STANDARDS		
87 STANDARDS			60 MISCELLANEOUS RESIDUES		
89 SCRAP ALLOYS			61 IRRADIATED METAL		
90 MISCELLANEOUS			62		
91			63		
92			64		
93			65 TOTAL - RESEARCH & DEVELOPMENT		
94 TOTAL - RESEARCH & DEVELOPMENT			IRRADIATED		
REMARKS:			103 IN REACTORS		
			104 COOLING		
			105 SEPARATION		
			106		
			107 TOTAL - IRRADIATED		
			PREPARED BY: LOCATION PHONE		

FIG. 9-17 Composition of Ending Inventory.

(3) by maintaining piece-count and number verification of all manufactured elements (various internal records substantiated by the control group's over-all records).

9-7. MATERIAL BALANCE REPORT

Forms for recording the monthly inventory have been patterned as much as possible after the Monthly Balance Report that is submitted to the AEC Operations Office.

The Core Manufacturing Substation uses five major forms in submitting its inventory to the Central SS Group. Four of these are particularly applicable to the enriched-uranium inventory, of which the fuel elements make up a sizable proportion. These forms are the SS Material Ending Inventory (Fig. 9-16), the Composition of Ending Inventory (Fig. 9-17), the SS Material Expendability Report (Fig. 9-13), and the Summary of Material Balance (95% Confidence) Uncertainties (Fig. 9-18).

SUMMARY OF MATERIAL BALANCE (95% Confidence) UNCERTAINTIES

For_____, 195

Ending Inventory	±	grams
Transfers During the Month	±	"
Material Which Changed Form	±	"
TOTAL SUBSTATION UNCERTAINTY	± _____	grams

FIG. 9-18   Summary of Material Balance (95% Confidence) Uncertainties.

The ending inventory report is divided into two parts. The left side of the report lists greater than 75 percent enriched uranium, broken down first by material form and then further subdivided by material type. The Core Manufacturing Substation Control Group obtains this information from a compilation of two reports. First, from the fuel alloy and filler plate production area, it summarizes the SS and U^{235} inventory by the breakdown listed on its inventory report. It then summarizes the piece count inventory of fuel plates, subassemblies, clusters, and miscellaneous materials from the other manufacturing areas, converts this into SS and U^{235} values, combines applicable figures with those from the fuel-alloy and filler-plate production area, and completes the left side of the report.

The material types on this report are listed as either analyzed or estimated. All material that was analyzed by the chemical and isotopic laboratories is listed in the analyzed section. Material whose weight was calculated using percentage weight composition or material that was analyzed by external SS stations is listed as estimated. In the event this material remains on the Core

Manufacturing Substation's inventory until it is analyzed, it is transferred to the analyzed column on the ensuing inventory report. An SS and U^{235} uncertainty column is also included for each material type. The SS uncertainty for material of each type is obtained from an "uncertainties graph" on which is plotted uncertainty in grams of SS material versus quantity of material by material type. The U^{235} uncertainty is obtained similarly from another graph. The right section of this report, i.e. quota (by project) breakdown, is easily obtainable from the journal totals. The totals of both sections should be equal.

The Composition of Ending Inventory form is an exact duplicate of the form submitted by the SS station as part of its Monthly Balance Report. The information necessary to complete the greater than 75 percent enriched uranium section is obtained by the Core Manufacturing Substation Control Group from the inventories submitted by the various internal areas.

Every type of B-PID is reported in the expendability report. In the Core Manufacturing Substation all losses of enriched uranium occur in the fuel alloy and filler plate production area. Every effort is made to keep these to a minimum by such means as obtaining analyzed values for all measurable scrap material; maintaining strict outlets for all possibly recoverable material, especially solutions; and adopting acceptable techniques for estimating SS amounts in such materials as filters and contaminated scrap jacketing material. However, normal operating losses do occur from machining, shearing, etc. These losses are very small. Most entries made in the expendability report are the result of account differences. These account differences occur whenever a change is made from the use of values based on nominal percentages to values based on chemically analyzed percentages. By nominal percentage is meant the uranium percentage that fuel alloy production is trying to achieve. If, for example, uranium alloy ingots were reported with values based on calculated percentage weight composition on one month's inventory and then during the next month these ingots were fabricated into fillers and chemical analysis data were obtained, the project carrying this material would show either a positive or a negative account difference, depending on whether the analyzed percentages were higher or lower than nominal.

The last sheet submitted by the Core Manufacturing Substation Control Group is the Summary of Material Balance (95% Confidence) Uncertainties. This report lists and combines the two sigma uncertainties for the substation's ending inventory, transfers during the month, and material that changed form into a total uncertainty for that particular month.

Once the information is collected, it is incorporated into a monthly inventory report, three copies of which are prepared. The original is sent to the Central SS Group, the second copy is sent to Industrial Hygiene Department, and the third copy is retained in the Substation Control Group's files. The copy sent to the Industrial Hygiene Department at their request is used in conjunction with the over-all criticality-control program. Since each substation submits a copy of its monthly inventory report to Industrial Hygiene Department criticality personnel, a plant-wide distribution of enriched uranium can be ascertained and controlled. The original copy of the report is received at the Central SS Group, where it is checked against central records. Any discrepancies that occur are immediately reconciled. This report is combined with the sixteen others received from the various substations into a Station Monthly Balance Report.

9-8. CHARTING BOOK-PHYSICAL INVENTORY DIFFERENCES

One of the important means of maintaining a check on the material-control effort of the substations is through the figure reported by each substation each month for its B-PID.

A chart is maintained by the Central SS Group of the cumulative B-PID's reported by each substation plotted against time. Inspection of these charts readily reveals trends, and the charts have thus proved useful in assessing substation performance.

Frequently, however, B-PID's have been reported by the substation which have raised a question as to their acceptability. The first method contemplated as a basis for assessing the B-PID's was that of establishing control limits by accepted quality control procedures. For this to be done effectively, however, it is necessary to select a period of operation in which the variable to be controlled varied within acceptable limits. These limits are not easily determined because of lack of an accepted basis for comparison. Since B-PID's are obtained by comparing substation records and inventory results, and since it could be assumed that the substation records were accurately kept because of the double-entry bookkeeping system employed, the most likely explanation of the B-PID's lies in the manner in which the inventory quantities were determined or in the uncertainties of the uranium content of the removals from the substation.

In the operation of the Core Manufacturing Substation and in particular the fuel alloy and filler plate area where the B-PID's for that substation originate, the material transferred out of the area in the form of filler plates is carefully controlled; the other material leaving the area is mainly in the form of reclaimable scrap. It was recalled that the findings of the reclamation facility did not always agree with the shipper's figures. An investigation was made to determine whether there was a correlation between shipper-receiver differences for scrap shipments and B-PID's reported by the Core Manufacturing Substation. This investigation has shown that the shipper-receiver differences balance out the B-PID's for the period from start of operations until the present; however, this is not considered to be conclusive evidence that the full explanation of the B-PID's has been found.

Chapter 10

PLUTONIUM FABRICATION *

10-1. INTRODUCTION

The element plutonium does not occur naturally to any practical extent. It is produced artificially in nuclear reactors from neutron capture by the naturally occurring U^{238} isotope (see Sec. 13-1).

Ordinarily plutonium is chemically separated from uranium and decontaminated from fission products by the Purex process[1] (tri-n-butyl phosphate solvent extraction). It is then concentrated by ion exchange methods into a purified nitrate solution containing up to 400 gm of plutonium per liter. Additional processing yields an anhydrous halide salt, which is thermally reduced to metal by alkaline-earth metals.

Plutonium is a hazardous material to work with. If ingested, it lodges in the bone where its 5.2 Mev alpha particles seriously damage marrow. In addition, the consequences of assembling enough plutonium under the proper conditions of geometry and moderation to produce a self-sustaining chain reaction are severe: lethal doses of neutron and gamma radiations are produced. Consequently special precautions are taken to protect the health and safety of personnel.

The principal merit of plutonium is its ability to maintain a chain reaction, under proper conditions, thereby releasing a considerable amount of useful energy. It shows promise for use in both slow reactors (utilizing thermal neutrons) and fast reactors (utilizing epithermal neutrons). Thus its fabrication into reactor fuel components is of interest.

10-2. PROCESS METHODS

Finished plutonium reactor fuel elements are produced by three main operations—metal fabrication, metal production, and salvage or recovery, as well as

* W. J. Maraman, University of California, Los Alamos Scientific Laboratory, Los Alamos, New Mexico. The author acknowledges the contributions and assistance of R. D. Baker, W. D. McNeese, P. J. Peterson, A. N. Morgan, Jr., J. W. Anderson, J. A. Leary, and R. L. Thomas, all of whom contributed substantially to the preparation of this chapter.

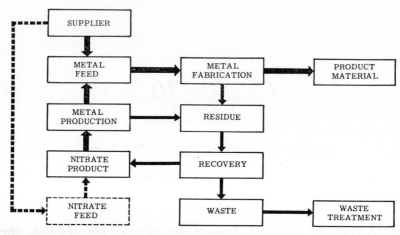

Fig. 10-1 Flow sheet for plutonium processing. The dashed lines represent the alternative plutonium nitrate feed from a supplier.

attendant waste treatment and disposal operations. A process flow diagram is shown in Fig. 10-1, and some physical properties of the element are given in Table 10.1. Owing to the present state of technological development and because of certain criticality limitations, plutonium is processed on a batch basis.

TABLE 10.1. SOME PHYSICAL PROPERTIES OF PLUTONIUM[2]

Phase	Stability Range, °C	Structure	Density, gm/cm^3	Coefficient of Thermal Expansion per °C × 10^6
Alpha	<122	Monoclinic	19.7 (25°C)	51
Beta	122-206	Unknown	17.6 (150°C)	38
Gamma	206-319	Face-centered orthorhombic	17.2 (210°C)	35
Delta	319-451	Face-centered cubic	15.9 (320°C)	−10[a]
Delta prime	451-476	Body-centered tetragonal	16.0 (465°C)	−120[a]
Epsilon	476-640	Body-centered cubic	16.5 (500°C)	26

[a] The negative coefficient of thermal expansion of the delta and delta prime phases, as well as the contraction during solidification, presents problems in metal fabrication.

The metal-fabrication facility converts metal feed from a supplier and from the metal-production unit into the finished product through a series of casting and machining stages. The recovery operation reclaims the plutonium from the scrap produced by the fabrication and production units and converts it into a purified plutonium nitrate solution. The metal-production unit transforms plutonium nitrate from the recovery operation into metal through a series of chemical processes. An alternate feed from a supplier, plutonium nitrate, is also processed in this unit. Waste treatment reduces the plutonium content in waste streams to a safe level for discharge into ground or surface water and yields a plutonium-contaminated sludge for storage or disposal.

Plutonium transfers are executed by product transfer receipts on which are entered the lot identification number, the amount of material, and the signatures of the originator and the recipient. The receipts enable SS-control records to be maintained.

Feed material into, as well as product material from, the metal-fabrication and -production units is measured. Residues, which are diverted to the recovery operation, are assigned by-difference values based on the feed and product material. These residues are evaluated as soon as practicable in the chemical processing steps. Evaluation requires dissolution of the residues so that a homogeneous system can be sampled and analyzed. Since only about 2 percent of the metal production feed and 3 percent of the metal-fabrication throughput is diverted to recovery, individually received lots are not evaluated separately. Statistical variations in sampling and analyses and a considerable expenditure of analytical and processing time require that large composited lots of residues be handled. Consequently a time period or a quantity throughput is selected as a basis for evaluation. At the end of such a period, called a "receipt area," all residues are removed from the enclosures of the operation being studied and are evaluated in a separate block. An operation of this type does not preclude the evaluation and recovery of residues in a current receipt area.

The time lag between receipt areas is determined primarily by the economics of processing, but this time should not be long enough to allow a loss of control to go undetected for any extended period. Short time lapses further assure better over-all processing conditions and can frequently assist in determining operational difficulties in the primary operation.

10-3. METAL FABRICATION

The metal-fabrication facility converts plutonium-metal buttons into an inspected reactor component. A typical flow sheet is shown in Fig. 10-2. Basically the process consists in casting the metal into an ingot, machining the ingot into the final shape, and canning it to protect the surface from oxidation. In subsequent handling operations, the canning prevents leakage of plutonium to the surrounding area. Inspection stations are required to obtain density and dimensional measurements and to take samples for analysis. Although plutonium can be formed by many conventional fabrication methods, the flow sheet in Fig. 10-2 was selected for simplicity. Similar material management procedures would apply to other methods.

10-3.1. Storage. Plutonium-metal feed from a supplier and from the metal production unit is stored in sealed containers inside "bird cages"—metal cans supported by angle iron in a cubical framework. The outside dimension of the cube is 20 in., allowing the storage of 4.5 kg of plutonium in each bird cage. Filled bird cages can be stacked in a cubical array and will satisfy both requirements for criticality safety; namely, 4.5 kg maximum in a single lot and a spatial density of 1 kg/cu ft. The storage site is so constructed that water flooding is impossible, and other reflector materials are not permitted inside the space.

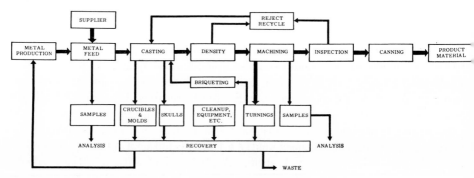

FIG. 10-2   Metal-fabrication flow sheet.

The storage of plutonium metal is further complicated by self-heating due to the absorption of the energy of emitted alpha particles. The equilibrium temperature of 4.5 kg of bare metal in moderately static air is about 50°C; consequently metal is stored in containers having good thermal conductivity properties. Direct cooling of the storage site is not required; however, the site is located so as to prevent abnormally high temperatures. Sufficient cooling is achieved from the health-safety ventilation requirement of 10 room-air changes each hour.

The as-received bird cages are surface monitored for alpha contamination as well as for gamma emission. The storage site is periodically surface monitored and surveyed for gamma emission, and the room air is sampled for airborne contamination. Removed bird cages are also monitored.

Long-term storage of plutonium leads to two problems. First, the continuing growth of Am^{241} makes the material increasingly gamma active. Second, the emitted alpha particles from both americium and plutonium become helium atoms; this results in a build-up of pressure inside the sealed container. The production rate of helium is about 0.3 micromole per day for each kilogram of plutonium.

10-3.2. Evaluation of Feed Material. For an evaluation of the quantity of plutonium received, the sealed container inside the bird cage is brought into the metal-fabrication facility and then opened. Surface oxidation on the metal not only complicates the evaluation of the metal from a material-management viewpoint, but, if it contains suboxides (or hydrides), the material becomes extremely pyrophoric.

The evaluation of plutonium metal feed material is accomplished by weight, density, chemical analysis, and neutron-emission rate measurements. All metal feed must be weighed in order to prepare casting lots. Density is obtained by weighing the metal in air and then in an inert liquid such as bromobenzene. The material is sampled by core drilling with a drill press, and the plutonium content, as well as metal impurities, is determined by chemical analysis. The neutron-emission rate of a certain geometry is directly obtained. This measurement indicates the Pu^{240} content of the feed material.

Statistical analysis of the above data yields a complete evaluation of the quality and quantity of the feed material.

10-3.3. Casting. Plutonium metal is cast into ingots by vacuum melting in a ceramic crucible and pouring into a mold. A typical casting setup[3] is shown in Fig. 10-3. The casting furnace contains a vacuum furnace can

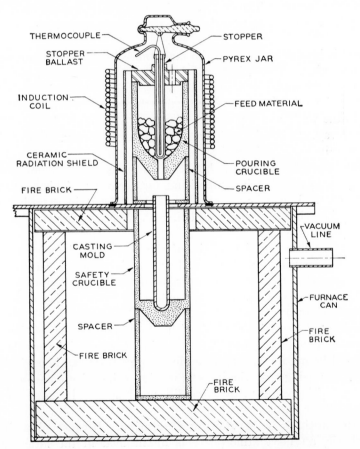

FIG. 10-3 Mold and crucible for plutonium-metal casting.

(attached to the enclosure floor) which support a Pyrex bell jar. The mold is located in the furnace can, and the pouring crucible is in the bell jar. The pouring crucible is a cylindrical magnesia crucible with a funnel-shaped bottom. The metal is melted in the crucible and is poured by means of a hollow stopper rod that can be pulled by rotating a drum above it. The drum and rod are connected by a wire. The crucible is supported by a ceramic spacer above the furnace can, and the mold is supported from the bottom of the furnace can and is surrounded by a safety crucible.

After the feed material has been loaded, the unit is assembled, evacuated, and outgassed to a pressure of less than 1 μ. The power to the induction coil surrounding the bell jar is turned on. When the appropriate casting temperature has been reached, as indicated by the thermometer inside the hollow stopper rod, the rod is pulled, and the melt flows into the mold. During the heating cycle a vacuum of less than 10 μ is maintained in the system.

After the melt has been poured, the power is turned off, and helium is admitted into the system. The equipment is dismantled, and the mold and ingot are removed. Dismantling must be done at an assembly temperature of below 75°C because of the danger of combustion.

The mold is broken away from the ingot, and the fragments are sent to the recovery operation. The weight and density of the ingot are determined. In certain cases split metal molds can be re-used many times before being sent to recovery. The pouring crucible contains the "skull" (a thin layer of metal adhering to the wall) and a permeated layer of plutonium dioxide. The skull is peeled away, weighed, and transferred to recovery. Since the skull contains certain metallic impurities and oxides, the weight serves only as an approximate plutonium measure, but it is useful as an approximate check on the casting cycle and batch compositing for recovery. This casting loss is about 3 percent. It can be materially reduced in certain cases by remelting the skulls and casting them into usable ingots. The pouring crucible is usable for about 20 casting cycles.

The difference between the weight of the casting feed and ingot product is assigned to the residues. The skull weight is then subtracted from this difference, the value (less than 0.1 percent of feed) being approximately the plutonium content of the crucible fragments. This number is useful for batch compositing in recovery.

Certain elements can be alloyed with plutonium in the casting step by slight procedural modifications. The plutonium content of the cast ingot must be determined before the appropriate plutonium values can be assigned to the residues. After being cast, the ingot is machined in a dry box to dimensional specifications. Plutonium metal is readily machined, and tolerances achieved are similar to those for other metals.

10-3.4. Precautions in Machining Operation. Because plutonium chips are pyrophoric, an inert atmosphere is maintained in the lathe or milling machine enclosure (see Fig. 10-4). The inert gas inlet can be attached to the tool piece, and the gas can be directed onto the tool bit. This procedure not only cools the piece but also assures the presence of inert gas where it is most needed. Lubrication is achieved with carbon tetrachloride, which subsequently evaporates. The enclosure exhaust duct contains the inert-gas detection device, and machining is not started until the inert-gas content is at least 30 percent. Since the ventilation rate is materially reduced to conserve inert gas during machining, an automatic bypass line on the exhaust system

Fig. 10-4 Hooded enclosure for controling contamination and maintaining an inert atmosphere during the machining of plutonium metal.

allows the enclosure to exhaust an additional amount when the enclosure tends to become pressurized during glove insertions.

Chips and turnings are constantly removed from beneath the piece and are packaged in tared metal containers. This eliminates the possibility of a single burning chip's igniting a large quantity of plutonium. If a burning chip should fall from the tool bit, it can be readily extinguished by smothering it with a massive piece of brass. A maximum of 1 kg of plutonium turnings is stored in a container. The enclosure floor and the machine surfaces are kept clean at all times.

The final machined piece is weighed, and its density is determined. If the machine turnings are not allowed to oxidize, material control is readily achieved by weights. A small amount of plutonium is obtained in the form of enclosure sweepings, which are weighed and transferred to recovery. The machining chips that are not oxidized can be cast into usable ingots for direct recycle. These turnings can also be recycled through the recovery operation.

Ordinarily one or more of the chips from the finishing cut is weighed for transfer for sample chemical analysis. The analysis is considered to be typical of that of the finished piece. Homogeneity can be determined from separate analyses of top and bottom samples as well as from those obtained intermediately. A sample is also submitted for isotopic analysis or for neutron emission level.

10-3.5. Canning. The machined piece is canned in a metal container—e.g., one made of copper, nickel, or tantalum. The piece, which has been dimensionally inspected and stored in a vacuum chamber over a desiccant, is inserted into the container. Extreme care is necessary to prevent the outside of the can from becoming contaminated. A lid is then either soldered or welded on the container. The canned assembly is dimensionally inspected and weighed, and its density is determined. It is also radiographed. From these and the machining measurements, the assembly is accepted or rejected.

10-3.6. Reject Recycle. Any piece not meeting specifications because of dimensions can be recycled through the casting operations. Pieces not meeting specifications because of low density normally contain excessive amounts of impurities; these must be processed through recovery.

10-3.7. Other Metal-Fabrication Side Streams. In addition to the rich residues, many lean residues are sent to recovery. These include cleanup rags, internal-enclosure filters, tools, gloves, containers used in intermediate storage and transfers, discarded equipment, and bromobenzene. Ordinarily, at the end of a receipt area the enclosures and their contents are thoroughly vacuum cleaned and wiped off. These filter bags and rags, like all residues, are transferred to recovery. Values assigned are determined by difference similar to the residues discussed in Sec. 10-3.3. Some plutonium is entrained in the enclosure air, which is continually monitored. The data are evaluated, and the plutonium content is written off inventory as a measured loss. Vacuum-pump oil and circulating water are also measured for plutonium content.

10-4. METAL PRODUCTION

The metal-production line produces plutonium metal from plutonium nitrate feed solution obtained from a supplier or from the recovery operation. A typical flow sheet[4] is shown in Fig. 10-5. Plutonium peroxide is precipitated from the nitrate and converted to plutonium tetrafluoride by anhydrous hydrogen fluoride. Calcium and iodine are mixed with the fluoride powder; the mixture is placed in a ceramic crucible, which is sealed in a steel pressure

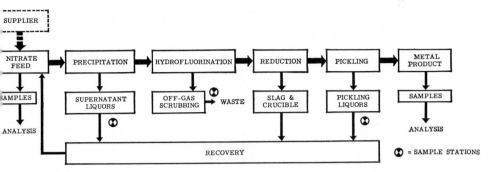

FIG. 10-5   Metal-production flow sheet.

chamber and is fired by induction heating.   The resulting metal button is separated from the slag and crucible and is pickled in dilute nitric acid, washed, dried, and weighed.   The operation is conducted remotely in the metal-production facility.   Fig. 10-6 is a view of the operating area.

10-4.1. Feed Material.   The plutonium nitrate feed material is received from the recovery operation and from outside suppliers in 350-gm lots in stainless steel or plastic bottles or in 1500-gm lots in a geometrically safe 6-in.-

FIG. 10-6   Plutonium-metal production line.   Operations are carried out in the dry boxes in the background remotely by manipulation of controls on consoles.

diameter stainless steel container. The plutonium concentration ranges from 100 to 450 gm/liter. The containers are stored in a critically safe configuration. The storage problem is complicated by the generation of helium from alpha particles and by the decomposition of water through the action of the emitted nuclear particles inside the solution. Accumulated gas is vented at the time of use, rather than during storage, to prevent escape of plutonium from the container. Plastic bottles with blowout vent plugs are adequate for short-time storage containers; pressure vessels of stainless steel are required for long storage.

The nitrate solution is homogenized by agitation and sampled for chemical analysis. In addition to the plutonium assay, iron and acidity determinations are made for process control. The weight measurements of the nitrate container before and after emptying, plus results from the solution analysis, provide the data necessary for determination of net plutonium content. Solids in the feed material can cause a biased analysis to be reported; consequently the feed is filtered through a fritted glass filter of medium porosity before being loaded into the container. If the plutonium content differs from the supplier's value by more than 1 percent or 5 percent for recovery lots, the contents are resampled after agitation.

10-4.2. Peroxide Precipitation. The plutonium nitrate feed material is vacuum transferred into the precipitation vessel, which is geometrically safe or batch safe. The container is thoroughly rinsed into the precipitation vessel, the dilute acid rinse water serving to adjust the plutonium concentration to the proper value. The contents of the vessel are cooled to 0°C, and 30 percent hydrogen peroxide is added slowly enough to maintain the temperature at less than 5°C. When precipitation has been completed, the slurry is filtered, and the precipitate is washed and dried. The filtrate, which contains excess peroxide, is collected in a receiver to which concentrated caustic had previously been added. The peroxide is continuously destroyed, and the plutonium in the filtrate is precipitated as the hydroxide. This slurry is made acidic, cooled, agitated, sampled, and transferred to recovery.

The only side stream from the peroxide precipitation process is the filtrate, which contains about 1 percent of feed plutonium. The filtrate is relatively dilute (0.1 gm/liter) in plutonium and is assayed by radioanalysis. Since the americium present in the feed is quantitatively transferred into the filtrate, an americium correction is made. The specific activity of the plutonium in the filtrate must be determined to correct the radiochemical analysis. From these data the appropriate amount of plutonium to be charged to recovery, as well as the amount to be charged into the hydrofluorination process, can be determined.

10-4.3. Hydrofluorination. The dried plutonium peroxide cake is transferred to a hydrofluorination furnace. The material is heated, and anhydrous hydrogen fluoride is admitted through the cake; the inlet gas also contains oxygen to assure conversion to plutonium tetrafluoride. After reacting at 600°C for 3 hours, the fluoride powder is removed and allowed to cool to room temperature. Excess hydrogen fluoride in the off-gas stream is absorbed in a tower of aqueous caustic. The caustic serves as a seal liquid for a vacuum pump, which maintains a slight negative pressure on the system so that any leak will leak into and not out of the unit. A hydrofluorination furnace and boat are shown in Fig. 10-7.

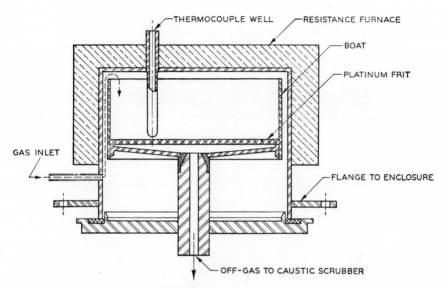

THERMOCOUPLE WELL   RESISTANCE FURNACE
BOAT
PLATINUM FRIT
GAS INLET
FLANGE TO ENCLOSURE
OFF-GAS TO CAUSTIC SCRUBBER

FIG. 10-7   Hydrofluorination furnace and boat.

The caustic absorbent is recirculated until it is spent to a pH of 11; then it is agitated and sampled for plutonium assay by radioanalysis. Since it contains a trivial amount of plutonium, it is transferred directly to the waste-treatment plant. The plutonium value of the peroxide cake is assigned to the fluoride powder.

10-4.4. Metal Reduction. The plutonium tetrafluoride powder is transferred into a mixing device, and calcium metal and iodine crystals are intimately mixed with it. An effort is made to exclude water vapor from the charged materials since a calcium-water reaction can cause a premature reduction reaction in the mixer. The mixer charge is transferred into a ceramic crucible pre-positioned in a steel pressure chamber; the annulus between the two is packed with ceramic fines. A metallic gasket is placed on the chamber, and the unit is sealed with a lid. The chamber is purged with argon and heated to 400°C by an induction heating coil around the unit. At this temperature the calcium-iodine booster reaction takes place, and the temperature inside the crucible rises sufficiently to cause the calcium–plutonium tetrafluoride reaction to occur. The unit is disassembled when it cools, the crucible is broken into fragments, and the slag is separated from the plutonium-metal button. Fig. 10-8 shows an example of a pressure chamber, crucible, and button.

The button is pickled in nitric acid to free it of any adhering slag and crucible material. After being rinsed with water and dried, the button is

FIG. 10-8   Pressure-chamber crucible and product from metal-reduction process.

weighed and sampled by core drilling with a drill press. Chemical analyses for plutonium and impurity concentrations, as well as a density determination, complete the necessary data requirements for complete evaluation. The button is then transferred to the metal-fabrication facility.

10-4.5. Reduction Residues. The combined button pickling and water rinse solutions are sampled for plutonium radiochemical analysis. Since this solution may contain solids, the assay value is reliable only if the solution has been filtered. However, only a small amount (less than 0.1 percent) of the charge is diverted, and the assay value serves as a process guide. The solution is transferred to recovery after it has been used to treat several buttons.

The slag and crucible combination is assigned the by-difference number between the fluoride charge and the button weight. Routine production diverts about 1 percent of the charge to these residues, which are composited along with the reduction-chamber gaskets into convenient batches for transfer to recovery. An abnormally low reduction yield may necessitate the dissolution and evaluation of the reduction residue for the particular batch.

10-4.6. Other Metal-Fabrication Residues. The steel reduction pressure chamber is occasionally pickled in hydrochloric acid. This pickling solution

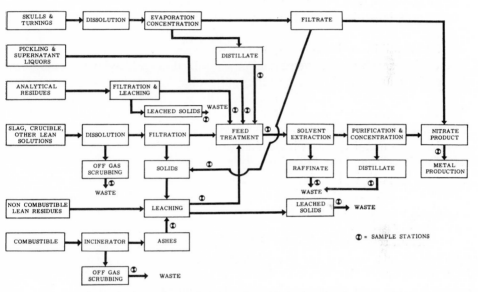

Fig. 10-9 Recovery-process flow sheet.

and other residues, such as cleanup rags, tools, ventilation filters, and dismantled equipment, are transferred to recovery. Ventilation air and coolant water are monitored for plutonium content.

10-4.7. Coreduction. Elements that form homogeneous alloys with plutonium can be added to the reduction charge in the metallic state (and in certain cases, as the fluoride) to produce a desired alloy.[5] The production of alloys by this method adds certain complications to the evaluation of the process in that the homogeneity of the produced button must be determined.

10-5. RECOVERY PROCESS

The recovery operation reclaims the plutonium in the residues produced by all processes and converts it into a nitrate solution suitable for feed to the metal-production line. A typical recovery flow sheet is shown in Fig. 10-9.

The operations required are metal dissolution, slag and crucible dissolution, solvent extraction, precipitation, incineration, and leaching.

10-5.1. Feed Materials. The categories of residues which are the feed to the recovery operation are:

1. Metal in the form of skulls, turnings, samples, and dry-box sweepings from metal-processing operations.

2. Peroxide filtrate and button pickling solutions.

3. Analytical wastes.

4. Slag and crucible from metal reduction and crucibles from casting.

5. Noncombustible lean residues such as tools, filters, and dismantled equipment.

6. Combustibles such as cleanup rags.

Since the exact value of the plutonium contained in each residue is unknown, the residues are stored on a by-difference value assigned to various receipt areas. These lots are stored chronologically according to type and source. The common transfer procedure for removing solid residues from an operation involves packaging them in sealed plastic bags. The plastic bags are accumulated in metal drums with tight sealing lids. This storage method not only facilitates handling but also serves as fire protection. Liquid residues are normally packaged in plastic or metal containers surrounded by a secondary metal container. Blow-out plugs are attached to the primary containers. The secondary container for both solids and liquids can further serve as a spacer for criticality safety.

Americium segregates with the richer plutonium residues, particularly with peroxide filtrate and casting crucibles, and is usually in sufficient amounts to be a gamma-radiation hazard. The slag and crucible are not only gamma active but are also a neutron hazard. Consequently these residues are not stored in the immediate proximity of operating personnel.

When the residues are processed, receipt areas are kept segregated, and the plutonium recovered is credited to the proper receipt area from which it originated and is debited to the current receipt area in which the recovery operation is working. It is often desirable to receive residues from several receipt areas into the recovery operation to eliminate storage of immediately recoverable material, i.e. material which fits into a particular recovery scheme without additional treatment. When this occurs, residues from different receipt areas are evaluated separately. Examples of such residues are peroxide supernatant, unused portions of metal samples from chemical analysis, and certain other analytical wastes.

The recovery operation must be checked by periodically having a thorough cleanup and inventory at the end of its receipt area. All materials on hand are evaluated, and appropriate material-control balances are struck.

10-5.2. Metal Dissolution. Plutonium skulls and other metal residues are weighed on a triple-beam balance into nominal 360-gm lots. The material is dissolved by refluxing in a mixture of nitric and hydrofluoric acids.   The lot is concentrated by distillation, and the product filtered.   After being diluted, the batch is transferred to metal production.

The residue is weighed after vacuum drying on the filter, and the feed minus residue weight is tentatively assigned as the plutonium content of the product. The metal-production group samples the solution, and, if the assay differs from the by-difference value by more than 5 percent, the lot is sampled again. The feed weight serves as a qualitative check on the value received from the metal-fabrication facility.

Solids resulting from routine dissolution are accumulated into separate lots and are processed by repeated treatment with fresh acid.   The final residue is transferred into the lean residues account (for example, incinerator ash from other recovery operations) for further leaching and ultimate discard.   The distillate from evaporations is composited, agitated, sampled for radioanalysis, and transferred to other recovery operations where the nitric acid content can be utilized.

The plutonium loss from this main recovery scheme is less than 1 percent, the amount depending on the completeness of leaching to which the dissolver solids are subjected.

10-5.3. Slag and Crucible Recovery.   Slag and crucible, as well as reduction pressure chamber gaskets and button-pickling solution, are charged into steam-jacketed reactors.   The by-difference plutonium value assigned to the residues charged in each batch must be critically safe.   These residues are dissolved by refluxing with nitric acid and aluminum nitrate.   The dissolution procedure leaves a small heel in the dissolver, which remains nearly constant from batch to batch.   This heel must be dissolved at the end of a receipt-area evaluation.

The iodine, which is liberated from the slag upon dissolution, is sparged into aqueous caustic.   The spent caustic is agitated, sampled for radioanalysis, and discarded.   Plutonium discarded in this manner is less than 0.01 percent of the total charged to production, and the amount is credited to the feed-storage inventory.

The dissolver solution is filtered, and the filtrate is agitated and sampled for radioanalysis.   Because this measurement serves both as a credit to the feed storage and as a debit to the recovery account, an americium and plutonium specific-activity correction is made on the analysis.

The removed solids are acid leached in the dissolvers, and the leach solution is filtered and combined with the filtered dissolver solution.   The residual solids are hydrofluorinated for silica removal, and the residues from this treatment are further leached before being combined with lean residues from other recovery processes.   The hydrofluorination off-gas is treated with caustic in a manner similar to that in metal production.   The plutonium diverted in this caustic is trivial; however, it is credited to the feed storage account.   The diversion of plutonium from the main recovery stream is normally less than 1 percent, but the amount depends on the degree of leaching that the residual solids receive.

The filtered and analyzed dissolver solution, having an approximate plutonium concentration of 0.5 gm/liter, is contacted with 35 vol. % tri-n-butyl phosphate (TBP) in an inert diluent. The plutonium is quantitatively extracted into the solvent in appropriate solvent-extraction equipment. The raffinate is analyzed for plutonium content and transferred to the waste-treatment plant. Under extraction conditions for plutonium transfer, the americium originally present in the feed remains in the raffinate; consequently a major correction to the raffinate radioanalysis value is required. Diversion of plutonium to the raffinate is less than 0.1 percent.

The enriched solvent is contacted with dilute acid, which strips the plutonium from the solvent. The solvent, which suffers a certain amount of radiation damage, is periodically treated with caustic to remove the hydrolysis products formed. This caustic is sampled for its plutonium content and is transferred to the waste-treatment plant.

The aqueous product from solvent stripping is concentrated by distillation. The distillate, which contains a negligible amount of plutonium, is sampled for radioanalysis and transferred to the waste-treatment plant.

The evaporator bottoms are again solvent extracted with TBP for additional purification. The raffinate and solvent treating solution are recycled through the feed stream, where the solvent is stripped with a dilute acid solution containing a reducing agent. The aqueous product is treated with oxalic acid, which precipitates plutonium trioxalate. The slurry is filtered, and the filtrate is recycled through the evaporators. The oxalate crystals are ignited in air to plutonium dioxide at 250°C. The plutonium dioxide is weighed on a triple-beam balance, and this weight, after being corrected by the gravimetric factor, becomes the tentative plutonium value of the batch. After being combined into 350-gm batches, the dioxide is dissolved by the procedure previously described for metal. The nitrate product is filtered, diluted, and transferred to the metal production. The distillate is recycled through the evaporators. The raffinate, solvent treating solution, oxalate filtrate, and distillate are occasionally analyzed for process evaluation. The plutonium holdup in these recycle streams is not significant.

10-5.4. Other Residue Recovery. Casting crucibles from the metal-fabrication facility are processed in a manner similar to that used for the slag and crucible material. Certain obvious steps are omitted.

Peroxide filtrates are combined and analyzed and, after concentration by evaporation, are added to the slag and crucible dissolver solution.

Aqueous analytical wastes are combined, analyzed, and added to the dissolver solution. Solid residues are leached to discard level. The leach solution is analyzed and combined with the dissolver solution.

Combustible material is burned in an enclosed incinerator. The off-gases are filtered and scrubbed in aqueous caustic in a manner similar to the hydro-fluorination furnace off-gas in the metal-production facility. The small amount of plutonium deposited on the filter is removed by leaching. The caustic, which contains a negligible amount of plutonium, is sampled and trans-ferred to the waste-treatment plant. The residual ash is leached with a mix-ture of nitric and hydrofluoric acid by a process similar to metal dissolution. The leached ash, which is combined with other lean plutonium residues, is further leached until the plutonium content reaches a level where additional treatment is uneconomical. The residue is dried, sampled by quartering, and is then ready for disposal. The sample is dissolved by a potassium fluoride–pyrosulfate fusion for radioanalysis. The ash leach solutions are sampled and combined with the slag and crucible dissolver solution. In certain cases the usual americium and plutonium specific-activity correction must be applied to obtain the proper plutonium content for transfer.

Noncombustible materials, such as tools, filters, and dismantled equipment which contain plutonium surface contamination, are leached in a bath at room temperature with nitric-hydrofluoric acid. The acid-leached residues are water washed and discarded. The leach solutions are combined, analyzed, and transferred to the slag and crucible dissolver solution.

FIG. 10-10 View of special recovery dry box area. Note plastic bag in-stalled in left foreground for collection of residues to be stored or discarded.

The processing of recovery residues requires highly specialized equipment such as steam-jacketed reactors, multistage solvent contactors, and incinerators. A liberal amount of enclosed work space is required for handling the wide variety of residues. Such an enclosure is shown in Fig. 10-10.

10-6. WASTE DISPOSAL

All waste streams from a plutonium-processing plant must be analyzed before discharge into the surroundings in accordance with health and safety requirements. The only exceptions are the enclosure and operating ventilation air streams. Although monitoring these gives after-the-fact data, adequate filtration prevents the discharge of harmful amounts of plutonium. The processing wastes that must be treated include caustic from off-gas scrubbers, raffinate from TBP solvent extraction, acidic distillate, steam condensate from reactors, and miscellaneous process water from overflows in coolant water systems and sinks and drains. Solids that must be handled are trash from the operating area, mildly contaminated equipment and material, and residues from the recovery operation.

10-6.1. Ventilation Air. Ventilation air is filtered through successive banks of ultrafilters before it is discharged into tall stacks. Operating-area air is given moderate filtration before discharge through tall stacks. As has been mentioned, data from monitoring instruments provide the basis for inventory write off of the contained plutonium.

10-6.2. Processing Wastes.[6] The caustic wastes are combined with the raffinates and adjusted to a pH of 9. Calcium chloride and a filter aid are added. The slurry is filtered, and the precipitate is buried in sealed steel drums. This procedure coprecipitates the plutonium as the hydroxide, along with the iron present in the solution, and precipitates calcium fluoride, leaving the supernatant liquor free of these contaminants. Other wastes are treated with iron and lime to a pH of 11. The slurry is filtered, and the precipitate is buried in sealed steel drums. The iron flocculation frees the solution of plutonium. The residual nitrate ion in the filtrates may or may not be important. Process-waste streams are sampled continuously as they are received into holding tanks. Analysis of the combined sample serves as an additional process control. The treated effluent streams are also analyzed for plutonium before discharge.

10-6.3. Trash. The trash accumulated in the processing area can be buried directly or incinerated and the residue buried in steel drums. Contaminated equipment and processing residues can be buried in minimal containers or in steel drums.

Gamma and neutron detectors serve as monitors on solid residues to determine if a significant amount of plutonium is being discarded inadvertently.

10-7. PLUTONIUM MATERIAL BALANCE

Material balances are achieved through analytical methods that include plutonium-metal weights and chemical and radiochemical analyses of solutions. Volumetric measurements and representative sampling are equally important in determining accurate data. The accounting system that accumulates the data is extensively treated in Chapter 18; hence it will be referred to only briefly in the following sections.

10-7.1. Critical Measurements. Plutonium metal is weighed to 0.01 gm on analytical balances of appropriate capacity. The balances are periodically standardized. Metal transferred between different operations is weighed twice; once by the shipping area and again by the receiving area. This serves as a check on each balance employed.

Volumes of plutonium solution require accurate determination. Weights of concentrated plutonium solutions are converted to volume by specific gravity measurements. The over-all accuracies possible are to within 0.1 percent. Volumes of dilute plutonium solution are measured by calibrated manometers or sight gauges to accuracies within 1 percent. Manometer lines and sight gauges are kept clean by purging. Adequate agitation of solutions is required to ensure homogeneity for representative sampling; the high salt and nitric acid concentrations of the process solutions generally result in stratification that is difficult to disperse. Solutions are sampled by vacuum transfers out of purged dip tubes.

Chemical analysis of plutonium is performed by potentiometric titration of plutonium (III) to plutonium (IV) with ceric sulfate. The plutonium is reduced with zinc amalgam after conversion to the sulfate. The analyzed solutions must be relatively free of interfering ions; the primary impurity, iron, is determined colorimetrically, and its equivalent is subtracted from the ceric sulfate value. The standard deviation of the analysis is ±0.2 percent.[7]

The radiochemical procedure for plutonium consists in alpha counting a prepared plate containing 500 to 40,000 counts/min in a 2π-geometry counter. The counter background and the salt absorption of the specimen are subtracted from the raw data. Americium and Pu^{238} are determined by alpha-pulse analyses. Plots of Pu^{238} content variation with plutonium specific activity yield corrections for the plutonium content. The precision of the corrected analysis is ±1 percent.[7]

10-7.2. Assembly of Data. Product transfer receipts for plutonium are issued when measurements have been made. These receipts are the basis for entries in journals for subsequent ledger postings in standard accounting procedures. The metal-fabrication and metal-production records show the source, designation, and amount of incoming material and the recipient, designation, and amount of outgoing material. Simple records are maintained, since there are only three possible sources (a supplier, recovery, and metal production) and five possible recipients (customer, metal fabrication, recovery, analytical, and waste disposal).

Accounting records required by recovery are more complex, since these records must cope with receipt areas for various accounts. All areas require records showing batch locations for process control.

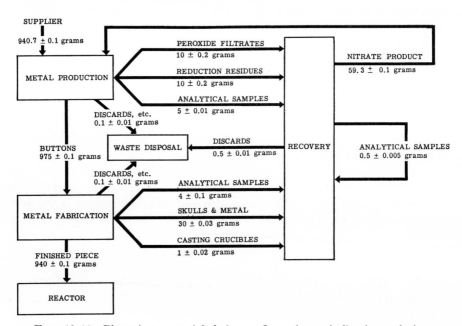

Fig. 10-11   Plutonium-material balance flow sheet, indicating relative quantities involved in important flows.

10-7.3. Inventories. A physical inventory of the metal fabrication facility can be taken without seriously disrupting processing. In general all items are counted and a statistical sample is chosen to determine the weight, density, chemical analysis, and neutron level. The by-difference value to recovery can be estimated and the in-process inventory proved.

A physical inventory of the metal production line is more difficult. The feed material is evaluated in a manner similar to that used in the metal fabrication facility. The in-process material is evaluated on the basis of product value after completion of the required chemical steps. The by-difference value to recovery is estimated. The feed material to the recovery operation cannot be determined until after dissolution. The recovery in-process inventory is determined by chemical analysis of the solutions on hand. Analytical reliability is substantiated by the submission of standardized samples under "blind" sample numbers.

Good housekeeping habits greatly facilitate the inventory and minimize errors of duplication and omission. The maintenance of good process records supports the control records and greatly assists reconciliations when necessary.

10-7.4. Material Balance Flow Sheet. The plutonium book-physical inventory difference and diversions to recovery and waste disposal depend on such factors as throughput and processing methods. A material balance flow sheet is shown in Fig. 10-11. The values indicated are somewhat idealized, assuming high-purity feed material and simple metal-fabrication operations that have highly efficient internal recycle. Recovery efficiency is largely dictated by the economic value of the plutonium as well as the health hazards involved in its disposal.

10-8. SUMMARY

Because of the high value of plutonium and its hazardous nature, careful material control is exercised over plutonium. Control over the major material flow in the fabrication of fuel elements is relatively simple. From the discussions it is readily apparent that the control revolves about the various residues generated in the process. A sizable effort is involved in the evaluation and recovery of these residues.

The discussion of the accounting system developed to implement control of materials has been brief. A discussion of our central control accounts is contained in Chapter 18, complementing the information in the foregoing sections.

REFERENCES FOR CHAPTER 10

1. E. R. IRISH and W. H. REAS, The Purex Process-A Solvent Extraction Reprocessing Method for Irradiated Uranium, in *Symposium on the Reprocessing of Irradiated Fuels, Held at Brussels, Belgium, May 20-25, 1957*, USAEC Report TID-7534 (Bk. 1), pp. 83-106, 1957.
2. A. S. COFFINBERRY and M. B. WALDRON, A Review of the Physical Metallurgy of Plutonium, in *Progress in Nuclear Energy*, Series V, Metallurgy and Fuels, Vol. 1, pp. 354-410, Pergamon Press, 1956.
3. J. W. ANDERSON and R. L. THOMAS, *A High-Vacuum Casting Furnace for Plutonium*, USAEC Report LA-1508, Los Alamos Scientific Laboratory, 1953.
4. A. N. MORGAN, R. D. BAKER, W. C. HAZEN, A. V. HENRICKSON, W. D. McNEESE, and R. L. THOMAS, *The Los Alamos Plant for Remotely Controlled Production of Plutonium Metal*, Second International Conference on the Peaceful Uses of Atomic Energy, Vol. 17, pp. 537-544, Geneva, 1958, A/CONF. 15/P/531.
5. A. N. MORGAN, *The Preparation of Plutonium Alloys in the Reduction Process*, USAEC Report LA-2231, Los Alamos Scientific Laboratory, 1958.
6. C. W. CHRISTENSON, Los Alamos Scientific Laboratory, personal communication.
7. C. F. METZ, The Analytical Chemistry of Plutonium, *Anal. Chem.*, 29:1748-1756 (December 1957).

SUGGESTED READING

G. I. SEABORG, J. J. KATZ, and W. M. MANNING (Eds.), *The Transuranium Elements: Research Papers*, National Nuclear Energy Series Division IV, Volume 14B, McGraw-Hill Book Company, Inc., New York, 1949.

W. H. LANGHAM, The Application of Excretion Analyses to the Determination of Body Burden of Radioactive Isotopes, *Amr. Ind. Hyg. Assoc. Quart.*, 17:305-318 (September 1956).

R. D. BARKER (Ed.), *General Handbook for Radiation Monitoring*, USAEC Report LA-1835, Los Alamos Scientific Laboratory, 1954.

A. D. CALLIHAN, W. J. OZEROFF, H. C. PAXTON, and C. L. SCHUSKE, *Nuclear Safety Guide*, USAEC Report TID-7016, Los Alamos Scientific Laboratory, 1958.

U. S. ATOMIC ENERGY COMMISSION, *Major Activities in the Atomic Energy Programs, January-June 1957*, pp. 42-43, U. S. Government Printing Office, Washington 25, D. C., July 1957.

Chapter 11

FABRICATION OF U²³³ *

The isotope U^{233}, known since about 1941, is a product of the neutron irradiation of thorium. Thorium-232, by way of an (n, γ) reaction, becomes Th^{233}; this decays by beta emission to Pa^{233} which in turn decays by beta emission to U^{233}. The Th^{233} and Pa^{233} have relatively short half-lives, rapidly producing U^{233}, an alpha emitter of about 1.62×10^5 years half-life.

The separation of U^{233} from the thorium and protactinium associated with it is accomplished by chemical means, usually by a solvent-extraction procedure.[1]

The chemistry and metallurgy of U^{233} are the same as for the other isotopes of uranium; thus no unique methods are employed except those required on account of radiation hazards. These methods are briefly discussed.

11-1. PROCESSING

Processing procedures make use of several valences of uranium. The most common state is the U^{+6}, usually as the uranyl ion, UO_2^{+2}, in such compounds as $UO_2(NO_3)_2$ or its hexahydrate form. The U^{+4} state is useful in such compounds as UO_2 and UF_4. Other apparent whole or fractional valences exist in various oxides and the peroxide. The compounds $UO_4 \cdot xH_2O$ and U_3O_8 are used in processing.

Uranium-233 appears as a silver-white metal in its pure form. The color gradually changes to black on oxidation. Normally, U^{233} has a density of about 18.7 and a melting point around 1133°C. It is amenable to a large number of ordinary metal-working operations such as casting, machining, rolling, extrusion, forging, swaging, drawing, and welding. Because of the ready tendency of the metal to burn to the oxide in air, inert gases and lubricants or coolants are used in most operations.

* J. A. Kircher, University of California Los Alamos Scientific Laboratory, Los Alamos, New Mexico. Acknowledgment is made of the assistance of the following personnel of the Los Alamos Scientific Laboratory in the preparation of this chapter: John W. Anderson for metal-fabrication procedures; A. L. Henicksman for analytical procedures; and W. J. Maraman.

Uranium-233 metal reacts with a wide range of reagents, but only a few of the reactions are useful in the purification of the metal. Most important is its reaction with nitric acid to form uranyl nitrate solutions, the starting point in many purification procedures. Massive metal is rather slow in dissolving in any concentration of acid, but chips formed as a result of machining dissolve readily in a wide range of HNO_3 concentrations, 5 M to 10 M being commonly used.

The slow dissolution of massive metal can be circumvented by conversion to an oxide, U_3O_8, which is readily soluble in nitric acid. Usually a temperature of 100 to 200°C in air is sufficient to start burning, and complete conversion to U_3O_8 can be accomplished by raising the mass to a higher temperature, usually 800°C, after the initial burning has subsided.

A third reaction is that with HF. Chips can be quantitatively converted to UF_4 with anhydrous HF under controlled conditions. This is not a purification process in the strict sense, since few impurities are volatilized; but when used in conjunction with other procedures, it can provide a partial purification.

Careful management of U^{233} is essential from three standpoints: health, criticality, and economics.

11-1.1. Health Aspects. Like other heavy metals, U^{233} is injurious if ingested. In addition, since it is a strong alpha emitter, minute quantities ingested can do serious damage to the biological system.

Although the alpha emission of U^{233} is of little concern externally, there is associated with it a small quantity of U^{232}. This isotope also decays by alpha emission, generating a decay chain of very strong gamma emitters. With time the gamma activity builds up and becomes a serious hazard. A 5-cm sphere containing 20 ppm U^{232} will have a surface activity greater than 90 r/hr at the end of a year.[2]

Ideally, all work should be done in remote-controlled shielded facilities, but this is not always possible. Therefore, for the safety of personnel, material control is a vital function.

11-1.2. Criticality. The second consideration requiring careful management of U^{233} is criticality, since U^{233} is capable of producing a critical reaction. Limits on the mass, volume, etc. are essential. The limiting data have been published.[3] Control over batch sizes and volumes is necessary to eliminate the possibility of building up potentially dangerous quantities.

11-1.3. Economics. The monetary value of U^{233} is also an important consideration. A purchase price has recently been established by the AEC [4] at $15 per gram of U^{233} as nitrate.

In connection with the valuation of the material, it might be well to give briefly the philosophy of measurement procedures. Sources of U^{233} batches fall into two categories, external and internal. Both, of necessity, are sampled. More rigorous sampling procedures are applied to the material from external sources to eliminate errors or even possible loss which may have been

involved as a result of shipment. This does not imply that lax methods are
employed on batches generated internally through processing operations. On
the contrary, sampling and analytical procedures are held at the highest possible levels consistent with the quantity and value of the material involved.
That is to say, batches known by experience to be rich in U²³³ have very precise methods applied, whereas batches known by experience to contain small
quantities are sometimes evaluated by use of reasonable estimates and somewhat less precise analytical methods. However, these smaller batches eventually form parts of a richer batch which must be used elsewhere, and here
the more precise methods again apply. In summary, the measurement procedures fit the quantity and value of the material.

11-2. MAJOR PROCESSES

Fig. 11-1 is a summary flow sheet of the process for the fabrication of U²³³
metal. The various stages and the management of the materials will be discussed in some detail.

It will be assumed that the product desired in this discussion consists of a
number of reactor fuel elements. The shape, size, and weight of these would

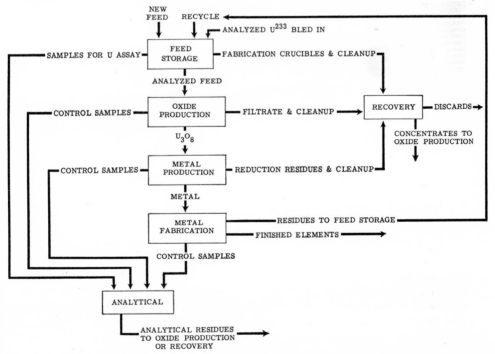

FIG. 11-1 General flow sheet, fabrication of U²³³.

depend on reactor design, but elements with a diameter of 1 in. and an over-all length of 4 in. would seem reasonable. The elements are enclosed in suitable aluminum cans 5 mils thick to contain fission products and prevent corrosion of the metal.

The process is broken down into categories to allow control of the U^{233} as it passes through several steps on its way to a fabricated fuel element. Each of these comes at a logical chemical break point which also provides an excellent SS control point. It is possible at these points to sample with comparative ease, and it is possible also at these points to remove material from the main stream if desirable or necessary. These operating areas are designated as feed storage, oxide production, metal production, metal fabrication, and recovery. Together these areas and processes make up a system capable of taking U^{233} as a nitrate solution, turning it out as a finished metal part, and completely recovering all the residues resulting from the operation.

11-3. FEED STORAGE

Consider first the feed storage area, Fig. 11-2. A number of U^{233} batches, each a nominal 250 gm of uranium in nitrate solution, may be received for conversion to metallic fuel elements. These will arrive from a shipper with

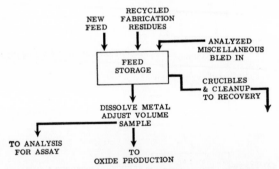

FIG. 11-2   Flow sheet of U^{233} feed storage.

the quantities of U^{233} contained indicated; however, policy requires that these solutions be evaluated. Or a quantity of U^{233} may have been recycled as a result of metal fabrication; it is desired to return this to metal fabrication in a usable form. The method by which a value was assigned to these residues again requires that they be evaluated. For this reason, both new feed material and recycle material from metal fabrication are given a type of intermediate status conveniently called "feed storage." Only after analytical evaluation is this U^{233} considered to have entered a processing area.

When the material is received, all pertinent data, such as quantity, enrichment, and number of containers, are recorded on a flow record. Also recorded is any other information that will help in the future to positively identify the batch or batches. Personnel handling this material make notations on the sheet as to when and how it was handled. This flow record ultimately shows the disposition of the batches as they enter a processing area.

The usual procedure is to divide the U²³³ from feed storage into nominal 250-gm batches. This may already have been done, as with new feed, or may require nitric acid dissolution of the appropriate quantity of metal from fabrication residues. In either case the resultant solution is quantitatively transferred to a volumetric flask of convenient size and adjusted to volume.

11-3.1. Feed-Storage Sampling. A volumetric pipet is used to withdraw a sample for SS-control purposes. There is room for some flexibility here. Duplicate samples are usually submitted on an individual basis; however, as a matter of expediency, composite samples are taken on occasion. This assumes equal volumes of sample from equal volumes of solution.

The samples are submitted to the analytical group, where the uranium content is determined by volumetric titration. In this procedure the nitrate is given several fuming treatments with concentrated sulfuric acid to convert it all to the sulfate form. The sulfate is passed through a Jones reductor (3 percent mercury on zinc) to yield a mixture of U^{+3} and U^{+4}; then it is air oxidized to U^{+4}. This solution is then titrated with ceric sulfate, using Ferroin as an indicator, and the uranium content is calculated.

When the analytical result has been received, the entire batch, including the samples, is charged to the oxide production area. The batch can be physically transferred as soon as samples are taken so that no delay will result in processing when the results become available.

11-3.2. Feed-Storage Residue. There are two minor residues or diversions that originate in feed storage owing to the practice of transferring relatively pure, readily dissolved residues to this account. The first of these consists of pouring crucibles, which are transferred together with attached skulls for recycle of the latter. These crucibles can be dissolved in nitric acid, evaluated, and transferred to recovery for solvent extraction of the uranium. The quantities of uranium involved are small, and their evaluation is discussed in Sec. 11-7.

The second minor residue consists of such rags as may be necessary to clean up the dry boxes after dissolution and sampling of skulls and other recycle residues. These combustibles are ashed, leached with nitric acid, evaluated, and transferred to recovery. This operation is also discussed in Sec. 11-7.

11-3.3. Feed Side Streams. It is possible to bleed other materials into the processing scheme, and these are usually entered into feed storage. In this case it is obviously necessary for the quantity being bled in to have been previously evaluated. An example of this might be a small quantity of metal or oxide remaining after analyses. These materials can be conveniently and accurately weighed, and the remainder of the batch can be made up from an approximate weight of impure metal. The analytical result for the sample will encompass the entire batch, and the exact contribution of the impure material can be determined by difference.

In this manner the entire amount of U^{233} in a particular feed storage area can be evaluated. The sampled batches can be transferred to the oxide production operation. The samples have provided evaluation for transfer, whereas the rags and casting crucibles involved in any area are eventually treated to permit evaluation and then recovered by solvent extraction.

11-4. OXIDE PRODUCTION

Oxide production feed is analyzed uranyl nitrate solutions from feed storage. The object of this part of the processing is to remove contaminants from the U^{233} as the first step to pure metal.

As outlined in Fig. 11-3, the uranium is precipitated with 30 percent H_2O_2 (hydrogen peroxide), and the $UO_4 \cdot xH_2O$ is collected by filtration. The UO_4

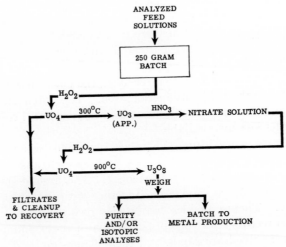

FIG. 11-3   Flow sheet of U^{233} oxide production.

is heated to provide a cake that has the approximate composition of UO_3; no attempt is made to produce a stoichiometric compound, since the function here is to change a slow dissolver (UO_4) to a faster dissolver (UO_3). The oxide is dissolved in nitric acid, and the precipitation step is repeated. This may be done as many times as needed to reach the desired purity, the final oxidation step being the calcination of the peroxide cake to U_3O_8. Treatment is the same for new feed and for recycled feed.

Batch data being generated are recorded on lot sheets. The batch number, origin, quantity, and any other pertinent information are first recorded, and as the batch proceeds through the process, the sample numbers and treatment are recorded. The date, final weights, calculations, condition of the material, and receipt numbers are set down in detail. It may be noted that the lot sheet provides a complete history of the batch from entrance into the operation to exit.

11-4.1. Oxidation-Process Residues. Two residues occur during oxide production. The first is cleanup rags. These are treated with the same ashing and leaching technique as the cleanup materials from feed storage; however, rags from different areas are handled separately.

A larger residue is in peroxide filtrates. The quantity of uranium in filtrates varies but is almost never over 1 gm/liter and is sometimes as low as a few milligrams per liter. On a balance-area basis, filtrates are collected, concentrated in stills, sampled for uranium content, and transferred to recovery for solvent extraction. Filtrates of this type can be concentrated from 100-150 liters to 5 liters. Filtrate sampling is discussed in Sec. 11-7.

11-4.2. Oxide Measurement. The final product of the oxide production step is a good stoichiometric compound, U_3O_8. The uranium content of a weighed batch of the oxide can be calculated quite accurately in the usual manner. Errors in the factor due to contaminants will be negligible for a pure oxide. This is controlled by a spectrochemical analysis for impurities. The procedure used involves transferring the U_3O_8 to a tared container, gross weighing, and making the necessary calculations for uranium content.

Evaluation of uranium feed and efflux of oxide production is simple; the influx consists of analyzed solutions, and the U_3O_8 product and its samples are the stoichiometric end quantities.

11-5. METAL PRODUCTION

The metal-production area consists of two processing steps: conversion of U_3O_8 to UF_4 and reduction of the UF_4 to metal (see Fig. 11-4).

The U_3O_8 is first converted to UO_2 by reduction with hydrogen, and the UO_2 is converted to UF_4 with anhydrous HF. The cycle is continuous. When the U_3O_8 is reduced, the HF treatment is begun. The flow of hydrogen is continued at a reduced rate during the HF portion of the cycle. This results in a conversion to UF_4 of 99 percent or better.

The reduction of UF_4 to the metal is carried out in an iron reactor or "bomb," using induction heating. The reaction takes place in a ceramic crucible which is insulated from the bomb wall with a fine sand. The UF_4, calcium, and iodine make up the charge. The iodine is added to promote better separation of slag and metal.

The reduction bomb is sealed by bolting on a lid with a gasket, and air is evacuated. The bomb is filled with argon three times to assure complete removal of oxygen from the interior; then it is heated by induction heating until the reduction reaction occurs. After the contents of the bomb have cooled, they are removed, the sand, crucible, and slag being set aside for recovery. The biscuit or button is pickled, weighed, and sampled. Yields in excess of 98 percent are usual.

It is also possible to convert U^{233} metal chips directly to UF_4 by direct treatment with HF. This is not a purification step but a matter of expediency, and its use will depend on the desired purity of the metal product. Reduction is the same as for UF_4 prepared from U_3O_8.

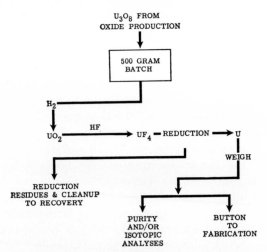

Fig. 11-4   Flow sheet of U^{233} metal production.

Diversions of U^{233} in all these metal-production steps are few in number but fairly large in the quantity of uranium involved, being in the neighborhood of 1 percent of the total feed to the process.

11-5.1. Reduction Residues. The principal reduction residue is the slag. A temporary uranium value can be assigned to the slag by difference between the amount of uranium in the charge and that in the metal button. Slag, crucible, and sand are treated as a single entity, and for this purpose all reduction residues are transferred to the recovery operation for eventual evaluation and solvent extraction. Rags from cleanup of dust created by transfers of oxide and fluoride are treated like those from other areas but are identified separately and kept segregated.

A very minor residue is the dilute acetic acid solution used to pickle the button. The uranium content of this solution is usually on the order of milligrams for multiple picklings. This is also transferred to the recovery operation to be evaluated with slag and crucible.

11-5.2. Measurements. Since there are two steps involved in metal production, two sets of batch data are kept: the first for the U_3O_8 to UF_4 stage and the second for the UF_4 to metal production. These are kept as separate lot sheets for each stage to provide convenience should it be desired to remove and store UF_4 rather than to reduce to metal immediately. Both these sheets are essential to proper control of the material and determination of yields. The hydrofluorination sheet contains the usual spaces for batch numbers, names, and dates. After these come spaces for recording weights and calculations. Specifically, the gross and tare of the boat and the net weight of U_3O_8 are required. All calculations for determination of conversion are dependent on U_3O_8 weight.

Calculations here are based on the assumption of a 100 percent conversion of U_3O_8 to UO_2 during the cycle. The extent of conversion of the UO_2 to UF_4 is then calculated as a function of the gain in weight actually achieved during hydrofluorination as opposed to the theoretical gain.

The weight of UO_2 produced by reduction of U_3O_8 is calculated by:

$$\text{Weight of } UO_2 = (0.961)(\text{weight } U_3O_8) \tag{11.1}$$

The extent of conversion of UO_2 to UF_4 is calculated by:

$$\text{Percent conversion} = \frac{\text{wt. of } UF_4 \text{ (actual)} - \text{wt. } UO_2}{\text{wt. of } UF_4 \text{ (theoretical)} - \text{wt. } UO_2} \times 100 \tag{11.2}$$

It is reasonably assumed that no uranium is lost during hydrofluorination. Therefore, for future use of the fluoride after transfer, a factor for converting this particular batch of fluoride is calculated.

$$\frac{\text{Actual weight of uranium}}{\text{Actual weight of } UF_4} = \text{factor} \tag{11.3}$$

This factor is then applied to any samples or other portions removed from the fluoride or to the entire batch if it should be necessary to transfer it for storage purposes. It is therefore possible to make this a break point if desired.

If the UF_4 batch is to be processed immediately, it is entered upon a reduction lot sheet. This sheet also contains the usual data on batch number, dates, and names. Other data are included in the following order: weight of UF_4, weight of uranium, weight of calcium and iodine required, weight of button, amount in residues (by difference), yield, weight of sample, weight of button after sampling, and amount to recovery as a result of sampling.

Transfer of a fluoride to a bomb always involves some dusting, which accumulates in dry boxes and filters, but the charge is not weighed into the bomb. The amount to recovery by difference includes this dusting loss and makes it essential that residues from the metal-production operation be treated as a unit.

The U_3O_8 entering the process is a good stoichiometric compound, chips are weighable, and the end product, a metal button, forms a fine basis for control by weighing. If it should be necessary to remove some of the uranium from the operation as the fluoride, the UF_4 itself is a good stoichiometric compound, and weights are dependable. All the factors and calculations applied are based on this premise.

11-5.3. Residue Sampling. Most residues in the metal production process lend themselves to reasonably easy evaluation. Even cleanup rags and reduction residues have well-developed processes for eventual recycle of the material.

Samples for quality control and for chemical and isotopic analysis, whether as fluoride or as metal, are as weighable as the batches from which they originate. It is usual to remove a sample of each batch at the fluoride stage. Normally, buttons are only sampled for chemical analysis by the spectrochemical method. Total impurities by the process described above are almost invariably less than 500 ppm and usually less than 200 ppm; thus the reliability of metal weight as an SS control point is readily seen.

11-6. METAL FABRICATION

In the metal-fabrication process the usual procedure is to first melt one or more buttons of U^{233}, then cast to approximate size for subsequent machining to exact dimensions. Fig. 11-5 illustrates the material flow. Owing to the

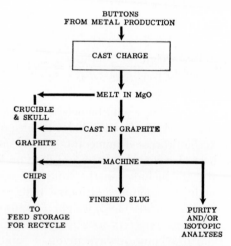

FIG. 11-5 Flow sheet of U^{233} metal fabrication.

pyrophoric nature of the uranium, it is essential that all these operations be carried out within inert-atmosphere dry boxes.

Although metal fabrication constitutes only one area with respect to materials management, two separate operations are involved. The feed material, in the form of buttons, is melted in a high-fired MgO crucible equipped with a pour rod or plug. When molten, the metal is poured into an aluminum oxide–coated graphite mold of the desired shape, from which it is removed after cooling. This results in a clean cast metal product ready for the machining process. Here, by conventional machining methods, the metal piece is cut to the desired dimensions. At this point the finished piece is weighed prior to being sealed into the aluminum can.

11-6.1. Side Streams. A fair-sized residue occurs during the casting operation in the form of the thin shell or skull of metal formed in the bottom of the pouring crucible. This may be as much as 1 to 3 percent of the total charge to the crucible. The crucible itself will absorb U²³³ metal at the rate of about 40 mg of uranium per pound of crucible. Skull and crucible are transferred to feed storage for dissolving and recycle of the contained uranium. The coated graphite mold absorbs negligible quantities of uranium and can usually be used several times before recovery is necessary.

The only material residue from the machining operation are the chips created during machining, and the necessary quality-control samples can be obtained from these.

11-6.2. Material Control. Batch data are also necessary for the metal fabrication area. The essential data are the identity and weights of the buttons used for the charge and the weight of the finished piece. Other data concern only the mechanical details of the casting and machining operations.

Uranium residues in the metal-fabrication area are easily evaluated but only on a tentative by-difference basis. The weights of the charge and of the finished piece are simple, but precise accounting for the residues must wait until the material is recycled through oxide production and recovery. It is possible to obtain weights for skulls and machined chips, and these can be used for an approximate material balance.

Because this balance can be only approximate, the residues or diversions are placed into the feed storage category already described. There all the metal residues are treated and evaluated as recycle material. Evaluation of the pouring crucibles cannot be made until they have been transferred to the recovery area; this procedure is discussed later.

Quality-control samples removed from the machining operation are sent to the analytical laboratory for chemical analysis.

11-7. RECOVERY SYSTEM

Recovery, sometimes called "salvage," is a part of the U²³³ processing scheme to which all the areas contribute. Anywhere from 5 to 20 percent of the total throughput of an operation will eventually have to go through recovery before it can be returned to the main stream. Recovery is thus an important operation. Fig. 11-6 illustrates the flow of material through the recovery operation.

Feed to the recovery area consists of the various residues contributed by other processing areas.   These are as follows.   Feed storage contributes MgO pouring· crucibles and rags.   Oxide production contributes peroxide filtrates and rags.   Metal production contributes reduction residues, acetic acid pickle solutions, and rags.   Other miscellaneous residues occur from time to time.

Nearly all residues are physically within the recovery area before evaluation; moreover, they usually enter in small batches that are not very rich in U^{233}, the quantities ranging from a few milligrams to several grams.

11-7.1. General Treatment.   The general scheme of the recovery operation consists in treating the residues to form nitrate solutions suitable for solvent

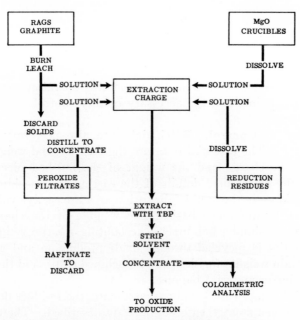

FIG. 11-6   Flow sheet of U^{233} recovery.

extraction.   This includes such treatments as ashing, leaching, dissolution, and concentration.   It is after this preliminary treatment that actual measurement by sampling and analysis of the U^{233} entering recovery takes place.   Prior to this, U^{233} content has usually been evaluated by difference only.

After the U^{233} content has been determined, the various solutions are combined into batches for solvent extraction.   The solution is adjusted to desired specific gravity and nitric acid normality, then is solvent extracted with TBP in kerosene.   The aqueous raffinate from this is low enough in uranium to discard.   The enriched solvent is stripped of U^{233} with dilute nitric acid.

This solution is then concentrated to a convenient volume with a concentration factor of 100 or more, the only limiting consideration being criticality. The quantity of U^{233} is determined from the solutions fed to the still.   The concentrated solution from the still is then transferred to a volumetric flask of convenient size and an aliquot is removed for uranium analysis.

Batches are transferred directly to the oxide-production operation, where they are treated as a small-scale peroxide precipitation. Impurities run high; so a crude U_3O_8 is the result. Small batches of U_3O_8 are weighed, and U^{233} content is calculated. When a sufficient quantity of this crude oxide has been accumulated to make up a nominal 250-gm batch, the oxide is dissolved and the uranium is further purified by peroxide precipitation the same as with material from other sources. Since this uranium has already entered the oxide-production area at an analyzed figure, no further analyses are necessary.

11-7.2. Specific Treatment. All cleanup rags, regardless of source, are treated alike, although those from different production areas are kept segregated. The procedure is to first ash and then roast at a high temperature (900°C) in air for 12 to 16 hours. The ash is then leached several times with heated concentrated nitric acid and vacuum filtered to remove the remaining insoluble material. Batches of nitric acid rag leach can be transferred to convenient-sized flasks for accurate sampling. These leaches are used as feed for solvent extraction. Infrequently, graphite molds are treated in a similar manner.

The insoluble ash from a leach presents a difficult problem when further recovery is considered. Some additional recovery is possible by HF treatment to remove silicon or by caustic fusion methods. The total U^{233} in the ash will average only a few milligrams for many kilos of uranium processed, and it is possible that the value will not warrant the effort involved.

The recovery of U^{233} from peroxide filtrates is a simple operation. These can be concentrated easily by a factor of 20 or slightly higher; the residual H_2O_2 being decomposed by the concentration process. The filtrate concentrates are large and the volume is ascertained in especially calibrated tanks. Quantities of U^{233} involved are small, resulting in a negligible effect from small errors. Samples from these tanks are sent to the chemical laboratory for uranium analysis. The concentrated and analyzed filtrates form a convenient part of the feed to the solvent-extraction procedure.

MgO fabrication crucibles and reduction residues are treated alike; both are dissolved in a nitric acid and aluminum nitrate solution. The aluminum salt serves as an additional salting agent for solvent extraction, and in the case of the reduction residues, the aluminum serves as a complexing agent for the fluoride present. The acetic acid pickle solution from metal production is usually added to the dissolver solution.

11-7.3. Recovery-System Measurements. The approximate quantity of U^{233} in a dissolver charge is based on the by-difference values previously assigned to the residues to be dissolved. After dissolution, samples are taken of the solutions for chemical analysis. Large calibrated vessels are used to ascertain the volume. A 1 percent error in estimating the volume of a solution containing 10 gm U^{233} is not great, and such errors tend to average out over a large number of estimates. These dissolved residues and the other recovery solutions form a solvent-extraction batch.

Residues from recovery contain small quantities of uranium, consisting only of samples and cleanup rags. The samples are evaluated at the time the analytical result is received. Cleanup rags are treated like those from other processing areas but need not be evaluated, since they originate from material previously charged to the receipt area. Those from a final cleanup will need evaluation for proper credit to the originating receipt area.

All the residues reaching the recovery area have batch data associated with them. Lot sheets are kept for dissolver products, extraction products, concentration products, and rag leaches. In addition to the essential processing data, these also contain data on source, sample numbers, volumes, sample volumes, total assay, and disposition. As mentioned before, even though items are physically present in the recovery area before actual evaluation, they are not transferred in the records until analysis has been made.

The complexities caused by the many sources and the criticality problems inherent in the large volumes processed necessitate careful control and management.

All the solutions from the recovery area are analyzed by the colorimetric method. In this procedure thiocyanate salts are added, forming uranium thiocyanate complex. Stannous chloride is added to reduce any iron present to the ferrous state since ferric iron is a strong interference element. Samples are diluted to appropriate volumes to provide a uranium concentration range of 1 to 40 μ gm/ml. The uranium concentration is then determined by spectrophotometric comparison with standards of known concentration.

In addition to providing a physical separation of the U^{233}, the various processing areas described also provide an accounting separation, which makes it possible to determine how well the material is being managed and provides a check on possible losses and diversions. This check is accomplished through internal material balances based on routine inventories. A description of a particular SS material control system is given in the following section.

11-8. SS-MATERIAL CONTROL

As a quantity of U^{233} is received, it is assigned a lot number for a feed storage area, and the appropriate record is made. There are no set rules regarding the lot quantity, but it should be of such size as is compatible with its being processed and evaluated within some reasonable period of time. The lot quantity is regulated by the throughput rate and should be as large as possible in keeping with the plant situation in order to simplify records and prevent having too many lots in process at one time.

The lot is split into batches (governed by criticality). Each batch is sampled and analyzed, and as analytical results are obtained, the batches are transferred to the corresponding oxide production area. As the various diversions of fabrication crucible and cleanup rags are evaluated, these wastes are transferred to recovery and are credited to the lot.

At this point it is customary to thoroughly clean all dry boxes used in the feed storage area and to recover and evaluate all solutions and cleanup materials generated in the process. When all the residues have been accounted for and evaluated, the general cleanup takes place. What remains on the books at this time, whether over or under the originally assigned value, is the book-physical inventory difference (B-PID) for that lot. Since all containers and contents are recorded on flow records, it is a simple procedure to determine when all the U²³³ belonging to a particular feed storage lot has been evaluated.

One small discrepancy occurs in the evaluation of the feed-storage material. Certain items that have been previously evaluated are bled into a batch prior to its evaluation; they are taken into account when the U²³³ contributed by feed storage is being determined. In a strict sense some portion of the cleanup materials should be assigned to such additional material. However, the percentage contributed by this additional material is a very small part of a small quantity of U²³³; thus no attempt at separation is made, and the entire value of the cleanup materials is considered as having originated from the feed storage. The small error contributed by this omission is compensated for by the subsequent handling of the U²³³.

Within reason, the batches from a particular feed storage lot form the bulk of the corresponding oxide production lot. The reason for this procedure, followed also in subsequent areas, is logical enough. Some small error in analysis or weighing can occur during the transfer of U²³³ from one area to another, and if such should occur undetected, the analyses or weighings of the same material in the following area are likely to correct the original error. However, this does not imply reliance upon compensatory errors. An example would be a batch that was analyzed slightly low and was transferred with this error undetected from feed storage to oxide production. This material will reappear in the records when the batch is removed from the oxide-production area as U_3O_8 and residues, although it may not be detectable as an individual discrepancy in a large mass of material. In this manner possible small errors are corrected by subsequent proper procedures.

Batches are fed into the oxide production area as uranyl nitrate solutions, and they emerge as purified U_3O_8. As U_3O_8 they can be evaluated. If proper batch data have been kept, it is an easy matter to determine when the end of the lot has been reached and whether or not all the U²³³ has been evaluated, including that which has been diverted in the form of peroxide filtrates and rags. It is possible to receive other evaluated materials, such as clean metal and oxide, into the oxide production lot. These materials are usually handled as additions to the batches and are treated as described in Sec. 11-3.

The termination of processing a lot in the oxide production area is also the occasion for a thorough cleaning of dry boxes and equipment, the resultant solutions and rags being transferred to recovery.

A batch from oxide production forms a batch to be processed in metal production. The U^{233} enters the area as evaluated U_3O_8 or chips for direct conversion and leaves as evaluated metal. Proper batch data will record all the U^{233} entering the area as leaving the area, whether in the form of metal or of residues. The equipment and dry boxes used in metal production are cleaned at the completion of the lot, and the residues are transferred to recovery.

Metal fabrication is considered a separate entity. The feed consists of buttons, and the final product is the canned slug or rod. Everything else, crucibles, skulls, and chips, are residues. These go to feed storage on a by-difference basis. With this procedure the lot is always returned to a zero balance, and no U^{233} remains in the account after completion of a particular fabrication job.

The feed to a recovery area consists of the residues from feed storage, oxide production, and metal production. Residues from each of these areas are evaluated separately and then become part of a charge to the solvent-extraction process. The end product is the concentrated nitrate solution returned to the main stream in the oxide-production area after analysis. As in other lots, a final cleanup of equipment and dry boxes results in further material for evaluation. This is usually transferred to the following recovery lot. Only regular discards are removed from the recovery lots. These will be discussed later.

In addition to the various records already discussed, consisting mostly of batch data, bookkeeping records of the U^{233} entering and leaving each of the processing areas are essential. Sections for corresponding lots of feed storage, oxide production, metal production, and recovery are set up and run concurrently, with the material progressing from one process to the next in the manner described.

Each of these operations is charged with the feed and credited with its own end product. When all the batches and all the residues from each of these lots have been accounted for and evaluated, a general cleanup takes place, and the cleanup residues are evaluated and credited to the lot and transferred to recovery. Upon completion of a recovery lot, the residues accumulated during final cleanup are evaluated and are transferred to a subsequent recovery lot.

Material balance areas are evaluated by difference between total U^{233} entering and leaving the lots. What remains on the books after final evaluation, whether a negative or positive quantity, represents the B-PID for U^{233} in the lot.

These lots are set up on a quantity rather than on a time basis to permit almost continuous processing. No attempt is made to process a given quantity of U²³³ in a month, and no attempt is made to accurately evaluate all the U²³³ on hand at the end of a monthly report period. Instead, an approximate inventory is taken. All batches and containers on hand are listed, and where an exact evaluation is available, it is used. Otherwise, the batches or containers are evaluated by difference or by estimate based on experience. This inventory is then compared with a book balance for the same date, and the inventory is assumed to be correct if it compares favorably with the book balance. It is difficult to assign any arbitrary figure to the agreement to be expected between these two because there will be variations dependent upon the type of processing and the nature of the residues on hand. From experience, agreement within ±5 percent is fairly reasonable.

The only true balance occurs when a lot has been processed through all areas; this is the only time a complete and accurate evaluation has taken place. There is no material on inventory at this time since each of the final residues has been removed from the lot inventory and the quantities remaining on the books are B-PID quantities. Similar lots should represent, within reason, different processing of U²³³ batches. In this way the B-PID quantities in each lot can be considered in the light of the other related lots and the over-all figure.

Table 11.1 is a summary of some typical B-PID quantities in terms of percent of U²³³ processed. Negative quantities denote apparent loss of uranium and positive quantities apparent gains.

TABLE 11.1. PERCENT B-PID FOR AREAS OF MATERIAL BALANCE[a]

Area	Range, %		Average, %
	Low	High	
Feed storage	−1.07	−0.94	−0.98
Oxide production	+0.35	+1.58	+0.87
Metal production	−0.47	−0.22	−0.33
Metal fabrication	(None, returned to zero balance)		
Recovery	−6.22	+0.36	−3.62
Net (all areas)	−0.29	−0.18	−0.25

[a] In some cases the figures are probably within the limits of analytical and weighing errors. No bias correction has been applied to these data.

The large range and magnitude of the recovery B-PID values are due to the nature of the operation. Quantities of U²³³ are small, usually only a few grams per batch, and volumes are large. Many of the solutions are difficult to analyze accurately. In view of these facts the results are actually quite good.

The recovery area is the only area from which U²³³ is regularly discarded.

The rule used for discard is to discard solutions averaging 0.1 ppm if they are not capable of being re-used in some other part of processing. The main discards are distillates from the concentration of peroxide filtrates or extraction product and the aqueous raffinates from the solvent-extraction process. Distillates will average about 50 μg of uranium per liter, and raffinates will average slightly over 100 μg of uranium per liter.

Other special discards may be necessary on occasion when small quantities of U^{233} are contained in residues difficult to recover without an effort far in excess of the worth of the material. Each of these is considered a separate case as it arises. In all cases discards are credited to recovery.

REFERENCES FOR CHAPTER 11

1. F. R. BRUCE, J. M. FLETCHER, H. H. HYMAN, and J. J. KATZ (Eds.), in *Progress in Nuclear Energy, Series III, Process Chemistry*, Vol. 1, pp. 212-222, McGraw-Hill Book Company, Inc., New York, 1956.
2. J. J. DEVANEY, *Radiation Intensity from Spheres of U-233 Contaminated with U-232*, USAEC Report LAMS-1892, Los Alamos Scientific Laboratory, February 1955.
3. D. CALLIHAN, Nuclear Safety in Processing Reactor Fuel Solutions, *Nucleonics*, 14:(7):38 (1956).
4. *Federal Register*, p. 10965, Dec. 28, 1957, Sup't of Doc., Dep't of Commerce.

Part Five

REACTOR OPERATION

Chapter 12

ENRICHED-URANIUM-FUELED RESEARCH REACTOR *

12-1. INTRODUCTION

The Materials Testing Reactor (MTR) was designed to furnish a very high flux of neutrons to a number of experimental locations within the core and reflector of the reactor. Its purpose is to provide a means for obtaining engineering data regarding the performance of materials under conditions simulating those to which it is desired to expose the materials. The MTR began operating March 31, 1952, at the National Reactor Testing Station near Idaho Falls, Idaho. The first experiments were inserted in August 1952; since then the irradiations in this reactor have increased in number and complexity.

Two principal types of SS materials are involved at the MTR. The first are the fuel materials used in the reactor's operation; the second, the many samples of SS materials that are irradiated in experiments.

Fuel material is received at the MTR in the form of finished fuel elements of extremely high value in both material content and fabrication costs. After the fuel material is used in the reactor, a portion of the U^{235} has been consumed and large quantities of fission products have been produced. At the same time, a significant amount of U^{235} remains in the fuel elements. This U^{235} is recovered at a chemical-processing installation.

All experiments received at the MTR are packaged for irradiation in such a manner that their SS material cannot be inspected physically. Fortunately, very little nuclear material is involved in these experiments. Their primary value lies in the cost of fabricating the often elaborate equipment for the experiments and in the scientific data that will result from a study of the effects of irradiation upon the materials. The experiments do have an effect upon the operation of the MTR because they disturb its reactivity. Improper handling of an experiment may seriously disrupt operation and may even result in hazard to the health and safety of personnel. Consequently, MTR people acquire extensive information about all materials put in their reactor and carefully control each experiment.

* F. P. Vance, Phillips Petroleum Co., Idaho Falls, Idaho. The author acknowledges the contribution and assistance of F. H. Tingey in the preparation of this chapter.

12-2. BASIC PRINCIPLE: ITEM CONTROL

Item control has been established as the basic principle of control because of the nature of the operation. The MTR, referred to since its conception in 1945 as the "High-Flux Pile," was constructed to accommodate a large number of experiments and to subject these experiments to neutron fluxes considerably in excess of those previously available.

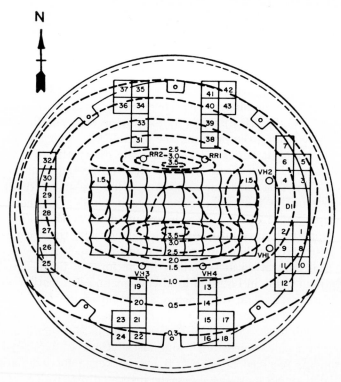

Fig. 12-1 Diagram of reactor tank showing fuel positions, experimental blanket positions and neutron flux patterns. The numbers on the contour lines represent highest thermal-neutron flux in that position, $nv \times 10^{14}$.

A plan view of the reactor tank is given in Fig. 12-1. Lattice positions are designated by coordinates. Positions 11 through 39 are occupied by fuel assemblies and fuel shim safeties; positions 44, 46, and 48 are occupied by beryllium shim safeties; other lattice positions, 41 through 59, are occupied by various experiments having a sufficiently low nuclear cross section that reactor operation is not seriously perturbed. The reflector, surrounding the fuel core within the tank wall, is solid beryllium with 43 removable pieces which provide space for additional experiments at somewhat lower flux. Many of the experiments inserted in the reactor contain SS material in some form. At the MTR, SS materials are received as capsules, slugs, or elaborately instrumented pilot-scale devices ready for insertion. In all cases, the packaging of these materials prevents verification of the SS content. Accordingly, their receipt is acknowledged by noting the item identification code. Following irradiation these items are returned to the sender at the same value; no report is made from the MTR regarding estimated results of nuclear processes, e.g. fission loss or SS material production.

☐ U-233   ☐ U-235   ☐ Normal U   ☐ Depleted U   ☐ Pu239   ☐ Th

FORM AED - 84 (R 4 - 19 - 57)

PHILLIPS PETROLUM COMPANY
ATOMIC ENERGY DIVISION
IDAHO FALLS, IDAHO

Experiment No.

DATE

SS MATERIAL TRANSFER

	AEC Form 101 No.	Item No.	Item No.
Remarks:			
Signature of Sender			
Signature of Receiver			

White copy to Sender
Pink copy to MTR SS **Control**
Yellow copy to Receiver

*List each item to be identified by the experiment No. assigned above.

FIG. 12-2   SS Material Transfer form.

A technical liaison section, organizationally designated "Project Engineering," was staffed early in the MTR operation. This section serves as the intermediary between experiment sponsor and reactor operator. These men estimate the effects of nuclear processes, such as heat developed, influence on flux, and activity generated, as well as the duration of irradiation to accomplish the results for which the experiment is being conducted. This information serves as a guide to those who approve the experiment insertion. The technological value of an experiment by the time it is fully prepared for insertion is usually many times the nominal dollar value of the material content. Hence the precautions necessary to safeguard the experimental data are entirely adequate for the protection of the material content.

Experiments approved for irradiation at the MTR are given an identification number; e.g. for the thirtieth program approved for Westinghouse Atomic Power Development for conduct at these facilities, the number WAPD-30 would be assigned. Individual insertions under this program would be numbered serially. Thus each slug or capsule has a unique label, e.g. WAPD-30-40. Each experiment is thus readily identifiable by SS Control, Project Engineering, Operations, and Health Physics. Many experiments consist of more than one discrete item. Under such circumstances control is often complicated by the difficulty of maintaining the identity of particular items, e.g. when slugs, following irradiation, are handled under several feet of water.

A form (Fig. 12-2) has been devised for local use in assigning material-control responsibility to a custodian. This individual, usually a project engineer, has nominal custody of the item during its use in the reactor. Local custody terminates when the item is returned to the experiment sponsor.

PHILLIPS PETROLEUM COMPANY, ATOMIC ENERGY DIVISION

AED Form 39
MTI Form 3

FUEL ELEMENT ITEM STATUS CARD

AEC 101 Forms: ....-MTI-.................., MTI-..................-.................., ...-MTI-.................., MTI-..................-..................

Date Rec. .... Shipper ORNL

	CS	REACTOR	REACTOR	HS	HS
Location					
Date					
Location					
Date					
Location					
Date					

		SS NET	U-235			SS NET	U-235
Received From Shipper		....	....	Run #	..............MWD	....	....
Run #	..............MWD	....	....	Run #	..............MWD	....	....
Run #	..............MWD	....	....	Run #	..............MWD	....	....

ITEM NO. I-.................... TYPE.................... SS MATL.. AREA

FIG. 12-3 Fuel Element Item Status Card.

Each fuel element is given a history card (Fig. 12-3) on which is recorded all information relevant to preirradiated SS quantities, burn-up (by cycle), and postirradiated SS quantities. Derivation of burn-up calculations is described in Sec. 12-4.2. These calculations are based on the experience of about 20 MTR cycles. When an element has been discharged from the reactor for the last time, it must cool a minimum of 120 days prior to shipment to allow short-lived fission products to decay, thus substantially reducing the hazard to personnel.

12-3. BASIC ACCOUNTING SYSTEM

A punched-card control system utilizing an IBM 419 tabulator and card sorter was devised to facilitate maintenance of records of the very large number of items on reactor inventory at any one time. The prime considerations in setting up this system are to (1) effect item control and (2) obtain a balance of material on hand. For these objectives to be realized, it was necessary to separate SS materials into two categories: reactor fuel for which burn-up calculations were to be made and experiments for which burn-up calculations were unnecessary. Since each category is handled differently, a separate approach was set up for each.

Data from the SS Material Transfer form (Fig. 12-2) and AEC Form 101 are recorded on an IBM data sheet; then the necessary information can readily be punched into a master deck of control IBM cards. The following information is punched on each control card: type of transfer (receipt or shipment), material type, experiment number, 101 number, date of 101, allotment number, custodian, and amount of SS material. A special control board for the IBM 419 printer is wired to fit each need of this system. The main elements of the system are the sorter and printer, the routine being to sort and then print and, if desired, accumulate totals concurrently with printing. One card is punched for each item (slug, capsule, or discrete element of whatever description). Only cards representing new activity, i.e. receipts or shipments, need be handled each month for preparation of the material balance statement, inventory, and other tabulations.

After the necessary tabulation has been made from the cards, the new cards are added to the master inventory deck. Cards representing shipments are then collected and matched with the original receipt card for the item, and this pair is removed from the deck. When SS material is transferred to a different area, and hence to a different custodian, as shown by the local SS Material Transfer form, a new card is punched to replace the one in the master deck.

12-4. ACCOUNTING FOR REACTOR FUEL

Since experimental items are controlled by a perpetual inventory and item-identification system, there are few problems other than clerical error or inventory omission. The fuel, however, presents serious problems.

12-4.1. Receipts. The SS content of unirradiated fuel assemblies is determined upon receipt at the MTR by a nondestructive assay technique. This method, based upon both gamma scanning and neutron attenuation, has been described.[1,2] In order to calibrate the device, individual MTR plates were specially fabricated and assayed versus a standard plate. Destructive assay of these special plates provided calibration curves for comparative scans on additional MTR plates; these in turn were assembled into complete fuel elements to serve as standards. Calibration curves were then derived from these data, providing reference standards whose content is known with high precision. Using this technique, a limit of uncertainty of the order of ±1 percent (precision and accuracy; 95 percent confidence level) has been achieved.

12-4.2. Irradiation. Variations in fission rate within the core are large and have a major effect upon the reliability of any estimate of U^{235} consumption in a given lattice position. This was not a major problem at first since whole cores were replaced with new fuel, even including the fuel shims. However, such a practice does not achieve optimum utilization of the fuel elements. With a higher fuel density it became practical to switch the fuel assemblies from the periphery to the center after one cycle and to remove the burned-out center elements.

Further complications resulted as the volume of experiments increased. Many of these experiments were tied into reactor control circuitry, and these produced more frequent scrams. When it is not possible to get back up to power within 30 minutes, the reactor flux level is poisoned by the growth of xenon. Unnecessary delay is avoided by inserting fresh fuel assemblies; in these experiments, only a few partially spent elements are replaced. After a week or so these partially spent elements can be returned to the reactor. Thus the spent fuel elements have an extremely heterogeneous history.

12-4.3. Measuring Power Output. The integral of fissions per cycle or for any particular period is computed from a measurement of the gross energy dissipated to cooling media.

The only direct measurement possible of this energy is gross flow of the primary cooling medium and its temperature differential. Demineralized water is pumped through the reactor tank at a rate of about 20,000 gal/min. Temperature differential is measured at points immediately upstream of the tank in the inlet and downstream of the tank in the outlet. The fraction of the total heat dissipated to air circulated through the graphite zone surrounding the reactor tank is very small in comparison with other variables.

Temperature differential is measured by the signal generated from many thermocouples located in the main 36-in.-OD flow lines. The temperature differential has also been measured at different points (for instance, in the process-water building about 300 ft from the reactor) with apparently negligible differences in the readings. Based upon repeated calibrations of the instrument, the error in the measurement of temperature differential is believed to be less than $\pm0.5°F$.

The major task involved calibration of the 30-in. flow tube at expected process rates. It was decided to use the sump tank to feed the reactor coolant under controlled conditions. The sump has a capacity of about 100,000 gal, and it was desirable to make runs at greater than 20,000 gal/min. Thus, some of the runs had less than 5 minutes' duration. Test equipment was installed on the sump tank to enable observers to read the drop in water level and the corresponding time interval. The tank circumference was measured several times and at several levels to ensure an accurate value for the volume delivered between level readings. During a run the flow tube differential was carefully read. These data, rate versus flow tube differential reading, were then subjected to analysis, yielding the following equation for the "best estimate" of water flow:

$$\log F = \hat{y} = 3.45 + 0.56 \log \Delta P \tag{12.1}$$

where F = flow (gal/min)
ΔP = differential (in. Hg).

The variance of this value based upon the scatter of points computed from 12 calibration runs is given by the following relationship:

$$s_{\hat{y}}^2 = s_r^2 \left[1 + \frac{1}{n} + \frac{(x - \overline{x})^2}{\sum_{i=1}^{n} (x_i - \overline{x})^2} \right] \tag{12.2}$$

where $s_{\hat{y}}^2$ = estimate of the variance of $\hat{y}$
$\quad\quad s_r^2$ = residual error, or variance, indicating "goodness of fit" of the data to the equation
$\quad\quad n$ = number of observations in the calibration run–in this case, 12
$\quad\quad x$ = any value for log ΔP
$\quad\quad x_i$ = observed value for log ΔP during calibration for run i
$\quad\quad \overline{x}$ = mean of all observed log ΔP during calibration run.

Statistical analysis of the data yielded the following:

$$s_r^2 = 1.573 \times 10^{-4}$$
$$\overline{x} = 1.31482$$

$$\sum_{i=1}^{n} (x_i - \overline{x})^2 = 0.34484$$

Thus we have

$$s_{\hat{y}}^2 \times 10^4 = 4.56[0.37356 + (x - 1.31482)^2] \tag{12.2a}$$

Substituting values of x in Eq. 12-2a, e.g. 10, 15, 20, et seq., values are obtained for $s_{\hat{y}}^2$ versus values for the best estimate of flow. Upper and lower limits for this best estimate are defined by

$$(\hat{y} - ts_{\hat{y}})_x \text{ and } (\hat{y} + ts_{\hat{y}})_x$$

respectively, where t is Student's t, described in every elementary reference on mathematical statistics. The value for t was taken to set the confidence level at 95 percent; i.e. there is a chance of 1:20 that the flow is actually outside the limits so computed. This calibration curve is illustrated in Fig. 12-4.

After reactor operating power was raised to 40 Mw, process water flow became 22,000 gal/min. At this rate the uncertainty of water flow is +1700, −1600, or about ±8 percent. When this uncertainty is combined with the uncertainty in energy per fission and in reactor temperature differential, the total limit of uncertainty in a determination of reactor power is ±8.5 percent.

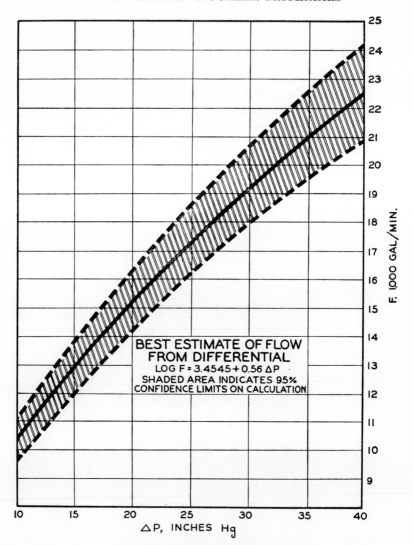

BEST ESTIMATE OF FLOW
FROM DIFFERENTIAL
LOG F = 3.4545 + 0.56 ΔP
SHADED AREA INDICATES 95%
CONFIDENCE LIMITS ON CALCULATION

F, 1,000 GAL/MIN.

ΔP, INCHES Hg

FIG. 12-4 Graph of flow from pressure differential, indicating 95 percent
confidence level.

12-4.4. Computing Burn-up from Power. The burn-up of U^{235} involves
both the loss due to fission and that due to conversion to U^{236}. The fission loss
is computed from the power generated expressed as megawatt days (Mwd)[2,3]

$$\text{Fission loss} = (1.06)(\text{Mwd}) \qquad (12.3)$$

The conversion of U^{235} to U^{236} by the (n, γ) reactions is related to the capture-
to-fission cross-section ratio α.

$$\text{Burn-up} = (1 + \alpha)(\text{fission loss})$$
$$= (1 + \alpha)(1.06)(\text{Mwd}) \tag{12.3a}$$

Taking $(1 + \alpha) = 1.185 \pm 0.008$ (from Ref. 2), we have

$$= 1.26(\text{Mwd})$$

The summation of all uncertainties in the burn-up computation is:

$$\text{Uncertainty} = \pm\sqrt{(0.08)^2 + (0.03)^2 + (0.005)^2 + (0.007)^2}$$
$$= \pm 0.086$$

For the usual purposes of computing burn-up for material control records, this is rounded to ± 9 percent. Note also that this error is nonattentuating; i.e. the uncertainty in energy integral is also ± 9 percent.

12-4.5. Correlation of Computed Burn-up with Recovery. In April 1956 a segment of MTR spent fuel was processed at the Idaho Chemical Processing Plant, and the data given in Table 12.1 were collected.

TABLE 12.1.   APRIL 1956 RECOVERY OF MTR SPENT FUEL (GRAMS)

Fuel content before irradiation

SS net	$26{,}429 \pm 300$
U^{235}	$24{,}656 \pm 300$

Fuel content after irradiation

MTR CALCULATION:

SS net	$21{,}450 \pm 538^a$
U^{235}	$18{,}745 \pm 611^a$

ICPP MEASUREMENT:

SS net	$20{,}875 \pm 221$
U^{235}	$18{,}177 \pm 193$

[a] Includes uncertainty in fuel fabricator's values.

The MTR estimate of U^{235} burn-up was 5911 gm, and the ICPP measurement, by-differencing pre- and postirradiation U^{235}, was 6479 gm. The original enrichment level in this fuel was 93.3 percent U^{235}; when the spent fuel was processed, this was observed to be 87.07 percent, based upon measurements performed on 33 batches of dissolver solution. By an easily derived stoichiometric relationship, it is possible to compute the quantity of fission loss which accompanies the measured quantities of total uranium and U^{235} present in spent fuel. Thus, it can be shown that

$$\text{Fission loss} = \frac{U_0(E_0 - E_1)}{1 + \alpha - E_1} \tag{12.4}$$

where U_0 = original total uranium in the fuel prior to irradiation
E_0 = enrichment level prior to irradiation
E_1 = enrichment level following irradiation

$$\alpha = \frac{\sigma_{n,\gamma}}{\sigma_{n,f}}$$

A similar equation can be derived:

$$\text{Fission loss} = \frac{U_1(E_0 - E_1)}{1 + \alpha - E_0} \tag{12.5}$$

where U_1 = residual total uranium in spent fuel.
Thus we have, using Eq. 12.4

$$\text{Fission loss} = \frac{26,429(0.9330 - 0.8707)}{1.185 - 0.8707}$$

$$= 5240 \text{ gm}$$
$$\text{Burn-up} = (5240)(1 + \alpha) = 6210$$

Then, using Eq. 12.5, we have

$$\text{Fission loss} = \frac{20,875(0.9330 - 0.8707)}{1.185 - 0.933}$$

$$= 5160 \text{ gm}$$
$$\text{Burn-up} = (5160)(1 + \alpha) = 6115$$

The enrichment level E_0 in this case had been measured on a mass spectrometer at a different installation. By means of several hundred comparisons, it has been established that the two instruments, ICPP versus the other, are biased 0.12 ± 0.02 absolute percent with reference to each other. This was taken into account in using this equation. In order to evaluate the uncertainty attending the calculation based upon enrichment level degradation the following equation was derived from Eq. 12.4:

$$\frac{\Delta FP}{FP} \approx$$
$$\sqrt{\left(\frac{\Delta U_0}{U_0}\right)^2 + \frac{(1 + \alpha - E_1)^2 \, \Delta E_0{}^2 + (E_0 - E_1)^2 (\Delta \alpha)^2 + (1 + \alpha - E_0)^2 \, \Delta E_1{}^2}{(E_0 - E_1)^2 (1 + \alpha - E_1)^2}} \tag{12.4a}$$

and similarly, for Eq. 12.5

$$\frac{\Delta FP}{FP} \approx$$
$$\sqrt{\left(\frac{\Delta U_1}{U_1}\right)^2 + \frac{(1 + \alpha - E_1)^2 \, \Delta E_0{}^2 + (E_0 - E_1)^2 (\Delta \alpha)^2 + (1 + \alpha - E_0)^2 \, \Delta E_1{}^2}{(E_0 - E_1)^2 (1 + \alpha - E_0)^2}} \tag{12.5a}$$

Accordingly, Table 12.2 can be constructed.

TABLE 12.2. COMPARISON OF MODES FOR ESTIMATING
U^{235} CONSUMPTION IN THE MTR

Mode of Estimation	U^{235} Burn-up, %
MTR energy integral	5911 ± 529
$E_0 U_0 - E_1 U_1$	6479 ± 356
Equation 12.4	6210 ± 230
Equation 12.5	6115 ± 300

12-4.6. Burn-up Record. For record purposes at the MTR a mode of reporting gross burn-up has been adopted as an expedient. As pointed out in Sec. 12-4.2, fuel elements are shifted from the periphery to the center of the core after one cycle. Barring unscheduled insertions, net reactor fuel inventory remains fairly constant. Furthermore, these fuel elements suffer no physical change whatever in their traverse of the reactor and environs. Accordingly, fuel is transferred nominally from "cold" storage (the vault) to "hot" storage. The reactor is carried on the books at a nominal inventory of 4600 gm of U^{235}. Hot storage is debited with fuel elements directly from cold storage and is credited with gross burn-up computed as was described in Sec. 12-4.4. The actual physical inventory of the reactor is essentially irrelevant. Exactly to the extent that it is overstated, the canal cooling area will have been understated, and vice versa. Since the fuel element is shipped at this value, this will also mean an overcharge to the chemical processing plant.

Apportionment of gross burn-up to individual fuels is, however, more of a problem. For some time a careful analysis of this matter was made after each cycle by a reactor physics group. Factors were derived for each cycle and position. After a considerable accumulation of results from these computations, these values were fitted to empirical equations to be used as approximations for material-control purposes.

12-4.7. Burn-up Apportionment. It has never been possible to collect sufficient data for a measurement of fission rate or integrated fissions by lattice location. However, means are available for estimating relative fission rate by position. Results from 20 cycles of operation of the MTR were collected and compared by standard regression analysis. It was assumed that percentage burn-up was a linear function of both lattice position and uranium content at the beginning of the cycle. Since several lattice positions can yield essentially the same rate of burn-up, each was compared with others to determine whether a significant difference in burn-up rate did exist. In cases where no significant differences were found to exist, the data were combined. It was observed that the rate of burn-up was nearly equal during any given cycle for many positions (see table below). Additional groupings were determined by plotting percentage burn-up versus uranium content by lattice position on graph paper and comparing the plots. This comparison gave a set of five equations which define the percentage of the total burn-up attributable to each position of the lattice.

In cases where the scatter of two or more positions intermingled, the data were combined. An equation of the form $Y = A + BX$ was fitted to the data for each grouping, where Y = percentage burn-up and X = uranium content at the beginning of cycle. These equations are listed below with the lattice positions for which each is valid.

LATTICE POSITION	EQUATION
11, 19, 21, 29, 31, 39	$Y = -0.44 + 0.020X$
12, 18, 24, 26, 32, 38	$Y = 0.08 + 0.020X$
13, 14, 16, 17, 23, 27, 33, 34, 36, 37	$Y = 0.32 + 0.020X$
15, 25, 35	$Y = 0.73 + 0.020X$
22, 28	$Y = 0.93 + 0.020X$

Since five separate equations are used to predict the burn-up in all positions, the total of the Y's will not be 100, except fortuitously; hence it is necessary to normalize the values by dividing by the total of all Y's as determined by computing total burn-up from gross power generated.

12-5. GENERAL PROBLEM OF SURVEILLANCE

By means of adequate manufacturing process control, the uncertainty in new fuel elements can be held sufficiently low that the term $\Delta U_0/U_0$ (Eq. 12.4a) will contribute very little to the over-all uncertainty. It is still necessary, however, to obtain a representative sample of the core to establish E_1. Such a sample will not usually be available until the fuel has been dissolved, probably a minimum of four months after its discharge from the reactor; however, an interim basis for computing U^{235} consumed can be provided by a sufficiently careful calibration of flow- and temperature-sensing devices. As described above, this was a physically awkward problem at the MTR because the sump tank out of which the process water is pumped has a capacity of only 100,000 gal. The test time, to calibrate the flow tube at expected rates, was thus less than 5 minutes. The flow rate is now 22,000 gal/min, which accounts for the large limit of uncertainty in reactor energy measurements, since this is an extrapolation of the original calibration.

In a chain such as fabricator-to-reactor operator-to-fuel recovery plant, the problem of minimization of material-control costs is exceedingly complex. The reactor operator, being in the middle, will probably find it advantageous to have a resident inspector at both the fuel fabricator's shop and the fuel-recovery plant. Data reflecting the content of unirradiated fuel assemblies are comparatively easy to verify. Data on spent fuel reflecting accuracy of burn-up are considerably more difficult to collect and interpret.

The direct calibration of large-scale coolant metering devices cannot be accomplished inexpensively. The procedure has been to calibrate moderate sizes, say less than 10 in., and to extrapolate to larger diameters operating within the same range of Reynolds numbers. A Pitot tube traverse of the larger installation will serve as a verification of the manufacturer's rating, but a large uncertainty still attends these measurements.

The uncertainty in energy per fission will remain near ±3 percent until much more reliable data on reactor power and measurement of spent-fuel quantities have been collected. However, it is feasible for the total uncertainty to be brought down to ±5 percent compared with the ±9 percent experienced at the MTR. In a research reactor of scale similar to the Engineering Test Reactor recently placed in operation, burn-up will be about $90,000 to $100,000 worth of U^{235} a month. At an uncertainty of, say, ±4 percent, this is equivalent to about ±$4000 a month at the 95 percent confidence level, and ±$6000 a month at the 99 percent confidence level.

The fuel recovery plant operator will not usually measure discrete increments of reactor fuel as illustrated in Table 12.1. Instead he may be operating continuously to minimize his own out-of-channel time; and to reduce unit processing costs, he may be feeding spent fuel from other programs into the recovery system. Hence the only measurement relevant to values computed by the reactor operator will be on run tanks of dissolver solution. Although the reactor is operated on essentially a batch system, confirming data must be derived from scrutiny of a continuum.

If an apparently large discrepancy is observed between the reactor and fuel recovery plant operators, and if, even after a searching analysis, no evidence can be produced indicating whether the measurements by one can be credited over the other, the only recourse is to interrupt processing long enough to sweep down the fuel recovery system and collect all material in the form of radiologically cold product in order to obtain a clean-plant, gravimetric, nearly rigorous material balance. The costs and other consequences of such an interruption must be evaluated against the gain in information.

In the exchange of material between AEC contractors, it has usually been sufficient to dismiss apparent differences if it can be shown these are not statistically significant. This can only be shown conclusively, of course, when all measurement reliability is firmly established and all sources of uncertainty are identified. By this means, statements of mathematical probability to be associated with the inferences can be made, and risks and ventures can be assessed on an intelligent basis. Propagation of errors by any less formal means than the methods of mathematical statistics will usually lead to a misdirection of effort and unnecessary expense.

12-6. MATERIAL BALANCE

The basic material balance data are provided by punched-card runs on the program described in preceding sections. In any reactor where the fuel is received as discrete segments of material, packaged beyond direct scrutiny, material inbalance is physically impossible. Furthermore, research reactors operated as irradiation facilities handle a heterogeneous multitude of experimental items, each of which is returned to its sponsor inviolate except for the results of nuclear processes, which are irrelevant to the local problem of material control. Hence, if all items are located on inventory, the usual sources of small B-PID quantities are attributable to rounding.

The summation (beginning inventory plus receipts, less ending inventory and removals) will accordingly always equal zero, within rounding and clerical errors.

REFERENCES FOR CHAPTER 12

1. R. V. Babcock and S. L. Ruby, *Nuclear Materials Control System (NMCS). Phase II. The Fuel Assay Scanner,* USAEC Report WCAP-6039, Westinghouse Electric Corp., February 1960.
2. F. P. Vance and F. H. Tingey, Phillips Petroleum Co., unpublished data, October 1955.
3. G. C. Hanna, *Total Energy Released in the Slow-Neutron Fission of U^{235},* Report CRR-489, Atomic Energy Project of Canada, May 1951.

Chapter 13

NATURAL-URANIUM-FUELED PLUTONIUM-PRODUCTION REACTOR *

13-1. REACTOR PROCESS

Plutonium is not found in nature but is produced in a "production" reactor from the neutron capture by the naturally occurring U^{238} isotope. This nuclear reaction is

$$_{92}U^{238} + _0n^1 \rightarrow {}_{92}U^{239} \rightarrow {}_{93}Np^{239} + {}_{-1}e^0 \rightarrow {}_{94}Pu^{239} + {}_{-1}e^0$$

The neutrons are produced by the fissioning of the U^{235} isotope. This nuclear reaction may be represented as

$$_{92}U^{235} \rightarrow \text{fission products} + \Big\langle \begin{array}{l} _0n^1 + {}_{92}U^{235} \rightarrow \text{fission products} + \Big\langle \begin{array}{l} _0n^1 \\ _0n^1 \end{array} \\ _0n^1 + {}_{92}U^{235} \rightarrow \text{fission products} + \Big\langle \begin{array}{l} _0n^1 \\ _0n^1 \end{array} \end{array}$$

A good deal of heat is released by these reactions and is removed by cooling water. The temperature rise of this cooling water is a measure of the number of the above reactions occurring. Thus the amount of plutonium produced and uranium consumed can be computed.

The United States plutonium production centers are the Hanford Works near Richland, Washington, and the Savannah River Plant near Aiken, South Carolina. The Hanford reactors are graphite moderated, the Savannah River reactors are heavy-water moderated. This chapter is devoted to a discussion of the management of nuclear materials at the Hanford Works production reactor. A typical reactor area is shown in Fig. 13-1.

* Donald W. Hoba, General Electric Company, Hanford Atomic Products Operation (HAPO), Richland, Washington. The author acknowledges the contributions and assistance of V. D. Donihee and C. J. Shortess, Jr.

A Hanford reactor is a large, homogeneous cube of graphite, approximately 30 ft on a side, built up of thousands of small blocks of graphite. Aluminum tubes extend horizontally through the reactor: these tubes convey the coolant support the uranium fuel element, and provide a convenient means of charging and discharging the fuel elements. The fuel elements are supported on two ribs that are extruded as a part of the tubes. Cooling water is pumped in the annulus between the fuel elements and the inside of the tube.

Fig. 13-1 Typical reactor area.

The fuel element is a short cylinder of natural uranium called a "slug." The fuel element is enclosed in an aluminum jacket well bonded to the fuel element. This jacket prevents both escape of fission products and corrosion of the fuel elements by the cooling water. The aluminum jackets, or cladding, must be well bonded to the uranium to insure rapid transfer of heat produced by fission in the uranium to the cooling water.

A reactor is loaded or charged with fuel elements by means of charging machines on the front face of the reactor. By pushing in fresh elements, and sometimes nonfuel spacers, irradiated elements are shoved out the rear of the reactor into a water-filled storage basin.

These elements, discharged after irradiation, contain uranium, plutonium, and highly radioactive fission products. Since direct exposure to them might be lethal to operating personnel, the area that encloses the discharge face of the reactor is heavily shielded with massive concrete walls and is cleared of all personnel during discharging operations.

The discharged fuel elements fall from their reactor tubes onto heavy rubber plates under several feet of water. Then they roll down inclined chutes to the bottom of the pool, where they are under 15 to 20 ft of water. Operators, shielded by the water and working with long tongs, pick them up from the floor, sort them, put them in buckets, weigh the buckets and store them elsewhere under the water of the pool, in "keys" until their radioactivity cools enough for shipment.

When a discharge has been accumulated in a key, an average weight, or

Fig. 13-2   A specially constructed railway car for transporting irradiated fuel elements.

"factor weight," for each uranium fuel element is determined. The plutonium produced and the U^{235} and total uranium burn-up are also determined. These determinations are made monthly in addition to the time when a discharge has been accumulated. Transfers from each key utilize the factor weight value to determine the total uranium weight of the transfer; plutonium weight and U^{235} content are determined by applying the applicable content percentage to the total weight transferred.

When the fuel elements are removed from the water, the reactor crane operator places them in lead casks and locks the lid of the cask with a remotely operated impact wrench. The casks are then placed in a water-filled well on a specially constructed railway car.

The irradiated fuel elements, still encased within the aluminum jackets, are transported from the reactors to chemical separation facilities in these cask cars. The cars normally have three compartments filled with water in which the containers of fuel elements are placed. This loading is done remotely owing to the high radiation level of the elements.

The separation of plutonium from uranium and the fission products has already been discussed in Chapter 10.

13-2. SS-MATERIAL CONTROL

13-2.1. Reactor Charge. All phases of fuel-element handling are governed by written standard operating procedures. A production scheduling group places an order for reactor fuel-element requirements with the Fuels Preparation Department. Such a production scheduling group acts as a clearing station for each of the reactors. The expected requirements of each reactor are forwarded to this group. Fuel elements are received from the Fuels Preparation Department in sealed vans, and a physical count of the elements is made by the responsible custodian. This custodian also directs and maintains the storage of all fuel elements assigned to the reactor. The fuel elements are taken from the van either directly to the reactor charging area or to a storage area, where they are kept under seal until needed. All fuel elements received into the charging area are inspected for quality. Each shipment, whether a receipt or a return of rejects to the Fuels Preparation Department, is documented on consecutively numbered material transfer forms. This form is initiated by the shipper, and two copies are forwarded to the SS Group. One copy is the original prepared by the shipper, the second is a copy showing the signature and acceptance of the receiver.

During storage of fuel elements in the reactor charging area, physical inventories by piece count are required at the beginning and end of each 8-hour shift. The piece count and identification are recorded in an operative log record. The fuel-element storage rooms are locked, and a numbered door seal system is used to control entry. A physical piece count is made before and after every material movement. The custodian maintains a record of these movements and conducts a weekly physical inventory of both work and sealed storage areas. Results of these inventories are recorded in his records and are also forwarded to the production scheduling group for over-all control purposes.

The month-end physical inventory is taken by the custodian in the same manner as his weekly inventories, and the results this time are forwarded to both the production scheduling group and the SS Group. This system provides a double check of piece count, one by the production scheduling group and the other by the SS Group.

Unscheduled interreactor transfers are at times necessary because of unprogramed reactor outages. The respective reactor supervisors must authorize each such transfer. The responsible custodians are notified in writing; they, in turn, notify production scheduling and the SS Group.

Fuel elements charged into a reactor are reported on consecutively numbered

Charge-Discharge Reports ("C-D Reports"), which show number, type, and factor weight of the fuel element charged. The discharge portion of the C-D report shows this information together with the associated number of megawatt days, number of tubes, average megawatt days per tube, and the sum of the squares of the individual tube exposures. The C-D report is the basic source data used by the SS Group in making the proper accounting entries for the movement of SS material through the reactor.

Copies of the C-D report are distributed to the receiver, to the receiver's SS Group, and to the shipper's SS Group; one copy is maintained by the shipper. This information is also reported to the production scheduling group by the custodian. A charge card is punched with the information contained on the C-D report. A complete tube-by-tube record of the loading charges is printed from these cards, and this provides the data necessary for the maintenance of a current record of fuel elements in a reactor.

Transfers of uranium are posted on work sheets by C-D report number and date. These work sheets are segregated by type of fuel element, factor weight, and account. At the month's end the work sheets are summarized, journal entries are prepared, and postings are made to the proper reactor account for number of pieces charged by fuel element type and total pounds of uranium and U^{235}. The U^{235} is calculated by multiplying isotopic concentration (0.7115 percent for normal uranium) times total pounds of uranium. After posting has been completed, a trial balance is drawn and cross checked with the month-end physical inventory.

Confirmation of receipts and shipments from and to other components within HAPO are obtained at the month's end via telephone. These movements of SS material are further verified at the time of the trial-balance cross check by the SS accounting group through interdepartmental eliminations.

The last C-D report for the calendar month is marked "ending report" so that a strict count of all charges and discharges is maintained.

All entries are based on factor weight times piece count. Factor weights are established by the measurements unit for each type of fuel element. Periodic reviews of factor weights in use are conducted and appropriate changes are made, based on independent measurements of material received from offsite manufacturers.

13-2.2. Reactor Discharge. When material is charged into the reactor, it is considered to be immediately irradiated. It leaves the charging area, where it can be physically inventoried, and enters an area where physical count is not practical (except by discharge); thus records must serve as the basis for inventory. All movements into and out of the reactor, except those in research and engineering controlled test holes, are covered by standard C-D reports that are completed by the custodians. These reports cover the movement of pieces or slugs only; no reference is made to any production during their time in the reactor.

Regular production material to be charged or discharged is specified by a production scheduling group. Special materials to be charged or discharged, such as production test material, can be scheduled by either production scheduling or reactor physics and engineering personnel.

Discharges from the reactor (uranium, U^{235}, and plutonium) are posted on work sheets by C-D report number as they are received after the proper calculations, based upon data contained in the C-D report, have been made. Total plutonium, U^{235}, and uranium discharged and transferred to the cooling basin is determined and posted on work sheets. At the month's end the work sheet is summarized, and journal entries are prepared and posted to the ledger (by reactor account) for grams of plutonium, pounds of uranium, and U^{235} transferred from the reactor to the cooling basin.

In addition to the above calculations, two more are made—monthly fission loss and plutonium production in the reactor. These two calculations are determined on the basis of by-difference accounting:

	Grams of Plutonium	Pounds U^{235} Consumed	Pounds Total Uranium Burn-out
Ending inventory in reactor	X	X	X
Plus: Discharges during month	X	X	X
Subtotal	XX	XX	XX
Less: Beginning inventory	X	X	X
Actual fission loss and plutonium production for the month	X	X	X

The resultant figures are posted to the reactor accounts in the journal and to the appropriate nominal accounts—i.e. Plutonium Produced and Fission Loss.

Physical inventory of reactor holdings is impossible; however, a book inventory of pieces by type of fuel geometry is maintained and cross checked with that reported by production scheduling.

A file of charge cards is maintained for each tube in each reactor. Each tube-loading card is kept current on a daily basis, describing the current loading of the tube, the production rate, the cumulative production in megawatt days, and several other reference or calculated quantities. When a reactor is shut down to discharge, the cards representing the loadings being discharged must be replaced with new cards representing the loadings being charged, (Fig. 13-3).

A C-D report and a charge card for each new tube loading are sent to the production scheduling group and the data processing group. The old tube-loading cards that match the new cards are removed from the tube-loading card file, and the information from the two cards is combined in a new tube-loading card. A printed single-draft report is prepared automatically by an accounting machine, which reads the tube-loading cards and prints the results in megawatt-day heat output. The single-draft report is a listing of each tube processed since the previous shutdown; the pre- and postshutdown loadings are described. The production of plutonium in the discharge is included. Before the new tube-loading cards are filed, the single-draft report is reviewed to determine which new tube loadings are changed enough to require new tube production factors. The factor corrections are made on the basis of the

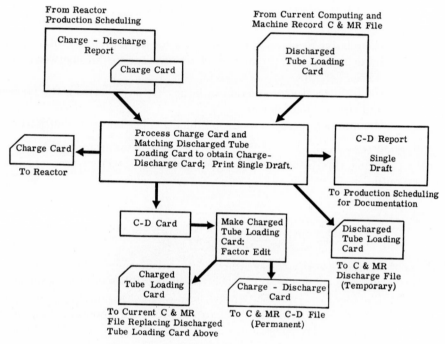

FIG. 13-3 Replacing a tube-loading record.

known variations that result from changes in tube loadings or slug geometries.

Each time a reactor is shut down for the discharge of a significant number of irradiated uranium charges, the calculated production of each tube record is updated to the time of the shutdown. At any particular time the current record deck for each reactor will contain the individual tube productions as of the previous discharge.

The tube record is updated by calculating a production increment and adding it to the tube production calculated at the previous shutdown. This computation can be expressed mathematically as

$$p_2 = p_1 + \Delta p_2 \qquad (13.1)$$

where p_2 = the tube production in megawatt days at the time of the present
shutdown

p_1 = the tube production in megawatt days at the time of the previous
discharge

Δp_2 = the individual tube production increment in megawatt days between the present and previous shutdowns

For purposes of routine machine calculation, individual tube production
Δp_2 is expressed as:

$$\Delta p_2 = FC_2 = \frac{F \, \Delta P_2}{N_2} \tag{13.2}$$

where F = the relative production rate or factor for the individual tube loading

C_2 = by definition, the production of the average loading between shutdowns

ΔP_2 = the total reactor production in megawatt days between the present
and the previous shutdown

N_2 = the number of active power-producing tubes between shutdowns

Individual tube loadings usually remain in the reactor from four to twelve
months. During this residence time, new production factors are calculated
once a month.

The difference of

$$\sum_{i=1}^{N_2} (p_2)_i - \sum_{i=1}^{N_1} (p_1)_i = \sum_{i=1}^{N_2} (\Delta p_2)_i = \Delta P_2 \tag{13.3}$$

is the method used to verify the accuracy of the calculations. Thus, the reactor
production ΔP_2, is assigned to all the heat-producing tubes in proportion to the
individual tube factors.

Large quantities of individual tube data are processed to obtain the production factors (Fig. 13-4). The following equation is used to calculate these
factors:

$$F = (\text{tube flow}) \times (\Delta T) \times (\text{constant}) \tag{13.4}$$

Tube coolant flows are calculated by feeding tube and header pressure data
to an electronic data processing machine. A deck of cards containing the individual tube flows then is combined with the difference between inlet and
outlet temperatures for the tube. The temperature difference data is in the
form of maps (T maps) and punched paper tapes. Three sets of temperature
data are usually taken with each set of flow data to calculate a single set of
factors representative of the average reactor operation. Each factor calculation is an average of these three sets of data.

Each factor calculation is edited for transcription and instrumentation
errors. For each factor a limiting range of deviation from the average of

surrounding tube factors is defined. The actual deviations are calculated for all tubes by a calculator, which automatically identifies tubes having factors outside the limiting ranges. The data pertinent to these tubes are listed, and then experienced editors determine any necessary corrections. The factors for the heat producing tubes are corrected, and some minor adjustments generally

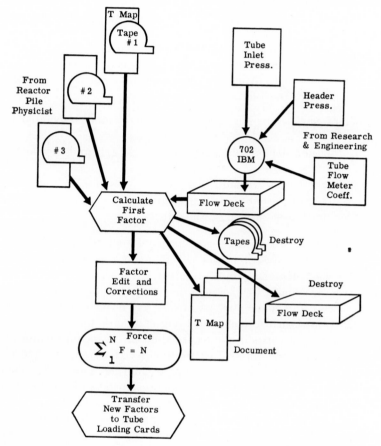

FIG. 13-4 Relative production rate (factor) calculation for a single reactor.

are necessary to make the sum of the factors equal the output of active production tubes.

13-2.3. Cooling Basin. The C-D report from the discharge area and the single draft report constitute the input source data for the cooling basin. The amount of depleted uranium, U^{235}, plutonium, and the associated megawatt days are calculated from data on the reports; these values are then posted to the appropriate subsidiary basin account, posted to a work sheet, and assigned a key (identification by date of discharge for cooling purposes).

Using prorated piece and megawatt-day data supplied by production scheduling, processing personnel complete a bucket loading summary. This form lists each bucket (approximately 1 ton per bucket) of the discharge, giving its location in the storage basin, its weight, the number of pieces contained in it, and the assigned megawatt-day value. The report is submitted to production scheduling in duplicate for verification, and then one copy is sent to the SS Group for use in shipping the discharge to chemical separation facilities after a suitable cooling period.

Additions to a basin are reconciled with the bucket loading summary and with an attached memorandum inventory work sheet. Reconciliation is made as to the number of fuel elements discharged, the associated megawatt days, and the disposition of the fuel elements as follows:

1. Number of buckets in key, pieces per bucket, and associated megawatt days
2. Number of fuel elements being held for research and development purposes
3. Partial bucket held without key number assignment (since only full buckets are transferred to the separations process, partial buckets are held over until next discharge and filled).

Transfers from the basin are made primarily to the chemical separation facilities with some to research and development groups and off site as per AEC instructions. Material transfer forms are received from the area clerk when transfers are made to chemical separations. The data (key number, number of pieces, and associated megawatt days) recorded on the form are compared with data on the bucket loading summary for that particular key to ensure that no error exists in the recorded data. A memorandum is received from chemical separations indicating the facility that is to receive the metal. Further calculations are necessary for accounting purposes; namely, the pieces are multiplied by the factor weights assigned to depleted uranium for that particular key to obtain total pounds of depleted uranium transferred. In turn, total pounds of depleted uranium transferred are multiplied by factor weights assigned U^{235} and plutonium, respectively, to compute the amount of U^{235} and plutonium shipped.

The data on the transfer form and the data resulting from the calculations are posted to a work sheet (one for each separations facility) by transfer number. The transfer slips are numbered consecutively for each balance area and recorded in a log book, thereby assuring control of all transfers.

A standard form is used to record the receipt and transfer of metal to and from research and development groups. It is prepared by the area clerk and forwarded to the SS Group in case of shipment from the basin, or it is prepared by the research and development custodians and forwarded to the SS Group in cases of transfers to the basins.

Form AEC-101 is prepared by the SS Group on the basis of memorandum data prepared and forwarded on forms by the area clerk and production scheduling in cases of off-site shipments.

At the month's end the individual work sheets are summarized; data are entered in a journal and posted to the ledger accounts. Also, shipments to separations are verified by telephone with the SS Groups and at the time of consolidation of area reports by the SS Group.

Basin ledger balances are then compared with the inventory taken and reported by the area clerk at the month's end.

Calculations in regard to the basin inventory, which is maintained on the basis of uranium, U^{235}, plutonium, and associated megawatt days, are as follows:

1. Quantities of depleted uranium discharged, as indicated on the bucket loading summary and attached memo inventory work sheet (segregated per disposition, key, research and development holdings, and heel), are divided by the number of applicable pieces. This results in a depleted uranium factor weight applicable to each fuel element.

2. Total U^{235} and plutonium divided by total depleted uranium results in a factor weight applicable to each fuel element for the respective SS material per inventory group.

These factor weights are also documented monthly and forwarded to SS Group for use in determining the amount of SS material received.

Weekly basin inventories are logged in the central SS inventory ledger. Monthly basin inventories are forwarded to production scheduling and the SS Group.

13-2.4. Measurement of Power Level. The power levels of the reactors are measured by special power calculators that integrate the total heat output to the process cooling water. Heat is transferred to the cooling water from the process tubes, the thermal shield, and the horizontal rods. Heat is lost to the reactor gas atmosphere, some to the rod cooling water, and an additional percentage is liberated from the slugs and graphite after shutdown or after discharge; but the total of these losses is insignificant when calculating the reactor's production.

Instruments measure the heat output during each irradiation process. Evidence of heat output is the increase in temperature of the cooling water during its passage through the reactor. The product of temperature rise and the quantity of water flow directly measures the quantity of energy being produced. Two methods of measuring these variables are used. One employs the average of bulk values of flow and temperature and the other is based on a measure of individual tube values of flow and temperature.

Bulk System. The rate of water flow is obtained from venturi or orifice plates in the water supply lines to the reactor. Each reactor has from two to four such elements. Differential pressure across such a device is proportional to the amount of flow. The device is connected to a sensing meter in the control room. These meters are calibrated in gallons of water per minute. Temperatures are obtained from resistance temperature-sensitive elements inserted in the inlet and outlet water headers. Each reactor requires four to six temperature-sensitive elements with interconnecting wires leading to the control room.

The accuracy of water-flow measurement is maintained at ±2 percent of total flow at operating levels. Reactor influent water-flow meters are head checked and calibrated at six-month intervals by instrument technicians. In addition, the total recording of these meters is checked against the drop in water level of process-water storage tanks during a fixed time interval. This drop test is supervised by process engineers. Temperature data are checked daily with a certified standard thermometer.

Total energy calculations based on bulk measurements have an estimated accuracy of ±2 percent.

Individual Tube System. The system for individual tube heat output is much more extensive. Individual tube flows are controlled by inlet venturi or orifice plates that have been calibrated before installation. An individual tube outlet flow can be determined from measurements of pressure at a tap downstream from the orifice or at the venturi throat end of the supply header pressure. The pressures for each tube and each header are indicated in the control room on individual pressure gauges calibrated in pounds per square inch. Inlet water temperature-sensing primary elements are similar to those used in the bulk system. However, outlet water temperatures are obtained from a primary element (thermocouple or temperature-sensitive resistance element) at the outlet end of each tube. Long lead wires are required to bring the signal from the reactor rear face to the control room. An automatic scanning system presents successive signals to a potentiometric recorder.

The individual tube water-pressure gauges are checked by master gauges during each reactor shutdown. It is estimated that the basic accuracy of calculations for the individual flow measuring devices is ±1 percent. Expected errors in the upstream and downstream pressure measurements account for an additional possible error of ±2 percent. The conclusion is that the present estimation of individual tube flows is no more accurate than ±3 percent. However, this ±3 percent figure represents the estimated possible error in the calculated flow rate for a single tube. If a large number of tube coolant flow rates is calculated, most of these errors will be canceled, and the average tube flow rate can be calculated to within ±1 percent.

The inherent accuracy of the individual tube effluent-water temperature instrumentation is estimated at ±1 percent of reading at the time of installation. However, neutron bombardment at the rear face deteriorates the signal system, and periodic replacement of critical circuitry has been necessary. The numerous components required to scan, measure, and record these individual tube outlet temperatures introduce errors with the passage of time.   Over a period of years the average accuracy of this system is estimated at ±2 percent of operating values.

13-2.5. Computing Plutonium Produced.   The   amount   of   plutonium produced by neutron irradiation is computed from heat output and is distributed among the reactor tubes in accordance with the individual tube production factors (Eq. 13.4).   The amount of plutonium produced is proportional to the heat output; however, the conversion ratio decreases as heat output (megawatt day per ton) increases.   This conversion ratio, reduced from a convergent power series, is of the form:

$$\text{Conversion ratio} \left(\frac{\text{grams Pu}}{\text{ton U}} \right) = aEe^{-bE} \qquad (13.5)$$

where a and b are constants that are different for each type (geometry and U^{235} content) of uranium and E is the heat output in megawatt days per ton. Equation 13.5 can also be used to derive total uranium consumed or U^{235} consumed with different values for the constants.

These equations are generally derived by combining actual recovery data with theoretical precepts.   The constants are semiempirical and fit a small amount of experimental data.   Liberal use of extrapolation techniques is made when determining constants for new and different fuel element types. It is necessary in utilizing such techniques to make certain assumptions regarding neutron temperature, heat of fission, cross-section values, and initial conversion ratios.

Uncertainties in these equations are due to:

1. Neglecting all terms beyond the first in the power series
2. Limited amount of experimental data over the entire operating range
3. Changes in fuel element types
4. Changes in reactor charge patterns
5. Uncertainties associated with cross sections and other physical constants
6. Variances of the measuring devices

Of all the uncertainties, the one it is most necessary to eliminate is the lack of adequate experimental data.   Sufficient and reliable experiments could either eliminate or hold the other uncertainties to a minimum.

A system of data-processing machines located in one of the reactors is utilized to perform the calculations and to maintain tube loading record cards containing inventory, production, and scheduling information.   The processing of punched cards includes: (1) the replacement of the tube-loading record card as each loading is discharged, (2) the periodic updating of the calculated production of all loadings, and (3) the periodic processing of reactor data to yield relative production rates for all tube loadings.   Figs. 13.3 and 13.4 illustrate the flow of information and the calculations.

The stability essential for these conversion computations is impractical for efficient and progressive operating reasons. With the advent of mixed tube loadings and multiple reactor patterns a definite need for an entire new approach to computation of transmutations has been recognized. Therefore a more highly monitored reactor or another method of computing conversion, such as a correlation with the isotopic content of the reactor coolant or flux, is necessary.

The individual tube transmutations can be computed from heat outputs determined by either of two methods: averaging the total reactor heat outputs or using individual tube heat output records already on a data processing card. The former method requires a bias correction, since the conversion expressions are not linear. The latter method has become economically possible, regardless of reactor pattern or tube charge, with the advent of high-speed data computing machines. In practice this amounts to simply making an additional pass through the machine. A summary of this program is as follows:

1. Convert the heat output of each tube into transmutation units at the time of
   a. Month-end inventories
   b. Discharge
2. Sum all values, plutonium, U^{235}, and total uranium by fuel element type
3. Compute each month the sum of the reactors' activities
4. Detect errors or omissions
5. Eliminate the necessary bias corrections and the usual numerical round-overs necessary with manual calculations

13-3. ACCOUNTS

The accounting for SS material is maintained through the use of a standard journal-entry system, fully supported by working papers, and a double-entry ledger. This system adapts itself to internal control as well as accurate and speedy reporting.

The SS Group uses four ledgers to maintain individual nominal and real accounts for SS-material transfers. The title of each ledger and the SS material accounted for are as follows:

TITLE	SS MATERIAL ACCOUNTED FOR
1. Reactor Operations—Normal Uranium Ledger	U
2. Reactor Operations—Depleted Uranium Ledger	U, U^{235}, plutonium, megawatt days
3. Reactor Operations—Enriched and Special Nuclear Materials	U, U^{235}, plutonium, and other SS material, as occasion arises
4. Engineering Operations—All SS Materials	U, U^{235}, plutonium, megawatt days

The normal flow of material through the process is as follows:

1. Receipt of normal-uranium fuel elements from the Fuels Preparation Department
2. Charging into the reactor
3. Discharging into the cooling basin
4. Transfers to chemical separations and off site

In addition, there are side transfers between components of the Irradiation Processing Department as well as transfers between components of the Irradiation Processing Department and the components of other departments and operations.

Each movement of material, regardless of its position in the flow pattern, is accompanied by a material transfer form signed by both the shipper and receiver so that the physical location and condition of the material can be followed.

Source data include the following:

1. Interdepartmental SS material transfers
2. Charge-discharge report
3. Material transfer (irradiated material to Research and Development)
4. Material transfer (separations)
5. Bucket loading summary
6. Cold-material inventory
7. Hot-material inventory in basin (depleted)
8. Hot-material inventory in basin (enriched and special)
9. Irradiation Processing Department—SS Material Inventory (Research and Development components, all materials)
10. Production report, Irradiation Processing Department, issued and documented monthly
11. AEC shipping form
12. Miscellaneous memorandum inventory papers

The accounting procedure, reduced to its barest essential, is that of inventory accounting (beginning inventory plus receipts minus shipments equals ending inventory).

The only calculation performed is that of piece count times applicable factor weight to obtain weight of SS material in inventory or associated with a specific transaction.

Research and Development components receive metal from Reactor Operations or other HAPO components at the material content the shipper's accounts reflect. It is booked at this weight and returned to other HAPO components at the same weight unless there is a loss of material through testing. Such loss is recorded in the proper account, and the inventory account is adjusted to reflect the proper valuation.

Monthly inventories are reported on an unnumbered form entitled Irradiation Processing Departments—SS Material Inventory, which lists the number of fuel elements by factor weight by material category. Also listed are the identifying allotment and quota numbers.

All movements of SS material are summarized at the month's end, entered into journals, and posted to the proper ledger accounts. Month-end inventory balances by balance area are compared with inventories reported by the SS material custodian.

A separate account is maintained for each cold storage area, reactor, and cooling basin. The same account number is used for each category of material within each cold storage area, reactor, or cooling basin. For example, storage accounts would be used to identify inventories of normal uranium, special depleted uranium (unirradiated), enriched uranium, and thorium. The same would apply to in-reactor accounts, and in-basin accounts for different material categories. The description of accounts that follows is applicable to all SS-material categories unless otherwise specified.

The description of accounts states that they are debited and credited for movement of SS material and U^{235}. Uranium-235 is accounted for separately in order to provide memorandum control of isotopic content.

13-3.1. Inventory Accounts: *In-Storage.* In-storage accounts represent the unirradiated-metal inventory and are established primarily for the purpose of receiving and storing unirradiated fuel elements until they are needed for charging into the reactor. These accounts are debited with the following:

1. Weight of SS material (piece count times factor weight) received from Fuels Preparation Department (primary source of metal), other HAPO components, and off site.
2. Uranium-235 associated with any special depleted and enriched uranium (calculated on the basis of percentage of U^{235} times the amount of uranium received) included in (1) above.
3. Inventory differences, i.e. the excess of the physical over the book inventory.

These accounts are credited with the following:

1. Weight of SS material transferred to other SS-material balances, other HAPO components, and charged into the reactor (piece count times factor weight).
2. Uranium-235 associated with any special depleted and enriched uranium (on the basis of the percentage of U^{235} times amount of uranium transferred), included in (1) above.
3. Inventory differences, i.e. the excess of book over physical inventory.

The balances in these accounts represent the weight of SS material and the U^{235} content of any depleted and enriched uranium on hand in cold storage.

In-Reactor.   In-reactor accounts represent the material being irradiated and reflect amounts of material in process, consumed, and transmuted (production).   These accounts are debited with the following:

1. Weight of SS material received (piece count times factor weight) from other SS categories and direct from cold-metal storage.
2. Uranium-235, if any, associated with the above SS material charged into the reactors (calculated on the basis of percentage of U^{235} times the amount of uranium charged).
3. Plutonium produced based on the amount of megawatt days generated in each reactor during the month.
4. Inventory differences, i.e. the excess of the physical over the book inventory.

These accounts are credited with the following:

1. Weight of SS material discharged from the reactors to the basins.
2. Uranium-235 associated with any depleted and enriched uranium included in the SS material mentioned in (1) above.
3. Fission loss of U^{235} and U^{238} in reactors.
4. Inventory differences, i.e. the excess of the book inventory over the physical inventory.

The balances in these accounts represent the weight of SS material on hand in the reactors.

In-Basin.   In-basin accounts represent irradiated material being held in the cooling basins until either the proper degree of cooling has been achieved or until the material is required by the separation plants.   These accounts are debited with the following:

1. Weight of SS material discharged from the reactors to the basins (piece count times factor weight).
2. Uranium-235 associated with any depleted and enriched uranium discharged.
3. Weight of SS material returned to the basins from other components of HAPO (primarily research and development components).
4. Uranium-235 associated with the above SS material noted in (3).
5. Weight of SS material and the U^{235} associated with such SS material received in transfers from one basin to another.
6. Inventory difference, i.e. the excess of the physical over the book inventory.

These accounts are credited with the following:

1. Weight of SS material and the U^{235} associated with such SS material removed from the basins to separation plants, other HAPO components, or off site.

2. Weight of SS material and the U^{235} associated with such SS material removed in transfers from one basin to another.
3. Inventory differences, i.e. the excess of book inventory over the physical inventory.

The balances in these accounts represent the weight of SS material and the U^{235} associated with such material on hand in the basins.

Research and Development Accounts. Research and development accounts represent inventories held by groups in Research and Engineering Operation and Facilities Engineering Operation. The same account number is used for each type of material in the possession of the group because of the uniform system of accounts. These accounts are debited with the SS material weight of:

1. Normal, depleted, or enriched uranium received from other components of HAPO and other operations offices.
2. Uranium-235 associated with the above-mentioned depleted and enriched uranium.
3. Plutonium associated with the above-mentioned depleted and enriched uranium.
4. Inventory differences, i.e. the excess of the physical over the book inventory.

These accounts are credited with the SS material weight of:

1. Normal uranium, depleted uranium, and enriched uranium removed to separation plants, other HAPO components, or off site.
2. Uranium-235 and plutonium associated with the above-mentioned depleted uranium and enriched uranium.
3. Inventory differences, i.e. the excess of book inventory over physical inventory.

The balances in these accounts represent the SS-material weight of normal uranium, depleted uranium, enriched uranium, U^{235}, and plutonium in the component's possession.

13-3.2. AEC Control of SS Material Accounts: *Fiscal Year Beginning Inventory.* This account represents the SS material responsibility accepted at the beginning of the fiscal year. No entries are made during the year to this account, other than adjustments of the prior fiscal year's inventories. At the end of the fiscal year, adjusting entries are made, closing the nominal operating accounts.

Production. This account is credited with the weight of SS material produced in the reactors based on the megawatt days generated in each reactor during the month.

The balance in this account represents total SS material produced for the fiscal year to date.

At the end of the fiscal year the balance in this account is transferred to the Fiscal Year Beginning Inventory account as part of the year-end closing entries.

Other SS-Material Balances—Normal Uranium.   This account is credited with the SS material weight of:

1. Normal uranium withdrawn from storage and charged into reactors.
2. Uranium-235 associated with the above normal uranium charged into reactors and calculated on the basis of 0.007115 times the weight of uranium charged.

At the end of the fiscal year the balance in this account is transferred to the Fiscal Year Beginning Inventory account as part of the year-end closing entries.

The balance in this account represents total material received from Other SS Material Balances—Normal Uranium for the fiscal year-to-date.

Other Operations Offices; Fuels Preparation Department—Engineering; Fuels Preparation Department—Manufacturing; Irradiation Processing Department—Engineering; Irradiation Processing Department—Manufacturing; and *Hanford Laboratories Operations.*   These accounts are credited with the following:

1. Weight of SS material received from off site and from the above-listed HAPO components.
2. Uranium-235 associated with depleted uranium and enriched uranium included in (1) above.

At the end of the fiscal year the balances in these accounts are transferred to the Fiscal Year Beginning Inventory account as part of the year-end closing entries.

The balances in these accounts represent total SS material received from the above-listed HAPO components and other operations offices for the fiscal year to date.

Removals—Book-Physical Inventory Differences.   This account is debited with the difference in SS material weight between book and physical inventory of SS material.   Corresponding credit is to the proper inventory account.

Credits to this account represent the difference in SS material weight between the physical inventory and the book inventory.   Corresponding debit is to the proper inventory account.

At the end of the fiscal year the balance in this account is transferred to the Fiscal Year Beginning Inventory account as part of the year-end closing entries.

The balance in this account represents Inventory Differences (book and physical) for the fiscal year to date for the specific SS material.

Approved Inventory Write-offs; Stored; and *Discarded.*   Debits to these accounts represent the SS material written off the books. As the account titles indicate, it may be stored in suitable containers and be available for recovery at a later date, or it may be discarded and, therefore, unrecoverable.

At the end of the fiscal year the balances in these accounts are transferred to the Fiscal Year Beginning Inventory account as part of the year-end closing entries.

The balances in these accounts represent the total of Approved Inventory Write-Offs for the fiscal year to date.

Fission Loss. Debits to this account represent fission loss of U^{235} and U^{238} in reactors. At the end of the fiscal year the balance in this account is transferred to the Fiscal Year Beginning Inventory account as part of the year-end closing entries.

The balance in this account represents total fission loss in reactors of U^{235} and U^{238} for the fiscal year to date.

Other SS-Material Balances—Depleted Uranium. Debits to this account represent the SS material weight of:

1. Normal uranium withdrawn from storage and charged into the reactors.

At the end of the fiscal year the balance in this account is transferred to the Fiscal Year Beginning Inventory account as part of the year-end closing entries.

The balance in this account represents the total normal uranium removed to Other SS-Material Balances—Depleted Uranium for the fiscal year to date.

Material Removed to Other Operations Offices; Fuels Preparation Department—Engineering; Fuels Preparation Department—Manufacturing; Irradiation Processing Department—Engineering; Irradiation Processing Department—Manufacturing; Hanford Laboratories Operation; and *Chemical Separations.* Debit these accounts with the following:

1. Weight of SS material transferred off site and to the HAPO components listed above.
2. Uranium-235 associated with depleted uranium and enriched uranium included in (1) above.

At the end of the fiscal year the balances in these accounts are transferred to the Fiscal Year Beginning Inventory account as part of the year-end closing entries.

The balances in these accounts represent total SS material transferred to the above-listed HAPO components for the fiscal year to date.

13-4. REPORTS

The principal reports prepared monthly are the Trial Balance Report, Production Report, Report to Cost, and Report of Receipts and Shipments.

13-4.1. Trial Balance Report. This report reflects month-end book balances in the inventory accounts (by balance area), fiscal year beginning inventory in the AEC Control Account, fiscal year to date totals for receipts and removals by account, and the fiscal year to date total AEC-Control. There is a total of 10 trial balance reports covering all SS material categories on hand for Reactor Operations and Engineering Operations. These reports are forwarded to the SS Group for consolidation with the reports of other SS control units for transmission to AEC.

13-4.2. Monthly Production Report. This report (plutonium production) is also forwarded to the SS Group and is made an attachment to the associated Trial Balance Report.

13-4.3. Report to Cost. Three in number, one for Engineering Operations, one for Reactor Operations (normal and depleted uranium), and one for Reactor Operations (enriched and special nuclear materials), these reports summarize the month's transactions by accounts (beginning inventory plus receipts, less shipments plus or minus adjustments, ending inventory) for use in dollar accounting for cost purposes.

13-4.4. Report of Receipts and Shipments. This report reflects total receipts from and shipments to other AEC operations. The operations office involved, type of material, and weight are reported. Distribution is to the SS group, AEC, and publisher's file.

Part Six

RECOVERY

Chapter 14

ENRICHED-URANIUM SCRAP RECOVERY *

14-1. INTRODUCTION

This chapter is devoted to the recovery of unirradiated highly enriched uranium fuel-element fabrication scrap. The approach is one that is applied in the job-shop recovery of fabrication scrap from a number of different fuel systems. The recovery facilities described supply the recovery needs of a number of fuel element fabricators.

The recovery of highly enriched uranium (e.g. uranium enriched to a U^{235} concentration of 20 percent or greater) is complicated by factors not present, at least to the same degree, in the recovery of natural uranium.

14-1.1. High Value of Enriched Uranium. First, since the uranium is highly enriched, it is considerably more valuable than natural uranium. The value of the material requires a control effort more intense than that applied to the less costly materials. Careful attention must be given to the smallest chances for losses, accumulations of in-process holdup, and in areas where different isotopic concentrations are processed, the possibility of crossover.

Of particular importance is the design of methods and equipment. The system used to process highly enriched uranium is designed to contain all the uranium within it. There are no unmeasured effluent streams. All exhausts are carefully filtered, and the stacks are equipped with samplers to detect filter leakage. When dry and dusty materials are handled, they are contained within gloved boxes provided with filtered exhausts. These filters consist of porous carbon or paper roughing filters backed by absolute filters. Period- ically, all filters are removed and burned to recover the contained uranium. There are no process drains in the enriched processing areas. All spills are cleaned up with sponges or mops, and the solutions are returned to the system. Liquid effluents are first routed to tanks for sampling and, if the concentration is low enough, then to settling ponds. If the concentrations are above the economic discard level, the solutions are reprocessed. The measurement

* R. F. Hibbs, Union Carbide Nuclear Company Y-12 Plant, Oak Ridge, Tennessee. The author gratefully acknowledges the assistance of J. R. Barkman, R. R. Levey, and J. E. Smyrl in the preparation of this chapter.

357

methods, including weighing, sampling, and chemical and isotopic analysis, must be of the highest quality. Small systematic errors in these measurements will result in apparent losses of a large number of dollars, or what is more serious, obscure actual losses.

14-1.2. Nuclear Safety. A second complicating factor in the processing of enriched uranium is the requirement for nuclear safety. Since processing of this type is done with unshielded equipment, stringent measures must be taken to avoid a critical accumulation of uranium in the process area or equipment. A number of methods are used to prevent this accumulation.

Geometric control, which relies upon equipment design and placement to build safety into the system, provides the best nuclear safety precaution. This type of control, however, is not sufficient without good administrative practices. For example, a given solution of enriched uranium can be safely handled in a tank or extraction column of restricted geometry, i.e. less than 5-in. in diameter and placed more than 2 ft from other uranium-containing material. But the collection of this solution from a leak in the tank or column in a 30-gal drum could result in a nuclear reaction with subsequent property damage and loss of life. Since it is beyond the scope of this chapter to discuss nuclear safety in detail, the reader is referred to Refs. 1 and 2.

14-1.3. Health. The third complicating feature of unirradiated enriched uranium processing is the health hazard. As U^{235} is enriched in the gaseous diffusion cascade, U^{234} is also enriched. This isotope is intensely alpha active, being approximately three thousand times more active than U^{235}. The external radiological damage resulting from the alpha activity of U^{234} is minimal; but when this material is ingested or inhaled, the hazard becomes acute. Therefore, it is necessary to prevent the uranium from entering the body.

Inhalation of enriched uranium compounds of low solubility is serious, and equipment and processes must be designed to prevent it. In particular, the processing of dry, dusty materials must be carefully controlled. Processing of this type is generally best accomplished in gloved boxes operating at a negative pressure with respect to ambient and thus permitting only in-leakage and preserving the cleanliness of the general work area. Generally speaking, the use of open-face hoods is not satisfactory for this purpose since the high-velocity air flow may create turbulence, releasing significant amounts of the material into the work area. For a more detailed discussion of this problem, reference is made to the various publications of the National Bureau of Standards and others.[3-10]

14-2 SURVEY OF MAJOR PROCESSES

The job-shop recovery of enriched uranium from a number of sources is accomplished in three main steps; head-end processing to permit sampling, purification, and metal production.

14-2.1. Head-End Process. In the job-shop recovery of enriched uranium, the material must first be processed to a point where a representative sample can be taken. Combustible material for example, must first be reduced to ash by burning; the ash must then be ground or milled to ensure homogeneity; and finally the ash is sampled by a suitable technique. Such processing must be accomplished without mixing the material from one source with that from another. The process must also be quantitative to ensure that all the uranium contained in the combustibles is retained in the ash.

Presampling processing is required also for other materials received for recovery. Uranium-zirconium alloy fines are generally shipped immersed in oil and must be separated from the oil and dissolved prior to sampling. Many solutions are recived with suspended or settled solids. These materials must be separated, and each phase must be homogenized and sampled. In all presampling treatments, provision must be made for quantitative handling and careful segregation of materials from various sources so that proper credit can be established.

14-2.2. Recovery. The second main step in job-shop recovery is the recovery and purification of the uranium contained in the scrap. The most common technique used for this is solvent extraction. This technique requires the dissolution of the solid materials in acids and the contacting of these solutions with a suitable organic material that preferentially removes the uranium from the feed solution. The organic material is then further contacted with water under proper conditions to produce a pure solution of uranyl nitrate. Other systems, such as ion exchange, precipitation, pyrometallurgical processes, and fluorination, are also applied to the purification problem.

14-2.3. Metal Production. The final step in the scrap recovery plant under consideration is the conversion of the purified uranyl nitrate to uranium metal. This is accomplished by denitrating the solution by either chemical or thermal means and treating the resulting UO_3 with hydrogen to yield UO_2. This material is then processed to UF_4 by reacting it with anhydrous HF. The UF_4 is reduced to metal with a suitable alkaline earth metal such as calcium or magnesium. The uranyl nitrate resulting from the purification facility can also be processed to yield other reactor fuel materials such as uranyl sulphate and uranium dioxide.

14-3. RECEIVING AND STORAGE

14-3.1. Containers. The shipment of large amounts of highly enriched uranium poses some unique problems. Not only must the containers be of sturdy construction, but they must also be fabricated of material that will withstand, in many cases, the attack of acid solutions.

A further requirement is that of nuclear safety. There are essentially two types of containers used to transfer enriched uranium scrap. The first of these is the restricted-geometry type in which the actual volume of the container is limited. With this type an angle-iron cage surrounding the actual container physically separates similar containers. Fig. 14-1 shows a restricted-geometry

container used to ship dry materials such as metal, highly concentrated alloys, and compounds. Fig. 14-2 shows a restricted-geometry container used to ship concentrated solutions. The container is 5 in. in diameter, and the pipe cage prevents improper spacing. Fig. 14-3 is a sketch of a standard 55-gal drum modified to provide proper spacing for several 1-gal cans of enriched scrap.

The second general type of container used to ship enriched scrap is more standard. Steel drums and polyethylene carboys (Fig. 14.4) are used to ship dilute solutions, dry low-concentration scrap, such as combustibles, and con-

FIG. 14-1   Dry-material shipping container.

taminated nonuranium fabrication scrap.

Proper identification of the shipping containers is extremely important in the job-shop recovery plant. It is desirable that each container be identified as to shipment and container number and that it show the gross, tare, and net weights. These identifying items should be listed on the transfer form so that an item-count and gross-weight verification can be obtained immediately upon receipt at the recovery plant. It is also desirable that similar items be grouped on a single transfer form. In this way material of high concentration which is suitable to fast recovery can be processed ahead of dilute material, and the completion of the measurements and transfer forms will not be held up by the slower processing of low uranium material.

14-3.2. Materials Storage. Frequently the job-shop recovery plant will operate on a campaign basis for processing similar materials for a given period of time. An operation of this type requires the storage of materials until such time as their chemical composition is appropriate for the processing campaign. For materials that are to be warehoused while awaiting processing, the gross weights of the containers are verified and all items are accounted for. Should a discrepancy occur between shipper and receiver data, it is resolved at once. The shipment is then placed in storage, and the storage records indicate the shipment number, source, number of containers, type of material, bulk weight, and estimated uranium content. This information is tabulated for the supervisory personnel of the recovery facility to permit planning of the processing campaigns. All containers from the shipment are kept in a single storage lot, each lot being properly identified. Nuclear safety provisions are recognized, and care is exercised to prevent the violation of safe storage limits. Fig. 14-5 shows a typical storage area for concentrated solutions. The individual containers are of the restricted-geometry type, and their spacing is ensured by the rack shown. The standard shipping containers (i.e. drums and carboys) are stored edge to edge with a 3-ft aisle separating row from row, as shown in Fig. 14-6.

FIG. 14-2 Liquid-material shipping container.

14-3.3. Shipper-Receiver Discrepancies. It is not uncommon for discrepancies to occur between the shipper's stated uranium content of a shipment and that determined by the recovery plant. The most common cause of this is the by-difference estimation made by the shipper of the uranium content of scrap unsuitable for sampling. Errors in weights and item count can be easily adjusted; however, sampling and analytical errors by either the shipper or the receiver are more difficult to resolve.

In all cases the retention sample is held by the recovery plant until the final determination of the amount of uranium in the shipment. This sample is large enough to allow reanalysis by the shipper and the receiver as well as by a referee laboratory, if necessary. Generally, the receiver's measure-

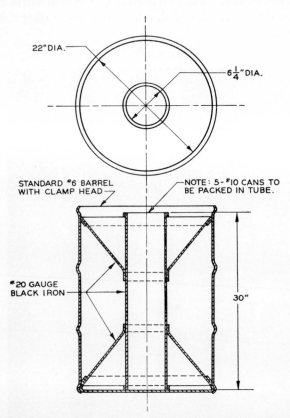

FIG. 14-3 Modified drum arrangement for enriched-scrap shipment.

ments are accepted on materials not suitable for sampling when the shipper has used the by-difference method in estimating their uranium concentration.

14-4. HEAD-END PROCESSES

The recovery plant contains a variety of head-end processes used to process the scrap to a point where its uranium content can be reliably measured and prepare it for a common purification system. These head-end systems are designed to produce material suitable for sampling with the minimum number of operations possible. The systems process material from only one source at a time to prevent mixing it with material from other sources. When a shipment is brought into the processing area, a numbered processing batch card is

FIG. 14-4 Typical containers for low-concentration scrap.

assigned to each container. These numbers, together with the following information, are then entered in the processing log:

Source
Transfer form number
Bulk weights: gross, tare, and net
Estimated uranium and U^{235} content
Matrix elements
Anions
Physical state
Previous processing history (if available)

FIG. 14-5 Storage area for high-concentration materials.

As the batches move through the processing sequence, each container is accompanied by its batch card, and a record of the processing operations is kept in the processing log.   As they become available, the results of the analytical measurements are entered in the log, and all calculations of uranium content are maintained in it.   Frequently, as the material is processed from the original containers to the sampling point, consolidation of batches will occur.   This consolidation is done on a weight basis, and the data are entered in the processing log.

FIG. 14-6   Safe-storage arrangement for shipping containers.

The chemical treatment given the scrap to process it to a sampling point in the head-end process varies with the type of scrap received.

14-4.1. High-Purity Solids.   Highly concentrated, relatively pure materials such as metal, oxide, and other compounds are dissolved in nitric acid in restricted-geometry equipment, and the resulting solution is filtered.   The dissolvers used are shown in Figs. 14-7 and 14-8.   The filtrate is sampled, and any residue is burned, milled, and sampled.

Alloys are dissolved prior to sampling; the solvent used will depend upon the alloy being processed.   Uranium-zirconium alloy is dissolved in hydrofluoric and nitric acids; stainless steel–uranium alloys are either dissolved anodically in nitric acid or dissolved in aqua regia.   Uranium-aluminum alloys are dissolved in caustic to remove the aluminum as sodium aluminate solution, and the residual uranium oxide is dissolved in nitric acid.   The caustic solution is sampled and discarded, and the nitric solution is sampled and pumped to the purification system. Flow sheets for these operations are shown in Figs. 14-9 and 14-10.

14-4.2. Scrap-Uranium Solutions. Solutions are homogenized and sampled unless there is evidence of suspended or settled solids or other immiscible

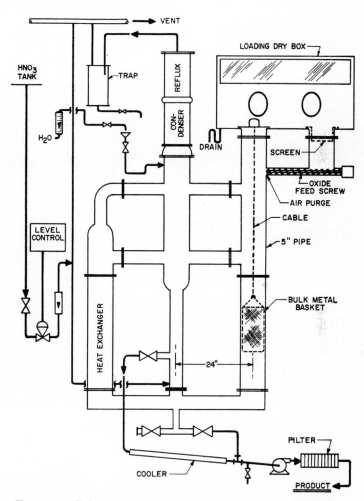

FIG. 14-7 Safe-geometry uranium metal and oxide dissolver.

materials. In this case the phases are separated, and each is homogenized and sampled. Combustible materials are burned to ash in batch incinerators, and the resultant ash is milled to ensure homogeneity prior to sampling.

14-4.3. Contaminated Nonuranium Scrap. Contaminated nonuranium fabrication scrap is sorted by conveying it over scintillation counters; material showing significant activity is leached in acid, and the resulting solution is

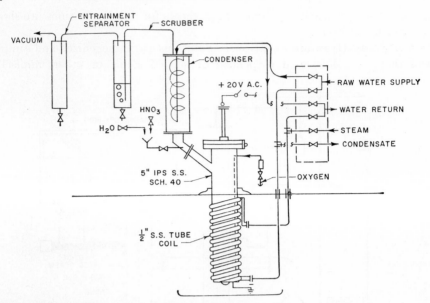

Fig. 14-8   Chip burner and dissolver.

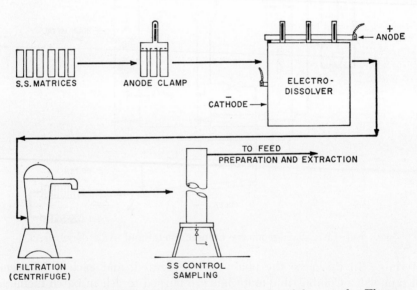

Fig. 14-9   Flow Sheet for anodic dissolution of stainless steel. Electro-dissolver operating conditions are: current density 0.49 amp/cm², voltage 5 to 6 volts, dissolution rate 364 gm/kw-hr, operating temperature 100–105°C, electrolyte 4 M HNO₃, anode holder is a stainless steel clamp; cathode is a stainless steel tank.

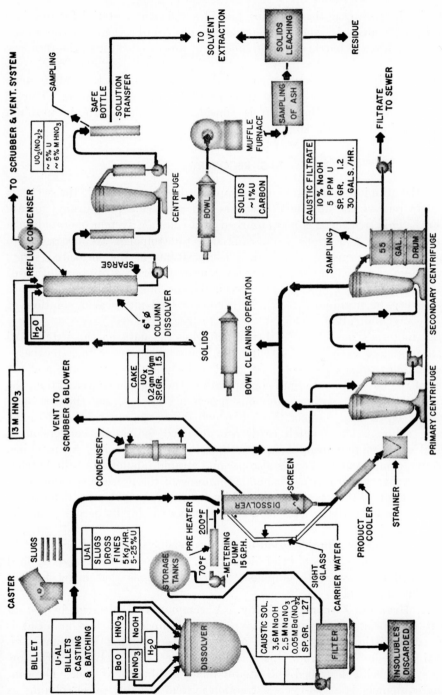

Fig. 14-10 Flow sheet for uranium–aluminum alloy processing.

sampled. In each case the sampling provides sufficient material for uranium analysis, U^{235} analysis, and a retention sample. After these measurements have been made, the batches are combined and processed through the recovery system.

Unfortunately, on occasion the cost of the effort expended to produce some of these batches will exceed the value of the uranium contained. This is particularly true when the scrap is considerably more dilute in uranium than was estimated by the shipper.

14-5. RECOVERY

Once the uranium content of the scrap has been established, the scrap is treated to remove the unwanted elements and produce a pure uranyl nitrate solution. This treatment is accomplished in a common system operated on a campaign basis. Variations from campaign to campaign are necessary to accommodate the variety of chemical compositions of the measured scrap. For example, a system operated to recover uranium from a dilute solution of uranium and stainless steel in aqua regia is not immediately adaptable to the recovery of uranium from a hydrofluoric acid–nitric acid solution of uranium-zirconium alloy.

Scrap materials are identified by transferring the data on the batch card that accompanies each batch through the head-end processes to a recovery-system batch card. This card is designed to include the gross, tare, and net weight of the batch, the uranium concentration, the isotopic concentration, the anions present, other cations, previous processing history, and the head-end processing batch-card number through which the batch can be traced to the shipping source. These batch cards are designed for simple conversion to punched cards so that uranium accounting can be done rapidly by machine. The conversion to punched cards also permits a rapid tabulation of the batches awaiting recovery, permitting economic planning of the processing campaigns. The summation of the uranium received by the recovery system as determined from these batch cards is used to charge the system for its receipts for the accounting period.

A detailed technical presentation of the recovery system is not pertinent to this discussion; however, a brief description of some of the more typical systems will be given, with emphasis placed on details that affect nuclear material management.

14-5.1. Uranium-Zirconium Alloy. A common fuel element in use at present is a uranium-zirconium alloy. Scrap composed of this material is dissolved in nitric and hydrofluoric acids prior to sampling. Uranium is recovered in a pure form from this solution by the use of solvent extraction. In the system being described, the organic phase is dibutyl carbitol. The contacting equipment is a tyo-cycle extraction system utilizing pulse columns as contactors and an approximate 4:1 evaporation in restricted-geometry evaporators between cycles. Fig. 14-11 is a general view of enriched-uranium processing equipment of this type.

The incoming solution is adjusted to the proper specific gravity and acidity, and the fluoride is complexed with aluminum in a restricted-geometry tank provided with recirculating agitation. Fig. 14-12 is a sketch of this equipment.

The uranium in the adjusted feed is extracted into the clean recycling organic phase, and the stripped phase or raffinate is discarded following measurement of its uranium content (usually below 0.25 ppm uranium by weight). The

Fig. 14-11 Uranium processing equipment.

uranium-containing organic phase is then scrubbed with an appropriate salt solution to remove residual impurities. The scrub solution is added to the incoming feed solution, and any contained uranium is extracted from it. The scrubbed organic phase is then contacted with demineralized water under the proper acidity conditions, and the uranium is extracted into the product aqueous phase. The cleaned organic is recycled to the first extraction column. This operation permits the discard of the feed-solution impurities in the first extraction-cycle raffinate.

Intercycle evaporators concentrate the product of the first cycle by a factor of about 4, thereby disposing of a large amount of the water originally contained in the feed solution in the form of condensate. The first-cycle concentrated product is then subjected to a second extraction cycle operated in a manner similar to the first, except that conditions are such that only extremely pure and concentrated uranyl nitrate solution is obtained as product. This operation leaves some of the uranium and essentially all the impurities in the raffinate. For the recovery of this uranium and the disposition of the impurities, the second-cycle raffinate is returned as part of the feed to the first extraction cycle. Figure 14-13 is a simplified flow sheet for this operation.

14-5.2. Material Control. From the foregoing description of the purification, it can be seen that it is possible to draw a material balance around the

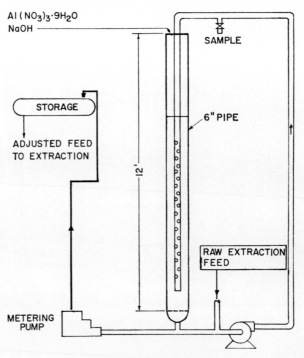

FIG. 14-12 Safe-geometry extraction feed adjustment station.

extraction system. The feed to the system is a measured solution of uranium and zirconium in acid. The product is a very pure concentrated uranyl nitrate solution which can be accurately sampled and analyzed. The only discards have been the raffinate from the first extraction cycle and the condensate from the intercycle evaporator. The sampling of the raffinate can be readily accomplished with good accuracy, and although the analysis of this very dilute solution is subject to large percentage errors, the absolute effect of these errors is small. The same holds true for the condensate since its uranium concentration is approximately 0.25 ppm by weight.

The recovery and purification of other nitrate solutions is accomplished in essentially the same manner as that described above, changes being made in extraction conditions to permit efficient operation.

Since the extraction system is fabricated of stainless steel, any solutions containing chlorides must receive a preliminary treatment to remove them. In the system being discussed, this removal is accomplished by a modification of the Oak Ridge National Laboratory (ORNL) Darex process[11] in which the

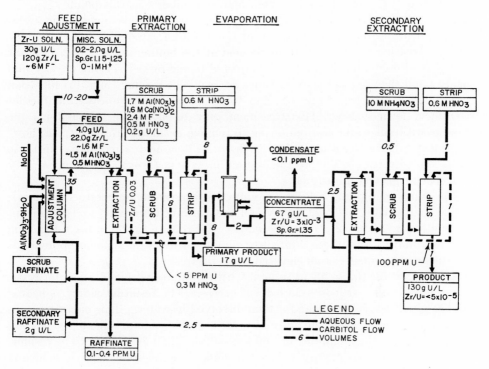

FIG. 14-13   Flow sheet for dibutyl carbitol extraction.

chloride-containing feed solution is distilled in a glass still in the presence of strong nitric acid. The chlorides are distilled off as nitrosyl chloride, and the chloride-free still bottoms containing the uranium are extracted in a manner similar to that described above. This chloride removal step introduces another discard stream that must be measured. The comments made concerning the condensate and raffinate discard streams also apply here, and the over-all material balance is not seriously affected by this discard.

14-6. SIDE STREAMS

The discussion thus far has been confined to the introduction of solutions resulting from head-end processing into the purification system. As already noted, solid materials are also generated by head-end processing. These solid batches, notably incinerator ash, are also assigned a purification-system batch card similar in form and content to that used for solutions, and the uranium contained in these batches is charged as feed to purification system material balance. The sampling and analysis of these batches is subject to larger errors than is the case with solutions, and a larger uncertainty is introduced into the purification-system material balance at this point.

14-6.1. Solid Uranium Scrap. It is necessary in preparing solid material for purification to dissolve as much of the uranium as possible. This is done by first treating the solids with nitric acid at the boiling point. The resultant slurry is filtered, and the filtrate is adjusted to the proper specific gravity and acidity and then fed to the extraction system. The residue from this filtration is not sufficiently free from uranium to be discarded, generally, and further treatment is necessary. This treatment may be as simple as repulping the residue with hot water and refiltering to remove occluded uranyl nitrate; however, generally, at least one other leach with nitric acid is required. In these cases the filtrates are sent to the extraction system through the usual acidity and specific gravity adjustments.

For solids containing a large amount of silica (most incinerator ash does), nitric acid leaching will not remove all the contained uranium, and significant amounts, e.g. 0.1 to 0.2 percent by weight, will remain in the solids. Uranium can be removed from these solids in a number of ways; a common approach is treatment with caustic at an elevated temperature.

In this process the solids are slurried with sodium hydroxide, enough caustic being added to bring it to a 25 percent excess. The resultant slurry is heated at 400°C for several hours and is then dissolved in water. This operation converts a large amount of the silica to water-soluble sodium silicate, which can be filtered from the remaining insolubles, sampled, and discarded. The residue, which has now been greatly reduced in bulk, is redigested in nitric acid and filtered once more. The filtrate is sent to the extraction system, and the acid-insoluble final residue is sampled and discarded.

The preliminary treatment of the solids prior to extraction produces two more discard streams that affect the purification-system material balance. The first of these is the water-soluble stream resulting from the caustic treatment, and the second is the final acid-insoluble residue. The sampling of the aqueous stream is simple, and, since its uranium concentration is low (0.5 to 1.5 ppm by weight), large percentage errors in the analysis have little absolute effect. Both the sampling and analysis of the acid-insoluble final residue are subject to sizable errors, but, fortunately, the over-all bulk reduction of the process works to minimize the effect of them.

14-6.2. Contaminated Nonuranium Scrap. A third general type of material received for recovery is the nonuranium fabrication scrap. As mentioned above, this material, which consists of rolling-mill cladding (generally, mild steel), crucibles, floor sweepings, process equipment, and some discarded tooling, is segregated by conveying it above scintillation counters. The equipment used for this purpose has been described by Arnett et al.[12] The uranium-containing segregated scrap is leached in nitric acid as part of the head-end process, and the decontaminated scrap is discarded following another survey with the counting equipment. The solutions resulting from this process are charged to the purification system on the basis of their analysis.

In addition to the measured streams introduced into the purification system, there is the scrap generated by the recovery process itself, i.e. pumps and flanges will leak, spills will occur, and it is necessary to decontaminate process equipment removed from service. Generally, this scrap, consisting of combustibles, mop water, decontamination solutions, etc., is reprocessed within the purification system; and although these streams do not affect input or product measurements, they can have an annoying effect upon the determination of the in-process inventory. The measurement of the in-process inventory and a comparison of the book-physical inventories is discussed in more detail in Sec. 14-11.

14-7. METAL PRODUCTION

The third main step in the job-shop recovery plant is the conversion of the purified uranyl nitrate solution into a form useful for refabrication into fuel elements. Two principal materials are used in fuel-element fabrication—metal and uranium dioxide. These operations are well known and are documented in the literature. Only points pertinent to material management will be presented here.

14-7.1. Denitration. The conversion of uranyl nitrate to metal usually requires as a first step the denitration of the material to yield the orange oxide of uranium, UO_3, by either thermal or chemical methods.

Thermal Denitration. Uranyl nitrate can be readily pyrolyzed to UO_3 at temperatures of 130 to 150°C. Several proven types of equipment have been used to perform this thermal operation, in which a wide range of feed concentrations can be used and a variety of particle sizes can be produced. This equipment includes batch type pot calciners, continuous horizontal-paddle agitator units, continuous horizontal-screw conveyor units, and continuous fluidization systems.[13] Material balances can be drawn around any of these systems, since the inputs and outputs can be accurately measured and the discard stream is the gaseous effluent containing water vapor and oxides of nitrogen. These off-gases are, of course, filtered or scrubbed to remove entrained uranium, and the filters or scrubber solutions are duly evaluated in the determination of the in-process inventory.

Chemical Denitration. Chemical means can also be employed to denitrate the uranyl nitrate solution. These consist in precipitating the uranium with ammonia or hydrogen peroxide. The precipitate is dewatered by filtration or centrifugation, and the cake is then converted to oxide by calcination. This type of denitration produces effluent streams which, for highly enriched uranium at least, cannot be discarded. The principal side stream formed is the filtrate, containing from 20 to 50 ppm uranium by weight, from which uranium is recovered by evaporation and extraction of the evaporator product. This stream will be difficult to measure accurately, especially in a continuous operation, and will introduce errors in the determination of the input to the purification system material balance.

14-7.2. Uranium Tetrafluoride Production. The uranium trioxide produced by denitration is next converted to UO_2 by reduction with hydrogen, which is then converted to UF_4 by reaction with anhydrous HF. Both these steps are carried out in continuous gas-solid contactors at approximately 1000°F. The material balance around this operation can also be measured. The effluent streams are gaseous, being hydrogen and water vapor from the reduction step and HF and water vapor from the hydrofluorination operation. These streams can be effectively cleaned of entrained uranium through the filters or scrubbers. Since these materials will contain uranium, they must be processed in the recovery operation.

The production of UF_4 from the uranyl nitrate solution, in a continuous plant process, is closely coupled with the purification operation, and it is simpler to draw a material balance around the entire operation from the input of measured scrap to the output of UF_4 than to separate the two steps. In this way it is not necessary to obtain costly and inaccurate measurements of the internal recycle streams such as filtrates, gas filters, and cleanup solutions. The determination of the in-process inventory becomes increasingly difficult, although handling it as a whole rather than as the sum of several parts actually simplifies the problem.

14-7.3. Reduction of Tetrafluoride to Metal. The reduction of the uranium tetrafluoride to metal is generally accomplished by the thermite reaction with calcium or magnesium as the reductant.[13,14] In this operation a bomb type reactor is used in which an intimate mixture of the UF_4 and reductant is contained in a refractory liner. The metal bomb is sealed with an inert atmosphere. The reaction, which is rapid once initiated, is started by heating. The uranium metal is formed in the molten state and, owing to its higher density, agglomerates at the bottom of the vessel forming a "derby" or "biscuit." The other reaction product containing slight amounts of uranium, and unreacted reductant fills the space immediately above the derby. This product is calcium or magnesium fluoride, depending upon the reductant used.

Once the reactor has cooled, it is opened, and the massive uranium is separated from the CaF_2 or MgF_2 slag and the refractory liner. The metal derby, after being cleaned of adhering slag and weighed, is ready for fabrication uses. The reduction slag, refractory liner, and derby cleanings, which all contain small amounts of uranium, are batched for recovery. The direct determination of the uranium content of these materials is difficult owing to the inhomogeneity of the mass; by-difference determination is also subject to large errors. This type of feed to the purification system is a further reason for drawing the material balance around the whole plant rather than drawing several balances around its component parts.

14-8. ANALYTICAL MEASUREMENTS

The number and types of measurements necessary in the operation of a recovery plant require chemical and isotopic analyses of a wide variety of solutions and solids. Because the plant processes material valued from $3000 to $17,000 per kilogram,[15] the quality of these measurements must be of the highest order. This calls for a well-equipped, well-staffed laboratory, utilizing the best analytical methods available. At the same time the measurements must be performed rapidly and at a minimum cost. The laboratory must perform precise analyses of concentrated solutions, solids, and metal, as well as of more dilute materials. The laboratory is also called upon to measure trace amounts of many elements for process control and specification purposes. These trace amounts are usually measured by spectrochemical techniques.

The recovery plant will probably process uranium of different isotopic concentrations, and it will be necessary to measure the amounts of at least the three natural isotopes of uranium. The concentrations of these isotopes will vary, and, in the case of scrap resulting from decontaminated spent reactor fuel, a fourth isotope, U^{236}, will be present. The instrument most commonly used for the isotopic concentration measurements is the mass spectrometer. An instrument of this type, capable of measuring uranium isotope concentrations, is an expensive, complicated piece of equipment requiring specialists trained in its operation. Another instrument that can be used less precisely for this work is the optical spectrograph, employing the spectral shift method of analysis. A discussion of many of the analytical methods used in uranium work is presented by Burkhart.[16]

For the control of laboratory analyses, two types of disguised samples are submitted to the laboratory by the production group. The first are the synthetic samples containing most of the impurity and matrix elements of the production sample being controlled and a precisely known amount of uranium. The results of these analyses are collected on a quarterly basis and are used to compute the random and systematic errors of the analytical method used.

The second type of disguised sample is used in a slightly different way. Certain production batches are selected for replicate sampling, and each of the samples is forwarded to the quality-control organization. To each of the samples is quantitatively added a precisely known amount of uranium. All the samples are then sent to the laboratory for analysis. From the results of these analyses, the random and systematic errors of the analytical method used can be computed as well as a good estimation of the error inherent in the sampling of the production batch.

Each analytical method routinely used for material balance measurements is under the quality-control program outlined above, as is each scale or balance used for this purpose. These data are collected quarterly, and computations are made to estimate the random and systematic errors of the material balance resulting from the measurements. These data are also plotted on Shewhart[17] control charts to help laboratory and production supervisors maintain the quality of the measurements.

All quality-control information is placed on punched cards so that computations can be done rapidly. In addition to the results of the measurements, other data, such as date, balance or scale number, analytical method, and name of operator or analyst making the measurements, are entered on these cards. These data can be used to trace the source of variances, and they are extremely helpful in estimating operator and analyst biases.

14-9. STATISTICAL QUALITY CONTROL

The management of nuclear material relies heavily upon measurements of many types. Weights, volumes, and chemical and isotopic concentration measurements are vital to the efficient handling of the uranium. These measurements, like all measurements, will vary and some method must be used to judge their reliability. The most efficient way to determine the reliability of the measurements is by statistical quality control. Through the use of these statistical techniques, statements can be made concerning the random and systematic errors of the measurements and sources of variances can be identified and their contribution to the over-all variance of the measurements can be estimated. Sampling plans can be devised for routine production streams which will obviate the necessity of 100 percent sampling, thereby saving significant amounts of money.

The function of the routine quality-control program is to control the reliability of measurement procedures and to investigate methods of improved accuracy as they may be applied to the present program. In nearly all cases the bulk amount of material being processed is measured by weight. All scales and balances are checked at regular intervals by weighing control objects whose weights are in the range normally encountered by the instruments. The results of these control weighings are compared with the expected variance of the scale or balance being used. If the control object weight does not fall within the expected weight range, the instrument is immediately taken from service and repaired. Monthly summaries are prepared of the results of all control weighings, and the variance of the weighings is computed.

In addition to the routine work described above, the quality control organization helps in the design of experiments, evaluates new or special measurements, and draws correlations between production variables. For example, it is necessary to evaluate a number of dependent and independent variables to maximize the operation of an extraction procedure. Through the statistical examination of a large amount of production data supplemented by in-plant variation of the control features, it is possible to determine the best set of operating conditions. Also, correlations can be drawn between the effects of several variables. Such data, together with a knowledge of the reliability of the measurements, makes it possible to optimize operating conditions to a degree that would not otherwise be possible.

The statistical approach is also invaluable in determining the quality of production. Through a statistical examination of product concentration, impurity level, or other specification, coupled with a statistical evaluation of the measurement reliability, it is possible to rapidly detect significant changes in product quality. Even more important, such an examination can detect the cause of the observed quality change and can estimate its significance. This will prevent unwarranted alterations of the production process when the observed change is statistically insignificant or is caused by a change in measurement quality. On the other hand, changes in the process can be determined early, and the appropriate measures for improvement can be indicated.

Indeed, no well-run production organization can do without the services of a well-organized quality-control program. The group that administers this program is more effective if it is independent of the production and laboratory organizations.

14-10. MATERIAL BALANCE

The determination of the material balance around the recovery plant follows fairly standard accounting practices. The book inventory is computed, a physical inventory is taken, and the results are compared and evaluated. The receipts for the accounting period are obtained by summing the uranium contained in all batches charged to the purification system. To the total amount of uranium received for the period is added the amount contained on beginning inventory at the start of the period. From the sum of the beginning inventory plus the receipts, the shipments and discards are subtracted, and the difference is calculated as the amount of the ending or book inventory.

14-10.1. Receipt Records. The material balance calculations require additional computations beyond those found in conventional accounting systems. The batch cards representing the receipts contain the net weight of the bulk of the batch, the uranium concentration and the isotopic concentration expressed as the weight fraction of U^{235}. For the uranium balance the bulk weight of each batch is multiplied by the uranium concentration, and the results are summed for all the receipts. For the U^{235} balance the computed uranium content of each receipt batch is multiplied by the weight fraction of U^{235}, and the results are summed for the total U^{235} receipts to the system.

14-10.2. Transfer Records. The determinations of the transfers from the system require consideration of the product shipments and the discards. The amount of uranium and U^{235} contained in the product shipment is based upon the precise measurements that must accompany the transaction. These shipments are recorded on the shipping forms, and computations of the uranium and U^{235} contents are straightforward.

Discards from the system are recorded on a waybill initiated for each discard at the time of the action. This waybill records the bulk weight of the solid or solution being discarded and the sample identification number. The various types of discards from the recovery plant include raffinates, condensates, final acid-insoluble residues, decontaminated nonuranium fabrication scrap, and stack losses. The waybill record of all these transactions is maintained, and the sum of the uranium contained in them is added to the product shipments to determine the removals from the system.

14-11. PHYSICAL INVENTORY

The determination of the physical or in-process inventory is considerably more involved than the computation of the book inventory. The uranium is distributed throughout the recovery plant in a variety of forms and locations, including such diverse matrices as filter elements, scrubber solutions, raffinates, condensates, organic materials, aqueous solutions, combustible materials, mop water, metal reduction slag, and contaminated equipment. The measurement of the uranium content of the physical inventory must include a considerable amount of cleaning and processing prior to sampling.

14-11.1. Material Balance Areas. In practice a material balance is established by segregating the processing facility for inventory purposes, processing the bulk of the material to a form suitable for sampling, stopping all material movement, and listing and sampling the entire inventory. During this inventory period those receipts in process to a sampling point are inventoried at the shipper's estimate. The inventory is adjusted to the measured concentration of these materials when sampling and analysis have been completed.

Segregation of the plant for inventory purposes is done by dividing the physical system into its several parts: the combustible and ash leaching area, the extraction area, the denitration and uranium tetrafluoride production area, and the metal reduction area. A schedule is drawn up setting forth the date and times of the final transfers of material between these areas and the detailed plans for the preinventory cleaning methods. Responsibilities are assigned to various individuals for each inventory area and cleaning program. Since the best physical inventory practice requires that the bulk of the material in process be processed to a form suitable for sampling, the inventory listing and sampling will take place over a period of several days. This is to say that although each one of the inventory areas mentioned above will be listed and sampled at a given time, the times of listing and sampling for the four sections will vary. Generally speaking, this time will follow the scrap-processing flow.

14-11.2. Metal-Reduction Unit. The first area in which processing is stopped is the metal reduction unit. All the uranium tetrafluoride on hand in this area is reduced to metal. The processing equipment is cleaned, and all scrap is transferred to the purification or combustible area. This will include bomb reduction residues, gloved-box cleanings, contaminated filters, mop water, etc.

All duct work is then surveyed with scintillation counters to detect the presence of possible uranium build-up. The detection of any significant activity is cause for dismantling and cleaning, and the cleanings are transferred to the recovery area. As soon as the cleaning and scrap removal has been completed, the individual responsible for the inventory authorizes the listing of the inventory, which now consists only of uranium derbies. These pieces of massive metal were each identified and weighed at the time of production. They were also sampled in accordance with the statistical sampling plan at that time.

In this area then the physical inventory listing is simply a matter of counting items. As each item is counted, it is reweighed. The identifying batch number, which is marked on the piece and its accompanying batch card, together with the inventory weight, is entered on the inventory listing sheet. These sheets are then transferred to the SS Group, and a punched card is prepared for each batch. The SS Group also has a punched card record of all batches initiated during the month in its files. A machine comparison is made of the number of items on inventory with that predicted by the batches initiated during the month, and any discrepancies are immediately resolved. Once the predicted and actual inventories are in agreement, the metal-reduction process can commence operation again, although no scrap can be transferred from the area until the entire plant inventory has been completed.

14-11.3. Combustible Area. The next section to cease processing for inventory is the combustible processing and ash leaching area. This takes place several days following the completion of transfer of scrap from the metal reduction area. No further transfers of combustibles will be received from the presampling processing area, the metal reduction area, the purification system, or the denitration and green salt areas. Prior to a listing of the inventory, all combustibles will be burned and all ash will be leached. The ash leach solution will be transferred to the purification area, as will all other cleaning solutions. A cleanliness inspection will also be made. The batches of leached ash on hand at this time will then be weighed and sampled. This weight, the batch number, and the sample identification number will be listed on the inventory listing sheets, which are forwarded to the SS Group.

14-11.4. Uranium Tetrafluoride Area. Shortly after the cessation of production activity in the combustible area, the transfer of purified uranyl nitrate solution from the purification area to the denitration area will stop. All nitrate solution on hand will be processed to UF_4, and the entire system will be washed free of uranium. The wash solution, together with other cleanup solutions, will be returned to the purification system, and a cleanliness inspection will be made. There will, of course, be small amounts of combustibles generated during this time. However, the amount of contained uranium is small, and it is estimated on the basis of experience factors.

The inventory in this area will consist of weighing the batches of UF_4 on hand and measuring the volume and sampling the off-gas scrubber solution. These data are also listed on an inventory sheet and sent to the accounting group.

14-11.5. Purification System Area. The final area to be inventoried is the purification system area. It is operated after all receipts have stopped and until the bulk of the uranium is contained in the purified product tanks. At this point the entire system, with the exception of these tanks, is flushed with acid, and these acid solutions are fed to the primary extraction system. Once this feed has been exhausted, the extraction system is depleted of its uranium inventory by recycling raffinate, and the uranium is concentrated as intercycle evaporator product. A cleanliness inspection is made; and the volumes of all solutions are then measured, and the solutions are sampled. These volumes and sample identification numbers, together with the batch numbers, are entered on the inventory listing sheet. Once this has been completed, the production operation is resumed, and material transfers are begun again throughout the plant.

14-11.6. Tabulating Results. The results of the analyses of the samples taken are reported to the SS Group as they become available. The data on all the inventory listing sheets are transferred to punched cards, and the analytical results are also added to these cards. The uranium content of the physical inventory is then computed, and the results are compared with the book inventory. A limit of error calculation is made, taking into account those sources of error which are known and measurable, primarily sampling and analytical errors, and an evaluation of the significant book-physical inventory differences is made.

However, there are other sources of error which, although they are recognized, are not so easily measured. Of this type the most important is the human factor. Even the best trained personnel will make mistakes. Whether these mistakes are of omission or commission, some of them will not be detected by any of the reasonable precautions taken. The probability of such errors will increase with the opportunity; that is, the larger the number of items, the greater the chance of error. Some way then must be devised to judge, relatively at least, the contribution of this factor to inventory uncertainty. One method of judging is to compare current results with past performance. It is possible to relate the current and cumulative book-physical inventory differences with past experience. This is best done by converting these statistics to a common denominator such as a percentage of the throughput. The definition of throughput is arbitrary, and the only requirement is consistency throughout the period under examination. With this approach, the relationship of opportunity for error and performance is recognized. Using this criterion, book-physical inventory differences that might appear significant when based only upon consideration of the measured errors may well be insignificant. Statistically significant deviations from the past experience criterion should give cause for concern and should result in reevaluation of inventory procedures, hidden inventory estimates, sampling plans, and analytical methods. The matter of deliberate diversion also requires consideration.

REFERENCES FOR CHAPTER 14

1. A. D. CALLIHAN, Nuclear Safety in Processing Reactor Fuel Solutions, *Nucleonics*, 14(7): 38 (July 1956).
2. G. A. GRAVES and H. C. PAXTON, Critical Masses of Oralloy Assemblies, *Nucleonics*, 15(6): 90 (June 1957).
3. H. M. PARKER, Health Physics, Instrumentation, and Radiation Protection, *Advances in Biol. and Med. Phys.*, 1:223-285 (1948).
4. S. T. CANTRIL and H. M. PARKER, *The Tolerance Dose*, USAEC Report MDDC-1100, Argonne National Laboratory, 1945.
5. R. D. EVANS, Health Physics: Instrumentation and Hazard Evaluation, Chap. 16, in *The Science and Engineering of Nuclear Power*, Addison-Wesley Press, Inc., Cambridge, Mass., 1947.
6. L. S. TAYLOR, The Basis for Standards for Radiation Protection, *J. Soc. Non-Destructive Testing*, 14 (1): 10-15 (1956).
7. NATIONAL COMMITTEE ON RADIATION PROTECTION, *Safe Handling of Radioactive Isotopes*, Natl. Bur. Standards, Handbook 42 (1949).
8. INTERNATIONAL COMMISSION ON RADIOLOGICAL PROTECTION, *Recommendations of the International Commission on Radiological Protection and of the International Commission on Radiological Units 1950*, Natl. Bur. Standards, Handbook 47 (1951).
9. NATIONAL COMMITTEE ON RADIATION PROTECTION, *Control and Removal of Radioactive Contamination in Laboratories*, Natl. Bur. Standards, Handbook 48 (1951).
10. NATIONAL COMMITTEE ON RADIATION PROTECTION, *Maximum Permissible Amounts of Radioisotopes in the Human Body and Maximum Permissible Concentrations in Air and Water*, Natl. Bur. Standards, Handbook 52 (1953).
11. J. E. SAVOLAINEN and R. E. BLANCO, Preparation of Power Reactor Fuels for Aqueous Processing, *Chem. Eng. Prog.*, 53 (2):78F-81F (February 1957).
12. O. ARNETT, Uranium Salvage Monitor (to be published by USAEC).
13. C. D. HARRINGTON and A. E. RUEHLE (Eds.), *Uranium Production Technology*, D. Van Nostrand Co., Inc., Princeton, N. J., 1959.

14. J. J. KATZ and E. RABINOWITCH, *The Chemistry of Uranium*, National Nuclear Energy Series, Div. VIII, Vol. 5, p. 122, McGraw-Hill Book Company, Inc., New York, 1951.
15. U. S. ATOMIC ENERGY COMMISSION, *Major Activities in the Atomic Energy Programs, July-December, 1956*, p. 343, U. S. Government Printing Office, Washington 25, D. C., January 1957.
16. L. E. BURKHART, General Discussion of Analytical Measurements, *Industrial Technical Information Meeting on Cold Process of Enriched Uranium, Septmeber 1956*, USAEC Report TID-7158 (Pt. 1), p. 37.
17. W. A. SHEWHART, *Economic Control of Quality of Manufactured Product*, D. Van Nostrand Company, New York, 1931.

Chapter 15

NORMAL-URANIUM SCRAP RECOVERY *

15-1. INTRODUCTION

From the time uranium ore or concentrate is introduced into the refining system until the metal emerges as an encased fuel element ready for use in a nuclear reactor, the uranium involved has been subjected to many operations. The product of each operation contains less uranium than was introduced into the operation, the "loss" remaining behind in some form of scrap or residue. The following discussion deals with the origin and treatment of these process residues and the material control procedures applied to them.

This chapter is based on operations of the natural-uranium scrap-recovery plant at the Atomic Energy Commission's Feed Materials Production Center (FMPC) at Fernald, Ohio. The source of most of this plant's feed is the FMPC itself, though the plant does also receive residues from many other AEC installations. Research and development facilities contribute only a small percentage of the feed for the plant, yet this small portion is so varied that the plant must employ extremely versatile and complex techniques for recovery of the uranium.

Only a few of the types of residues processed are amenable to sampling in the form in which they are received. Most residues require some preparation or processing before a representative sample can be taken. These residues are transferred from the point of origin with a best-guess evaluation of their uranium content, this value being adjusted as soon as a representative sample can be taken. Since so much normal-uranium scrap has not been analyzed at the source, this scrap-recovery plant serves as a key material control point for uranium in the United States. Fig. 15-1 is a photograph of the FMPC scrap recovery plant.

15-2. RECOVERY

The complexity of recovery techniques varies with the type of residue. Some materials require only screening to remove trash before they meet the

---

* P. N. McCreery, National Lead Company of Ohio, Feed Materials Production Center, Cincinnati, Ohio.

specifications of the refinery for feed material. Others require crushing, leaching, roasting, or a combination of these processes and more. Even a single batch or lot being processed may require various steps to process side streams resulting from portions of the original lot. A workable SS-control system can be established only when this multiplicity of operations is kept in mind.

FIG. 15-1 Scrap-recovery plant.

The first step in facilitating residue recovery is proper control of the methods of identification and segregation at the point of origin. Each residue must be analyzed to determine its most probable mode of recovery, and procedures established to isolate residue side streams by recovery categories. Table 15.1 shows a proposed categorization of residues which would make them most compatible with the scrap-recovery system. Note (Sec. 15-2.1) that contaminants require an even further breakdown of each category.

15-2.1. Contamination Categories. All the materials in the general categories of Table 15.1 (unless otherwise indicated) which contain the contaminants listed below are segregated from materials of the same general type which contain no such contamination. The contaminants:

1. Chlorides
2. Fluorides
3. Boron or other contaminants with high thermal-neutron capture cross sections
4. Thorium or rare earths
5. Depleted or enriched uranium
6. Low-melting salts or metals

7. Substantial quantities of foreign matter

8. Beryllium or other health hazards.

A system for adequate initial categorizing will greatly reduce the cost of the recovery operation without adding appreciably to the operating cost of production plants. Materials that have not been properly separated or identified must be processed by more laborious and expensive methods.

15-2.2. Storage. The next step in the control of materials to be recovered is storage during the interim between generation or receipt and processing.

TABLE 15.1. SEGREGATION OF RESIDUES

TYPE OF MATERIAL	REMARKS
Uranium-metal chips, turnings, and sawdust	Can be collected as a group without segregation if desirable. If the turnings are briquettable and briquetting is desired, the sawdust should be categorized separately.
Uranium-metal sludge	Primarily uranium metal and uranium oxides and contaminated with little foreign matter. Sludge with a high foreign-matter content should be segregated as a miscellaneous uranium-bearing residue.
Uranium-alloy chips, turnings, and sawdust	This category is segregated from pure uranium scrap of the same physical form. In addition, it is necessary to segregate alloy scrap according to the individual alloying constituent.
Uranium-alloy sludge	This category is segregated from pure uranium scrap of the same physical form. In addition, it is necessary to separate alloy scrap according to the individual alloying constituent.
Uranium-metal scrap	Segregated according to its suitability for remelting; for example, if high in impurities, segregate for acid dissolution rather than remelting.
Uranium-metal scrap (clad)	All uranium-metal scrap that is clad with other metals such as stainless steel, copper, and zirconium is separated according to its type of cladding.
Uranium-alloy scrap	Separated from pure uranium scrap of the same physical form. In addition, it is necessary to segregate alloy scrap according to the individual alloying constituent.
Uranium-alloy scrap (clad)	Must be divided according to both the alloying components and the cladding material.
Uranium oxides	Containing less than 2 percent free metal to be segregated from oxide containing free-metal concentrations in excess of this value.
Pickle liquors (HNO_3)	
Cake from neutralized pickle liquors	
Uranium-contaminated salt bath sludge	
Filter cake	
Scrap UF_4	
UF_4 + Mg reduction residue	

Recovery cannot be on a first-in-first-out basis simply because the more lucrative feeds hold priority over the low-content feeds or those that are more difficult to recover. A basic familiarity with recovery operations indicates the possible length of time a given residue will remain in storage before the recovery plant can accommodate it, and plans for storage should be made accordingly. Indoor storage is beneficial from the standpoint of container life, but it is expensive and may be dangerous for hydrogen-evolving materials. If outdoor storage is felt to be necessary, a metal drum is the most suitable container. Wood, cardboard, and containers of similar construction are obviously not recommended for outdoor storage.

If a container is filled with a corrosive material or is abused in handling, it may in time develop a leak, resulting in the loss of uranium or the admission of water. Frequent checks should be made for leaks in drums from which uranium might be lost.

Uranium is somewhat pyrophoric, especially when in the form of grinding wheel fines, machining turnings, and saw chips. Storage time for these materials must be held to an absolute minimum. They are kept under light fuel oil to retard oxidation. All precautions should be taken to keep water away from uranium fines. Hydrogen, produced by chemical reaction between water and uranium, and the tendency for uranium to spark from friction can be a dangerous combination.

15-2.3. Storage Accounts. A perpetual inventory of the card type, periodically confirmed by physical examination, has been found to be quite adequate for control of material in storage. Inventory cards show:

1. Lot number
2. Number of containers in the lot
3. Total gross weight
4. Tare weight
5. Net weight
6. Location in the storage area

If there is more than one drum in the lot, the control card will have attached to it the generating plant's notice of production, which lists the individual gross, tare, and net weight of each container. At the FMPC, a material lot is composed of material of sufficiently uniform uranium content to be represented by a single analytical value; thus an activity involving a partial lot can be controlled on a simple weight proportion basis.

Production scheduling for the recovery operation does not follow the formal concept usually applied to production units. The plant may be assigned a production quota for a given month based on the capacities of its various components and the calculated generation rates of residues from the metals fabrication plants.

Specific items scheduled for recovery, however, include only the highest grade of the current residue production, and these are processed on an as-generated basis. The remainder, more that half the total number of items, is selected from a tabulated listing of the storage inventory. Approximately a

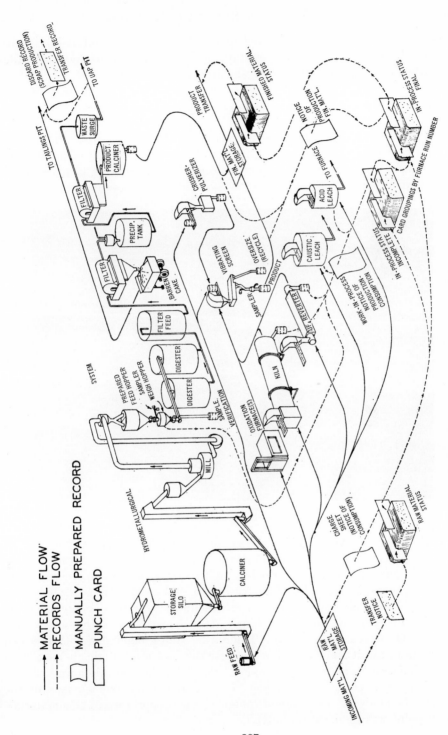

MATERIAL FLOW
RECORDS FLOW

MANUALLY PREPARED RECORD

PUNCH CARD

Fig. 15-2 Flow sheet for the recovery plant.

387

month's feed supply can be selected at one time. This material is visually inspected by the supervisors to ascertain the authenticity of the identification and is then dispatched from the storage area as requested.

15-3. PROCESS SYSTEM

The recovery facilities are depicted schematically in Fig. 15-2. They consist of a continuous process system for reclaiming the uranium content of the UF_4-to-derby reduction slag and several isolated batch-process furnaces, leach tanks, and so forth. The slag-recovery system will be described first.[1]

Fig. 15-3   Digest tanks.

15-3.1. Slag-Recovery Unit. Magnesium fluoride, a by-product of the reduction process, contains uranium metal in various degrees of agglomeration plus trace quantities of uranium oxide. This slag is fed to a surge hopper in which the process begins. It is first crushed to −4 mesh and roasted for 1 hour at 800°C to oxidize the contained metal, facilitate grinding, and prevent the formation of hydrogen during leaching. After being roasted, the slag is pulverized to 90 percent −325 mesh. The roasted and ground slag is then stored in hoppers to await leaching. For the first time since its origin the slag is in a form that can be accurately sampled, and as batches are discharged into a weigh hopper, a continuous sampler removes representative portions of the stream to be analyzed for uranium content. The importance of this material-control point will be discussed later.

The slag is leached with hydrochloric acid for 3 hours at 85 to 90°C with an oxidant added to promote uranium dissolution. The digest tanks are shown in Fig. 15-3. The slurry is then filtered, the cake is washed with water, and the depleted slurry cake is discarded to the tailings pit. The filtrate is treated with phosphoric acid and ammonium hydroxide to precipitate the uranium in the form of uranyl ammonium phosphate.

FIG. 15-4   Box furnace.

The precipitate is filtered from the liquor and roasted in a multihearth furnace; the product is suitable for refinery feed. The barren liquor is neutralized, and if the uranium concentration is within discard specifications, it is pumped to the tailings pit; if not, it is filtered, and the filter cake is returned to the process stream, the liquor being discarded.

15-3.2. Batch Recovery Units. The batch recovery operations consist of the following major units:

1. *A box furnace.* This is a small (approximately 6 sq ft) gas-fired single-hearth furnace (Fig. 15-4) designed for easy cleanout. The primary use of this furnace is the recovery of relatively small lots of readily combustible residues. Since the SS material content of these residues is calculated on the basis of the uranium content of the recovered product, recovery must be car-

ried out quantitatively, and lot segregation must be strictly maintained.   Residues are ignited in this furnace by a gas flame.   The material is periodically hand rabbled to assure complete oxidation of the metallic uranium.

2. *A stoker-fed furnace.* This furnace is about 2 ft wide and 10 ft long, with no provision for supplying external heat.   For this reason it is used only for burning easily ignited materials, and because of its relatively large capacity compared to the box furnace, it is utilized primarily to burn the larger receipts of uranium turnings and sawdust in a campaign or continuous operation.

3. *A muffle furnace.*   This furnace differs from the box furnace in size (being somewhat larger) and heating characteristics; in addition, a rotating mechanical rabble is provided to promote more efficient oxidation.   This furnace has sufficient heat input to calcine the less combustible residues as well as readily combustible material such as uranium metal turnings and sawdust. Because of this feature it may also be utilized to oxidize some alloyed forms of uranium.

4. *A multihearth oxidation furnace.*   This furnace is equipped with rotary rabbles designed to calcine residues requiring relatively long retention periods with a minimum bed thickness.   Owing to its size and design characteristics, it operates more efficiently when handling large quantities of material in a continuous operation.   For this reason it is seldom employed for the recovery of off-site receipts of uranium residues.

5. *The rotary kiln.*   This is a unit 5 ft in diameter and 40 ft long.   Its basic function is the drying of wet solids.   Again, owing to size, it is not amenable to frequent cleanout or to the recovery of small lots in a segregated fashion.

6. *The reverter furnace.*   This consists of an electrically heated tube about 15 ft in length.   Material is conveyed through the furnace by means of a rotating ribbon conveyor.   This unit is especially designed for one application— i.e. the conversion of contaminated UF_4 to a U_3O_8 product that is essentially free of fluoride.   The fluoride is removed by exposing the heated UF_4 to an atmosphere of steam.

7. *Leach tanks.*   Three tanks are employed both for aqueous and chemical leaching of uranium residues.   One of these three units is used for the removal of soluble halides and carbonates from otherwise suitable refinery feed materials.   It is also capable of acid leaching uranium from low-grade and chemically inert residues.   An iron tank is used for nonmetallic residues requiring a caustic leach.   A smaller caustic-leach unit situated in the open, outside the building proper, is used to dissolve aluminum jackets from reject slugs or to digest the aluminum content from uranium alloyed pieces.

15-3.3. Crushing and Pulverizing. A portion of the residues consigned for scrap recovery requires only a simple pulverization to produce a suitable refinery feed.   Other residues for which a multiplicity of recovery steps are necessary may require additional pulverization prior to a given operation.   A combination crushing and pulverizing unit is provided for this purpose.

The product obtained from many of the above units contains particle-size fractions that exceed the maximum size specifications for refinery feed ($\frac{1}{8}$ in.). All such material is passed over a rotating screen prior to sampling and packaging; the oversize pieces are rejected and returned to the recovery stream for further processing.

15-3.4. Waste-Gas Recovery. Off-gases from the furnace and dryer and fumes from the digestion tanks are vented to the atmosphere through venturi type gas scrubbers. Spent scrubber liquors, process spills, and pump seal water are used as make-up water in digestion batches. All operations that involve the handling of dry solids are vented to dust collectors.

15-4. SAMPLING AND MEASUREMENTS

When slag is fed to the storage silo in the slag recovery system, its uranium content has been determined only by a by-difference figure in the plant in which it originated. This residue, as received by the recovery plant, is not homogeneous and may consist of particles whose maximum linear dimension is several inches. For this reason the residue is not amenable to any conventional sampling technique.

After conversion to a finely pulverized prepared feed, however, the material can readily be sampled, this being the point at which the uranium content of the material is first evaluated. Of necessity, then, the uranium content of the material in the feed-preparation portion of the system is carried at its by-difference figure, continually adjusted on the basis of receipts into the silo and discharges of measured quantities of prepared feed. Over a period of time this by-difference value may deviate considerably from the actual uranium content of the system; however, this can be reconciled only by cleanout of this portion of the system. When this is done, the difference can be adjusted back to the originating plant.

The remaining portion of the slag recovery system is regarded as a material balance area in which the batches of prepared feed represent the consumption and the drummed product and the side streams represent the production. The input to this material balance area is measured in weighed batches prior to digestion of the prepared feed. The material is discharged from the weigh hopper through a vertical downcomer, and it is in this discharge chute that the material is sampled.

15-4.1. Prepared-Feed Sampler. This sampler, shown in Fig. 15-5, consists of a 1-in.-diameter 1-in.-pitch screw positioned in a trough and placed horizontally through the wall of the downcomer. As material is collected in the trough, it is continuously removed by the auger to a receptacle located outside the downcomer. This auger is motor driven through a system of variable-reduction gears so that speeds can be varied from about $\frac{1}{2}$ to 5 rpm. Approximately 5 lb of sample is collected from each 6000 lb of prepared feed.

Samples collected from this continuous sampling system are blended and sub-divided into sizes more suitable for handling in the laboratory. These are analyzed by precise analytical techniques for total uranium content. The precision and accuracy of this weighing and sampling system is periodically checked by diverting the sampled stream to a drumming station immediately below the downcomer. The drummed batches are reweighed and resampled by the best techniques presently available. The analytical precision being known, a comparison of weighing and sampling techniques affords data for a

Fig. 15-5 Feed sampler.

statistical comparison between the two systems and allows a calculation of the limits of error.

15-4.2. Side-Stream and Product Sampling. Side streams containing uranium at low concentrations are sampled and analyzed by fluorimetric techniques. Random pipe samples are removed from batches of tailings cake and composited. The composite is blended, subsampled, and analyzed. The filtrate from the ammonium phosphate precipitates is agitated and sampled prior to being discarded.

In the downcomer from the vibrating screen, through which recovery plant product passes prior to packaging, there is located a rotary continuous sampler. This sampler consists of a rather flat cone with its vertex pointing upward and revolving about its axis. In the edge of the cone are three equidistant indentations of about 1 in. toward the axis over arcs of about 30°. Sample-collecting pipes extend through the wall of the downcomer up to and under the edge of this cone. Their open ends are covered by the cone except when exposed by these indentations. At these intervals the sample portion is collected and dropped into containers placed adjacent to the unit. The material that has been sampled is packaged in 30-gal steel drums, for which tare weights have previously been obtained. All dust from this packaging and screening operation is collected by a unit which serves this unit only and provides for return of the dust to the packaging station. The filled containers are then gross weighed and are identified with an appropriate lot mark and container number. Containers comprised in any given lot are numbered sequentially as they are produced. Sample evaluation of the product sampling unit is made in the same manner as described above for the prepared feed sampler.

15-4.3. Dust Collection. Dust-collector effluent to the atmosphere is sampled by a unit of the same type as has been described for measuring material crossover. These units operate in the exhaust ducts continuously, and a log is maintained for each sample obtained as to unit number and total time in stream. The uranium analysis of the sample is multiplied by the duct sample head ratio, and this quantity is then included in the measured loss credit to the plant's material balance. The intake air velocity of these units is adjusted to the average velocity of the duct under normal operating conditions. If a dust-collector bag should rip, the air velocity in the duct will increase, as will the ratio of suspended particles. The sample obtained under such conditions is invalid, and the loss can only be estimated by extending the average input rate to the collector by the time duration of operation with the split bag. This at best is only a rough, conservative guess. A well-executed program of preventive maintenance of dust collectors can reduce this problem to insignificance, and the cost of such a program is justified through direct savings of material otherwise lost. If a bag should tear, smoke detectors in the stack can be used to shut the system down immediately and thus minimize the loss.

15-4.4. Liquid Waste. Liquid waste is sampled as a batch in tanks prior to discharge to the sewer. If the uranium content exceeds specifications for discharge, the liquor is either returned to the process stream as make-up water or its pH is adjusted until the uranium precipitates as a salt. The precipitate slurry is then filtered, and the uranium content is recovered as filter cake. The filtrate is then returned to the discard tanks for resampling prior to discard.

15-5. MARKING SYSTEM

The first marking system is a numerical and alphabetical combination code, referred to as the "lot mark." It appears on both the containers of material and the records pertaining to the material. The second marking system is one of colors, which distinguishes major chemical elements or isotopes.

The lot-marking system consists of four groups of numbers or digits which identify:

1. The material-balance area in which the material originated: a two-digit (or letter) code.

2. The year in which the material originated; a one-letter code, which began with the letter A in 1951, each succeeding letter representing a succeeding year.

3. A three-digit code represents any type of material that must be distinguished from any other type for reasons of sampling control, production control, recovery method (for residues), cost determinations, material control, criticality considerations, etc. Specific groups of numbers are assigned to materials of each type.

4. A four-digit code represents the lot sequence of production in a given year. As a rule of thumb, lot quantities of residues consist of 20 containers or one month's production, whichever occurs first. Lot sizes of product items are adapted to suit the producing plant.

There are some specific exceptions to the above. If the material is received from off site, the consignor's SS station symbol is used in place of the plant number and year of origin. The transfer sequence number applicable to the consignment is used in place of the lot sequence number. Also, in many special orders, the production order number is used in place of the lot sequence number. The material type code number, however, is never compromised.

In addition to the lot-marking system, a color code has been adopted:

    Yellow, normal uranium
    Green, depleted uranium
    Red, enriched uranium
    Blue, thorium

White, plus any of the above, indicates an alloy of the above. The coding for enriched uranium (red) has been extended to include stripes of gray, black, and orange to identify various percentages of enrichments.

Additional information may be included on containers as deemed useful. Gross, tare, and net weights are shown with few exceptions. The chemical symbol of weight percent of alloys or chemical impurities is included where applicable. The percentage of U^{235} with respect to total uranium may also be shown.

15-6. SS MATERIAL CONTROL

Material-control aspects can now be considered in the light of the technical functions of the scrap recovery plant. In the recovery plant, because of the varied requirements for SS content evaluation, each batch recovery unit must be regarded as a material balance area. Since material crossover occurs between units through flue and scrubber systems and since multiple-unit processing may be required on many batches, a records system set up for a formal report on each area would require an intolerable amount of paper work.

The system in use is based upon assigning a code letter to each unit operation and a sequence number to each campaign of batches of material (from one complete cleanout until the next) through that unit. The combination of these two codes is termed the "furnace run number." The final evaluation of a given lot of residues is usually based on the weight of the total product from a given furnace run extended by the analytical result of a sample of that product, plus any measured diversions from the furnace.

15-6.1. Group Batching. Campaigns of feed materials for the unit operations are made up of similar materials from the same consignor. Batching several receipts results in a considerable economic savings by reducing the total down time spent cleaning out the unit, as compared to a cleanout between each receipt and the next run individually.

Any batch undergoing evaluation is kept completely segregated from all other uranium-bearing material until it is in a physical state amenable to conventional sampling techniques. At the first process opportunity the sample is taken, and from then on the batch can be combined with other evaluated batches for more economic processing.

In some instances only a part of the batch will emerge suitable for sampling; the remainder (screen oversize, agglomerates, and nonburnable trash) must be processed in as many additional steps as are necessary to extract the recoverable uranium. Identity of the parent lots is retained until all materials have been worked up to some final batch suitable for recovery feed.

The SS content values determined from the batch samples and analyses are accumulated and credited to the parent lots. Differences from received values are reflected in B-PID (if an FMPC lot) or shipper-receiver differences (if an off-site receipt).

15-6.2. Loss Control. The furnace-loss factors are based on measurements of the dust-collector ducts and flue gases. Some units are serviced by a common dust-collecting system, which in turn discharges into one of the systems serviced. Measurements are made by a simple sampling device placed in a flow section of the duct. The material collected is analyzed for total uranium content and is interpreted as a ratio of total flow through the duct. Several such measurements are statistically analyzed for a loss factor to be assigned to a given furnace processing a given type of material. Flue gases are scrubbed prior to being discharged to the atmosphere, and samples of the scrub liquor are taken to determine the loss factor by this route. The sum of the two factors is then applied to the furnace for a given material type.

The term *loss* as used above applies only to the unit under discussion, not to the plant as a whole, since this material is eventually recovered. The factor-determined amount of SS material is credited to the recovery unit from which these particle laden gases are emanating and is debited to the stream into which the dust collector or scrubber product is being discharged. The batches of scrubber liquor are directed to a specific tank for evaluation purposes, then recovered in the slag recovery system.

15-6.3. Control Records. Material control records originate concurrently with the activity represented by them. There are five basic activities as well as supplemental transactions which occur only as memoranda. For future reference they are defined as follows:

1. *Physical inventory:* A listing of all or any part of the uranium-bearing material which has been physically accounted for on a specified date, in a given location, with a specific identity and quantity.

2. *Receipt:* A record of items of uranium-bearing materials which is debited to a given material balance area. Receipts are further identified as being of external origin (received from off site) or internal origin (received from another material balance area).

3. *Consumption notice:* A statement of items of uranium-bearing materials whose status category has been changed from raw material to work in process.

4. *Production notice:* A statement of items of uranium-bearing materials whose status category has been changed from work in process to either finished material or scrap.

5. *Shipment:* A record of items of uranium-bearing materials which is credited to a given material balance area. Shipments are further identified as being internal or external, depending upon their destination.

6. *Adjustments:* Each change of identification within a given material balance area must be credited to the former identity and debited to the revised identity. An example of the use of identity adjustments would be to reflect changes in cost codes or material codes wherein the material does not change form, location, or status category. This should not be confused with reevaluations of uranium content, which must be reflected from a processing account into the originating account. Such revisions are handled as shipments or receipts for the amount of the difference only.

The term *status category* refers to one of the following four steps of processing:

1. *Raw material:* Feed material for a given process area which has not yet been introduced into the system.

2. *Work in process:* The intermediate status of material after it has been put into process but prior to its acceptance as product or its discard as residue.

3. *Finished material:* Acceptable product.

4. *Scrap:* Any residue or discard that contains sufficient uranium to warrant recycling into some previous processing step or through the recovery facility.

The basic system of accounting consists of a simple double-entry ledger in which additions and removals are reflected as changes in the inventory. The accounting is done mechanically on automatic tabulating equipment from punched cards.

15-7. ACCOUNTING METHODS

Each transaction is identified on a punched card and on lists produced from these cards. The basic and supplemental activities described above are coded with the following numbers:

CODE NUMBER	IDENTIFICATION
1	Beginning inventory from prior month's ending inventory
2	External receipt
3	Internal receipt
4	Production
5	External shipment
6	Internal shipment
7	Consumption
8	Coding change, "to"
9	Coding change, "from"

Codes 1 through 4 and 8 are carried as debits; codes 5 through 7 and 9 are carried as credits. A control punch in the latter group signals the tabulator to subtract values assigned to these cards. In order that the lists necessary for the various reports can be prepared, several codes are punched into the cards.

15-7.1. Breakdown of Coding System. A three-digit code is used to identify the account involved in a transaction. The first two digits represent the plant or area, and the last represents the status category described in Sec. 15-6.3.

In the case of alloys the lot mark is appended to a number code, which identifies the chief alloy constituent.

With codes 4, 7, 8, and 9, an additional three-digit code is employed to identify furnace and run number.

For external receipts the SS station code is used to identify the shipper.

Each external receipt and shipment is identified by the AEC operations office in control of the external station.

All transactions are identified by a two-digit cost category code. This code is usually based on the lot number and represents a grouping of material having a particular monetary value as determined by the end use of the material.

All transaction cards contain a one-digit analysis code, which identifies the method by which the weight percent uranium was obtained.

In addition to the nine types of transaction cards, other cards are used in the course of the machine procedure.

Ending-inventory cards contain a four-digit standard inventory identification number for AEC use. Inventory cards are calculated by machine after the initial calculation of ending inventory has been checked and corrections have been made. These cards are used for three purposes: (1) the breakdown of inventory by standard inventory number for the current month's AEC report, (2) the breakdown of inventory by material type, and (3) the opening inventory transactions for the following month's business.

Analysis cards are reproduced from certain inventory cards, external receipt cards, production cards, and code change "to" cards or are key punched from special punch sheets. They contain identification as to cost code and lot number and, in addition, the analysis and analysis code applicable to transactions of the identified lot.

Adjustment cards are punched from manually prepared punch sheets. They contain identification as to the accounts to be adjusted, the transactions adjusted in each account, the cost code, and the lot number, in addition to weight, analysis, and identification data necessary to complete the adjustment.

Material type code master cards contain, in addition to the plant or area and material type code identification, the cost code ordinarily associated with a particular material and the furnace identification that can accommodate the cost code.

15-7.2. Record of Receipt and Shipment. Year-to-date external receipt and shipment cards are calculated monthly. They are identified as to SS station code, AEC operations office code, and material type code. They contain the total weight shipped or received for the year to date identified by material type, station, and operations office.

Generally, documents are prepared manually by each plant or area on the site, and it is from these documents that transaction cards are punched. External receipt, external shipment, code change "to," and code change "from" transactions are not punched from such documents. The external receipt and shipment transactions, as well as code change "to" and code change "from" transactions, are punched from documents or instructions originated by the SS Group.

15-7.3. Tabulating Transaction Records. In the tabulating department the transaction cards are prepared by manually key punching the pertinent data from the document into the proper transaction card. The following list represents the minimum data categories entered: (1) transaction number, (2) account code, (3) lot number, (4) piece count, (5) net weight, and (6) date.

In addition, the following could be punched into a transaction card:

> (a) Account code "to" and account code "from" are punched into internal receipt cards.

(b) Station "from," account code "to," and operations office are punched into an external receipt card.

(c) Account code "from," station "to," and operations office are punched into an external shipment card.

(d) Interplant transfer numbers are punched into all receipt and shipment cards.

(e) Identification, such as hopper number, is often punched into production and consumption cards.

(f) Furnace run numbers are punched into all recovery plant production, consumption, code change "from," and code change "to" cards.

(g) Analysis and analysis codes are punched into all production, external receipt, and external shipments cards.

(h) A credit punch is entered on all credit transaction cards (shipment, consumption, and code change "from" transactions).

(i) The cost code, analysis, analysis code, SS weight in pounds, and SS weight in kilograms is punched in some original transaction cards and all corrections to transaction cards.

Certain transactions are manually key verified by the tabulating department. In general, cards are verified when no independent check on their accuracy otherwise exists or when it is not timely to use this check.

15-8. STANDARD CARD PROCEDURE

With few exceptions all cards are key punched according to a standard card punching layout. Wherever the key punching is not done according to the standard layout, it is necessary to reproduce the information on other cards which do conform to the standard layout and contain at least the minimum information necessary on transaction cards.

Wherever possible, advantage is taken of material flow in the plant to combine transactions and reduce manual key punching. In all cases an internal shipment card is reproduced from an internal receipt card (this is done after the receipt card is complete). In some cases a production card can also be made from a receipt card, and a consumption card can be made from a receipt card.

15-8.1. Analysis Cards. Periodically throughout the month the analysis cards are prepared. Code and analysis data are mechanically reproduced from the external receipt, production, and code change "to" transaction cards. Some of these analysis cards have cost codes and some do not. Those that do not have cost codes are assigned the proper cost code based on plant or area and material type code. This is done using the material type master cards.

After these cards have been completed, they are sent to the SS Group where they are checked for accuracy and completeness.

Before the monthly tabulated lists can be prepared, additional preparation of the source data is necessary. Final checks of the analysis cards must be made; checks for coding changes must be made; the transaction cards must be merged with the analysis cards; the SS weight must be calculated; and the cost codes must be punched. At this point, too, the internal receipt transaction cards must be reproduced into shipment cards.

After all new analysis cards have been prepared and checked, they are put in lot-number order and merged with the analysis file, which represents material on inventory from prior months. At the same time a check is made to see that no duplicates are allowed to get into the files. Such duplicates as are found must be narrowed down to the one final analysis card for the lot in question.

15-8.2. External Receipt and Shipment. At this point the tabulating department prepares mechanically reproduced copies of the external receipt and shipment transaction cards. The original cards are used to prepare over-all summaries of receipts and transfers. The duplicates are used in balancing procedures and in reports by individual accounts.

The original receipt cards are put in order by transfer sequence number within shipping station within operations office for the first external receipt summary list. The original shipment cards are put in order by transfer sequence number within receiving station within operations office for the first external shipment summary list. The duplicate cards are put with the other transaction cards.

15-8.3. Cost Cards. A special tabulating department procedure is necessary to obtain cost code changes in the recovery plant. Only consumption cards are used. These cards are sorted to furnace number order within plant or area* within material type order. The cards in this order are matched against the material type code master cards that have a furnace number. Consumption cards that match in both cost and furnace code represent normal consumption of material and can be merged with the other transaction cards. Consumption cards that do not match represent an unexpected handling of material which will require a change in the cost code.

Cards that match a master card on material type and plant or area only are merged behind that master card, and the cost code representing the way the material was intended to be handled is punched into the transaction cards from the master cards. The revised cost code is also punched into these consumption cards. The consumption cards that do not match a master card are assigned a standard and a revised cost code, and this is manually punched into the cards. (Occasionally this manual assignment will mean that analysis master cards must be changed also.) At this point all consumption cards that have an old and new cost code (thus representing cost code changes) are as-

---

* Some of the recovery facilities are physically located in material balance areas other than the recovery plant.

sembled, and from them transaction cards for code change "from" and code change "to" are reproduced.

15-8.4. Transaction Cards Merged by Lot Number. At this point all transaction cards except beginning inventory are collected by the tabulating department and put in card number order within lot number order. The deck is then merged behind the proper analysis card from the analysis deck. Should there be transaction cards that do not match, analysis cards must be prepared for these, and the reason for the lack of an analysis card must be ascertained. From the analysis card, by the use of an electronic calculator, the following items are punched into the transaction cards: (1) cost code, (2) analysis and analysis code, (3) SS weight in pounds, and (4) SS weight in kilograms. Should any or all these data already be punched into the card, it will neither be repunched nor checked by the calculator.

15-8.5. Separation of Cards by Group. After the calculation step, the cards are separated into three groups—analyses, internal receipts, and other transactions. The internal receipts are reproduced to obtain internal shipment cards; all transaction cards, including beginning inventory, are merged together in the following order: card number within cost code, within lot number, within account code. This is the listing order of first balance list.

The first list can now be made to bring all transactions into balance with the physical inventory. Failure of this list to balance with the inventory can be indicative of several types of errors. Before the remainder of the month-end work can be accomplished, the discrepancies with physical inventory must be noted and reconciled.

The list is prepared on tabulating equipment, debits being added and credits being subtracted. Each time a cost code changes within a lot number, a subtotal of net weight, pounds SS and kilograms SS is obtained. Each time the plant or area and material type part of the lot number changes, another subtotal of pounds SS and kilograms SS is obtained. Each time the account code changes, a grand total of pounds SS and kilograms SS is obtained.

This list is compared with the physical inventory by lot and in total. This is done for raw material, finished material, and scrap subaccounts only because in these categories the physical inventory must agree exactly with the book inventory. The errors found are reconciled, and necessary changes are made in the transaction cards. When all accounts have been reconciled with inventory, the corrections to cards are sent to the tabulating department for repunching, and the incorrect cards are pulled and destroyed.

It is necessary to obtain the production and consumption chargeable to each furnace run in order to facilitate the current adjustment of material to an as-recovered value. The difference between production and consumption can then be charged back to the plant originating the material. Concurrent with the preparation of the first balance list, a list of duplicate recovery-plant production and consumption cards is prepared. The listing order of these cards is lot number within account code within furnace number. Production and consumption are listed separately, and totals are obtained by material type or producing plant and furnace run number. The difference between production and consumption for completed furnace runs is obtained. On the basis of this difference the consumption is adjusted, and other transactions on the lots involved are correspondingly adjusted. The adjustments are reflected on transaction cards.

When the final reconciliation has been made, summary totals of beginning inventory, receipts, production, consumption, shipments, and ending inventory are obtained in units of pounds of SS material, summarized by account code in total. As a cross check the total external receipts obtained from the over-all summary of external receipts is subtracted from total receipts to give internal receipts. This is compared with the difference of total shipments and total external shipments.

After all transactions have been brought into balance with the physical inventory, a new list is made. With the cards in the order, card number within cost code within lot number within account code, the list is prepared on tabulating equipment, adding debits and subtracting credits. Each time a cost code changes within a lot number, a total of drum count, net weight, pounds SS, and kilograms SS is obtained. If a balance remains in any of these categories, a new inventory card is produced. Each time the plant or area and material type part of the lot number changes, a subtotal of pounds SS and kilograms SS is obtained. Each time the account code changes, a grand total of pounds SS and kilograms SS is obtained. Over-all totals are compared with physical inventory totals to make sure that all corrections were made properly.

15-8.6. Sorting by Cost Code. After the final balance list has been completed, the activity cards are sorted by cost codes within material balance areas. These cards are then tabulated by cost totals in columns of:

(1) Beginning inventory
(2) Receipts (and adjustments thereto)
(3) Consumption or production (determined by plant process being recorded; i.e. if raw material, this column will show consumption; if finished material, production)
(4) Shipments
(5) Ending inventory

This listing constitutes a monthly production report for raw, finished, and scrap materials which is used as the basis for cost determination and for production scheduling.

Mention was made above of an inventory card being produced mechanically whenever a balance occurs for any given lot during the tabulation of the final balance list. These cards can be tabulated to show the total ending inventory of lot-marked material (other than work in process) by lots within material types within account code within material balance areas.

15-8.7. Summary. Briefly retracing this flow of paperwork and the punched card records we find that at any given time material that has been received into this plant and debited as a plant inventory item either remains on inventory or is consumed, with a corresponding credit to the plant's inventory which will balance to zero the original debit. The consumption of this material, however, results in a debit to a given furnace run. As material is produced, it is identified as a product with perhaps an entirely different lot number and, of course, a new series of weights and analytical information. It does, however, bear the same furnace run number as other material consumed during that particular campaign. The card that is punched to represent this product is a debit to the finished material inventory for this plant. It is likewise a credit to the given furnace run number. Once a given furnace run has been completed, these cards can be sorted from the deck by furnace run number, a recapitulation of debits and credits being totaled to arrive at the difference.

As already stated, the sum of the credit cards represents the evaluation result, and the difference between the debits and credits represents the adjustment that is made to the consignor of the material. This adjustment is made in the above mentioned receipt card by punching a similar card debiting or crediting the amount of the adjustment only. This adjustment must, of course, be followed up in any other material balance areas through which this material has passed until it is finally reflected either as an adjustment to an off-site consignor or as an adjustment to the B-PID in one of the internal material balance areas. An activity run of all cards representing debits and credits as inventory items, receipts, shipments, consumption, and production (this time ignoring the run number) would result in a balance that should tie in with the physical inventory of raw, finished, and scrap material at any given time. This inventory balance will identify all items thereon as to their inventory category. Such listings are compared with each physical inventory listing as a check between the inventory and the record system. Any discrepancy must be reconciled before recapitulation, for report purposes, can proceed.

15-9. STATISTICS

The method of propagation of error is used to assign a limit of error to a given measurement or series of measurements. This method provides an accumulative and reasonably accurate procedure for expressing the total variance due to all recognized measurement uncertainty as a function of the individual measurement variances. The resultant total variance can be used to calculate the limit of error (by convention the limit of error is equal to twice the square root of the variance).

15-9.1. First-Order Approximation. The limit of error obtained by use of propagation of error is, of course, only a first-order approximation to a 95 percent confidence interval for the true measurement value. Departures of the basic distribution of measurement errors from the normal distribution and departures of the function representing the combination of measurements from linearity tend to increase the discrepancy between the true 95 percent confidence interval and the approximation. Standard propagation techniques are employed except in cases where there is evidence dictating some other treatment.

15-9.2. Scale Control. Scale control charts are maintained by plant personnel. Control limits (upper control limit and lower control limit), the average $(\overline{X})$, and range (R) are established and presented for items normally weighed, and the results are reviewed statistically by the SS Group. Comments and suggestions for improving the reporting of data and remedial action to be considered for improving the over-all weighing program are transmitted to the plant supervisor and to scale maintenance personnel following each review.

Scale precision graphs are also maintained by production personnel. On these graphs the scale maintenance department and the scale operator plot date of inspection versus the maximum pounds error. The means of reporting and commenting on these graphs is identical to that for control charts.

15-9.3. Residue Analysis. Mention was made earlier of the use of some of the batch-recovery units for determining analysis factors, which, in turn, are used in maintaining more accurate material balance data in production areas where the product, especially residues, is difficult to sample for analytical purposes. An example of this would be the ingot top croppings produced in the metal-casting area. This residue consists of a continuous transition from good metal to oxide and slag. It is a heterogeneous solid and cannot be sampled by conventional techniques. Economics dictate that this material be dissolved in acid for return to the process stream in the refinery, and inasmuch as the dissolver is a continuous operation, it is unsuitable for SS-content evaluation purposes. A random sample of these pieces is therefore sent to the recovery plant to be burned to oxide; the resultant furnace product is then sampled and analyzed. The amount of contained uranium found in this product is divided by the net weight of the crops in the test, and a factor analysis is thus established. Similar examples can be related for many other residues; however, there are instances wherein the use of a factor determination must be ruled out. The feasibility of using a factor approach is determined by the following:

1. A sufficient decrease in the measurement cost to offset the expense of establishing and administering the factor program
2. A volume of production sufficient to ensure continual economic benefit

3. The feasibility of maintaining a factor on a current basis thereby ensuring an accurate factor

In some instances the adoption of a factor analysis will result in a decrease in the reliability of the SS evaluation. It is then necessary to evaluate the savings that can be realized and to weigh these against the indicated decrease in accuracy.

15-10. INVENTORIES

On the first day of each month a physical inventory is taken of all SS material in the plant. The inventory procedure is divided into three phases—preparation, execution, and recapitulation. Formal procedures are written to assure complete coverage of each phase. The highlights of these detailed instructions are summarized in the following paragraphs.

PREPARATION: A time is set for the inventory to begin, and a cleanout of the furnaces, filters, partially used containers, etc., is scheduled to be completed by this time. All drumming stations are to be vacuumed free of SS material, and then the dust collectors are emptied. All non-lot-marked production is properly lot marked, color coded, and assembled in the storage area by lots. The supervisor will have an operator prepared to measure the volume of the digestors and other tanks containing uranium-bearing liquors.

Furnaces with an inherent dead bed are rabbled free of material only in excess of this dead bed. The furnace hold-up is then listed on inventory at a constant predetermined value which is computed by multiplying a geometric calculation of volume by the ratio of uranium per unit volume as determined by the laboratory.

All tanks that will contain liquid at inventory time are calibrated immediately after installation by measuring the distance from a bench mark at the top of the tank to the surface of the liquid as measured increments of water volume are let into the tank. A chart is then plotted for these distances versus volume.

EXECUTION: All tanks of SS-material bearing liquor are agitated for at least one-half hour prior to sampling. After the sample has been taken, the agitation is discontinued, and a volume measurement is made. Sample bottles are filled between one-half and two-thirds full to allow for sufficient agitation in the laboratory prior to subsampling. Sample bottles are labeled as to type of material and source. Requests for chemical analysis bear the same information.

The inventory of drummed materials is made by strictly following a definite geometric pattern throughout the plant. Special inventory sheets are used which list the status categories of material, and, as each drum is encountered, it is listed on the proper sheet. The inventory contained in the prepared feed section of the slag recovery system is listed at a book value as previously explained.

If a furnace is not cleaned out because of some slow-burning material, the hold-up quantity will be estimated by the plant foreman. The plant will not be returned to operation without the mutual agreement of the SS Representative and the plant superintendent.

RECAPITULATION: For each tank, the volume will be computed by referring to calibration charts. The sample identification number will be listed beside each unit from which a sample was obtained. Lot totals from the inventory should be compared with record totals as a check for agreement of quantity and for omission from or duplication of inventory.

15-10.1. Statistical Evaluation of Inventory. The evaluation of the B-PID can be approached by either of two methods:

1. The total variance can be determined by accumulating variances for each measurement, sampling technique, and analysis made during the inventory.
2. The variance can be based on the experienced over-all variance of previous inventories.

Although the former might perhaps be better in theory, it is far too unwieldly to be adapted to inventories that are seldom duplicated from one month to the next. The second method is more practical and is currently in use. The B-PID, with all adjustments to prior period operations being considered, is recorded as a percentage function of the total removals from the in-process stream (i.e. finished material production, scrap production, measured losses, and B-PID).

The average B-PID for each material balance area is obtained, as well as for the plant as a whole, and the variance about this value is then determined at both the 2σ and 3σ limits. As the B-PID for each area is determined for each month, the appropriate value is noted on the chart for the given areas. If the value falls within 2σ limits, the process is felt to be in control. If it falls between 2σ and 3σ, the process is examined for peculiarities that might contribute to the conditions. If the 3σ limit is exceeded, the reason for the B-PID must be determined and appropriate action taken.

It is quite possible, of course, that offsetting errors can exist in a material balance area and that this can erroneously indicate good control. This possibility is not overlooked and is minimized by:

1. Checking yield data for various types of residues and finished material against consumption
2. Preparation of process inventories by two independent persons
3. Physical review of inventory procedures to ascertain that the standard operating procedure is being followed and suggesting revisions as deemed necessary

Each control chart is reviewed once every six months, new control limits being computed at that time. Significant changes revealed by these computations are investigated as to their cause.

If the B-PID exceeds the allowable limit of error, the inventory of the work-in-process material is first checked for errors of extension, both of calibration and analytical data. Technically trained personnel review these data in light of comparing results with values known from experience to be reasonable for the given measurements. Changes in operational techniques during the month are reviewed for their effects on the inventory. Measured-loss records during the month are reviewed for information on excessive dust-bag breakage or difficulties in meeting specifications for discarding liquors.

If all the above checks fail to reveal the cause of discrepancy, the SS Representative reviews all pertinent facts and then makes recommendations to management as to whether he believes (1) material has been compromised or lost through negligence and that security authorities should be notified, (2) the inventory does not represent the material on hand and that it should be reinventoried immediately, or (3) the inventory was as good as might be expected under certain extenuating circumstances and that a second inventory would not accomplish sufficient ends to justify the additional expense.

15-11. SUMMARY

The control procedures described above are designed to meet several specific needs, including process control, health and safety, conservation of materials, efficient and economic operation, and the generation of desirable management data to be reflected in a number of reports.

The reports recap the month's activity in a form that relates the beginning inventory, receipts, production or consumption, shipments, and ending inventory of every classification of material in the plant. The report can in turn, be used as a basis for plant cost computations and as a basis for production evaluation. In the latter category are included product yields, production scheduling information as to generation rates, inventories, and comparisons with goals previously established. A comparison of the physical inventory with the calculated value of material in process serves as a basis for evaluating the precision and accuracy of the physical inventory, which, in turn, determines the degree of control through which material losses, operational or by compromise, can be detected.

Other reports are intended to serve the needs of the AEC in its role of coordinator of all the various sites. These reports contribute to the over-all AEC picture much of the same information on a nation-wide scale as the above described reports contribute to individual plant operation.

Certain broad requirements (such as periodic reports, reporting units, etc.) are outlined by AEC policies and procedures. The balance of the program is left to the discretion of the individual station with the only additional stipulation being that it be conducted commensurate with good business practices. It has been our aim to accomplish this in the truest sense as reflected in the preceding discussions.

REFERENCES FOR CHAPTER 15

1. E. R. Johnson et al., *Chem. Eng. Prog.*, 53: 2 (February 1951).

Chapter 16

IRRADIATED ENRICHED-URANIUM FUEL RECOVERY*

16-1. INTRODUCTION

Nuclear material control as applied to the processing of irradiated enriched-uranium fuel elements in the Idaho Chemical Processing Plant (ICPP) is discussed in this chapter. The purpose of this processing is the recovery of uranium—the same purpose as the processes described in Chapters 14 and 15. The purpose of processing irradiated normal-uranium fuel elements, as described in Chapter 17, is the recovery of plutonium in addition to uranium. The processes described in this chapter differ from that described in Chapters 14 and 15 because of the greater radiation danger present.

Nuclear material control at the Idaho plant is basically a chemical engineering function. Chemical process engineers maintain surveillance over the collection of routine process control data. These flow directly to a small clerical staff, where it is used in the preparation of reports for management and the Atomic Energy Commission. All data are under rigorous statistical scrutiny. One administrator is responsible for statistical analysis, material control, and the analytical laboratory quality-control program.

Measurement effort is allocated as nearly as possible on the basis of the value of the information generated. Close liaison is maintained among supervisors of plant operations, shift process engineers, and analytical laboratory personnel. Personnel in each of these groups are alert to the specifications for operating levels of process variables and tolerable limits for measurements. The clerical personnel of the Material Control Section are similarly alert as an additional safeguard. A senior statistician reviews each material-balance statement for appropriateness of the limits of uncertainty of the statement's various items.

Significant economy of effort has been realized. For instance, input is determined by measurements made on accumulations of uranyl nitrate solution fed to run tanks from the dissolvers. When continuous processing of

---

* F. P. Vance, F. H. Tingey, and B. S. Lewis, Phillips Petroleum Company, National Reactor Testing Station, Idaho Falls, Idaho.

spent fuels was initiated, the practice of collecting three samples from each run tank batch was adopted. Each of these was analyzed for uranium concentration by the isotopic dilution method. In addition, specific gravity and acidity were determined for process control purposes. After the system had been run for a short time, operating conditions became essentially stabilized, and a good correlation was obtained among the variables—specific gravity, acidity, and uranium content of the solution—by regression analysis of process data. Also, the stoichiometric relation between U^{235} and U^{236} was utilized as a control. Through the use of the information generated by scrutiny of these data, many measurements were found to be no longer necessary and were eliminated.

16-2. PROCESS DESCRIPTION

16-2.1. Dissolution. Uranium-aluminum alloy fuel elements are dissolved in two vertical dissolvers which operate continuously. The solvent is nitric acid; mercuric nitrate is added as a catalyst. The solution of $Al(NO_3)_3$, HNO_3, $UO_2(NO_3)_2$, and fission products is filtered by gravity as it runs through line coolers to two hold tanks. Two dissolver solution-run tanks provide surge capacity and a means for measuring the volume and composition of the solution. The solution is fed to each dissolver run tank in turn until a predetermined level has been reached. After a suitable sparging interval, the solution is allowed to settle for sampling and volume reading.

During the final hour of vessel filling and for a minimum of 30 minutes after the flow is switched to the other tank, the solution in the vessel is air sparged to provide thorough mixing before sampling. After sparging has been stopped and the level in the vessel is quiescent, as indicated by the liquid-level manometer, a reading is taken from which run tank volume can be computed. Three samples are drawn, and the batch is transferred to the first-cycle feed tank. In this manner the batch is measured and then transferred forward through the process. Uranium in any solution transferred to the first-cycle feed tank from sources other than the dissolver solution run tank is measured before transfer.

16-2.2. Purification. The process of purifying uranium by solvent extraction involves a series of extraction-stripping cycles.[2] Uranium is preferentially extracted with hexone (methyl isobutyl ketone) from the aluminum nitrate solution in the lower section (extraction section) of the extraction columns. The bulk of the fission products remains in the aqueous phase, since these fission products are considerably less extractable than uranium. The uranium-hexone extract rises to the upper section (scrub section) of the extracting columns, where additional fission-product decontamination is accomplished by scrubbing with a counterflowing stream of aluminum nitrate solution. The solvent, containing the uranium and some fission products, is brought into contact with dilute nitric acid in a second column, and the uranium and fission products are back extracted (stripped) into the aqueous phase. A new feed is prepared from this solution by concentration is an evaporator, and the extraction-stripping cycle is repeated for additional separation from fission products.

Three extraction-stripping cycles are required before the uranium is sufficiently free of fission products to permit handling without shielding. The solvent-extraction system is continuous throughout the three cycles. The first-, second-, and third-cycle product stream concentration is carried out continuously in critically safe thermo-siphon evaporators before the stream is fed to the succeeding extraction columns or to storage as final product.

16-2.3. Product. The product solution from the third-cycle evaporator is collected in two transfer vessels. It is then transferred in batches into the product collection vessels by applying air pressure to the transfer vessel. The product is drawn by vacuum from the collection vessels with either of two product-bottle filling burets and subsequently is drained from the buret to the always-safe product bottles by gravity. Each product bottle is sampled, sealed, and then weighed on a balance accurate to the nearest gram. The bottle is then placed in a second container (bird cage) with outside dimensions (2 ft by 2 ft) that minimize the possibility of assembling a critical mass. The product is then ready for shipment to another site for additional processing.

16-2.4. Waste. The aqueous waste stream from the first extraction column is collected in geometrically safe tanks and sampled to determine the uranium content. If the solution is high in uranium, the waste is sent to the salvage equipment for recovery. Normally, the waste is concentrated to the minimum volume possible without freezing and is jetted directly to a 300,000-gal type 347 stainless steel permanent storage tank. This tank is encased in concrete under about 10 ft of earth.

Second- and third-cycle extraction raffinates are handled together in a manner similar to that for the first-cycle raffinate, i.e. sampled and ultimately stored in a separate 300,000-gal underground tank in the waste tank farm.

Two other classes of liquid waste, collected separately to facilitate treatment, are process-equipment waste, which has a low activity level, and cell floor-drain waste. The cell floor-drain wastes are collected for sampling in two 4000-gal stainless steel tanks in two cells in the deepest part of the process building. Normally, the uranium content and activity level of cell floor-drain waste are low enough for direct discharge to the ground, but during cell decontamination this waste can be transferred to the chemical waste evaporator system for concentration.

16-2.5. Spent Solvent. The spent solvent from the solvent-extraction cycles is collected in geometrically safe collection vessels and sampled for uranium. If high in uranium, it may be recycled to the first-cycle stripping column. Solutions from the process operations and laboratories, high in uranium content, are collected in geometrically safe vessels, sampled for uranium (primarily for critical-mass control), and then evaporated to minimum volume in a batch evaporator.   The concentrate is stored in another geometrically safe tank and then recycled to the process feed preparation vessels.

16-2.6. Sampling.   Samples of the radioactive process solutions are necessary for process-control purposes and to provide the data for an accurate accounting of the fissionable material in the process.   Special sampling equipment is required for the dissolver and raffinate batch solutions because of the high level of radioactivity present.

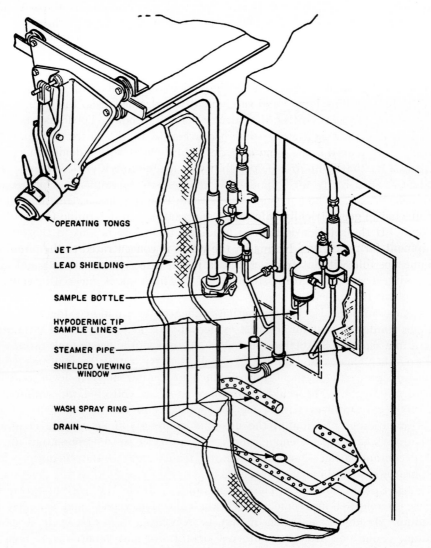

OPERATING TONGS

JET

LEAD SHIELDING

SAMPLE BOTTLE

HYPODERMIC TIP
SAMPLE LINES

STEAMER PIPE

SHIELDED VIEWING
WINDOW

WASH SPRAY RING

DRAIN

FIG. 16-1   Sample transfer station.

A sampler system was designed to meet the particular needs of the plant. Special sampling corridors were constructed at operating-corridor level for each cell tank. Samplers for several cells were grouped so that a continuous 4.5-in. lead shield having one entry for a sample carrier and a single set of sample handling tongs could be used. Fig. 16-1 shows a single air-operated sampling jet, tongs, and shield. The tip of the sampler is fitted with two hypodermic needles that punch through the neoprene cap on a sample bottle. The sample bottles are removed from the sample carrier, conveyed to the sample jet, and raised to sampling position. The sample is taken by drawing a vacuum on the bottle through the short needle with the jet, which in turn draws process solution from the vessel through the sampling line and long needle into the bottle. The solution is circulated through the bottle and returned to the process vessel for a few minutes before the jet is turned off and the bottle removed. The sampling operation is viewed through a lead-glass window directly in front of the sampler. The filled sample bottle is returned to the sample carrier and removed from the sampling station for delivery to the analytical facilities. The sampler stations are equipped with steamers that are used to steam the intake and discharge lines after samples are taken. The steamers are also used when the sampler is being decon-taminated.

16-3. INPUT SAMPLING AND ANALYSIS

Routinely, three 5-ml samples are drawn from each dissolver batch run tank solution. The first sample from a given batch is circulated for a minimum of 15 minutes through the sample bottle to purge the sample draw lines. The other two samples are circulated for a minimum of 5 minutes each.

Acidity and specific gravity analyses are made on two of the three samples drawn from each batch. Rerun or range limits are provided as a safeguard against nonrepresentative samples and analyses. These limits are determined by applying statistical methods to past analytical error and sampling error associated with the particular measurement. Depending upon the agreement between the duplicate specific gravity and acidity determinations, one or two of the samples are prepared for a uranium determination.

16-3.1. Acidity Determination. The free acid in the dissolver solutions is determined by potentiometric analysis. This method involves the utilization of a potassium oxalate solution at a reference pH of 5.80 to complex hydrolyzable ions including uranium (VI). Hydrogen ions in the sample solution, when added to the pH 5.80 potassium oxalate solution, causes the pH to drop. The quantity of standard base required to bring the pH back to pH 5.80 is a direct measure of the free acid in the sample.

16-3.2. Specific Gravity Determination. Since fission products are present in the dissolver solution and the specific gravity determination, therefore, must be made remotely, the falling-drop method is utilized. In this method the specific gravity of an aqueous solution is determined by measuring the time required for a drop of the solution to fall a fixed distance in an immiscible organic medium (reference liquid). The falling time is related to the specific gravity by an expression derived from Stokes' law. The organic liquids are prepared so that they have a slightly lower specific gravity than the aqueous solutions to be measured. The reference liquids are placed in graduated cylinders, which are kept at a constant temperature of $25.0 \pm 0.2°C$. A measured drop of aqueous sample is forced from the tip of a remote pipet beneath the surface of the reference liquid, and the drop falls in the liquid. The time required for the drop to fall a fixed distance is measured, and the specific gravity of the sample is then determined by comparison with a standard curve.

16-3.3. Uranium-Concentration Measurement: *Isotopic Dilution.* Prior to the analysis of the hot feed sample, a remote liquid-liquid extraction followed by a hydrogen peroxide precipitation must be made. The routine hot feed sample uranium concentration determination is known as "isotopic dilution." [1,3-5] This consists of introducing a known amount of a uranium isotope, not present in the sample, into a measured volume of the sample to be analyzed. The isotopic composition of the mixture gives a direct indication of the amount of uranium in the solution of unknown concentration.

The mass distribution is determined by means of a surface-emission mass spectrometer.[5] The sample is evaporated from the nitric acid solution onto a filament of tantalum ribbon. The material is deposited as U_3O_8. A 50-μg deposit is usually sufficient for analysis.

After the material has been introduced into the instrument through a vacuum lock arrangement, the filament is heated, and ions are thermionically emitted. The spectrum is scanned to receive UO_2 ions. These ions are then accelerated through a potential of approximately 6000 volts, and beam deflection is achieved by a permanent magnet. The masses are scanned electromagnetically by varying the current through a range of 250 ma upon windings around the poles of the permanent magnet. This is done electronically using an RC time-constant circuit. The ion beam representative of the individual isotope is received, and the signal is amplified by an electrometer type ion detector. The intensities of the ion beams are recorded by a Brown electric recorder as a series of peaks of various heights. These are recorded on a single roll of paper at preselected amplification factors. Measurement of the peak heights and the total signal received afford a relationship from which the weight percent can be easily calculated.

Coulometric Analysis. The isotopic dilution method, although explicit, requires a long analysis time and expensive equipment.[1] Thus fundamental research and development studies[6] have been in progress to provide a method less involved and of sufficient precision and accuracy to be used for SS-material control purposes. As a result of such studies, the coulometric determination of uranium (VI) at controlled potential has been developed.[6,7]

Rerun Criterion. A degree of control over the quality of these analyses can be achieved by using the high correlation of uranium content with specific gravity of the solution as a criterion for rerun of analyses. The range of values for the uranium content predicted from specific gravity is plotted from experience. If the analyzed uranium values lie outside statistically determined limits when compared with the predicted content, a rerun is required.

16-3.4. Isotopic Determination. The isotopic assay of feed samples is easily obtained from the mass analyses required by the isotopic dilution determination. In the manner previously described, the isotope used as a spike can be disregarded completely, and the desired mass ratio can be calculated.

In the chemical industry the derivation of stoichiometric relations between process variables is often possible. In the processing of enriched uranium fuel, a very effective control procedure for mass-distribution analyses can be based upon the stoichiometric relation between residual U^{235} and residual U^{236} fractions.

If we define

$$Z_0 = \text{preirradiated } U^{236} \text{ fraction}$$
$$E_0 = \text{preirradiated } U^{235} \text{ fraction}$$
$$Z_1 = \text{postirradiated } U^{236} \text{ fraction}$$
$$E_1 = \text{postirradiated } U^{235} \text{ fraction}$$
$$\alpha = \text{thermal-neutron cross-section ratio of capture to fission}$$

then we can derive the following relation:

$$E_1 = \frac{\alpha}{\alpha + Z_0}\left[E_0 + \frac{Z_0}{\alpha}(\alpha + 1)\right] + Z_1\left[\frac{E_0}{\alpha + Z_0} + \frac{Z_0(\alpha + 1)}{(\alpha + Z_0)\alpha} - \frac{\alpha + 1}{\alpha}\right] \quad (16.1)$$

An average value[8] for α is 0.185 ± 0.008. Z_0 and E_0 usually obtainable from fabricator's data.

The procedure then is to compare in any given case the residual enrichment E_1 as predicted from the residual U^{236} (Z_1) by the above equation and compare this with that actually obtained by mass analysis. From a knowledge of the magnitude of the errors involved in the constants of the equation and the analyses, rerun limits can be determined to provide protection against nonrepresentative analyses.

16-4. PRODUCT SAMPLING AND ANALYSIS

The problems associated with the measurement and control of product are not as complex as those for feed. The product is concentrated uranyl nitrate solution. The fission products have been sufficiently removed that the remote sampling necessary for feed measurements is no longer required. Furthermore, the sampling error associated with this solution would not be expected to approach that experienced in the feed. However, because of the large amount of uranium present in the product room and in the vault, procedures for criticality control in these areas are very important and must be followed exactly.

The product collection vessels consist of three banks of three 5-in.-diameter critically safe vessels. By means of valves and pumps, solutions in the banks can be thoroughly circulated and mixed prior to withdrawal. For the purpose of SS measurement, bottles drawn in sequence after circulation and mixing of a given quantity of solution in the banks constitute a bank draw. One 50-ml sample is taken from each bottle. The sampling is accomplished very simply from the product-bottle filling buret. Routinely specific gravity and acidity determinations are performed on each sample. Uranium and mass-distribution analyses are performed on the samples representing the first, second, and last bottle in each bank draw. Statistical range limits reflecting primarily analytical error are provided for each of these three sets of measurements so generated, to insure homogeneity of the material constituting the entire bank draw. Providing all limits are complied with, the average of the three uranium and mass determinations is applied to all bottles from the given bank draw; otherwise each product bottle is mechanically rocked end over end at 12 rpm for 20 minutes, resampled, and analyzed. Under the latter procedure each bottle content is computed from its own analysis. In the vast majority of cases homogeneity of solution is achieved within the banks. Consequently, a great economy of analytical effort is effected by this procedure.

The tare weight is measured on each bottle of uranyl nitrate product before it is filled. A gross weight is taken after sampling. An operations supervisor must be present during weighing to verify the weights used and during sampling to see that the prescribed procedure is complied with and the reference bottle numbers are correctly recorded.

16-4.1. Uranium Determination. The determination of the uranium in a product sample is made by the direct ignition method.[9] The solutions of uranium nitrate are weighed by differences from a Lunge weighing buret into tared platinum crucibles. Hydrofluoric acid is added, and the samples are evaporated to dryness and ignited at 900°C to the black oxide, U_3O_8. The hydrofluoric acid ensures stoichiometric conversion to U_3O_8. The impurity metals are spectrographically determined, and the results are corrected accordingly.

The fact that three independent samples are analyzed from each bank draw provides a basis for control over gross outlier values. Also an empirical relation relating specific gravity and uranium concentration can be derived which, in the manner described for feed samples, serves as an additional control technique.

16-4.2. Isotopic Determination. Routinely each sample from a product bank draw available from each product bottle is mass assayed. The equipment and procedure used are the same as those used for decontaminated feed samples. The control of mass-distribution analyses for product is identical with that for feed.

16-4.3. Specific Gravity. The specific gravity of an unknown liquid is found by weighing a plummet immersed in the liquid; the apparent weight is a function of the specific gravity of the unknown liquid. The Westphal balance, which is designed for this purpose, is used for product specific gravity determinations.

16-5. RAFFINATE SAMPLING AND ANALYSIS

16-5.1. Sampling. The sampling of raffinate streams is done remotely in the manner described for plant feed. These streams consist of solutions of fission products bearing minuscule quantities of uranium. Because of the low concentration and the fact that these solutions frequently bear particulate matter in suspension, considerable analytical and sampling error is experienced in many cases. It is, in fact, extremely difficult to establish precision or reproducibility for any measurement on these waste streams, since the errors have been found to depend to a large extent upon the particular solution being sampled. Because of the dilute nature of these solutions, high analytical precision is not justifiable on the basis of dollar value of the material. Accordingly a sequential type of analytical and sampling program is used.

For each type of process-waste solution and the associated measuring tank, two concentration limits are defined. These limits are derived in conjunction with the tank volume to reflect negligible amounts of uranium involved and appreciable amounts of uranium involved. What constitutes negligible and appreciable in any given case depends to a large extent on the difficulties involved in recovering the material. A simple guide is that effort and expense should be commensurate with the value of the material.

Initially a single sample is drawn from the process waste tank and analyzed. If the result of this analysis, plus the associated uncertainty (deduced from the most pessimistic estimates of the sampling and analytical errors associated with the solution), does not exceed the lower limit (negligible uranium), only the single analysis is made. The majority of waste batches fall in this category. If, however, the result of the first analysis falls between the two limits or above the upper limit, one or more samples are drawn and analyzed according to a defined procedure, which takes into consideration such things as the cost of additional sampling, the amount of uranium involved, and the precision required for the batch determination.

16-5.1. Uranium Determination. The analytical technique used for these dilute uranium samples is the fluorophotometric determination of uranium by the extraction method.[9] This procedure applies to both aqueous and organic solutions. Aqueous samples are first extracted with 25 percent tributylphosphate in kerosene to remove impurities; organic samples are used directly. The procedures are based on the quantitative measurement of the characteristic yellow-green fluorescence emitted by uranium when it is fused with sodium fluoride and subjected to ultraviolet radiation. The uranium content is determined by reference to a standard curve.

Owing to the dilute nature of the quantities being determined by this method, no elaborate control program is justified.

16-6. AUXILIARY CONTROL TECHNIQUES

In addition to the measurement and control programs outlined above, other programs may reinforce the control and contribute information useful in the maintenance of an efficient control system.

16-6.1. Chemist-Tester Performance Evaluation. It is apparent upon reviewing the entire process data validity problem that the competence, performance, and integrity of individuals intimately associated with the steps by which the data are generated are of prime importance.

Too often the quality level of the data being generated is accepted as a matter of course and that standard is maintained. This approach, although having some merit, fails to emphasize the importance of the individual in connection with the quality of the data. Ideally, therefore, what is needed is some method of performance certification.

For the chemical-plant operator who is responsible for the sampling and instrument readings that are associated with a given quantity of material to be transferred, this amounts to a certification that the operating procedure is being followed for each and every transfer. This is accomplished, first, by making every operator aware of the importance of the data for which he is directly responsible and how they are related to the rest of the process data; and, secondly, by having a process engineer present at transfer to verify and certify along with the operator that the procedure was complied with and that the data were correctly interpreted and recorded.

In the case of the laboratory technician who is routinely doing the chemical analyses on the samples submitted, this back-up procedure is not feasible for obvious reasons. Again the technician must be impressed with the importance of his results and how they are related to the other data accumulated. This can be accomplished through frequent discussions with the laboratory personnel. In addition, however, some assurance must exist that the individual is qualified to perform the analytical methods that are to be applied.

Admittedly the subject of technician qualification is a touchy one. The usual procedure in most analytical laboratories is simply a statement or feeling on the part of the shift supervisor that the individual has had sufficient training and practice to perform satisfactorily on the given method. There are obvious weaknesses in this subjective approach. A program directed toward the objective evaluation of individual technical performance has been established. Briefly, the program is as follows.

Each technician in the laboratory is given a period of intensive training and practice on each of the 23 analytical methods used routinely in the laboratory. When the individual feels that he is qualified on a particular method, nine synthetic control samples are submitted to him for single determinations on each sample. On the basis of the performance of the entire group of analysts on the given method and with reference to previous applicable data, the bias and the precision of the method with reference to the group are determined. The corresponding parameters are determined for each individual's set of nine determinations and are compared with the group values. Under the assumption that the group values are known, the tabulation of the normal probability distribution and the χ^2 distribution provide approximate statistical tests for a significant departure of the individual's performance from the group's. If the bias or precision associated with a given individual on a given method is significant at the 0.10 level, the individual is given further specialized training, after which a repetition of the series is required. The choice of criterion for acceptable and unacceptable performance was arrived at on the basis of a study of the power functions of the tests involved.

Results of this program have been gratifying. The acceptance on the part of the analysts of this method of evaluating their performance, contrary to earlier apprehension, has with few exceptions been wholehearted. The tests provide a key, even for those that pass, to where further effort should be concentrated to improve the quality of the data for which they are directly responsible. A significant bias on the part of an individual on a particular method indicates a need for a critical evaluation of the procedure as it is interpreted and applied by him; whereas significance with regard to precision indicates that a refinement of technique is in order. An increase in data quality cannot help but be a natural consequence of such a program.

16-6.2. Isolation of Error Components. The identification and subsequent estimation, within the limits of economic and physical feasibility, of component error factors is necessary if the most efficient and effective use is to be made of the quality-control techniques available. In fact, such a study is prerequisite to the formulation and administration of the entire data generative program. The number of samples per batch, the number of preparations per sample, the number of analyses per preparation, the time interval between analyses, etc. cannot be efficiently resolved until a fundamental knowledge of the magnitude of the corresponding error components is obtained. The area of mathematical statistics known as experimental design and analysis provides the techniques by which the components are identified and their magnitudes are estimated.

For example, the isotopic dilution technique is involved and complex and provides many sources of error. It is conceivable that the following sources of variability could contribute to any given result:

1. Sampling
2. Chemist doing the remote extraction
3. The pipet used to measure the aliquot of sample and to spike the solution
4. Sample preparation and decontamination
5. Mass instrument operator
6. Mass instrument
7. Time of analysis

A discussion of the various experimental designs applicable to this problem or of chemical processing plant data studies in general is outside the scope of this chapter. Suffice it to say that by proper experimental design the magnitude and significance of each of the sources in the example, as well as in similar problems, can be estimated and thus can provide the basis for optimum allocation of effort for maximum precision.

16-6.3. Stoichiometric Relations. In addition to the stoichiometric relation between residual U^{235} and residual U^{236} in spent reactor fuel (Sec. 16-3.4) two more relations of the same type are available for gross plant input computations. These are:

$$\text{Residual uranium} = \text{cold uranium} \left(\frac{\alpha + Z_0}{\alpha + Z_1} \right) \tag{16.2}$$

and

$$\text{Residual uranium} = \text{cold uranium} \left(\frac{1 + \alpha - E_0}{1 + \alpha - E_1} \right) \tag{16.3}$$

where α = thermal-neutron cross-section ratio of capture to fission
           Z_0 = preirradiated U^{236} fraction
           E_0 = preirradiated U^{235} fraction
           Z_1 = postirradiated U^{236} fraction
           E_1 = postirradiated U^{235} fraction
cold uranium = the preirradiated uranium content of the dissolved fuel

The cold uranium contents, Z_0 and E_0, are usually available from the fabricator of the fuel. The parameters Z_1 and E_1 are determined from a mass analysis of the feed solutions.

This computation is valid only for feed increments as determined for clean dissolvers without residual heels, since a residual heel would tend to bias the mass analyses if the equations were applied to a single batch without dissolver cleanout.

From a comparison of the values calculated from these relationships with those determined as previously discussed, the degree of reliance to be placed upon dissolver-solution measurements can be estimated.

16-6.4. Continuous By-difference Plant Material Balance. Certainly a fundamental part of any measurement control program is the construction of material balances. This problem is made quite complex in the processing of spent reactor fuel elements since considerable quantities are held up in process. Because of high radiation levels and lack of remote sampling facilities, these materials are inaccessible for direct measurements. Thus measurement and sampling techniques as well as process operation must be controlled by maintaining a control chart of the measured input less measured product plus raffinates difference. This chart is constructed, using the methods of mathematical statistics, to detect changes in the average quantity held up as well as changes in the inherent variation to be associated with the holdup figure.

In conclusion, it is worth noting that any good control program on process measurements must be based upon the methods of mathematical statistics. However, these methods alone cannot provide an all-inclusive and foolproof program; there are many variables that cannot be controlled or measured. A continuing awareness of operations, investigation of unusual fluctuations, and intelligent evaluation of information is essential to optimum control.

16-7. DATA RECORDING AND REPORTING

16-7.1. Journals and Ledgers. The record system for material control of irradiated fuel processing consists of one Transfer Journal, one Material Balance Summary Ledger, and one Bucket Record Card File.

The Transfer Journal (Fig. 16-2) is a book of original entry used for recording shipper's data and fuel transferred to the processing plant. Fuel measure-

OUT OF AREA TRANSFER JOURNAL

STATION ________ MATERIAL ________ UNITS ________

Year 19		101 FORM NO.	MATERIAL DESCRIPTION	MATERIAL SHIPPED							MATERIAL RECEIVED						
Mo.	Day			SS Net	L. E.	Net U-235	L. E.	No. Elem.	Area	Post Ref.	SS Net	L. E.	Net U-235	L. E.	No. Elem.	Area	Post Ref.

FIG. 16-2 Out of Area Transfer Journal.

ments are supplied by the shipper on a standard AEC-101 transfer form. The journal is divided into several sections, segregating the various operations offices within the AEC. Postings are summarized on a monthly basis and transferred to the Material Balance Summary Ledger. Contractor identifica-

CPI-SS-1 ☐ I Interplant Carrier Unloading Record No._____
     ☐ II Inter Bucket Transfer Record   Date_____

Material Type			From	To	Number	Cask Number
Batch No.	Bucket No.	Weight (Kg.)	Individual Element Identification or Count			
1		G				
2		T				
3		N				
4		G				
5		T				
6		N				
7		G				
8		T				
9		N				
10		G				
11		T				
12		N				
13		G				
14		T				
15		N				
16		G				
17		T				
18		N				
19		G				
20		T				
21		N				
22		G				
23		T				
24		N				

I. This constitutes an accurate record of materials transferred to the CPI SS Storage Area.

_____
Operator

II. The above listed material was transferred within the SS Storage Area from bucket(s) "A" to bucket(s) "B".

_____
Operator

Posted to Container Stock Ledger:

Clerk_____

Date_____

I. This certifies acceptance of responsibility for the above listed materials placed in the CPI SS Storage Area.

_____
Supervisor

Audited by:

Clerk_____

Date_____

FIG. 16-3 Interplant Carrier and Bucket Transfer Record

tion is readily available through the use of standard AEC station code symbols.

The ledger (book of final entry) consists of a plant control column and seven material balance areas; namely, fuel storage, chemical engineering development, process recovery, analytical laboratory, waste storage, chemical development, and product storage. The ledger was additionally designed to record beginning inventories, receipts, shipments, losses, ending inventories, and book-physical inventory differences. Each material balance area is identified by a number to facilitate proper interplant material control.

AEC-284   **SS MATERIAL TRANSFER RECEIPT**

SS Material on Transfer:_____ to _____ No. _____ ,
                                   (Station Symbols)

shipped on _____ , 19__ has been received

on _____ , 19_____

Material has been verified as follows: (Check one)

     Piece Count   Container Count   Gross Wt. Check

     Other:_____

(Shipper's weights and SS content are accepted pending final
   verification measurements and completion of Form AEC-101.)

                          By: _____
                              (SS Representative)

Fig. 16-4   SS Material Transfer Receipt.

The Bucket Record Card File is used for recording bucket weights, material type, piece count, individual element identification, vendor data, and batch numbers. The file is used primarily as a perpetual inventory record of the fuel storage basin.

16-7.2. AEC Form 101. Transfers of special nuclear materials between AEC contractors are accompanied by this standard transfer form. This form has provisions for recording both shipper and receiver data pertinent to the material involved. A list of procedures standardized for recording, handling, and issuing this form has been published by the AEC.[10]

16-7.3. Receiving Forms SS-1 and AEC-284. A locally conceived form, designated SS-1 (Fig. 16-3), is used to record bucket numbers, weights, and piece counts for materials entering the storage basin. When piece count has been entered by the receiving operator, form AEC-284 (Fig. 16-4) is issued notifying the contractor and operations office involved that verification has been completed.

FORM AED - 256 (1-15-55)

I   SS MATERIAL REQUISITION

No _____

Date _____

Material Classification	No. of Fuel Elements Requested _____	Storage Bucket Nos. _____ Requested by _____

II   CHARGER LOADING RECORD — Material Removed From SS Storage

Batch No.	Bucket No.	Weight (Kg.)	Individual Element Identification					
3		G						
4		T						
5		N .						
6		G						
7		T						
8		N						
9		G						
10		T						
11		N						

Charger No. _____ Loaded by _____ Time _____ Date _____

III   INTRAPLANT TRANSFER — CHARGER TO DISSOLVER

Contents of Charger No. _____ Charged to Dissolver No. _____

Slug Count _____ Time _____ Date _____ Batch _____

Operator _____

IV   SS CONTROL ENTRIES (All space below reserved for SS Control)

Batch Number	Canned Weights		MWD Factor	Net Irradiated Weights	
	SS Net	U-235		SS Net	U-235
Totals					

Audited by _____ Date _____ Calc. by _____ Date _____

Posted to: Cont. Stk _____ Date _____ T. J _____ Date _____

FIG. 16-5   SS Material Requisition.

Procedures for recording the SS-1 and issuing the AEC-284 are as follows:

1. SS-1 is posted to the storage-basin bucket-record cards. Bucket number, 101 serial number, date material was received, SS-1 form number, material description, element piece count, and bucket weights are entered.
2. SS-1 is signed and dated to indicate form has been posted.
3. Form is filed.
4. AEC-284 is then issued as follows:
    Copy 1—Shipper
          2—Division of Nuclear Materials Management—AEC
          3—Shipper's Operations Office
          4—Idaho Operations Office
          5—Retain in file

16-7.4. Charger Loading Record. The procedure for recording batch transfers to the dissolver is as follows:

1. Post Charger Loading Record (Fig. 16-5) to storage basin bucket record cards. Enter batch transfer date, batch number, elements removed, batch weights, and bucket inventory balance. Care must be taken to ensure that bucket numbers are identified with Charger Loading Record before posting is complete.
2. Sign and date (at time of posting).
3. File.

16-7.5. Coding. The material flows are varied and have been identified by a numerical system to facilitate control. The coding system now in use not only identifies the material flows but also the particular vessels involved in the transfer. The various material and sample transfer flows are illustrated in Fig. 16-6 and described in Table 16.1. Note that each transfer code accompanied by a solid line denotes bulk material transferred: whereas codes accompanied by a broken line denote only samples transferred to the laboratory. The heavy lines separate the basic material balance areas and indicate the requirement of a sample request and material transfer form.

The Sample Transfer and Sample Request and Material Transfer forms are precoded with the appropriate SS code number to maintain control on the various material control transfer stations. For example, the SS Group can determine material flow description from the SS code number or operational run code designation. Likewise, chemical operators can choose the correct precoded form to coincide with the particular material flow involved. Rigid SS control can be accomplished by using precoded forms in consecutive run code order. For example, should the operator fail to report a particular material flow on the precoded form, a run code will be missing in sequence thus notifying the SS Group that paper work on the transfer has been omitted.

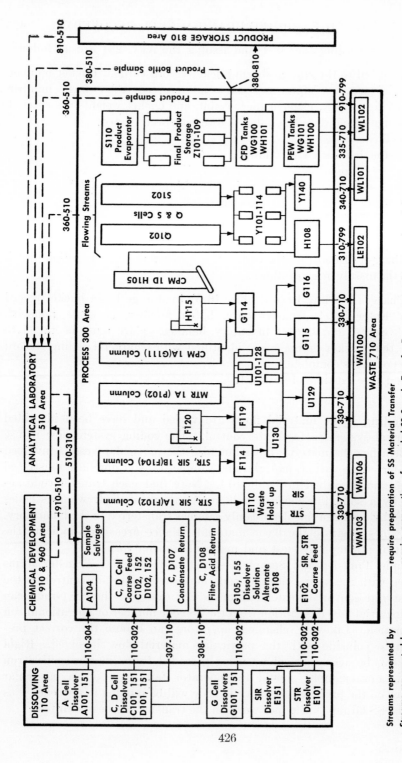

FIG. 16-6 Interplant transfer flow diagram.

426

TABLE 16.1. INTERPLANT TRANSFER FLOW DIAGRAM EXPLANATION

SS Code No.	Operation Run Code Designation	Description of Material Flow
110-302	I Fu	Dissolver solution transferred to feed run tanks (unadjusted) for input measurement, C-102, C-152, D-102, D-152, G-105, G-155
110-304	I Fu	Dissolver solution transferred to feed run tanks for input measurements (EBR fuel only), A-104
330-710	I Arm	First-cycle raffinate transferred from U-129, U-130, G-115, and G-116 to deep tanks WM-100
335-710	PEW	Waste streams collected in WG-101 and WH-100 from process equipment waste and transferred to deep tank WL-102
340-710	II and III Arm	Second- and third-cycle raffinate streams collected in Y-140 and transferred to WL-101
310-799	H-108	Aqueous waste solution transferred from H-108 to LE-102. Solution is discarded to burial ground
380-810	III Pm	Product transferred from Z-cell bank to product bottles (in product storage area)
360-510	II and III BP	Second- and third-cycle flowing stream extraction samples transferred to laboratory; also includes Z-cell samples
380-510	III Pm	Product bottle samples transferred to laboratory
810-510	III Pm	Product samples transferred to laboratory from product storage area
910-510	None	Uranium samples transferred from chemical development to laboratory
510-310	None	Salvage transferred from analytical laboratory to process for recovery

16-7.6. Handling Sample Request and Material Transfer Forms. The route of the various transfer forms from the time they are generated until the final information is entered in the Material Balance Summary (MBS) Ledger is illustrated by Fig. 16-7. Motion and time study symbols were used to represent form routing procedures. Table 16.2 lists the symbols and their meanings.

16-7.7. Calculating and Posting Material Transfer Forms: *Feed Measurements.* Dissolved fuel solution is transferred into two parallel feed-measuring vessels. Dissolver solution flows into one feed tank until the overflow valve is reached; the feed is then diverted to the second tank by means of a remote-control valve. The first tank is then sparged for approximately 30 minutes to ensure thorough mixing. When the sample is pulled, transfer form 110-302 is initiated (Fig. 16-8). The operator records the vessel liquid-level manometer reading, batch number, vessel number, data, and sample

TABLE 16.2.   ROUTING SYMBOLS FOR INTERPLANT
MATERIAL FORMS

Symbol	Name	Used to Represent
◯	Operation	Work being performed
○	Movement	Form moved from one location to another
▢○ ○▢	Origin of form	Form first being made out in duplicate
>---	Information Take-off	Information taken off form for entry into additional set of records
▭▯▯▯▯▭	MBS	Material Balance Summary Ledger
▽	File	Forms in file

analysis request.   The batch volume is calculated by precalibrated run tank data.   The 110-302 transfer form has provisions for entering this calculation. Note that space is also provided for entering analytical data such as concentration, specific gravity, acidity, and mass distribution.   With these data, total uranium and U^{235} content is readily available.   After the forms have been completed by the SS Group, they are bound (monthly) and totaled.   The sum,

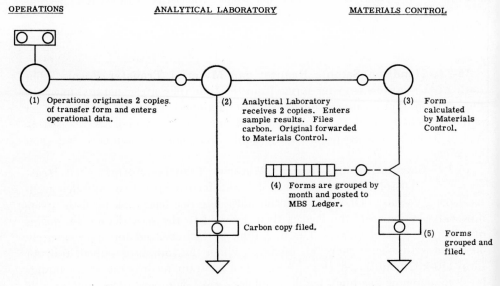

FIG. 16-7   Analytical laboratory material flow sheet.

SECRET WORK SHEET — Security Information (When SS Calculations Are Entered Within Box)
FORM AED - 159 (Rev. 3-27-56)

PHILLIPS PETROLEUM COMPANY

MATERIAL TRANSFER CODE

FROM   TO

ATOMIC ENERGY DIVISION

REPORT OF MATERIAL TRANSFER & SAMPLE ANALYSIS

Sample Code_____ Lab Log No. _____

Charge Account [√] _____ [x] _____ [o] _____   Date _____ Time_____

Est. Activity_____ mr./hr Rec'd _____ Logged _____   Process Engineer_____

Total Sample Vol._____ ml.   Sampled by _____   Shift Supervisor_____

Vessel No. _____ Vessel Temp. _____ °C   Material _____

I. Liquid Level_____
    Specific Grav._____

II. Liquid Level_____
    Specific Grav._____

III. Amount Transferred
     Volume_____

IV. Remarks:

X _____ =
X _____ = _____ = _____ (D¹)
X _____ =
X _____ = _____ = _____ (D²)

Vessel Calibration Equation:

Vol. = _____ + _____ (Depth)

NX _____ X _____ = _____

Calc._____ Ckd. _____ Post: _____

This Space for SS

Units (check): ☐ I ☐ gm.

_____ G
_____ T
_____ N

L. E. = _____

Determinations Desired	Sample Results		Average	Units
U				mg/g
U				mg/ml
Sp. Gr.				FD
t°C /20°C @ °C @ °C @ °C				WB P
Acid. or				NᴬNᴮ
Acid. Def.				
Mass 234				Wt. %
A 235				Wt. %
B 236				Wt. %
C 238				Wt. %

Determinations Desired	Sample Results		Average	Units
Red Norm				N
α				c/m/ml
β				c/m/ml
Beta Ratio				
γ (icn ch.)				Ra eq./ml
Pu				c/m/ml
Ru				c/m/ml
Nb				c/m/ml
Zr				c/m/ml
Ce				c/m/ml
Spectrochem (Results attached)				

Results Recorded by _____ Rpt. Ckd. _____ Date_____

Distribution:

White (Original)—SS Control

Pink—Analytical Laboratory

FIG. 16-8   Report of Material Transfer and Sample Analysis (Material Transfer).

SECRET WORK SHEET — Security Information (When SS Calculations Are Entered)
FORM AED-310 (Rev. 8-27-56)

PHILLIPS PETROLEUM COMPANY

ATOMIC ENERGY DIVISION
REPORT OF MATERIAL TRANSFER & SAMPLE ANALYSIS

| PRODUCT TRANSFER | |

Sample Code _____   Lab Log No. _____

Vessel No. _____   Date _____

Sampled By _____   Sampled At _____ hours

Charge Account [√] _____ [X] _____   Supervisor _____

380-810 PRODUCT BOTTLE	380-810 REFERENCE SAMPLES	380-510 LABORATORY SAMPLES
Units: grams	No. _____ No. _____	No. _____ No. _____
Gross _____	_____ _____	_____ _____
Tare _____	_____ _____	_____ _____
Net _____	_____ _____	_____ _____
	Total _____ gms.	Total _____ gms.

Net U %U-235 U-235	Net U %U-235 U-235	Net U %U-235 U-235
_____ X _____ = _____	_____ X _____ = _____	_____ X _____ = _____
Calc. _____ Ckd. _____	Calc. _____ Ckd. _____	Calc. _____ Ckd. _____

Determinations Desired	Sample Results		Average	Units	Remarks:
U				mg/g	
U				mg/ml	
Sp. Gr.					
Acid				N^A N^B	
Mass C D 234				Wt. %	Laboratory Time and Date Stamp
235				Wt. %	
236				Wt. %	
238				Wt. %	
γ (ion ch.)				Ra eq./gm u	
Spectrochem Analysis: (ppm as U_3O_8)					
Al			Mn		
Cr			Na		
Cu			Ni		
Fe			Si		Rec'd _____
Mg					

RESTRICTED DATA
This document contains restricted data as defined in the Atomic Energy Act of 1954. Its transmittal or the disclosure of its contents in any manner to an unauthorized person is prohibited.

Results Recorded By: _____   Rpt. Checked: _____   Date _____

Distribution: White (SS Control)   Pink (Operations)   Blue (Analytical Lab.)

FIG. 16-9 Report of Material Transfer and Sample Analysis (Product Transfer).

representing the monthly feed charged to recovery operation, is transferred to the MBS Ledger relieving the fuel storage basin (110 area) and charging process (310 area).

Raffinate Transfers (330-710, 340-710). Raffinate batches collected from first-cycle extraction are measured before transfer to waste storage tanks. Transfer data are entered on the 330-710 transfer series, similar in form to the 110-302 series. Data for raffinate batches collected from second- and third-cycle extraction are recorded on transfer series 340-710. Again, equations are available for precalibrated tanks to calculate batch volumes and total uranium content. Each transfer series is grouped, bound, and summed. The total is transferred each month to the MBS Ledger.

Waste-Stream Transfers (335-710). Condensates from process equipment are collected in vessels and are sampled and then transferred to permanent waste storage tanks. Volumes transferred are computed by direct chart readings calibrated in gallons per inch. The process equipment waste transfer form is similar to that shown in Fig. 16-8, with the transfer code prefix being 335-710.

Product-Storage Transfer. Product solution is collected in product storage vessels and accumulated until product withdrawal is feasible. Product bottles are filled at selected intervals, and the data are recorded on the 380-810 transfer series (Fig. 16-9). The transfer form represents a complete history of each product bottle.

Reference samples are pulled, and the data are entered in the space provided. Laboratory samples are extracted from the reference sample bottles and accompany the product transfer form to the laboratory for analytical determinations. The product reference samples are stored in the product storage vault pending product bottle content verification at another installation. Should no discrepancy exist, the reference samples are combined, analyzed, and shipped in the regular product container.

16-7.8. Entering Receiver's Data. Upon completion of a particular program, receiver's data (input measurements) must be formulated and entered on the AEC-101 forms affected. Since it is impossible to correlate input measurement data with individual 101's, receiver's measurements must be withheld until final dissolver-heel solutions have been transferred. Total receiver's measurements (110-302) are entered on the latest 101 affected, with notations such as: "This value represents the total batch input measurement of materials indicated on 101's BSL-CPI-1 through -100." Thus, BSL-CPI-1 through -99 would have the notation printed in the receiver's data portion of the form, "See BSL-CPI-100 for receiver's measurement methods and total accepted values on shipments BSL-CPI-1 through -100." Should partial dissolution occur on a particular 101 in the series, undissolved portions will be accepted at shipper's values and entered on BSL-CPI-100.

This figure will be added to the total input measurement value previously mentioned. The sum will equal the total accepted value.

16-7.9. Material Balance Summation. Material balances for the plant control and each material balance area are summarized in the MBS Ledger. Fuel shipments are recorded in the Out of Area Transfer Journal, are transferred to the Summary Ledger, entering the Plant Control and Fuel Storage Basin columns. Likewise, shipments enter the Plant Control and Shipping Storage columns. Next, monthly summations of the interplant transfer form series journals are entered. Each transfer series is posted separately, entering the various material balance area columns. After the postings have been completed, the ledger is summed and ruled. The plant-control balance series acts as a check against the ledger postings and should equal the summation of the material balance area inventories.

16-8. INVENTORY PROCEDURES

16-8.1. Fuel Storage Basin. Each month the fuel storage basin cardex file is recapped in columnar form listing bucket numbers and fuel content. Uranium values are entered from the shipping form AEC-101. The total uranium value from the cardex summation must equal the fuel basin inventory shown on the MBS Ledger less shipper-receiver differences that occur through feed input measurements. Physical verification of the fuel storage basin is performed at the discretion of the group.

16-8.2. Process Inventory. Process inventory forms, too numerous to include here, are issued monthly to operations. These forms include information on measurable vessel holdup, calculated by the SS Group. Unfortunately, owing to the nature of the recovery operations, holdup contamination in the extraction columns cannot be inventoried. Therefore, unless a book by-difference value is used, it becomes necessary to estimate contaminated volumes and concentrations. Fig. 16-10 is a schematic diagram of the line and vessel holdup.

Volumes were computed by the process engineering staff and represent design or ideal operating conditions only. In addition, each column contains a two-phase system (organic and aqueous), the quantity being dependent upon solvent and feed-stream pump rates. Since the organic and aqueous ratios within the columns cannot be determined, the assumption must be made that phase ratios are proportional to the solvent and feed pump ratios entering the column. This assumption indicates a uniform distribution of the phases throughout the vessel. Uranium concentration of each phase must be estimated utilizing an average feed input concentration derived from the isotopic dilution analysis and ideal vessel to vessel concentration ratio previously established by the process engineering staff. Concentration change ratios from column to column are applied to the average feed concentration to determine an approximation of vessel holdup. Again, a uniform mixture of the two phases in the extraction equipment must be assumed. Concentration ratios change with each material type, further complicating the situation. The SS Group makes the above assumptions and arrives at an estimate of contaminated holdup, which is added to the measurable vessel inventory. Any disagreement between this total and the book by-difference inventory falls into the category B-PID.

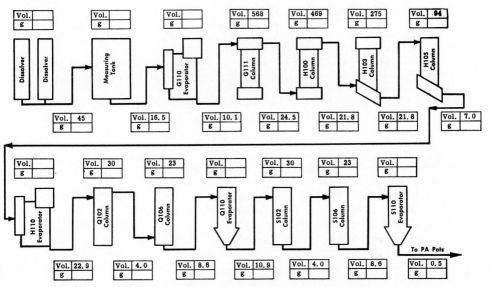

FIG. 16-10 Schematic diagram of vessel holdup.

16-8.3. Analytical Laboratory. Each quarter, inventory sheets are issued in duplicate to the analytical section for the purpose of recording quantities on hand, either in solid (such as standards) or solution form. All items on hand must be listed. After the inventory has been completed, the carbon is filed, and the original is forwarded to the SS Group.

16-8.4. Shipping Storage. The shipping storage inventory is composed of enriched uranium product solution. Items are listed in two categories, namely, product bottles and product bottle reference samples. Monthly listings of both categories are entered on the product shipping storage inventory sheets. Inventory calculation is based on weight and gravimetric determinations. Uranium-235 mass ratio percentage is given for each product bottle. Product bottles and their respective reference samples will carry the same gravimetric and mass ratio percentages.

REFERENCES FOR CHAPTER 16

1. PAUL GORIS and F. H. TINGEY, *Uranium Determination by the Isotopic Dilution Technique*, Part II, USAEC Report IDO-14366, Phillips Petroleum Company, 1956.
2. R. B. LEMON and D. G. REID, Experience with a Direct Maintenance Radiochemical Processing Plant, in *Proceedings of the International Conference on the Peaceful Uses of Atomic Energy*, Vol. 9, P/543, p. 532, United Nations, New York, 1956.
3. M. G. INGHRAM, Trace Element Determination by the Mass Spectrometer, *J. Phys. Chem.*, 57:809-814 (1953).
4. C. M. STEVENS and M. G. INGHRAM, *A Mass Spectrometer for Routine Solid Analysis*, USAEC Report ANL-5251, Argonne National Laboratory, 1954.
5. W. E. DUFFY, G. V. WHEELER, and T. D. MORGAN, *Manual of Mass and Emission Spectroscopy Methods Used at the Idaho Chemical Processing Plant*, USAEC Report IDO-14318, Phillips Petroleum Company, June 1955.
6. G. L. BOOMAN, W. B. HOLBROOK, and J. E. REIN, *Coulometric Determination of Uranium (VI) at Controlled Potential*, USAEC Report IDO-14369, Phillips Petroleum Company, April 1956.
7. G. L. BOOMAN, *An Instrument for Controlled Potential Electrolysis and Precision Coulometric Integration*, USAEC Report IDO-14370, Phillips Petroleum Company, April 1956.
8. F. H. TINGEY and F. P. VANCE, Phillips Petroleum Company, 1955, unpublished data.
9. M. J. SHEPHERD, JR., and J. E. REIN, *Manual of Analytical Methods Used by the Control Laboratory at the Chemical Processing Plant*, USAEC Report IDO-14316, Phillips Petroleum Company, January 1955.
10. *Handbook for Nuclear Materials Management*, Part I, Sec. IG.

Chapter 17

IRRADIATED NORMAL-URANIUM FUEL RECOVERY*

17-1. PROCESS DESCRIPTION

17-1.1. Purpose. The chemical processing plant recovers plutonium and uranium from irradiated fuel. Recovery involves the separation by solvent extraction of plutonium and uranium from each other and from the radioactive fission products.

The feed is small solid pieces of uranium encased in thin aluminum jackets, or cans. Between discharge from the reactor and chemical processing, these pieces are stored for 90 days or more to permit decay of short-life fission products. As charged to the recovery process, the plutonium and radioactive fission product content of these pieces is a function of their reactor exposure history and their cooling history. The solid feed to the plant contains in descending order of magnitude: uranium, aluminum, plutonium, and highly radioactive fission products.

The plant has two products, plutonium and uranium. The final plutonium product is a concentrated nitrate solution essentially free of impurities and radioactive fission products. The final uranium product is a uranium oxide powder, also essentially free of impurities and radioactive fission products.

The aluminum and fission products from the feed are removed from the main stream in the course of the processing and are discarded to underground storage.

17-1.2. Operations. The process consists of several well-defined unit operations; however, since all operations through to the final loadout of products must be conducted remotely, the process is more intricate than would be indicated by the type of unit operation involved.

The process consists of the following operations listed by material balance areas:

* W. H. Johnson and R. W. Doerr, General Electric Company, Hanford Atomics Products Operation, Richland, Washington. The authors wish to acknowledge the assistance of V. D. Donihee and C. J. Shortess, Jr., whose understanding of the problems substantially expedited preparation of this material.

1. Metal solution preparation
   a. Removal of aluminum fuel-element jackets with sodium hydroxide
   b. Dissolution of uranium pieces with nitric acid
   c. Centrifugation of the dissolved solution
   d. Chemical preparation of solution as column feed
2. Extraction
   a. Liquid-liquid extraction separation of uranium and plutonium from fission products
   b. Concentration and chemical adjustment for next cycle
   c. Liquid-liquid extraction separation of uranium from plutonium
   d. Concentration and chemical adjustment for next cycle
   e. Liquid-liquid extraction separation of impurities from uranium and plutonium
   f. Final concentration of plutonium for shipment and of uranium for the calcination step
   g. Concentration and neutralization of waste
   h. Acid recovery by use of absorber and fractionator
3. Uranium purification
   a. Further uranium purification in a silica gel contactor
   b. Feed storage for uranium denitration operation
4. Uranium concentration and denitration
   a. Concentration of uranyl nitrate hexahydrate (UNH) solution to 100 percent
   b. Continuous denitration of uranyl nitrate to UO_3 powder
   c. Recovery of nitric acid in absorbent fractionator
5. Recovered acid storage (storage area for acid to be used in (1) metal solution preparation and (2) extraction)
6. Analytical (analyses of samples from all operations)
7. Plutonium storage (concentrated plutonium nitrate held in shipping containers for off-site shipment)
8. UO_3 product storage (uranium oxide powder held in shipping containers for off-site shipment)

Chemicals used in the process include sodium nitrate, sodium nitrite, nitric acid, sulfuric acid, ferrous sulfamate, sodium hydroxide, tributy phosphate, and kerosene.

17-1.3. Receipt and Removal Streams. The plant has many potential SS-material-containing receipt and removal streams. The main receipts are irradiated slugs from reactors. Removals consist of the uranium and plutonium product streams, the major waste streams, and many potential waste streams. In the multiple balance-area system described here there will also be many internal transfers for which controls are necessary (see Fig. 17-1).

17-2. SS MATERIAL CONTROL PROCEDURES

SS material transactions include material movement between AEC stations as well as within AEC stations. A complete transaction may therefore involve off-site accounts in addition to the material balance areas listed in Sec. 17-1.2.

The SS Group implements and maintains a double-entry accounting system in accordance with AEC regulations and accepted accounting practice to record

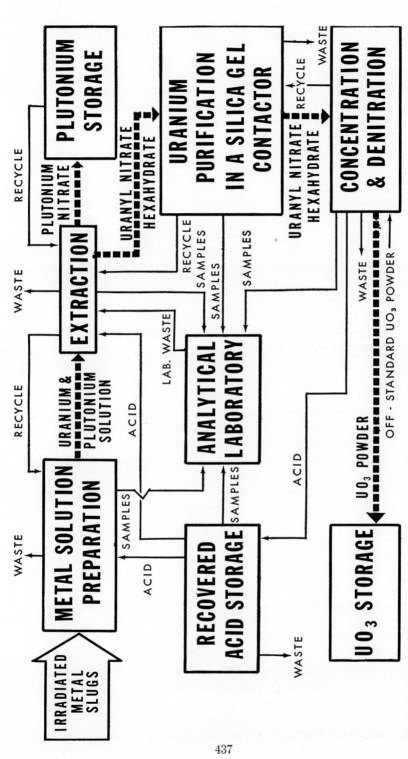

Fig. 17-1 Process flow diagram for uranium and plutonium recovery from irradiated uranium. Each operation indicated by box is a material balance area. Note the many internal transfers for which SS material control is necessary.

437

SS material transactions.   The basis of a double-entry accounting system is the change in the records of two balance areas for each transaction.   Thus, a transfer is recorded in one set of records as an addition to, or a deduction from, the custodian's inventory account, and in a second set of records as a decrease in the shipper's custodial responsibility or an increase in the receiver's custodial responsibility.

The effect of material movements on inventory and ownership balance is shown by nominal or current accounts that parallel custodial receiving and shipping or transfers.   Material-receipt accounts are credited with the quantity received as indicated by the custodian; the account balance shows the accumulated quantity received since the beginning of the fiscal year.   An offsetting charge is made to the appropriate inventory account.   Similarly, material-removal accounts are charged for the quantity shipped or transferred as indicated by the custodian; the account balance shows the accumulated quantity shipped or transferred since the beginning of the fiscal year.   An offsetting credit is made to the appropriate inventory account.

The frequency of routine SS material movement and the volume of resulting source records require that inventory records be kept current.

17-2.1. Measurement Policies.   An SS material control system should provide internal controls as well as over-all plant control.   Eight material balance areas are optimum in this fuel-recovery plant (Sec. 17-1.2).   The control system provides for measurement of all plutonium- and uranium-bearing streams entering or leaving each balance area potentially containing significant quantities of SS material.   Accurate records are maintained and are provided to the SS Group.   Main-stream transfer records are provided at least daily, and each main-stream transaction is calculated and recorded individually.

There will be some streams, such as exhaust air, cooling water, steam condensate, process condensate, equipment burial, and perhaps others, which ordinarily do not contain sufficient SS material to warrant measurement but will require monitoring to give reasonable assurance of insignificant SS material content.   Records of such monitoring are part of the SS Group records and are provided on a less frequent basis, perhaps weekly or monthly, depending on the stream content and experience.

The system of accounts is sufficiently flexible to take care of any special transfers occasioned by nonroutine operation.   Recycling or unusual occurrence may necessitate measurement in nonroutine tanks.   Operating personnel must have an intimate knowledge of material balance area boundaries so that proper records are maintained at the time of these nonroutine operations.

The services of accountants, statisticians, and engineers are necessary for adequate control.   The accounting group receives transfer data daily which must be checked closely for completeness and calculation accuracy.   Posting to proper accounts is done daily because of the large volume of transactions involved. Plant inventories are received monthly, at which time reports of monthly transactions must be compiled for control purposes.

The multiplicity of processing problems and changes, measurement method improvement, and procedural work affecting control will require the services of a chemical engineer. The maintenance of a statistical control system will require the services of a statistician. Although a large amount of the routine investigation and control-data collection can be done by competent nonengineers and high-level clerks, analysis of the control data must be performed by a technical group.

17-2.2. Source Data. Source data are normally the official records of plutonium or uranium transfers or inventories provided by the SS-material custodian or his personnel to the SS Group. They contain all data pertinent to the calculation of the quantity of material involved. Any correction to original source data, in a transfer or inventory, provided by the custodian is also source data. Any data having direct bearing on the quantities as recorded are considered source data. Source data can be generated only by the custodian.

In establishing and maintaining a system of record control, the SS Group relies upon written communication from the SS-material custodians in the development and production operations. These communications include:

1. SS-material forecasts
2. SS-material requisitions
3. SS-material schedules
4. SS-material movement data
5. SS-material verification data
6. Supplier and receiver confirmation
7. Development program and laboratory reports

Development programs and laboratory reports and production schedules aid the SS Group in planning personnel, facility, and record utilization. SS-material forecast, requisition, schedule movement verification, and confirmation data provide periodic data necessary to assure record integrity and timeliness.

Written communications from the SS-material custodian to the SS Group contains the following information in addition to measurement values:

1. Transaction description
2. Type of SS material
3. Time, date, or period of data
4. Control number or source record number
5. Authority reference—AEC, contractor, department, operation, program allotment, cost code
6. Titles, initiating and completing organizations, and authors

7. Measurement definition—processing areas or receiving, shipping, and transfer points
8. SS-material specification and weight units
9. Supervisory approval—AEC, contractor, department, component

17-2.3. Journal Entries. Special journals or working papers (one for inventory debits and one for inventory credits) are used to classify, analyze, and post source data during the accounting period. At the close of the period, the data are summarized by a standard journal entry. The following four journal entries are used to summarize the activity affecting each SS material type in a material balance area or areas:

1. Fiscal-year closing of shipper and receiver account
2. Decrease the shipper's responsibility and increase the custodian's inventory
3. Increase the receiver's responsibility and decrease the custodian's inventory
4. Adjust the custodian's inventory as a result of measurement, accounting, or physical verification differences

A fifth entry may be required to record an unusual incident or infrequent occurrence.

17-2.4. Accounts. The inventory, ownership, receipt, and removal accounts are given in Table 17.1. The accounts have been numbered and titled to agree, as far as possible, with the Material Balance Report (Fig. 2-8) in order to support directly the entries appearing on the report.

Source data are incorporated into the accounts and working papers as follows: (1) At the month's end the book inventory is derived from the beginning inventory and working-paper postings, (2) book inventory is then adjusted for differences between the book and physical inventory, (3) monthly receipts, removals, and internal transfers are then transferred to the journal entries (see Table 17.2). The ledger is posted from the journal entries.

At the fiscal-year end the nominal or current accounts are closed by debiting the receipts and crediting the removal account balances and crediting and debiting, respectively the AEC ownership of SS material account.

The material balance is arrived at by taking beginning inventory, plus receipts, less removals for an ending book inventory. The difference between the book inventory and the physical inventory is termed a B-PID. When the physical inventory is greater than the book inventory, there is an overage; this is credited to B-PID. Conversely, when the book inventory is greater than the physical inventory, there is a shortage; this is debited to B-PID.

17-2.5. Control Measures: *Multiple Material Balance Areas.* The plant is divided into several material balance areas to aid in the prompt detection and elimination of inventory or transfer errors. The size of the plant makes it

TABLE 17.1. LIST OF TYPICAL ACCOUNTS

ACCOUNT NUMBER[a]	ACCOUNT TITLE		POSTINGS
101	Metal solution preparation (MSP)	Dr.	Receipts from reactor, other balance area recycle, external recycle.
		Cr.	Removals to extraction, to waste, to laboratory.
102	Extraction	Dr.	Receipts from MSP, acid storage, UNH storage, analytical laboratory.
		Cr.	Removals to waste, to MSP, to laboratory, to UNH storage, to product storage.
103	UNH storage	Dr.	Receipts from extraction and uranium reduction.
		Cr.	Removals to uranium reduction, extraction, to waste.
104	Uranium reduction	Dr.	Receipts from UNH storage.
		Cr.	Removals to acid storage, to off-site product storage.
105	Recovered acid storage	Dr.	Receipts from uranium reduction.
		Cr.	Removals to MSP and extraction.
106	Analytical control	Dr.	Receipts from all balance areas.
		Cr.	Removals to waste and to extraction.
107	Plutonium product storage	Dr.	Receipts from extraction.
		Cr.	Removals to off site.
108	Uranium product storage	Dr.	Receipts from uranium reduction.
		Cr.	Removals to off site.
201	Control (used at end of fiscal year)	Dr.	Removals for fiscal year except B-PID balances that are overaccounted.
		Cr.	Receipts for fiscal year and B-PID balances that are overaccounted.
Plant Receipts			
301	Reactor 1	Dr.	Account balance closed out to 201 Control—end of fiscal year
302	Reactor 2		
303	Reactor 3 etc.		
304	Engineering Oper. 1	Cr.	Receipts from the operation shown.
305	Engineering Oper. 2		
Plant Removals			
401	Book-Physical Inventory Difference	Dr.	Amount by which the book inventory exceeds the physical inventory.
401.1	Metal Solution Prep.		
401.2	Extraction	Cr.	Amount by which the physical inventory exceeds the book inventory
401.3	UNH storage		
401.4	Uranium Reduction		
401.5	Recovered acid storage		
401.6	Analytical control		
402	Waste	Dr.	Removals of waste to storage or discard.
402.1	Stored		
402.2	Discarded	Cr.	Account balance closed out to 201 control at end of fiscal year.
403	Off-site Oper. 1	Dr.	Removals to the operation shown.
404	Off-site Oper. 2	Cr.	Account balance closed out to 201 control at end of fiscal year.
405	Off-site Oper. 3		
406	etc.		

[a] Accounts 101 to 108 are debited with a positive B-PID or credited with a negative B-PID.

extremely difficult to pinpoint inventory errors if only an over-all plant balance is determined since an error in the balance could be an inventory error at any location in the plant. If the plant is divided into several balance areas, errors in the over-all balance will show up in the particular area in which the error occurs. Furthermore, transfer errors causing shipper-receiver differences can be confirmed or denied by referring to the balance of the area in which the transfer originates.

A multiple balance-area system requires the establishment of several good internal measurement points. For this system to be effective, all SS material

TABLE 17.2. JOURNAL ENTRIES [a]

Journal entry 1:
Reserved for opening and closing entries at the beginning and end of the fiscal year.

Journal entry 2:
 Title: Receipts into Plant
 Posting: (1) Dr. 101 Metal Solution Preparation.
      Cr. 301 Reactor 1.
     (2) Dr. 101 Metal Solution Preparation.
      Cr. 302 Reactor 2, etc.

Journal entry 3:
 Title: Transfers from MSP
 Posting: Dr. Appropriate receiver account.
     Cr. 101 MSP.

Journal entry 4:
 Title: Transfers from Extraction
 Posting: Dr. Appropriate receiver account.
     Cr. 102 Extraction.

Journal entry 5:
 Title: Transfers from UNH Storage
 Posting: Dr. Appropriate receiver account.
     Cr. 103 UNH Storage.

Journal entry 6:
 Title: Transfers from Uranium Reduction
 Posting: Dr. Appropriate receiver account.
     Cr. 104 Uranium Reduction.

Journal entry 7:
 Title: Transfers from Recovered Acid Storage
 Posting: Dr. Appropriate receiver account.
     Cr. 105 Recovered Acid Storage.

Journal entry 8:
 Title: Transfers from Analytical Control
 Posting: Dr. Appropriate receiver account.
     Cr. 106 Analytical Control.

Journal entry 9:
 Title: Transfers from Plutonium Product Storage
 Posting: Dr. Appropriate receiver account.
     Cr. 107 Plutonium Product Storage.

Journal entry 10:
 Title: Transfers from UO_3 Product Storage
 Posting: Dr. Appropriate receiver account.
     Cr. 108 UO_3 Product Storage.

Journal entry 11:
 Title: Book-Physical Inventory Difference
 Posting and Source of Information:
     Prepared from a comparison of the book inventory and the physical inventory.
     If a shortage exists, the B-PID accounts are debited and the inventory accounts
     are credited. If an overage exists, the B-PID accounts are credited and the
     inventory accounts are debited.

[a] Journal entries 2 through 10 summarize quantities for each month and are based upon source data accumulated on worksheets as the transactions are completed.

received into, or removed from, each balance area must be accurately measured. Since no good method of continuous measurement is known, all receipts and removals from the areas established must be on a batchwise basis. In a normally continuous process, this requires a break in the continuity to provide a batch measuring step.

The value of the multiple balance area system is limited by the accuracy of the area receipt, removal, and inventory measurements. If the accuracy of the measurements gives an uncertainty of ± 5 per cent, only errors having a magnitude greater than 5 percent will be detected.

Inventory and B-PID Account. Each material balance area is provided with a separate set of books, each subdivided into three accounts to cover inventory, receipt, and removal. Source data related to material transfers in each material balance area are submitted by operating personnel to the SS Group. After all source data for a current month have been posted, the "working paper" columns are totaled and balanced. As of midnight of the last working day of the month, a physical inventory is taken by operating personnel, and the data are forwarded to the SS Group. Calculations are verified, and totals are obtained for each area. The difference between inventory based on SS Group records and the physical inventory is recorded as B-PID. An unusual B-PID gives rise to an immediate investigation by the SS Group.

For any material balance area, there are four quantities that are essential in judging SS control: the beginning inventory, the receipts, the removals, and the ending inventory. Inaccuracies and imprecisions in the measurement of these quantities contribute directly to the measurement error in the B-PID. In most instances the imprecisions in the measurement of inventories exceed those in receipts and removals for relatively short intervals. This is compensated by the fact that as longer periods of time are considered, errors in beginning and ending inventories for the shorter periods cancel out. Thus, for example, the individual B-PID's for successive one-month periods involve each monthly inventory; whereas the B-PID for a one-year period involves only the inventories at the beginning and the end of the year. In the first case, only the receipts and removals during a one-month period are involved; whereas in the latter case the total receipts and removals for the entire year must be considered. This is taken into account in the statistical treatment of the monthly and yearly control limits. The effectiveness of the system is judged by comparing material balance area B-PID's with the predicted limits of uncertainty.

At the close of an accounting period, material balance area B-PID's are summarized in a control report together with an independent evaluation based on measurement methods. When a particular B-PID is shown to be out of control, engineering personnel of the SS Group explain the nature of the discrepancy and also indicate what action was initiated to correct or to investigate the discrepancy. Where further investigation is warranted, a systematic study is made of measurement uncertainties, processing losses, inventory errors, etc. The control aspects needed to guarantee the reliability of these various items are discussed in the next section.

Measurement Quality Control. Each measurement has three phases: (*a*) volume (or weight) determination, (*b*) sampling, and (*c*) analytical determination. These are discussed in order.

(*a*) VOLUME CONTROL. Volumes are determined by use of liquid-level instrumentation and vessel calibration tables. Extreme care must be used in the original tank calibration. Any error in the final table will manifest itself as a bias in all subsequent measurements. Quality control of the original calibration is very important, and little if any recalibration should be necessary if the original work is good.

Liquid-level instrumentation is checked periodically. This includes changing manometer oil, cleaning and zeroing manometers, recalibrating transmitters, and checking the pneumatic system for leaks.

The loadout of plutonium product is on a weight basis. A check weight system provides constant quality control of the scales.

(*b*) SAMPLING CONTROL. A sample is good only if it is representative of the material from which it was drawn. Sample volumes are restricted in many instances because of the radioactivity level of the solutions. The ratio of solution volume to sample volume in some instances will be 1000 million to 1. Decontaminated stream samples will have a ratio of approximately 200,000 to 1. With such ratios of solution to sample volume homogeneity of solution is necessary if samples are to be representative. This demands good agitation of vessels; tests are required to show the length of agitation required to give a homogeneous solution. Such tests must be conducted before plant start-up. Since in routine operation sampling quality control is very difficult, much depends on sampler tests previous to plant operation.

In a remotely operated plant, sampling is by indirect means involving lengthy sample lines. Equipment for drawing samples must be thoroughly tested before start-up to guarantee adequacy and to provide knowledge for establishing procedures involving circulation periods and flushing necessary to give representative samples.

Agitation and sampling tests should be run, using solutions simulating those that will be used. Direct multiple sampling at different tank levels during the tests will provide the necessary data. Once the plant is in operation, comparatively little sampling quality control can be maintained. Knowledge of quality depends almost entirely on information gained from cold tests. Sampling quality control during operation consists of monitoring sampling procedures periodically to guarantee that procedures followed are in agreement with the original equipment qualification.

However, once the plant has started operations, sampling error can be determined roughly by multiple sampling using routine methods and a comparison of analytical results. Known analytical variation can be subtracted to give that error which is due to sampling only.

(c) ANALYTICAL CONTROL. The Analytical Section maintains a quality control program on all SS control analyses. The program is divided into two parts: one to determine analytical accuracy and the other to determine analytical precision. In the accuracy control program, about 5 percent of all samples analyzed are standard or test samples of known concentration analyzed by the routine techniques. The average result of a number of these analyses divided by the known concentration and multiplied by 100 gives the percent recovery. A calculation is also made of the precision (95 percent confidence level) of this recovery. From these data an estimate of possible bias can be made and corrective action can be taken if necessary. These data also contribute to the evaluation of material balance discrepancies.

The precision program consists of a reanalysis of 5 percent of the samples (selected at random) by a second technician. Statistical comparison of the original and the rerun gives the analytical precision and also provides supervision with a measure of technician performance. The precisions are used extensively in computing the limit of error for inventories and material balance control.

Waste-Control Limits. Limits have been established on the quantities of plutonium and uranium which can be written off to "measured discards" or "unrecoverable storage" in any one month without special approval from Nuclear Materials Management, AEC. These limits are based on a statistical analysis of total losses observed during a fiscal period. They are set statistically at a level that should be exceeded less than 5 percent of the time.

The purpose of waste-control limits is to prevent throw-away of amounts of SS materials in excess of predetermined practical operating quantities. It can be both a gauge of operating efficiency and an economic rework limit.

Statistical Control Limits. There is no such thing as a perfect measurement. Uncertainties exist in all phases. Measurements are improved until, for technological or economic reasons, further improvement is not feasible. At this point a statistical analysis of the precision and accuracy of the measurement will provide a means of predicting the variance to be expected. Knowledge of precision and accuracy shows whether balance area differences or shipper-receiver differences are due to normal measurement variation or to off-standard conditions requiring investigation and corrective action.

A reliable statistical control system can be an invaluable tool in the control of SS materials. However, to be reliable, the individual measurement precisions for both inventory and transfers must be good and must be kept current as precision changes occur. All uncertainties in each phase (sampling, analytical, and volume) must be considered when determining precision.

Transfer and Inventory Precisions. Individual transfer and inventory precisions are determined in an identical manner. However, the contribution of error made by transfer and inventory items to the over-all variance of a balance area during an accounting period must be calculated on a different basis.

Measurement errors can be of two types, random or fixed. A random error is one that can be either plus or minus, and if enough measurements are taken, it will average out to no significant long-term error. A fixed error is one that is always present and is of the same magnitude and direction in all measurements.

An inventory measurement is made only once for an accounting period. Thus, regardless of whether the error is a random error or a fixed error, it is the total error that affects the balance for the period, and this must be considered entirely as a fixed source of error in individual inventory measurements.

In the case of transfer measurements, the total error contributed to balance variance will be reduced by the number of transfers made. The random error variances for transfers are based on the relation:

$$\sigma_{R_T}{}^2 = \sum_i^N \sigma_{R_i}{}^2 \tag{17.1}$$

where $\sigma_{R_T}{}^2 =$ the total variance due to random error in the T grams of N transfers

$\sigma_{R_i}{}^2 =$ the random error variance of the i-th transfer

$\quad = (t_i P_R)^2$

$t =$ quantity in the i-th transfer

$P_R =$ the random-error precision factor for such a transfer

If the transfers are of uniform size,

$$T = t_i N$$

$$\sigma_{R_T}{}^2 = \sum_i^N (t_i P_R)^2 = N(t_i P_R)^2 \tag{17.2}$$

$$\sigma_{R_T} = \pm \sqrt{N}(t_i P_R) \tag{17.2a}$$

$$\sigma_{R_T} = \pm \frac{T P_R}{\sqrt{N}} \tag{17.2b}$$

Eq. 17.2 is used as a good approximation of Eq. 17.1 in the calculation of all random-error variances on transfers.

For the nonrandom, or fixed, sources of error (inventory total error), variances are calculated from the relation:

$$\sigma_{F_T}{}^2 = (T P_F)^2$$

where $\sigma_{F_T}{}^2$ = fixed-error variance

$\quad T \quad$ = quantity (grams or pounds)

$\quad P_F$ = fixed-error precision factor for such a transfer

The following example is the precision calculation on a uranyl nitrate product transfer:

Fixed Error

Tank calibration	Manometer	Total F.E.
0.34%	0.2%	0.39%

Random Error

Instrument reading	Sampling	Uranium analysis	Specific gravity	Total R.E.
±0.4%	±1.0%	±0.78%	±0.09%	1.33%

The totals were calculated by taking the square root of the sum of the squares of the individual errors.

All measurements made in tanks have the same types of possible measurement error. The magnitude of each type will vary with the tank and the equipment on it, and all must be determined separately.

Material Balance Area Control Limits. Monthly control limit calculations are made on each balance area for the current month and for the cumulative balance in the current fiscal year. The control limits include all recognized sources of uncertainty. They are calculated by the propagation of errors technique. The greater the detail in these summations, the more reliable the limit. However, the amount of detail should be limited to that which contributes significantly to the over-all variance, with due regard for possible changes that could at some time be significant. In general, only the transfers and removals that are significant as a percentage of throughput are considered. Waste transfers, for instance, normally need not be considered. Each transfer is considered individually and the variance of debits and credits are the summations of the individual transfers.

It has been the practice to assign a fixed precision to the inventory of an entire balance area. This is done by use of clean-out experience and knowledge of individual measurement precisions. It is not as reliable as a breakdown and summation of all individual measurement errors would be, but it eliminates considerable detail at the expense of some reliability in the control limit.

Shipper-Receiver Difference Control Limits. These limits are calculated from precision data on both the shipper's and receiver's measurements.

$$\text{Control limit} = \sqrt{\sigma_S{}^2 + \sigma_R{}^2}$$

where $\sigma_S{}^2$ = the summation of the fixed- and random-error variances in measurement of shipments

$\quad \sigma_R{}^2$ = the summation of the fixed- and random-error variances in measurement of receipts

17-3. ACCOUNTING REPORTS

The principal SS material control reports are the Trial Balance Report, the Material Balance Report, and the Production Report. The Trial Balance Report and the Material Balance Report are standard reports for an accounting office.

The Production Report may be considered a highlight report, since the principal factors employed point up net production. These factors concern the beginning inventory, receipts, removals, ending inventory, and net production. Waste losses, B-PID, and minor transfers and receipts to laboratories are not considered. This report is consolidated and submitted to Hanford Operations Office, AEC.

In addition to the principal reports noted above, the following minor reports are from the SS control records for control analysis:

Production Statistics—monthly
Statistical Data Report—monthly
Ratio Report—monthly
Product Cost Report—monthly
Unrecoverable Waste Summary—monthly
Waste Batches Out of Limits—weekly
Operations Report—weekly

17-4. ANALYSIS OF SS MATERIAL CONTROL

The SS Group constantly monitors the plants' SS material control system. All SS material control data are reviewed and analyzed to detect off-standard conditions. The status of plant SS material control is provided routinely to responsible plant management in the form of routine monthly reports. Frequent letters and memos are written as SS material control problems arise to point out problems to responsible management and make corrective recommendations.

Two routine monthly reports are written, the general SS Materials Control Report and the Inventory Verification Report. The SS Materials Control Report contains a narrative portion that describes all SS Group actions for the month and gives an analysis of the present control status. B-PID experience is given in table and graph form for both plutonium and uranium for the current month and for the fiscal year to date. Shipper-receiver difference for the current month and fiscal year are given. Statistical control limits for all balance areas and for shipper-receiver difference are given and compared with experienced differences.

The Inventory Verification Report is a detailed report on the current inventory. It is made by a member of the SS Group who has witnessed the inventory being taken by the operating personnel. It describes the quality of the inventory in regard to the following of prescribed procedures and methods. It will note unusual circumstances prevailing, if any. It points out possible uncertainties and aids in the improvement of methods and procedures for future inventories as well as assisting in maintaining a high level of present inventory quality.

The quality and efficiency of the SS material control program must be maintained. This includes keeping measurement precisions current for use in the calculation of statistical control limits and inventory uncertainties and for use in shipment precision statements and shipper-receiver difference control limits.

Changes in the SS material control system are made to incorporate changes in process or processing conditions or whenever technological advances or procedural changes permit better or less expensive equivalent control. The SS Group recommends such changes based on analysis of control data. All changes in the SS material control system having measurement aspects must be approved by the SS Group.

17-5. MEASUREMENTS OF RECEIPTS, REMOVALS, AND INTERNAL TRANSFERS

17-5.1. Volume Determination. The volume of plutonium nitrate product solution is calculated from the results of weight and specific gravity measurements. Most other volume determinations are made by tank-level instrumentation and tank calibration tables which relate the liquid height in a tank to the liquid volume.

Tank liquid levels are found by weight factor instrument whose reading is directly proportional to the liquid level in a tank by virtue of the differential pressure between the bottom and top of the tank. The reading can be made directly from the instrument, or on a chart receiving a signal from a transmitter between tank and chart. The reading must be corrected for solution density and transmitter calibration.

The most accurate method of computing the values in a tank calibration table is the increment weight method. In this method small increments of water are accurately weighed and dropped into the vessel to be calibrated. After each increment has been added, an instrument reading is taken. The water weight vs. instrument reading data are used to construct the calibration table giving pounds or gallons of water per inch. Such calibrations can be reproduced to within ±0.25 percent.

Process condensate, cooling water, and steam condensate are measured by orifices and weirs.

17-5.2. Weight Determination. Weighing is the most accurate method of measuring quantity. Weighing eliminates errors introduced by tank calibration and by liquid level instrumentation, and the errors introduced by weighing can be reduced to insignificant levels. The use of weighing techniques has been limited to direct measurements since the maintenance and operation of remote large-scale weighing devices has not been sufficiently developed.

The quantity of plutonium nitrate product and UO_3 product is determined by weighing. The scale used for plutonium solution is a portable upright platform scale capable of weighing to ± 25 gm. Weighing accuracy is considerably improved (to ± 1 gm) by use of a check-weight procedure, which consists of comparing the net weight of solution with the weight of an accurate check weight of approximately the same weight as the solution net weight. Net weights of solution are adjusted for the scale bias shown by the check-weight procedure. The check-weight procedure provides constant scale quality control.

The quantity of plutonium shipped is calculated by using the specific gravity analysis to convert solution weight to volume since chemical analysis is reported in weight per unit volume.

The UO_3 powder is weighed on 10-ton capacity platform scales calibrated to ± 2 lb. The scale is checked before each use with a secondary check weight weighing approximately that of an empty bulk container and once per day with a check weight equal to the normal gross weight of a full container. The scales are checked weekly by an instrument mechanic using primary certified weights and secondary check weights.

17-5.3. Sampling. All vessel samplers are identical in basic concept; the samplers differ only in sample size and in the technique of removing the sample from sample line to the laboratory. All samples are drawn from the vessels to the sample port by a small-capacity air jet. The samplers are of a continuous circulation type, solution being removed from a single point at the bottom of the vessel (Fig. 17-2). Those samplers pulling material an excessive height from the cell floor to the sample gallery are given an assist by an atmospheric air bleed system.

All samples containing gross fission products are less than 0.1 ml in size. These are taken from the sample line by a remote pipet and expelled into a dilution bottle in a shielded carrier for transfer to the laboratory. This is called an "A" type sampler.

Samples of a less radioactive nature are removed from the sample line by a capillary discharge tube set to give a specific sample size ranging from 1 to 100 ml. The sample bottle is in a shielded container during sampling. The shielded container is removed from the sampler and used as a carrier and shield in transferring samples to the laboratory. This is a "B" type sampler.

Solutions essentially free of fission products are sampled into an unshielded bottle for transfer to the laboratory. The majority of the cold vessels are equipped with this "C" type sampler for taking larger volume samples. Some samples of this type are taken directly from lines during bulk transfers, or if a standard sampler is not available, by dip samplers direct from the tank.

UO$_3$ powder samples are taken by a continuous screw sampler during the loadout of the powder. The sample is drawn from the loadout line directly above the loadout outlet. Samples are deposited in quart glass jars. Precautions must be taken to avoid exposure to atmosphere because of the hygroscopic nature of the powder.

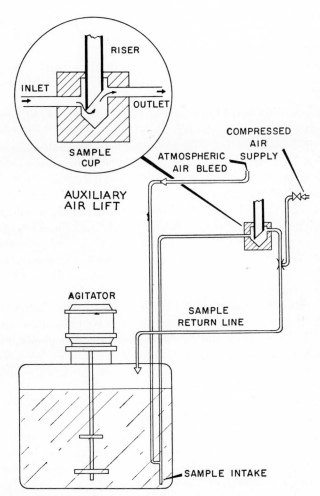

FIG. 17-2 Schematic diagram of a recirculating sampler.

The uncertainties involved in sampling solutions are similar on all three types, although more uncertainty exists in types A and B than in type C, and the greatest uncertainty lies in type A. The sampling uncertainty results primarily from two requirements: (1) the vessel must be agitated sufficiently to give a homogeneous solution (agitation time before sampling is based on pre-start-up tests); (2) after the solution is homogeneous, sufficient amount of solution must be drawn through the sample lines to flush out the residue of previous samples. Both A and B types are entirely enclosed systems. There is no way of detecting whether or not there is circulation and, if there is, what the rate of circulation is. Everything depends on the system's performing as tested before plant start-up. Procedures are followed which were shown to give representative samples during pre-start-up tests. The C type sampler provides visual evidence of circulation. The pipetting operation uncertainty, associated only with the A type sampler, is caused by the necessity of obtaining an accurate sample volume directly into a dilution bottle under conditions less ideal than normal laboratory conditions and by other than laboratory personnel.

Very little sampling-precision work has been done. What has been done indicates the sampling error to be considerably more than the random variance of the analytical methods used on the samples. Special samples of uranyl nitrate solution in unagitated storage tanks have shown a deviation of 4 percent, depending on the location of the tank sampled.

17-5.4. Analytical: *Coulometer.* The coulometer is an instrument for measuring the concentration of uranium or plutonium in a solution by electrically changing the valence state. The method has a precision of about ±2.5 percent. Although the coulometer is more versatile and less susceptible to bias than the X-ray absorption photometer, which has comparable applications, it is also more complex and time consuming. It is an alternate to the X-ray method of analysis.

X-ray Absorption Photometer. The X-ray absorption photometer (see Fig. 17-3) is an instrument for determining uranium or plutonium concentrations of solutions. It is based on the principle that heavy elements absorb a high proportion of X rays passed through them. When a heavy element is in solution, the X rays absorbed are in direct proportion to the concentration of the element in solution.

The method is fast, simple, and fairly precise (±2.0 to 2.5 percent), but it is subject to bias. Sources of bias have included the absorption of X rays by other materials in the samples (corrections can be made by impurities analysis), faulty standards, and technique errors. The method is useful on relatively pure and concentrated solutions. Some impure samples can be X-rayed after first removing impurities by extraction.

Fluorimeter. The fluorimeter is an instrument for the analysis of low concentrations of uranium in solutions, usually wastes. It operates on the principle that uranium fluoresces when exposed to ultraviolet light, the amount of fluorescence being proportional to the amount of uranium. The precision of the analysis ranges from ±5 to ±30 percent. These limits, although rather wide percentagewise, are considered adequate, since quantities involved are small, generally parts per million.

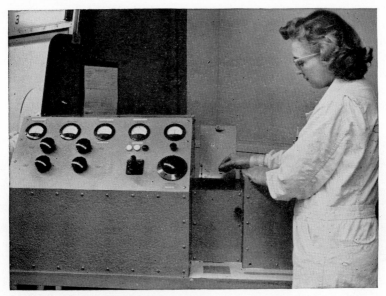

FIG. 17-3 X-ray photometer equipment.

Alpha Count (Radioassay). This method for determining plutonium concentration utilizes the rate of emission of alpha particles from decaying plutonium atoms. The accuracy of the counting-rate measurements depends upon how constant the geometry of the counting instrument remains as it registers the alpha particles emitted from a disk containing a dried drop of solution. This is checked frequently by means of standard disks whose counting rates are known.

FIG. 17-4 Drying hood for preparing plutonium samples for radioassay.

The major problem of the alpha-count analysis is the conversion of count rates to grams of plutonium. Different isotopes of plutonium have different emission rates. The method of conversion currently being used is an after-the-fact correlation of X-ray and radioassay analyses of the final product.

The count analysis has a precision of approximately ±5 percent as does the conversion factor. The over-all analysis precision of a gram's determination is about ±7 percent. Fig. 17-4 and 17-5 show some of the equipment used.

Fig. 17-5 The counting room, with instruments for plutonium radioassay. Charts on top of the counters are the control charts upon which are plotted daily the results of standard counts.

Mass Spectrometer. This is the standard instrument for measuring proportions of different isotopes in a sample. It has excellent precision (±0.24 percent) but occasionally develops bias through air leakage, etc., and the cost per analysis is high.

Uranium by Liquid Density. The uranium content is calculated from the solution density at 25°C. Corrections are made for other constituents of the liquid which add significantly to the density. This procedure is valid for hexone-free aqueous solutions. This method is convenient for use on highly radioactive streams, such as dissolver solution, since exposure to personnel is reduced to a minimum. The precision of the method is approximately ±3 to 5 percent.

Gravimetric Determination of Uranium in UO₃. Orange UO₃ powder is ignited and weighed as U_3O_8, and corrections are applied for impurities. The percentage of uranium is reported. Extreme care must be exercised to prevent sample contact with air since UO_3 powder is hygroscopic and any moisture pickup will introduce a low bias. The precision of this method is ±0.03 percent.

Plutonium Chemical Assay. This is a direct chemical analysis by a ceric sulfate titration method. The precision of this method is approximately ±0.15 percent.

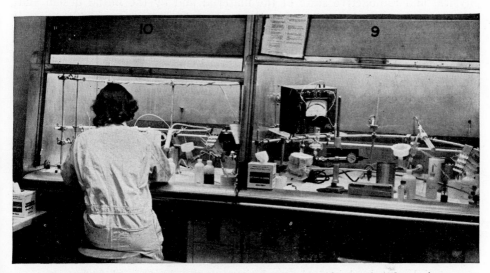

Fig. 17-6   The hot-sample hood that handles specific gravity determinations.

Specific Gravity. Specific gravity is determined by the pycnometer on decontaminated solutions requiring high accuracy. Specific gravity is determined by the falling-drop viscosity method on radioactive solutions and those requiring less than pycnometer accuracy. Fig. 17-6 is a view of a hot laboratory where these measurements are made.

17-5.5. Use of Factors, Calculation, or Estimation. In some cases where knowledge of SS quantities is required routinely, experience has shown that results are very consistent or are in some way predictable. In such cases there is an economical advantage in establishing a factor and sampling only infrequently for check purposes. Coating waste and condensate are examples of process streams handled in this fashion.

Some measurements require routine analytical corrections for errors contributed by impurities present. Whenever such corrections can be precisely estimated without analysis or when they can be calculated from analysis experience, analytical economies can be realized. Examples of such measurements are feed and product measurements. Analytical history at these points shows certain impurities to be constant for all practical purposes, and historical values can be used.

17-6. MEASUREMENT OF INVENTORY

Nuclear materials management is concerned with the systematic location, storage, and recording of materials. The type of inventory is determined by the physical and radioactive state of the material and by the initial design and capability considerations of process instrumentation. Some material, like irradiated fuel elements, cannot be readily identified and counted because of the radioactive hazard involved; other material, such as process solutions, is contained in equipment pieces or in vessels, and in these cases measurements must be taken and converted into physical units based on predetermined tables. Temperature, chemical analysis, and other factors also bear on the conversion. All these matters require that the tables, estimations, and formulas (the use of which precedes the derivation of inventory quantities) be reliable and applied as accurately as possible.

The inventory of nuclear materials in process is based on the following general types of measurement:

1. Measured inventory indicates that the stated quantity was physically determined by direct weighing, piece count, or physical measurement.

2. Calculated inventory indicates that the stated quantity was determined by the use of empirical or theoretical computations. This includes the quantity of material in a solution that cannot be sampled directly. The quantity of material contained in such a solution can be determined from sampling adjacent vessels or from a knowledge of the process technology; for example, the plutonium or uranium content of slugs in feed storage or of solution in the extraction columns.

3. Estimated inventory pertains to a quantity of material, such as that in dissolver heels, which cannot be determined by sampling and analysis and cannot be calculated from other data. It implies the application of judgment to other available process data.

The same tools available for transfer measurement are available for inventory. However, sometimes special care is necessary owing to the infrequency of the measurements; special consideration must be given to sampling, volume, and weight determination. The solutions must be sufficiently agitated to ensure that the sample is representative. Care must be exercised to avoid contaminating the sample with previously sampled material. This is usually done by recirculating the solution through the sample lines until any holdup from previous sampling has been thoroughly washed out. Only then is the sample ready to be extracted for analysis by the laboratory.

Seldom-used instrumentation must be checked to ensure good results. Special situations present at inventory time must be recognized and given proper consideration.

17-6.1. Specific Inventory Categories.   The basis of monthly inventory in the respective material balance areas is summarized under the following heads.

Feed Storage.   Irradiated slugs (fuel elements) in cask cars and in slug storage are reported at the SS value submitted by the slug canning area shipper.   For fuel elements not irradiated at Hanford reconciliation is accomplished on the basis of analytical determination after complete dissolution.

Metal Solution Preparation.   The quantities of uranium and plutonium in the dissolvers and in the metal solution storage tanks are based on measurements taken after dissolver heel has been removed; these figures are then adjusted for receipts to and removals from the metal solution preparation area occurring between the time of dissolver heel removal and month end.   When dissolver heel cleanouts are not done during the month, quantities of uranium and plutonium in this balance area are based on solution level measurements and chemical analyses together with an estimate of the amount of material in the dissolver heels.

Recovered Acid Storage.   The uranium content of recovered acid solution is determined by solution level measurement and chemical analysis.   Solution in transit in tank cars or trucks is reported in this category at the shipper's value arrived at by determination of volume and analysis.   Uranium content is generally negligible.

Recycle Storage.   Recycle cans are portable critically safe containers for storing and handling recycle solutions.   The quantity of SS material in a recycle can is calculated from the weight and chemical analysis.

Extraction Area.   The uranium and plutonium measurements in this area are based on solution level readings, chemical analyses, flow rate data, and extrapolation.   The material in process vessels is inventoried by taking solution level readings and laboratory determinations; the amount of solution in concentrators, strippers, and fractionators is calculated from flow rates and the analyses of related streams; column holdup is derived from standard values established on the basis of research and flow sheet extrapolation.

UNH Storage.   The uranium content of stored solution is determined by solution level measurement and an average analytical factor; in the absence of the average value (computed from recent material transfers), a sample is taken, and the volume and concentration are based on the analytical results. This portion of the inventory report includes the uranium heels in empty tank cars as well as the contents of vehicles in transit to the finished-products operation.

Product Storage.   Product cans are portable, critically safe containers for storing and handling plutonium solutions.   The amount of plutonium in a product can is determined from the solution weight and analytical results.

Analytical Control Laboratory. Plutonium from process samples is accumulated until a sufficient volume is attained to minimize handling. A daily inventory, based on a controlled average sample size, is maintained for SS control; this accumulated value is reported at the month's end.

Uranium Denitration. The uranium inventory in this area is in concentrated solution form in storage tanks and concentrators and in UO_3 powder form in continuous calciners, receiving hoppers, bins, off-gas equipment, and product containers. Prior to inventory, an effort is made to empty all hoppers, bins, etc. holding large amounts of uranium. Solution measurements are by volume and analysis; powder measurement is by weight calculated in equipment and actual weight in containers, converted to uranium content by load-out analysis average.

17-6.2. Direct Measurement: *Process Tanks Inventoried.* The inventory of process tanks is calculated directly using vessel solution level readings, specific gravity corrected for temperature, and analytical results of applicable SS control samples.

Process Tanks Normally Not Inventoried. Process solution movements are planned to ensure that cell sumps and tanks containing minor amounts of SS material are empty at the time of inventory to simplify the procedure. All waste solutions are sampled and analyzed for SS control prior to removal.

Centrifuges. During operation the inventory in the centrifuges is calculated directly using a standard holdup volume and analyses of the feed material. When the centrifuges are down, the volume is determined by weight factor instruments.

Silica Gel System. A calculated holdup is used when the system is operating; and zero is used when the system has been flushed.

17-6.3. Indirect Measurements. The dissolver charge is calculated using reactor area weight and factor data. Under normal operating conditions the dissolver heel is removed prior to shutdown, and an inventory is taken after the heel is removed. When this occurs, it is not necessary to take a physical inventory of the metal solution area at month end. Instead, the inventory taken after dissolver heel removal is adjusted for all receipts to, and disbursements from, the metal solution preparation area; this then provides the basis for month-end reporting.

On occasions, production requirements do not permit curtailment of the dissolver operation for heel removal. When more than 60 days have elapsed between dissolver cleanouts, a physical inventory is taken on the last day of the month.

For a more accurate estimate, fuel elements are added to a dissolver heel to produce a standard heel, and this value is used for uranium inventory purposes. The plutonium inventory is determined by multiplying the standard uranium heel by the ratio of plutonium to uranium in the last dissolver charge.

When heels are not removed, the amount of SS material in the dissolver heels is estimated using dissolving rates as the basis of the estimate.

17-6.4. Estimated Inventories: *Column Holdup.* Estimates of SS material holdup in the columns are based on a standard flow sheet. The following assumptions are made in performing the calculations:

1. The continuous phase occupies a constant volume percent of the packed-column section.
2. Stage heights are assumed to be equal.
3. The plutonium holdup is estimated on the basis of reactor irradiation history.
4. An empty or stripped column contains a negligible amount of SS material.

Plutonium Concentration Section. The operating volume must be determined before the amount of SS material can be calculated. The solution level readings from the weight factor instruments are proportional to the recirculation rate; they do not indicate actual solution level measurements. These instruments are satisfactory for operating the equipment but cannot be used to determine actual volumes. The amount of SS material present during normal operation is derived from past operating experience by measuring the contents under steady-state operating conditions subsequent to normal shutdowns.

Each time the building is shutdown, the equipment is drained and flushed according to building shutdown procedures. Past operating experience indicates varying amounts of plutonium buildup in the system. Based on this operating experience, a standard plutonium holdup is considered to be present in the system in addition to the material present under normal operating conditions. All material recovered in flushes after shutdown and prior to a physical inventory is deducted from this standard holdup.

UNH Storage Tanks. It is difficult to obtain representative samples of solution in the UNH storage tanks. The uranium analysis and specific gravity are obtained from an average analysis of transfers to UNH storage. After the average uranium and specific gravity analyses have been determined, the amount of uranium in storage is calculated.

Recovered Acid Storage Tanks. Representative samples can be obtained only during operational transfers to the dissolvers. Since transfers to the dissolver section are not usually in progress at the time of inventory, the storage tanks are not sampled. The amount of uranium in the recovered acid is based on an average of several analyses. The number of analyses to be averaged is determined by calculating the total volume of acid in the storage tanks and dividing this volume by the average transfer batch size.

17-6.5. Inventory Forms. In general, the SS inventory accounts parallel the material balance areas. The month-end inventories are recorded on four types of inventory forms (Fig. 17-7).

FORM A

DISSOLVER AREA SS INVENTORY		
Dissolver No.	Charge No.	Lbs. U in Charge

		APPROVED BY	DATE _____ 19____
U in Heel	Total U	Total Pu	Basis of Inventory

FORM B

METAL SOLUTION PREPARATION SS INVENTORY							
Vessel No.	Sample Source	Sample No.	Weight Factor	Specific Gravity	Liquid Level	Gallons	Lbs. U/Gal.

		APPROVED BY		DATE _____ 19____		
Lbs. U	AT c/m/gal	AmCm c/m/gal	Corrected AT	TC	Total Pu	Signed

FORM C

UNH STORAGE AREA SS INVENTORY			
Tank	Weight Factor	Specific Gravity	Liquid Level

	APPROVED BY	DATE _____ 19____	
Gallons	Sample No.	Lbs. U/Gal.	Lbs. U

FORM D

URANIUM REDUCTION SS INVENTORY				
Tank	Weight Factor	Specific Gravity	Liquid Level	Gallons

		APPROVED BY	DATE	
			_____19_____	
Sample No.	Weight % U	Lbs. U/Gal.	Lbs. U	Signed

```
Cyclones.............................................    _____
Hoppers .............................................    _____
Bag Filters .........................................    _____
Partial Containers ..................................    _____
Broken Bags .........................................    _____
Powder in Drums .....................................    _____
Waste Powder ........................................    _____
Lab Returns..........................................    _____
Calciners:
      (a) Bed Holdup .................................    _____
      (b) Collection Bin.............................     _____
      (c) Pickup Bin.................................     _____
Process Holdup.......................................    _____
Customer Samples ....................................    _____
Empty UO3 Containers ................................    _____
Full UO3 Containers .................................    _____

                    Signed _____
```

FIG. 17-7 Typical inventory forms (above and opposite page).

Form A. The inventories of the cask cars, dissolvers, and slug storage area are entered on this form. Process and material-handling operations personnel enter the charge numbers of the material in the dissolvers, the cask car number and station number for all loaded cask cars, and yoke number and station number for material in the slug storage basin. The remainder of the inventory is calculated by the SS control clerks.

Form B. The inventory for the remaining portion of the plant (with the exception of uranium denitration UNH storage, and column holdup) is entered on these forms. The sample number, batch number, weight factor, temperature, and specific gravity are entered on the form by the person taking the inventory.

For indirect calculations involving concentrators, the concentration factor is entered. All uranium and plutonium analyses are corrected by multiplying them by this concentration factor. The remaining calculations are made on a volume basis.

Form C. The UNH storage inventory and the column inventory are entered on this form. The UNH storage tank inventory is calculated on a volume basis as the sample calculation in the proceeding section. The standard values used for the column holdup have been discussed in a previous section.

Form D. The uranium denitration inventory is taken on this form. Data on each vessel containing uranium solution are entered on the form. This includes sample number, weight factor, and specific gravity. The remainder of the inventory consisting of UO_3 powder is calculated by equipment volume data and average powder analysis. Data on each piece of equipment are recorded. Product in inventory is stated at the loadout value.

17-7. CHECK PROCEDURES

There are many phases of SS control where the use of check procedures or special precautions is highly desirable to minimize the possibility of error arising as a result of process or operational circumstances. The following is a generalized discussion of such circumstances together with the procedures and special precautions which have been found useful in dealing with them.

17-7.1. Transfers. Transfers made just before or just after the month-end inventory cutoff can result in omissions or double charging. Several types of error in this category are possible: (1) A batch can be credited both as a transfer and as an inventory item by the shipper. (2) Credit for a batch can be taken by both shipper and receiver, the shipper taking it as an inventory item and the receiver as a receipt and consequently as an inventory item. (3) A transfer batch in transit might be omitted from the receiver's inventory.

Such errors can be eliminated by reconciliation of all transfers between shipper and receiver and by reconciling transfer time with transfer-tank inventory time. This is important for internal between-balance-area transfers as well as off-site transfers.

The accuracy of measurements can be affected by temperature. Errors have resulted when analytical results were not reported at a standard temperature or when the instrument specific gravity used was not adjusted to the temperature of the reported analysis. If an analysis is reported at 25°C, the volume used to calculate quantity must be the volume at 25°C. This problem can be eliminated by reporting all analysis at a standard 25°C. Instrument specific gravity is corrected for temperature to give a specific gravity at 25°C.

Unreliable tank calibration tables have resulted in irregular material balances. Tank calibration errors can be the result of errors made in the original calibration or of actual changes in the relation between tank volume and liquid level as indicated by the manometer. Changes can result from a tank dimension change (unlikely) or from the addition or removal of internal equipment. Small leaks and changes in line friction can cause changes in manometer instrumentation calibration. Calibrations can be checked remotely. The best method found has been the water increment method described in Sec. 17-5.1.

Shipper-receiver differences due to errors in scale weighing have been experienced. Errors have been reduced to insignificant levels by establishing an accurate check weight system of scale quality control.

Shipper-receiver differences have also necessitated detailed verification of the accuracy of analytical methods. Verification has been made by comparing routine analysis to analyses made of the same sample by an independent laboratory using more detailed and accurate analytical methods.

Determination of an isotope correction factor is necessary for converting plutonium alpha count (radioassay) to grams. The variation in isotopic content of plutonium recovered does not permit the use of a standard factor, and the determination of isotopic content at each radioassay measurement point is not economically feasible. The most realistic and usable approach has been the determination of a ratio of grams to counts in the final product, rather than a direct determination of isotopic composition. The factor used at present is an average ratio of grams to counts as determined in the final product measurement. The average ratio is calculated weekly and is used on all radioassay measurements to convert counts to grams for the following week. Since the factor is determined on material different from the material being measured, the accuracy of this approach depends on the complete randomness of the isotopic content fluctuation. To assume such randomness is not entirely correct; however, the error is considerably less than the other uncertainties in the measurements on which it is used.

Some transfers require material to be pumped from a lower level to a higher level or through overhead lines. This results in solution drain-back after the transfer pump is shut off. Errors have been the result of tank manometers being read before such drain-back has completed. Thus arises a high bias in transfers, since part of the material measured as-shipped drains back into the shipping tank. Error is reduced by observing the drain-back period and rigidly adhering to a time interval between pump stop and manometer reading sufficient to permit complete drainage.

The receipt or removal of material to or from a measurement point via a manifold can cause errors. Leakage through any of the valve outlets from the manifold can result in only partial measurement of solution received or shortages in quantities shipped. The only positive precaution is the avoidance of manifolds at such points.

Transfer errors have arisen when process changes, additions, or emergencies have required SS-measurement control changes, but, through breakdown in communications or failure of responsible personnel to realize the implications, the proper changes were not incorporated.

Operating and engineering units must fully realize the SS control requirements for their plant. At the operating level a familiarity with the building control system is essential. Process changes must be followed by suitable changes in measurement technique and, in emergencies requiring recycle or special handling, due regard must be given to SS control. The engineering units can save much time and effort and greatly aid material control by giving proper consideration to material control in the design and planning stages.

The use of incorrect manometer oil can introduce transfer bias. The correct oil to use is that which was used at the time the tank was calibrated. Small changes in the physical properties in density or viscosity can produce significant measurement bias. Tank calibrations are merely relations between manometer indication and quantity of solution in the tank at the time of calibration. The manometer must be maintained at all times at the same conditions as during the calibration.

Addition or deletion of possible measurement points or new transfers can make material balance area concepts obsolete. Balance area boundaries must be changed to give the most reliable balance possible. Balance area boundaries are always set at the point where the most reliable measurements are to be found. Boundaries should always be defined to incorporate the best measurements.

Verification of plant receipts presents a complex problem. The solid elements received cannot be measured in this form. The first measurement possible is made after the dissolving step. The material is then in solution and contains all the high-activity fission products. The uranium concentration is high, but the plutonium concentration is extremely low. The measurement limitations imposed by the high radioactivity and low plutonium concentration adversely affect measurement reliability.

Verification of individual receipts requires complete dissolution of each batch. This reduces plant capacity attainable per dissolver. In practice, individual receipts can be verified only to within approximately ± 3 to 5 percent. However, if uranium weight is accurately known, the plutonium can be analyzed and calculated on a ratio basis within ± 1 percent or better.

17-7.2. Inventory. The use of a continuous process such as solvent extraction, while economically advantageous, presents complications in terms of inventory measurement.

Solution Samples. The general characteristics of vessels and process streams must be understood by the SS Group if this group is to evaluate the influence of these characteristics upon the inventory data obtained. The following considerations provide a basis for illustration:

1. The sample may be drawn from a tank where material has been stored for a long time. The solution must be sufficiently agitated to permit the ma-

terial to become homogeneous. Sampling time can also be extended to permit a good sample to be obtained, or duplicate samples can be taken for comparison; where the results are doubtful, the solution is sampled again. Previous analyses are reviewed, and the concentration of materials added to, or removed from, the vessel are analyzed along with other pertinent data on record from flushes or cleanouts.

2. The inventory sample may be drawn from a large vessel where the material is involved in chemical or physical changes. Here it is difficult to get a satisfactory sample, and the data must be correlated with other process events.

3. Sampling from a flowing stream produces the optimum sample; however, correlation with other process events and timing of the sample are important.

4. Solutions containing a high percentage of salts tend to freeze out in the sample line. Even if the line is freed, there is doubt whether the salt present comes from the solution in the process or from the sample line.

An operating supervisor obtains sample analyses and assists in making the necessary extensions to arrive at the total uranium and plutonium in inventory. Limits are furnished for checking the analytical results of solutions normally contained in each of the vessels. Emphasis is placed on these procedures to ensure that the analytical determinations are properly applied and within the specified range.

Instrumentation. There are several causes of false readings on manometers: (1) too high a purge gas flow rate, which causes line friction and back pressure; (2) leakage in the instrument lead lines; (3) restrictions within the instrument lead lines. Manometers also give false readings through inadvertent use of manometer oil with a specific gravity different from that used during calibration. Any one of these factors can cause an inventory error by causing a false reading. The instrument systems are checked periodically and are checked against each other when transfers are made from tank to tank to keep such occurrences to a minimum.

The instrument must also be read accurately, taking care to eliminate parallax and to interpolate correctly between the numbered divisions of the scale. If the manometers are read with the eyes at a low level, a high bias will be introduced into the measurement. This can be corrected by providing ladders for the reader to stand on while taking readings.

A comparison of the instrument recording charts and manometers is made to determine their relative accuracy. When the two readings are not within reasonable agreement, further inquiry is made to locate the nature and extent of the discrepancy. Obviously, one instrument can serve as a check on the other; however, since they both are tied into the same instrument lines, use of this method is limited. Although the chart recorders have a greater potential for built-in error, their use is valuable in ascertaining previous operating experience and trends. Recorded chart readings are sometimes used for inventory purposes when the related manometer is out of service at month end.

Therefore, the accuracy of both instruments should be maintained routinely.

Errors may arise from the difficulty of interpolating correctly and also from the failure to make specific gravity corrections for temperature. When an interpolation is made between the "0 to 100" scale range, readings are usually made to the nearest 0.005 or to the nearest 0.003, depending on the instrument calibration. Unless an operator is quick to discern these differences, he might easily interpret the scale as 1.300 where it should be read as 1.030.

Tank Calibrations. When the calibration tables are used, proper correction for density or specific gravity is mandatory. If the table is entered by the manometer reading alone, the volume might be erroneously taken from the portion of the table where the volume is not directly proportional to the height; therefore the weight factor readings must be corrected for specific gravity before the table is entered.

Different calibration tables exist for the same tank, one for chart readings and one for manometer readings. Both tables are valid if used properly, but if a chart calibration is used with a manometer reading, or vice versa, the resultant error can be significant. The problem is resolved by issuing instructions to fully identify solution level chart readings on the inventory sheets. Manometer readings are normally required for the inventory.

Another problem is encountered in the preparation of calibration data in weight units for some vessels and in volume for others. Confusion will result from the use of tables that are not consistent in this respect.

Dissolver-Solution Inventories. Monitoring of dissolver solution for control purposes is not feasible for three reasons: (1) the presence of a variable metal heel, which introduces a large uncertainty in the volume measurement, (2) the tendency for sample lines to become plugged, and (3) the absence of agitators. The dissolved-metal solution is therefore transferred to other vessels where suitable dilution and agitation can precede sampling and analysis.

Dissolver-heel estimates are based on a standard, but experience has shown that the size of the heel in each dissolver may vary considerably from that amount. Records of all charges to the dissolvers and the amounts of material recovered during cleanout have been kept to establish the relative heel sizes. However, when dissolver-heel cleanouts are infrequent, the estimates are based on current dissolving rates. A good method for obtaining accurate dissolver inventories is to schedule cleanouts no more than 60 days apart.

UNH Storage. The UNH storage tanks are not equipped with mechanical agitators. Although the solution can be recirculated, this is time consuming and the results have not been satisfactory during past inventories. An average analytical value of the last 10 (or more) batches received is used for the inventory in order to secure a good estimate of the SS material content. Rod readings eliminate the necessity for a solution specific gravity determination.

Special inventories have been scheduled in the UNH storage area to reconcile differences between book values and the actual quantities reported. At these times the inventory procedure and measurement methods are observed by personnel of the SS Group. Some recommendations for improving the inventory procedure are:

1. That minimum recirculation times be observed
2. That sample lines be completely flushed of residue before taking the inventory sample
3. That all vessels in this area be rodded for inventory measurement as a check on the agreement between rod and manometer readings
4. That inventory be taken preferably on day shift

Cell Sumps. Cleanup and recovery of SS material from the cell sumps can be a recurring problem in some areas. The material, generated from leaks and miscellaneous drainage, must be transferred to a tank for sampling and volume determination. Because of other processing requirements, a tank receiver is not always available, and the material may remain unmeasured until the following month. If this solution can be jetted into a tank and measured within a few days, it can be added to the inventory. Care must be taken, however, to see that the solution that leaked after the inventory cutoff is not measured twice.

Plutonium Build-up. Instances of plutonium deposition may occur under off-standard conditions. The depositions are the result of (1) the formation of a plutonium precipitate (probably polymer) during long storage of solutions containing dissolved solvent and (2) improper handling of the solutions formed on dissolution of the precipitate in acid. Limiting the storage of plutonium solutions to a maximum of five days and controlling acid concentration should prevent the precipitate formation. If solution storage and the formation of precipitates becomes unavoidable, the precipitates can sometimes be dissolved in nitric acid, and the plutonium can be recovered without difficulty. Plutonium accumulation may occur in the columns as a result of polymers formed with the decomposition products of solvent used.

17-7.3. Records and Accounting Report Problems. Many of the errors that occur in this phase are derived from source data. Frequently, discovery of errors in laboratory analysis, solution level, or other measurements requires that the original data be corrected. This requires changes in the original record and in all book entries made. Such occurrences cannot be completely eliminated; in fact, custodians must continually be encouraged to follow through on the correction of all errors detected to give the most reliable data available. Likewise, they must be encouraged to keep errors to a minimum.

All parts of source data can be equally important. Even date, time, and batch number are important, particularly when sequence of events is critical. The SS Group must strive for 100 percent correct source data in all respects.

Reconciliation of accounts is extremely important to guarantee proper debiting and crediting in each accounting period. Transactions should be numbered consecutively by batch or type to avoid omissions. Complete back-up data must be retained on all entires and corrections to entries. Source data back-up on any entry should always be readily available.

The accounting system must be maintained on a current basis to coincide with process changes or control-system changes. All records must be easily accessible for investigative purposes and must be maintained in a manner that will provide the continuous control data necessary. Month-end report deadlines have always resulted in peak loads which require more personnel than are justified on a continual basis. The use of computing machines can alleviate this problem.

17-8. SUMMARY

The nuclear materials control methods, measurement tools, and problems presented here represent the system that finally evolved out of many years of experience in operations of this type. The control system has been an ever-changing one, marked by advances to meet process changes and to incorporate new ideas and new measurement methods to produce the most accurate and economically efficient control system possible. Changes will continue. The reader should recognize that much of this discussion concerns a specific plant. What has been deemed necessary in this plant may, for some reason, be unnecessary in other plants, or, conversely, even more necessary.

Part Seven

RESEARCH AND DEVELOPMENT FACILITIES

Chapter 18

LOS ALAMOS SCIENTIFIC LABORATORY*

18-1. INTRODUCTION

Methods for the management and control of SS materials at research and development installations differ in many respects from methods used at production facilities. In most instances the turnover of material at research and development installations is slow. An individual or group may have the same material for months and years; whereas at production facilities the material flows in and out of an operation, usually within a few days.

For the most part research and development work is not routine, and there can be no routine confirmation of quantities of material held. Owing to the many and varied projects that are being investigated, a similarly wide range of quantities and types of materials must be controlled. At production facilities there is routine generation of material control information, and there are sampling points and evaluations, set up primarily for production control, which can be used for SS material control. This type of information usually is not available in research and development activities.

18-2. ACCOUNTING

Adequate control over SS materials being used for research and development is maintained by centering responsibility in an SS Control Group that reports directly to top management (see Fig. 18-1). This arrangement ensures the necessary latitude of being able to cross divisional and departmental lines.

The group leader is also the SS Representative. He is responsible not only to the contractor's management for all SS material in the possession of the laboratory, but also for the receipt and shipment of these materials from and to other installations. The Representative is responsible to management and the AEC for ensuring that adequate records are kept, materials are safeguarded, and inventories are submitted so that a monthly material balance

* G. R. Champion, Los Alamos, New Mexico.

471

report can be prepared for management and the AEC.   This material balance report will reflect the status of SS materials at the installation.

18-2.1. Central SS Control.   The Central SS Control Group is composed of the Records Section, Transfer Section, an assistant group leader, and a chief clerk.

The Records Section, composed of three bookkeepers, checks the accuracy of the information shown on the documents of original entry and posts this in-

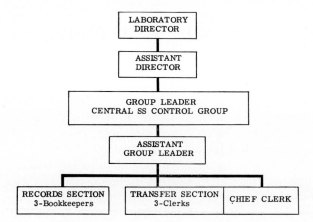

FIG. 18-1   Organization of the Central SS Control Group.

formation correctly to the proper accounts.   Three stations have been established to distribute the work load, and the bookkeepers are rotated among these stations every three months.   The available manpower is thereby efficiently utilized, and the Records Section personnel are familiarized with all phases of the bookkeeping system.

Station 1 is primarily the checking station, where all documents of original entry, from which the Subsidiary Ledger and the Factory Journal entries are made, are checked for:

1. Correct unit of measurement
2. Arithmetic accuracy
3. Proper extension of SS net weights where gross alloy weights are indicated (in the case of U^{235} and U^{233} the correct weight of these isotopes must be extended from the total uranium weight)
4. Account titles and numbers which are corrected, if necessary, or inserted when they are not indicated
5. Completeness, i.e. the proper date, signature, etc.

Station 2 receives from Station 1 all documents that serve as the bases for entries into the ledger accounts maintained by this station.

Station 3 receives from Station 1 and Station 2 all documents that serve as the bases for entries into the ledger accounts maintained by this station.

The chief clerk's duties include:

1. Receipt and recording of all incoming documents
2. Distribution of these documents to the proper individual within the group
3. Preparation of outgoing shipping forms and the completion of incoming shipping forms.
4. Final filing of all documents retained in the permanent files of the group

The assistant group leader posts the Factory Journal and the General Ledger and also prepares the monthly material balance report for the AEC. A flow chart for documents of original entry within the Central SS Control Group is presented in Fig. 18-2.

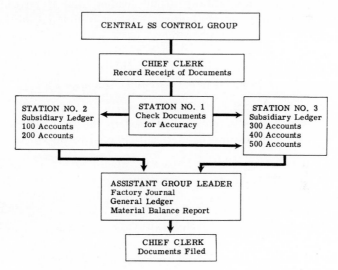

FIG. 18-2   Flow of source documents in the SS Control Group.

The Transfer Section, composed of three transfer clerks, is responsible for the physical movement of all SS materials between groups or individuals throughout the laboratory. It also checks the material transfer receipts that accompany each movement of material between material balance areas.

All the members of SS Control are concerned with, and participate in, the semiannual physical inventory verification of materials in the custody of the various individuals or groups in the laboratory. (The laboratory is composed of departments and divisions, which are further divided into groups.)

18-2.2. Material Balance Areas. The laboratory groups have been divided into material balance areas. These areas are identified by account numbers, which are incorporated into a Chart of Accounts (Sec. 18-2.3). A material balance area may be defined as an activity that receives a measured quantity of material for which it is responsible until the material is transferred to another activity. A material balance area may consist of an individual, a group, or a particular type of operation.

Each group of the Research and Development Division possessing SS materials is usually considered to be a material balance area. However, a group may be divided into more than one material balance area. For example, some groups may have feed material and process material in their custody, and they may also be concerned with research and development relative to the same types of materials. Separate material balance areas are established for each different activity.

The group leader is responsible for the SS materials in the possession of all members of his group regardless of the number of material balance areas into which the group is divided. Many group leaders find it advantageous to delegate the responsibility for SS materials to an individual working within a material balance area. It is advisable to have a second individual also become familiar with the material and the methods of accounting for it in case of illness or vacation of the assigned responsible person. It is the responsibility of the individual assigned in each material balance area to:

1. Account for the SS materials
2. Keep records of the material debited to the area
3. Report all expenditures of material charged to the area

When material is received by an area, the weight or other measurement is checked to be sure that the area is properly charged with the material received. When material is received or removed, the responsible person will be advised of the movement so that the records of the area can be kept current and the total quantity of material charged to the area will be available at all times.

Each material balance area is required to furnish the SS Group with a written monthly inventory of all its material (see Fig. 18-3). The SS Group forwards an inventory form to each material balance area at the end of each month; this serves as a reminder that an inventory is due. Those materials requiring a written monthly inventory are checked on the form to alert the material balance areas of the various types of material which they are required to report.

These forms are completed by each material balance area as of the last working day of the month. The method of determining the inventory is the responsibility of the group leader, and he signs the inventory form when it is completed.

The monthly physical inventory reports submitted by each material balance area are checked against the balance in the accounts, as shown on SS Control records, by the bookkeeper assigned to post those accounts. If there are any

SS MATERIALS MONTHLY PHYSICAL INVENTORY

Date _____

To   : _____

From: _____
        (Group)   (SS Account Number)

From inventories taken on _____ (last working day of the
month), the weight of each type of material in the possession of my group has been
determined as:

Weights to nearest .01

	B-PID	Measured Losses	Total Ending Inventory		
1. ENRICHED URANIUM (U^{235}): A. 90-100% Grams U :					
B. 75-90% Grams U :					
C. 50-75% Grams U :					
D. 25-50% Grams U :					
E. 0-25% Grams U :					
2. PLUTONIUM in Grams:					
3. U^{233} Grams U :					
4. DEPLETED URANIUM in kgs.:				Composition of Ending Inventory	
5. NORMAL URANIUM in kgs.:				Metal	Other
6. THORIUM in kgs.:					

Please explain unusual Book-Physical Inventory Difference on a
separate sheet and attach to this report.

I certify that, to the best of my knowledge and belief, the above total weights of SS
materials were in the possession of my group on the above date and represent the
entire amounts of these materials in the possession of my group on that date.

_____
Signature of Group Leader

FIG. 18-3   SS Materials Monthly Physical Inventory report.

discrepancies between the ledger figures and the reported inventory, the group concerned is contacted, and the difference is resolved. All accounts must agree before the monthly material balance report can be prepared.

A group or a material balance area may have relatively small quantities of SS materials in its possession. If these small quantities were reported monthly, technical personnel would lose valuable time. Therefore, it was decided that the following quantities of the materials listed would not require a monthly physical-inventory report:

Plutonium (all forms except residues)	30 gm
Plutonium (residues)	60 gm
Enriched uranium	150 gm
U^{233}	10 gm
Normal uranium (0.7115 percent U^{235})	65 kg
Depleted uranium	300 kg
Thorium	90 kg

These values are for an installation having rather large quantities of SS material in their inventory. Other installations should scale their quantities of SS materials accordingly.

During the first six calendar months of each year, members of the SS Group participate in a physical inventory taken in each material balance area. At this time all quantities of all SS materials in the custody of the area are physically inventoried, and adjustments are made to SS control records when quantities inventoried do not agree with the book balances. Thus, although some material balance areas are not required to report some SS materials in their possession every month, these materials are checked at least once a year by the above procedure.

18-2.3. Bookkeeping. A system of double-entry bookkeeping has been established to allow the SS Group to adequately control the quantities of SS materials charged to the various material balance areas. When one material balance area removes material and is therefore credited with that specific amount, another material balance area receives and is debited with the same amount of material. For every credit there is a corresponding debit.

The SS Group maintains the following ledgers: (1) Factory Journal, (2) Subsidiary Ledgers, and (3) General Ledger.

The Factory Journal is posted in total by type of account. The Chart of Accounts for the various material balance areas is divided into five basic inventory accounts:

1. The 100 accounts are feed-material areas
2. The 200 accounts are processing activities
3. The 300 accounts are research and development groups
4. The 400 accounts are concerned with reactor development

FORM NO. 431B 7-57-20M

SS MATERIAL TRANSFER RECEIPT

Use separate receipt for each material type.

White copy to SS Control at time of transfer.
Yellow copy to person receiving material.
Green copy to person from whom material is received.

Unit of Measurement_____ Type of Material_____
(Grams, Liters, etc.)   (U-235, U-238, Pu, etc.)

IDENTIFICATION NUMBER	COMPOUND, FORM, OR OTHER DESCRIPTION	NET WT. OF MATERIAL	SS NET OR T WEIGHT	PERCENT ENRICHMENT	U-235/U-233 WEIGHT
Totals					

Transferred to:_____ Acct. No._____ Date_____
(Group)

Transferred from:_____ Acct. No._____ _____
(Group)   Issued by

Transferred by _____

CHECKED
DEBIT
CREDIT
F. J. Fage _____

Received by

54962

Fig. 18-4 SS Material Transfer Receipt.

5. The 500 accounts pertain to inactive residues, such as material awaiting recovery for which no method has as yet been developed.

The five basic inventory accounts are further divided into individual accounts for each material balance area.

Subsidiary Ledgers are posted in individual accounts either in total or by separate items. In accounts that are kept by items, separate items are debited to the account; but credits are posted in total, and the separate items are checked off on the debit side.

FIG. 18-5 Sample journal entry form.

The General Ledger is a control ledger and is posted once a month using total debits and total credits in each basic account taken from the footings in the Factory Journal.

18-2.4. Internal Control Forms. SS material transfer receipts and journal entries are documents of original entry which are posted to the Factory Journal and the Subsidiary Ledgers. Transfers of SS materials between material balance areas are controlled by SS material transfer receipts (Fig. 18-4).

These receipts are numbered serially and are made up in books of 25. Each book contains a fly sheet, in duplicate, which is signed by the individual responsible for the receipts. The numbers of the receipts contained in the book are also listed on the fly sheet. The original copy of the fly sheet is retained by the SS Control Group and is used as a check list to ensure that the original copy of each receipt (even voided ones) has been forwarded to the SS Control Group. The receipts are issued in triplicate. The white copy (original) is forwarded to SS Control; the yellow copy goes to the person receiving the material; and the green copy is retained by the person sending the material. Very close control over the movement of SS material is maintained by virtue of the fact that the transfer clerks from the Transfer Section of the SS Control Group physically move this material between groups of the laboratory.

Journal entries (Fig. 18-5) are documents used for recording and posting adjustments (of a nature not covered by other documents of original entry) to the inventory accounts. These adjustments include such activities as

EXPENDITURE OF SS MATERIAL

Unit of Measurement _____ Type of Material _____

Identification No.	Description	SS Net Wt.	%

Explanation:

Credit Group _____, Acc't. No. _____

_____, 19 ___   Signature _____
Month Expended

FIG. 18-6   Sample form for Expenditure of SS Material.

book–physical inventory differences, measured losses, and expenditures of material.

When a journal entry is prepared, it should be supported by a written document from the material balance area concerned. This supporting information may be a simple memorandum that explains the circumstances or a notation on the monthly inventory form. When material is being routinely expended in tests, an Expenditure of SS Material form should be used (Fig. 18-6).

There are many activities that produce waste materials from which the SS material cannot be recovered economically. In such cases a record of the unrecoverable material must be kept on some suitable form, such as that illustrated in Fig. 18-7.

18-2.5. Trial Balance. After all documents of original entry have been posted for a month's activities and the balances in each account have been

48888088

compared with the monthly inventory from each material balance area, a trial balance is prepared to ensure that no errors in posting have occurred during the recording of the month's transactions and to provide a consolidation of the ending inventories for each type of SS material. These ending inventories are used in the preparation of the monthly material balance report.

UNRECOVERABLE MATERIAL

Materials from which the plutonium, thorium or uranium content cannot feasibly be recovered may be dropped from SS materials accounting records. Such write-offs shall be shown in the "Materials Removed" section of the monthly material balance reports.

Material Type	Source	Gross Wt. or Volume	SS Content	Method of Measurement	
				Assayed	Estimated

Explanation why recovery is not feasible:

Disposition:

Requested by: _____ (Group Leader)   Approved: _____ (Division Leader)

Approved: _____ Director's Office LASL   Approved: _____ Manager's Office ALOO

Date: _____

Submit in quadruplicate to SS Control

FIG. 18-7   Sample Unrecoverable Material report form.

The trial balance is compiled from information supplied by the bookkeepers, each of whom prepares a work sheet for all the individual accounts for which he is responsible. The balance in each account is listed for each type of SS material, and these balances are then totaled for each of the five basic inventory accounts. The trial balance is proved by taking the ending inventory for the preceding month from the General Ledger, adding to it the total debits from the footings in the Factory Journal, and subtracting from this figure the total credits from the Factory Journal. The figure thus obtained must agree with the total for each basic inventory account previously recorded on the trial balance. If the two quantities do not agree, an error has been made. This error must be resolved, even if it is necessary to check each transaction posted in the ledgers. When the trial balance has been checked, it is safe to assume that all the entries have been made and are correct and that quantities listed for each account represent the ending inventory for the month. This information can then be used to prepare the material balance report.

18-3. ANALYSES

The values used in debiting or crediting a material balance area are based on some type of measurement. Many materials are amenable to weighing. In the case of metals, weighing constitutes an acceptable method of measurement, but when the metal is alloyed, it is desirable to have an analysis of the material so that the ratio of SS material to alloying material can be definitely known.

When solutions are to be measured, the volumes must be known very accurately, and good sampling techniques are essential. After a representative sample has been procured, the amount of the various elements contained in it can be determined by one or more of the following methods of analysis.

18-3.1. Chemical Analysis. Chemical analysis is used, where possible, to determine the total quantity of the major element present, such as uranium. Spectrographic analysis is generally used to determine the kinds and quantities of impurities present in the material. It is often very important to know what impurities are in a material.

Certain radioactive materials, such as dilute solutions of plutonium, can be analyzed by radioassay. This is a counting method that makes use of the characteristic radiation of the element to be measured. There is a serious drawback to this method because the counter cannot differentiate between the alpha emissions of two types of materials such as plutonium and americium. Thus chemical separations are usually made to correct for the interfering element.

18-3.2. Isotopic Analysis. The most precise method for isotopic assay utilizes the mass spectrometer. However, this is a time-consuming analysis unless samples are being run routinely. Some excellent spectrographic techniques have been developed for determining the ratio U^{235}/U^{238}, as well as some acceptable fission counting procedures. For the other isotopes, such as U^{232}, U^{233}, U^{236}, and the isotopes of plutonium, the mass spectrometer is still the only reasonable instrument for analysis.

18-3.3. Evaluation of Data. When compounds are being analyzed, their stoichiometric characteristics are an important consideration. There are many compounds that are not stoichiometric; i.e. the atomic weight of an individual element divided by the atomic weight of the total compound does not result in a factor that represents the percentage of the element in the compound. In this case a factor can be determined by averaging a large number of analyses of the total element content. For example, it has been determined that U_3O_8 is not necessarily a stoichiometric compound. It has been necessary to examine numerous chemical assays of U_3O_8 to arrive at a factor that most accurately represents the true relation of uranium to the total atomic weight of the U_3O_8. This factor, 0.8452, is more correct than the theoretical 0.8465.

Wherever routine transfers occur, statistical treatment of data can estimate the uncertainties involved in the stated quantities. However, most of the material in research and development accounts is not involved in routine transfers. Hence experience and familiarity with the programs involved provide the best criteria for evaluating the transfers.

Experience is also a contributing factor in evaluating the authenticity of a material balance. After many reports of quantities relative to a material balance area have been received and accepted, a scanning of the information submitted by a material balance area will usually reveal the credibility of the information. When doubt exists, it is advisable to request a statistical verification of the plausibility of the information submitted. However, in the case of research and development accounts, this application is limited because of the infrequency of back-up information; there are just not enough data to evaluate the reliability. In such circumstances, experience is the only criterion available.

Chapter 19

ARGONNE NATIONAL LABORATORY *

19-1. INTRODUCTION

Argonne National Laboratory has two major areas of activity: it carries on fundamental research and development studies related to the understanding and use of atomic energy and it is responsible for the development of new reactor prototypes.

The scientific staff of the Laboratory represents most major fields of science and engineering. The major scientific divisions are Biological and Medical Research, Chemical Engineering, Chemistry, Metallurgy, Physics, Reactor Engineering, and Remote Control Engineering.

19-2. SPECIAL MATERIALS DIVISION

The AEC requires that each contractor be responsible for all SS materials in his possession. This responsibility includes setting up an accounting procedure, maintaining control of certain items, and designating a representative to be responsible for all SS materials in its facilities. At ANL the Director of the Special Materials Division is the SS Representative.

The Special Materials Division supplies technical services, administrative and operational, to the research staff of the Laboratory and its participating institutions and industrial organizations. It carries on the analytical, accounting, and auditing functions for AEC products supplied to ANL for its research activities. The division has a professional staff distributed among the major scientific divisions and an administrative staff localized in a strategic position close to the business offices, the AEC offices, and the Director's office.

For administrative purposes, the Special Materials Division is divided into the Analytical Laboratory, the Physical Control Section, and the Accounting Section.

* L. K. Hurst, Argonne National Laboratory, Lemont, Illinois. The author acknowledges the contributions and assistance of M. C. Nelson, B. D. Devine, J. H. Patterson, C. M. Stevens, and A. L. Harkness in the preparation of this chapter.

The Analytical Laboratory, administered by an associate scientist, provides independent analyses by chemistry (wet and dry methods) and by mass spectrometry. It develops analytical techniques, procedures, and equipment to be used. It calibrates balances and weights against standards prepared by the National Bureau of Standards.

The Physical Control Section, managed by an associate scientist, provides storage, protection, movement, and packaging facilities for materials and administers the procurement and the budgeting for materials in quantity and type adequate to fulfill the needs of the research program. The Physical Control Section is divided geographically into stock areas located in each of the research areas of divisions that utilize its services and materials. Each area is supervised by an associate or assistant scientist titled Special Materials Representative. These work areas conform with the major divisions of activity. Each work area operates independently in regard to material and record segregation, but all are subject to the same management control and over-all divisional procedures.

The Accounting Section, operated by an accountant, provides centralized material accounting for all products that require these controls. It provides independent audit and statistical studies on process flow records and stock area records and compiles monthly, quarterly, and yearly material balance reports as required.

Each section has a line authority within its own specific area and performs only a staff function at points where an overlapping of duties could occur. As an example, the Accounting Section is held responsible for the maintenance of all control ledgers, but the Physical Control Section has authority over the card system in use where actual material handling takes place. Hence the Accounting Section cannot effect entries of material changes in item cards, but it can report any imbalance of the cards with the quantities shown in the control ledgers.

19-3. SS MATERIAL CONTROL

The first step in establishing SS material control is the determination of a framework of procedures within which all control measures must be contained and then the establishment of internal accounting methods that will provide satisfactory control of material. The decisions made and the methods adopted are incorporated in a written procedure, which, after acceptance by management, becomes the guide for all material control activity. The written procedure serves three purposes: it is the contractor's statement of how management requirements are to be met, it establishes consistency in the methods to be employed in accounting for material flow between work groups, and it serves as the basis for auditing operations.

The basic objective is a system that provides the most efficient and the most accurate compliance with the management needs for material quantity information. The balance reported indicates the total SS material for which the organization is responsible; hence only those activities that result in increases or decreases in total balance figures have meaning in so far as report compilation is concerned. Most transactions affecting material balances are external; i.e. they are concerned with receipts of material from other installations or shipments of material to other installations. Internal activity becomes important in the total balance picture only in those instances where a material balance is changed because of the consumption of material during use or the production of material in internal operations.

19-3.1. Report Ledger. Because the Material Balance Report is so closely aligned with external activities and because these activities are recorded on AEC form 101, it is not difficult to establish an over-all control ledger (Report Ledger) using the same format as the Material Balance Report (Fig. 2-8). The advantage of using this format for ledger purposes is twofold: the preparation of the monthly report becomes a simple task of transcription and firm control of external document flow is automatically established.

This format needs only a few additions to make the ledger self-balancing. A control account for each type material must be set up, as well as a reconciliation account, to establish balance between the over-all control ledger and those subsidiary ledgers in use. Other than such additions, the ledger is developed with the same account headings as the line descriptions on the Material Balance Report. Further breakdown of accounts is required for those lines showing operations office totals when there are transactions with more than one station under a single operations office.

There are categories shown on the Material Balance Report that seldom if ever are affected by AEC transfer documents; yet these accounts become quite active in the Report Ledger. Such categories as Approved Inventory Write-Offs, Fission Loss, Procurement, and Production are almost always internal in nature; yet activities within these subdivisions result in increases and decreases in the material balances and must be shown on the report. Thus the format of the Material Balance Report presents a ledger arrangement that is practical in that it permits all activity affecting material balances to be easily and categorically recorded.

Posting to the Report Ledger is subject to individual interpretation as to how it should be done, when it should be done, and what documents are to be considered proper posting media. If the Report Ledger is to be useful as a control device for document flow as well as its more primary use, posting should be performed daily. A closely regulated use of forms has made it possible to record all information pertinent to the Report Ledger on not more than four forms. The AEC form 101 records all external activity; and within ANL itself a receiving report and an expendability report suffice for all other information that affects material balances. Occasional issues to licensees are removed from inventory balances by the use of the prescribed form.

The posting of AEC form 101 probably presents the most complex problems connected with the Report Ledger. Form 101 not only documents material

FIG. 19-1   Pilot plant production of UF_4.

shipped but also documents material received. Until a received 101 is dispatched, the AEC has on record in its control only the values recorded as shipped. Consequently the monthly report must, if it is to be in balance with the AEC control, list the value carried by the AEC. If the 101 could always be dispatched as soon as the material is received, the posting problem would be relatively simple. However, once the 101 is dispatched, acceptance of the values stated on its face is assumed. Incoming material is often of such value that an independent determination must be made. This independent check usually involves analytical procedures that are time consuming, and often the transfer document must be carried into a succeeding report period. There are other variations that affect the use of the 101 as a posting medium; e.g.

FIG. 19-2 Laboratory equipment for production of small samples of UF_6.

the 101 may be received during a report period but the material may still be in transit, or the 101 may have been in error and have to be corrected.

The complexities of handling the 101 affect the document flow to such an extent that a firm control has to be established. The accounting mechanism that provides such control requires the posting of the 101 forms in the chronological order in which they are received, regardless of whether or not the material has been received or accepted. A separate log book has been set up to record the receipt of 101 forms by number sequence to ensure that document control is maintained. The detailed control necessary to ensure that the monthly report contains only completed transactions is provided through a reconciliation account in the Report Ledger. The records forming the basis of the reconciliation account have their origin in the internal control system. This system is described next.

19-3.2. Control Records. The accounting problems of internal SS control in a research and development installation become complex not because of the accounting methods and devices involved, but because it is frequently difficult to obtain the necessary information, and thus the decision as to what constitutes a valid figure for record purposes must often be based on theory rather than actual knowledge.

A research and development installation is what its name implies—a place where new ideas are being formulated and tried and where development of ideas is first put into practical form. The problems of such an installation include the need for control over SS materials in amounts varying from minute amounts to substantial quantities and over materials that vary from those that can be measured directly to those that can only be determined by estimate. To illustrate the possible range in quantities of materials handled, Fig. 19-1 shows a setup which generates quantities of UF_4 on a pilot-plant scale, and Fig. 19-2 shows a portion of a smaller-scale laboratory unit for UF_6 production. Generally the types and quantities of material vary so widely that statistical methods cannot be applied, and, in cases where statistical evaluations can be made, the results would represent such a small percentage of the total quantity handled as to preclude the development of a method. Nevertheless control must be maintained, not only to make meaningful the report figures but also to assist in the scientific effort itself. It is not uncommon for a scientist to rely on the stated figures of the SS Group in his research or development work.

The most effective method of maintaining the degree of control necessary to account for material that is frequently changing in form and size, is often being transferred from one user to another, and at times disappears altogether into assemblies and other containers is to itemize the material and set up an individual card for each item. The Kardex system has proved to be the flexible method required for frequently shifting material balances.

Each work area maintains its own card system to record the materials on hand as well as a record of all users within the specific area. One person may have material in any one or all the locations within the areas, but the material belongs to the area and is recorded in the card system of the area. This method has two important advantages over one that would attempt control on a laboratory-wide basis. The physical control people in each area are most cognizant of the nature and history of the material and thus are more aware at all times of the use being made of the material. And the method restricts the uncontrolled movement of radioactive material since any movement between areas must be performed by physical control personnel.

Material may be received into any area from outside sources. Once it has been received, weights are taken, and the decision is made as to whether the shipper's weights are acceptable or further verification is necessary. If further verification is needed, the receiving report is marked as a temporary document, and any values shown are then known to be subject to change.

Upon receipt of the material, an item card is prepared to which the receiving report is posted. The card contains a complete description of the material as well as its weights. The card also contains a batch number, which has been issued to identify the material during its use. After this information has been posted, the card is placed in its appropriate tray and is then available for following the movement of the material it represents. Thus if the material is issued, the card is removed from a material-in-stock tray and placed in the scientist section under the name of the person to whom it has been issued. If only part of the material is needed, a new card is made out to record the part removed, the batch number is extended to indicate that a division of the material has occurred while allowing the new portion to retain its identity with its source, and the new card is placed in the section that indicates material whereabouts.

The batch numbering system has proved extremely useful in tracing material flow. Each type of material is identified with a number that is prefixed to the sequential numbering; e.g. normal-uranium numbering is prefixed with the number 4. Thus a piece of normal uranium might have the number 4-1000. If part of this piece of material is removed for issue, the new piece would be numbered 4-1000/2, and the identification of the parent piece would be extended to 4-1000/1. If the original piece is further reduced by issue, the issued piece would be numbered 4-1000/1B, and the identification of the original material remaining would be again extended, this time to 4-1000/1A. Thus the batch number tells which piece is the original, how many break-offs have occurred, and, in the case of the piece broken off, enables it to be traced to its source. Control of the batch numbering system is kept in the Accounting Section of the central office. In this way duplication of numbers is avoided.

Insofar as the control ledgers maintained in the central office for internal operations are concerned, the receipt of a receiving report is sufficient to initiate a posting. At this point it is of no concern whether or not an AEC-101 has been received or whether it is in accord with the receiving report. Document and material control both require the posting of the document to the control ledger. Conversely, to refer again to the Report Ledger, an AEC-101 is posted at the time of its receipt regardless of whether or not the material has been received.

When material is issued for use, a transfer document is prepared to record the issue, it is signed by the person in charge of the area office to indicate that the material and values stated are correct, and it is signed by the person to whom the material is issued. One copy is retained for posting to the area's card system, and copies are forwarded to the central office for posting to the scientist control ledger. If the material transfer is from one area to another, an interarea form is prepared to record the shipment, and distribution is made. Two separate forms are used, one for interarea transfers and one for intra-area transfers. The major reason for the distinction in forms is economic. Each person charged with material receives a copy of the document charging him. When the person transfers material to another user, he receives a copy of the transaction as proof of his release from responsibility. Hence an inter-area transfer, because generally more persons are involved, contains more copies for distribution. However, there are substantially more intra-area transfers made. To use the same transfer form for both types of operations would result in a considerable waste of unused copies. An additional advantage is found in quick identification. Area personnel can tell at a glance whether a transaction is entirely within one area or if records from other areas are involved.

Posting to area records, as well as to central office control ledgers, provides more effective material control if performed on a daily basis. This procedure cannot be made too rigid, however, because there are times in a research and development installation when the work activity becomes very demanding. There is a period when completion of accounting records does take precedence over activity, however, and that is at the month's end, when each area is required to send inventory reports to the central office accounting section for comparison with the control ledgers.

Much of the value inherent in a detailed control system is lost if the inventory reports from each area do not truly reflect the condition of the card system. It is possible to prepare an inventory by referral to previous reports and recording of pertinent documents. Such actions eliminate the proof of good control that prior balancing of the card system provides. Hence, the procedure is for areas to first be certain that all monthly activity is posted and that the card system is balanced; then the monthly inventory report can be prepared from the balanced card-system summary card.

When these reports are received by the accounting section in the central office, they are compared with the control ledger for agreement and posting balance. When such comparison has been made and existing differences have been corrected, the control ledgers are considered to represent the values of material in the work areas, and report preparation is begun.

The Material Balance Report is prepared from the Report Ledger, and a reconciliation account is required to balance the internal control ledgers with the Report Ledger (Sec. 19-3.1). This is necessary since posting internally is done to two decimal places, whereas posting to the Report Ledger is done with the rounded unit. Also recognition must be given to those external documents that were received and posted while material was still in transit and to values picked up on the records before final analytical figures were received. These instances all result in an imbalance between the internal control ledgers and the Report Ledger. Items are posted in the Report Ledger that are not properly to be included on the Material Balance Report. Such imbalances, as well as temporary entries, must be reconciled. When such reconciliation has been performed, the Report Ledger is balanced with the internal control ledger to a difference representing only the difference between the actual total, as shown in the internal ledgers, and the rounded figure, as shown in the Report Ledger. The reconciliation itemizes the rounding differences, not for purposes of complete balancing, but to indicate that the final existing difference as established is a rounding difference and not due to hidden errors attributed to rounding operations.

The Material Balance Report includes a statement of the composition of the ending inventory. The breakdown by forms of material is prepared in the areas and sent to the central office along with the monthly inventory report from each area. There are several ways of accomplishing such a breakdown, but the knowledge of changes in the form of material is best known to persons who staff the work areas. Consequently, the composition of the ending inventory is prepared in the work areas.

The composition of the ending inventory can be restricted to the breakdown required for reporting to the AEC, but generally it is widened in its scope to include categories that effectively aid management in following the progress of the various projects. The knowledge of where the various allocations of material may be and their forms at any designated time can be of considerable assistance to persons responsible for work progress.

19-3.3. Inventories. So far, this discussion has been concerned with various material movements. An adequate control system also requires that an actual physical count should be made of the material the accounting system records.

Certain questions are always encountered in a physical inventory. What is the best method? Should tags be used, or will they contribute to the possible spread of contamination when tags are collected for summarizing? Often the physical form of the material is such that tags large enough to contain the essential information would be extremely cumbersome.

Another consideration is timing. Material control is set up to permit scientific efforts to proceed in as uninterrupted a fashion as possible. Hence an inventory should be planned for the period when laboratory activity is known to be low. This is not to say that areas of activity using large amounts of material should be ignored except for quiet intervals. When an activity is such that considerable amounts of material are in use and large amounts of scrap are being generated, with possible losses of material, physical inventorying must be done to keep the material under control. The practice of monthly inventorying of holders of large amounts of material is established as routine. A laboratory-wide physical inventory is conducted annually.

The monthly inventories of large quantities are conducted by personnel in the work areas, and reports are sent to the Accounting Section. If losses have been incurred, an investigation into those processes is made to determine if they are the result of careless handling or if the process is such that losses cannot be avoided. Further examination is made to determine the

FIG. 19-3   Measuring induced activity in milligram samples to obtain cross-section data.

flow of the waste streams and the final disposition of the waste material. If there are no alternatives, such as the recovery of waste, the loss is accepted.

The annual inventory presents a larger problem because of the bulk of material that must be handled, even though it is in small individual lots divided among many users. Members of the Accounting Section prepare the inventory by a listing method that provides, by means of duplicate copies, a record of the card system in each area as it exists on a given day. Members of the Physical Control Section complete one part of the inventory sheets by entering quantities determined by physical methods (weighing, analysis, etc.). When the physical portion of the inventory has been completed, the data sheets are sent to the Accounting Section, where comparison is made with the duplicate documents prepared from the card system and retained by accounting personnel. Differences are marked, and quantities differing from the stated amounts are investigated for possible error. When there is assurance that a difference does exist, consideration is given to the possible uses made of the material during the year. If the handling of the material has been performed with the proper care and the operations have been such that a loss of material could have occurred, the loss is accepted.

FIG. 19-4 Experimental setup involving thousands of kilograms of uranium.

Once the inventory has been reconciled with the records, a report is made to management concerning the condition of the inventory, violations of procedure that have been noticed, suggestions for improvements in method, and any other observations pertinent to management needs.

19-3.4. SS Control Problems. SS control is complicated by the conditions inherent in the operation of a diversified research and development facility engaged in a variety of fields of basic research and in the development of reactor fuel elements, fabrication techniques, fuel recovery processes, reactor designs, materials testing, and the like. With such a wide diversification of effort, the requirements for nuclear materials are equally varied. As a consequence the nuclear material inventory includes items which vary in quantity from a few milligrams, such as a research sample being used in cross-section measurements (Fig. 19-3), to several thousand kilograms of material such as that in use in reactor experiments (Fig. 19-4). It may be necessary to apply extremely rigid controls in the case of a small sample representing the major portion of the available supply of that particular material, or controls may be somewhat less stringent if the material is readily available and is of relatively low value. The degree of accuracy necessary in establishing limits of control may depend upon this factor, upon the processes through which the material will pass, or upon the total quantity of material being processed.

SS control may be further complicated by the physical layout of the facility. The buildings may be so located that the distance between the office originating a nuclear materials transfer and its ultimate destination is 2 or 3 miles.

The fact that many lots of material may be stored for long periods of time makes accurate control methods more important, since opportunities for complete material balances over specific operations are not frequently encountered. In other cases the material may be tied up in a long series of related experiments on a single sample or group of samples or in the study of a complete fuel element cycle from fabrication through the actual operation and, finally, to fuel recovery. In such cases it may not be possible to obtain accurate and complete material balances for periods ranging up to several months. Such circumstances, although not common, demand that close attention be paid to the control of material at all stages of a particular study being undertaken.

Control is further complicated by nonroutine processes. The preparation of a small sample may involve many and varied chemical and physical manipulations before the material is in the form desired for the particular investigation. Similarly, fuel-element development studies result in the production of a large variety of compounds and alloys of nuclear materials. The processes used in these cases are frequently unique and quite likely of short duration. Even where entire reactor charges are fabricated, the application of routine control procedures is difficult, since only in extremely rare instances is the fabrication procedure duplicated or of a nature similar to a previous operation.

19-3.5. Physical Control Section. Complete historical background data for each lot of material are of major significance to the research groups because of the large variety of items, their long retention, and the nonroutine nature of the operations undertaken. Consequently the physical control system must provide the following information:

1. Type of material
2. Quantity of material
3. Analytical data (chemical and isotopic)
4. Identification of specific lots
5. Historical data (background of previous use or fabrication history)

The Physical Control Section implements this system. This group operates independently of the accounting control and analytical control organizations and is responsible for the actual handling of the nuclear materials, including the receipts, storage, distribution, and disposal of the items, and for the maintenance of records indicating the location and identity of the material.

This group operates most efficiently if its members have a technical background coupled with experience in administrative activities. It is apparent that administrative experience or education is valuable in the accounting area of such work, and when the technical aspects of the physical handling of nuclear materials are considered, the need for some scientific background becomes equally apparent. These requirements are dictated to a certain extent by the associated services this group renders. A considerable familiarity with the problems of handling various types of materials is essential from the standpoint of safety and is most helpful in the recognition of problems that may be encountered in the use of materials.

Procurement. The responsibilities of the procurement group begin with procurement of material requested by a scientific division. The material is requisitioned through the appropriate channels. At the same time an identification number is assigned to the request, which serves to identify the shipment and the associated papers. The identification number assigned previously assists in determining the nature of the shipment and the precautions to be observed in handling it. A receiving report is prepared immediately, presenting the data that are readily available: the source of the shipment, gross and net weights, identity of material, method of shipment, disposition of material, and any necessary administrative data, such as purchase order and subcontract number. A batch number is assigned to each lot in the shipment; this number will follow the material during its retention at the laboratory. At the same time samples are taken and forwarded to the analytical group for appropriate determinations. The issuance of a final receiving report will await the submission of such data by the Analytical Laboratory.

The final receiving report contains, in addition to the administrative details mentioned above, the following essential information:

1. The nuclear material content (in the case of alloys, compounds or clad material)
2. The isotopic content (if appropriate)
3. The batch number of each lot
4. The disposition of the material (whether held in storage or distributed to use)

This final document is used to clear shipping documents and provides primary data for the accounting records.

Internal Transfer. Distribution of the materials to the research staff is controlled by a listing of those authorized to withdraw these materials. The issuance of items to unauthorized personnel is prohibited.

An internal transfer document, prepared only by physical control personnel, records the transfer of material between individual scientists. After appropriate signatures have been obtained, copies are distributed to the accounting control group and to all parties involved in the transfer. A complete inventory of the materials in the hands of individual scientists is maintained on a daily basis through the use of these documents. The forms are designed to provide the essential, pertinent data associated with the material: basic identification, analytical data, etc.

After the material has been transferred, the Physical Control Section contributes assistance during the actual use of the nuclear material. This is usually of minor significance in cases where individual researchers are engaged in projects involving small quantities of material. In cases where larger quantities are handled, however, such as in fuel-element fabrication, the assistance provided by the Physical Control Section can represent a real contribution to the program. Active participation in operations can also aid material control. For example, effluent streams can be evaluated more accurately and losses through waste streams can be minimized.

Any process measurements made can ordinarily be expanded quite easily to provide necessary technical data for the fabricator, the ultimate user, and SS control. For example; in the fabrication of fuel elements for the Experimental Breeder Reactor, enriched uranium was cast into rods, rolled to approximate size, and machined to the final dimensions. Seventeen weigh points were established through the process to determine losses and waste quantities and to provide accurate data for the reactor loading. The weights so obtained, in conjunction with the analytical data, provided excellent material control, permitted careful study of the efficiency of the process, established quantities of materials in various waste batches, and afforded vital information to the reactor operating staff. This type assistance is beneficial both to the specific activity in process and to the establishment of the control required. It also provides valuable experience and information for the evaluation of subsequent similar operations.

The physical control system can also provide assistance to reactor research programs. Extremely accurate information is most helpful to programs of this type where variations in the nuclear material content of the fuel elements in use are of importance in the theoretical calculations and in the interpretation of accumulated data, as in the case of the determination of breeding gain in a breeder reactor. Proper identification of individual fuel elements and an accurate knowledge of the fuel content of each element can readily be provided by a good control system.

After the nuclear material has served its purpose, there remains the problem of disposition. The material may be in the form of spent fuel elements, fabrication wastes, small samples that are no longer needed, or unused material. Here, again, accurate information is essential. If the material is to undergo some recovery process, a complete history of its use will help to determine the type of processing necessary to restore it to a useful form. Obviously, the processing necessary to recover clean uranium turnings is considerably less complex than that necessary for the recovery of uranium from an alloyed clad fuel element that has been in an operating reactor for some time. The information that can be provided by the physical control system can be of considerable value to the chemical processing plant operator and can eliminate unnecessary expenditure of time, energy, and money.

Off-Site Shipment. There are several possible conditions that can initiate shipments of nuclear materials off site: the termination of some phase of research, cooperative research undertaken with or at other facilities, or samples transferred to other sites for insertion into reactors and returned for investigation. In any case the handling of such shipments must be controlled by a centralized organization to ensure flow of information to the Accounting Section for the maintenance of control records. The same information must be provided to the receiving installation.

The shipment of nuclear materials requires careful consideration because of the radioactivity hazard. If the material has been irradiated the level of activity may be extremely high and the handling problem difficult. The high intrinsic value of the material also requires that special precautions be taken to minimize the possibility of loss. In addition, many shipments are of such a nature that criticality conditions must be carefully reviewed. A complete description of the packing method and container design is submitted to a committee of physicists and reactor engineers for review and approval before a shipment of this type is made. The nonroutine nature of such shipments makes it impossible to establish simple standard procedures for such activities.

Regulations of the Interstate Commerce Commission, published by the Bureau of Explosives, American Association of Railroads, in Agent H. A. Campbell's Tariff No. 10, are very specific in outlining packing and labeling requirements for radioactive material. All nuclear materials are covered by these regulations, but the determination of the amount of shielding necessary for the attenuation of gamma radiation and the type of containment required for alpha-emitting items must be made by the shipper. The variety of materials and the many levels of activity encountered at a research installation make this determination one requiring educated judgment. These same conditions necessitate the maintenance of a large inventory of shielded containers of varying dimensions and shielding thicknesses.

The steps taken to safeguard material against theft or tampering during shipment are most frequently a matter of compliance with AEC security regulations; however, even this compliance requires the exercise of judgment in the interpretation of the regulations and their application to the specific shipment.

In addition to these physical handling details, the necessary documentation for the transfer of material and its removal from records is also the responsibility of the Physical Control Section. All pertinent data associated with the material are entered on the AEC shipping form, AEC-101, or on an appropriate document and are subsequently distributed to the appropriate offices.

19-3.6 Summary. A nuclear material control system at a research and development facility requires, in addition to an accounting control group and an analytical group, an organization with the responsibility for the physical handling and distribution of the materials, working in close liaison with the research staff. The responsible members of such an organization must be possessed of sufficient technical background and judgment to be able to function independently and to determine the appropriate steps necessary for the safe handling of these materials. There must be sufficient administrative experience to provide necessary controls and documentation for all activities undertaken with the materials, and there must also be a data-recording function to provide necessary information to investigators who require complete histories to verify results. The organization should be able to provide assistance in the establishment of operating procedures to maintain accurate and complete records to minimize losses and to ensure control over all waste streams. The group must be aware of all programs in progress and of any proposed activities so that adequate preparations can be made for the handling of material that will result. Complete familiarity with applicable regulations concerning shipment of nuclear materials is necessary to safeguard the material from loss and to protect personnel from any possible injury. The primary concern of the group should be the maintenance of the maximum practicable control of all nuclear material from the time of its receipt at the installation until the time of its shipment.

19-4. ANALYSIS

For an adequate accounting of SS materials, accurate estimates must be made of them. This entails chemical analysis for uranium, plutonium, or thorium in materials other than pure metals and isotopic analysis of uranium if it is other than normal. The shipper generally supplies analyses for materials received, but independent corroboration is needed to prevent error. Also, if the composition of the material is altered by alloying or chemical treatment after receipt, analyses will be needed. Waste materials and solutions for recovery or disposal must be analyzed for SS control. Occasional checks may be necessary for materials kept in storage for protracted periods of time.

A group separate from the general analytical facilities has been set up to supply the analytical data necessary for SS control. A disadvantage of this plan of operation is the possibility of waste of manpower and equipment funds through unnecessary duplication of effort. There are several advantages to offset this, however. This special group can devote its attentions to the development of improved methods of analysis for nuclear materials and to the determination and improvement of the accuracy of the methods. A close liaison can be maintained with those in charge of physical control so that the volume and type of analyses needed can be anticipated, which would result in greater efficiency and speed of analysis. The materials control analytical needs can be accomplished as needed without interfering with other activities.

The fluorophotometric assay of uranium in low concentration in wastes is obtained from the normal analytical sources since the quantities here are generally low. Also, spectrochemical analysis and the determination of such trace impurities as carbon, hydrogen, nitrogen, and oxygen are obtained from these sources. These analyses are of indirect interest for SS control since they may indicate the quality of the material as well as qualitatively confirm its elemental identity. Here the expense of equipment, space, and specially trained personnel far outweigh the advantages of having separate facilities.

The surface ionization mass spectrometer was chosen as the most suitable tool for the isotopic analysis of nuclear materials at installations of this type. Methods other than mass spectrometry, in general, do not give a complete isotopic analysis. The versatility and sensitivity of the surface-ionization mass spectrometer made it the choice over the gas type. Though the latter has somewhat greater precision, it is subject to memory effects when there is a wide variation of isotopic ratios in succeeding samples. Much smaller samples can be used in the surface ionization source, which is advantageous in the analysis of hazardous materials. The mass spectrometer is also used for the determination of the concentration of elements by the sensitive isotope dilution method.

Several methods have been used for the determination of uranium. Among the titrimetric methods the oxidation with standard permanganate solution after reduction with a Jones reductor has an advantage, since a direct stoichiometric titration can be made; however, the oxidant is unstable, requiring frequent standardization. Substitution of standard ceric sulfate for permanganate provides a very stable standard solution. A stoichiometric endpoint is obtained by adding excess oxidant and back titrating with ferrous solution. A lead reductor is now used for reduction of uranium instead of the Jones (amalgamated zinc) reductor, since the former reduces the uranium quantitatively to the tetravalent state, thus eliminating the necessity of air oxidation of the trivalent state before titration.

Under some circumstances spectrographically pure oxides or readily convertible salts, such as the nitrate, can be analyzed gravimetrically by direct ignition. The uranium can be precipitated with carbonate-free ammonia solution and ignited to the oxide and weighed, but there are many interfering ions. A gravimetric method consisting of precipitation with hydrogen peroxide followed by ignition to the oxide has fewer interferences, but a much larger sample is required to get quantitative results because of the solubility of the peroxide salt.

The spectrophotometric methods have been used. The measurement of the absorbance of the thiocyanate complex ion in acetone solution is comparatively free of interference and becomes quite precise when the differential method is used. The ferrocyanide complex method is used for a rough preliminary measurement before a more precise determination by another method.

Plutonium has been determined titrimetrically and by alpha counting. The alpha counting method requires only very small samples; thus the health hazard is much less, but the determination is much less accurate. In the titrimetric method the plutonium is first reduced to the trivalent state with either liquid zinc amalgam or solid amalgamated zinc in a Jones reductor before titration to the tetravalent state with ceric sulfate. Uranium interferes and must be separated before analysis.

Thorium is generally determined gravimetrically by precipitation as oxalate and ignition to the oxide.

In alloys where the uranium is present in far larger concentration than the other elements, the uranium may often be determined by difference more accurately than by direct determination. Details on most of these methods can be found in the unclassified USAEC Report ANL-5410, *Manual of Special Materials Analytical Laboratory Procedures.*

19-5. SAMPLING

The taking of representative and useful samples is as important to accurate accounting of nuclear materials as the analysis methods. This phase of control is often neglected, when actually it should receive the most careful attention. Many problems arise in sampling, the most important of which is that of obtaining a homogeneous and representative sample. Solid materials may not be homogeneous because of insufficient mixing, variation of particle size, or nonuniform physical or chemical treatment. Metallic samples may have oxide coatings or may be clad with another metal, and alloys may show segregation because of a wide variation in densities of the metals and their compounds. A solution will be inhomogeneous if it is not mixed properly if it has a precipitate or if it has more than one liquid phase.

Powdered or lumpy material can be sampled, quartered, and pulverized by ASTM approved methods, special care being taken to prevent loss if the material is very valuable or hazardous. If the total amount of material is small, the whole sample can be dissolved, and aliquots can be taken for analysis.

Oxide coatings on metals can be removed either electrolytically or by selective acid treatment. In clad material a whole plate can be dissolved and aliquots can be taken for analysis, or, as a second choice, a representative cross-sectional sample can be taken and analyzed. A common problem is the detection of segregation in alloys. This is done by taking samples from the top and the bottom of a casting and analyzing them separately. In two-phase liquids each phase is analyzed separately. If the solution contains a small amount of a finely divided precipitate, the liquid is mixed thoroughly and sampled before there is appreciable settling of the precipitate. Otherwise the solution is separated from the precipitate, and each phase is analyzed separately.

Sometimes only a limited amount of sample can be spared for analysis. This may require adaptation of more sensitive methods of analysis, with accompanying sacrifice of accuracy in the analysis as well as in the sampling. Samples for isotopic analysis can be taken on unclad metals and alloys by etching a few milligrams from the surface with an acid solution, since isotopic composition is usually homogeneous.

Care must be taken to ensure that errors in the analytical results do not occur because of a change in the samples before they are analyzed. Metallic samples must be protected by a dry inert gas against oxidation if they are to be stored for any length of time. Salts and oxides may gain or lose moisture on standing in contact with air. Solutions must be kept tightly sealed to prevent evaporation of solvent. In water solutions a high concentration of alpha activity causes decomposition of the water, which may lead to changes in volume and concentration. The volume should be measured accurately as soon as possible after the sample is taken. In this case the container should not be tightly closed, since the gaseous decomposition products would cause an increase in the pressure. When the container is then opened, the spray from the sudden release in pressure could lead to a high alpha contamination of the surroundings.

In some cases material precipitates from solution. Plutonium and zirconium are troublesome in this manner because they are hydrolyzed if the solution is not sufficiently acid. Also under some circumstances the material or solution reacts with the container, causing interferences in the analysis or loss of sample. If the amount of material is small, as in some isotopic samples, care must be taken to prevent contamination with material from natural sources or other samples. Accidental introduction of a small particle of uranium dust might change markedly an isotopic analysis of uranium.

The health hazards of nuclear materials, especially plutonium, require special handling of the samples. Containers must be carefully chosen so that there can be no loss by spillage. Yet the containers must not be airtight in the case of high alpha solutions; they are usually protected by secondary containers. Samples of plutonium larger than a few micrograms are opened and treated in glove boxes or hoods containing glove panels, especially if the material is in the solid form. Solutions can be handled in open hoods if adequate precautions are taken to prevent spray or evaporation to dryness of any small amount of the solution, which could lead to flaking and blowing of the solid salt deposited. Solutions are pipetted instead of poured to prevent spillage and drying of salts on the lip of the container. The responsibility for the sampling methods for nuclear materials lies with the analytical group. This group does some sampling, but most sampling is done by the scientists using the material, with the assistance of the SS Representative.

Any portions of samples of fissionable materials that are left in their original state after analysis are returned to the sender to be combined with his scrap. Waste solutions containing small amounts of plutonium and moderate amounts of normal or depleted uranium are sent to a reclamation group for disposal. Enriched uranium waste solutions are combined according to their U^{235} concentrations. The solutions are then evaporated to a wet solid and eventually recovered elsewhere.

19-6. CONCLUSION

The requirements for good material control in a research and development installation are best met by a specialized group working within a system based on sound internal control principles. The record keeping and accounting devices necessary to maintain control over the flow of materials in its myriad of uses is best assigned to those trained in the use of accounting mechanisms, but the actual physical handling and introduction of primary records into the system should be performed as a separate function. Given a sound systematic approach, however, a well-defined material control system can be of considerable usefulness in helping a laboratory to perform the work for which it was established.

GLOSSARY

accuracy The degree of concordance between an observed numerical value and the true numerical value.

assay, *noun* The mineral content in an ore; (restrictively) the isotopic content of enriched uranium.

assay, *verb* To analyze chemically for the constituents, as a sample of ore for metal content.

beginning inventory The quantity of materials on hand at the beginning of a specific time period.

bias A long-term systematic error in which the *average* value of the estimate of a quantity differs from the true value.

billet A product of the early passes of an ingot in the rolling mill. Further passes of the billet may produce a rod.

bird cage A shipping container for fissionable material in which the main container is surrounded by a structural network that prohibits the approach of other containers to distances below safe limits from a criticality consideration.

black oxide An oxide of uranium, U_3O_8, frequently referred to as urano-uranic oxide.

B-PID Book-physical inventory difference, the figure that brings the book inventory into balance with the physical inventory. It serves as an indication of the degree of control maintained over SS materials.

briquetting The process of compressing metal turnings into a cylinder of relatively high density.

brown oxide Uranium dioxide (UO_2).

calcining The process of heating materials to remove combustible or volatile materials such as organic matter and moisture.

cladding The outer metal jacket or can that is placed on pure uranium or on uranium-bearing fuel elements to protect the fuel from heat and corrosion effects. Typical cladding materials are aluminum, zirconium, and stainless steel.

cold Having negligible radioactivity.

composite The preparation of a single sample from several samples from several containers by combining them in the same ratio as the net weight of materials sampled; a sample prepared in such fashion.

confidence interval If the probability is $(1 - \alpha)$ that an unknown quantity θ lies between the values A and B $(A < \theta < B)$, then A and B are called $100\ (1 - \alpha)$ percent confidence limits for the quantity θ, and the interval between them is called the $100\ (1 - \alpha)$ percent confidence interval.

critical mass The minimum quantity of a fissionable material which, under ideal geometrical and moderating circumstances, will produce a self-sustaining chain reaction.

crossover The unintentional blending of two batches of uranium having different percentages of U^{235}, with the net result of a downgrading of the value of the material.

custodian An SS representative or his designee who is responsible for control of SS materials being processed.

cut A small percentage of a flowing stream removed in a representative fashion.

degree of reliability The converse of the degree of uncertainty.

degree of uncertainty A way of expressing the fact that a measured value is not certain to be the true value, usually stated as a limit of error assigned to the measurement.

dingot The uranium-metal product of the simultaneous reduction/casting operation suitable for introduction into the rolling mill (an abbreviation of "direct ingot").

ending inventory The quantity of materials on hand at the end of a specific time period.

enriched uranium Material which has been processed in such a fashion as to increase the relative percentage of U^{235} to concentrations greater than the 0.7115 percent which occurs naturally.

enrichment The process, or result of the process, of enhancing the relative percentage of U^{235} in uranium.

external receipts Materials received by a plant from external sources.

external shipments Materials shipped by a plant to external points.

fiscal-year-end inventory Material on hand on the last day of the fiscal year.

fission The physical process of an atom splitting into two nearly equal parts as a result of an upset in the nuclear balance by the absorption of energy, generally in the form of a neutron. The splitting is accompanied by the emission of neutrons and considerable energy.

fission loss The loss of material in a reactor either through the process of fission or absorption of neutrons to produce different isotopes.

fluorination The process of chemically reacting a material with fluorine or a fluorine-containing compound to produce a desired product, such as the reaction of UO_2 with HF to produce UF_4.

fuel elements The physical form in which uranium is incorporated into a reactor. It may take the shape of a right cylinder, rods, an assembly of plates, etc.

fuel slug A fuel element in the form of a right cylinder, generally composed of uranium and clad with a corrosion-resistant metal.

gravimetric Of chemical analysis based upon reactions that produce a material to be weighed.

green salt Uranium tetrafluoride (UF_4), an intermediate formed in the production of uranium metal and uranium hexafluoride.

gross weight The weight of a full container, including cover, brackets, etc.

head end The beginning of a chemical processing line.

header A manifold that feeds to, or accumulates from, more than one vessel.

heel A quantity of undissolved solid material deliberately left in a dissolver. Since the rate of solution is dependent upon the amount of material present, the rate will decrease as solution progresses; it is inefficient to completely dissolve all material charged to the dissolver.

hidden inventory The inventory in the gaseous diffusion cascade which cannot be measured because it is not in a gaseous form nor available for sampling.

hot Highly radioactive.

ingot A cylindrical casting before it has been reduced in the rolling mill.

in-process inventory The quantity of material present in the various processing vessels, machines, etc., at any specified time.

internal receipts Materials received by a material balance area from another material balance area in the same plant.

internal shipments Materials shipped by one material balance area to another in the same plant.

inventory The process of determining the quantity of material on hand at any given time; the quantity so determined. See also specific type of inventory.

isotope One of two or more species of the same element, nearly identical in chemical behavior but differing in atomic mass. Generally the elements occur as mixtures of isotopes, and the atomic weight is the weighted average of the isotopes constituting the element.

isotopic composition The ratio of isotopes for a given element; e.g. uranium in its natural form contains about 99.3 percent U^{238}, 0.7115 percent U^{235}, and trace amounts of U^{234}.

isotopic enrichment The act of processing, usually in a gaseous diffusion cascade, to increase the percentage of U^{235}; also, the percentage so attained.

leach To remove, generally by chemical dissolution, a desirable material from undesirable constituents, e.g. the leaching of uranium from crushed ore.

limit of error A value derived from the standard deviation and expressed as a confidence interval; by convention, a 95 percent confidence interval.

material balance The comparison of material quantities input and output for a process; generally, the comparison of beginning inventory plus receipts with ending inventory plus shipments for a specific time interval.

material balance area An area, usually based on some physical boundary delineation within the plant, on type of process, or on organizational lines, in which measurements and records are maintained to establish a material balance.

natural uranium Uranium whose isotopic composition as it occurs in nature has not been altered. See also *normal uranium*.

net weight The weight of the contents of a container, generally arrived at by taking the difference between the gross weight and the tare weight of the container.

nondestructive measurement A measurement that involves no loss of the utility of the material being measured, e.g. measurement of the content of a fuel element by neutron-multiplication methods.

normal uranium Uranium containing the same percentage of U^{235} as occurs in nature, but usually attained by blending uranium of different isotopic compositions or by processing in a gaseous diffusion cascade; loosely, natural uranium.

orange oxide Uranium trioxide (UO_3); formed as an intermediate in the production of uranium tetrafluoride.

ore concentrate The product resulting from the beneficiation of ores. In uranium processing the uranium content in the concentrate is greater than 50 percent as opposed to roughly 0.3 percent present in the ore.

parameter A quantity to which may be assigned arbitrary values, as distinguished from a variable, which can assume only the values that the form of the function makes possible.

physical inventory The quantity of material which is determined to be on hand by physically ascertaining its presence by sampling, weighing, and analysis techniques; also, the process by which the quantity is determined.

pickling The removal of the surface of a metal by immersion of the metal in acid solutions.

pile A graphite-moderated reactor.

plutonium Element 94, metallic in nature, which is produced by neutron irradiation of U^{238}.

precision The degree of consistency among observations determined by a particular method.

pulp A subsample, generally of ore.

quality control A technique, based upon statistical treatment of data, which permits the maintenance of a desired quality level.

raffinate In a solvent-extraction process, the liquor which remains after the major portion of desired material has been removed by extraction.

receipts The quantities of material which are received by a plant for its use.

reduction In metal production, the chemical process that converts a compound to the desired metal, e.g. the reduction of UF_4 with magnesium to produce uranium metal.

reliability See *degree of reliability*.

restricted geometry An arrangement (usually mechanical) that separates discrete quantities of fissionable materials to preclude a critical configuration.

safe geometry The geometrical arrangement of fissionable material which will not, under the worst possible conditions, result in a critical mass.

shipments The quantities of materials which are shipped by a plant to other plants for their use.

shipper-receiver difference The difference between the quantity stated by the shipper as having been shipped and the quantity stated by the receiver as having been received. It may result from the uncertainties associated with measurements or from the loss or diversion of materials.

skull A thin sheath of metal and dross left on the sides of the casting crucibles after pouring the casting.

solvent extraction A physicochemical separation process in which the desired material in solution is separated from undesirable materials by intimate contact with a solvent. The solvent used must preferentially dissolve the desirable material and must not be soluble in the solution, thus forming a separate phase from which the desired material can be recovered.

source material Uranium, thorium, or any other material that is determined by the Commission, pursuant to provisions of Section 61 of the Atomic Energy Act of 1954, to be source material, or ores containing one or more of the foregoing materials, in such concentration as the Commission may by regulation determine from time to time. This does not include special nuclear material.

special nuclear material Plutonium, uranium enriched in the isotope 233 or in the isotope 235, or any other material that the Commission, pursuant to the provisions of Section 51 of the Atomic Energy Act of 1954, determines to be special nuclear material. This does not include source materials or any material artifically enriched by any of the foregoing.

splitting limits Limits for measurement mutually agreed upon by the buyer and seller. If their measurement results are within these limits, the difference is split; i.e. the average will be accepted. Generally, if the difference in measurements exceeds the splitting limits, a sample of the material measured is submitted to an umpire to establish the acceptable value.

SS Source and Special (nuclear materials).

SS material Source material, special nuclear material, and other materials of unique interest to the Atomic Energy Commission in its operation.

SS Representative The individual to whom responsibility is assigned for the management of SS materials at any site handling those materials.

standard deviation The square root of the variance. Standard deviation may be used to describe the scatter of observations or the frequency distribution of observations.

stoichiometric Of the precise weight relationship of the elements in a chemical compound; (of quantities of reacting elements or compounds) in the same weight relationship as the theoretical combining weight of the elements involved.

survey A comprehensive examination, analysis, and evaluation of all phases of SS materials control, including material records, inventory procedures, measurement and statistical methods in use by an installation, and an independent test of the inventory.

tare weight The weight of an empty container including cover, brackets, etc.

thorium Element 90, metallic in character and of natural occurrence, designated as a source material by the Atomic Energy Act of 1954.

umpire Generally a laboratory of recognized capability chosen to determine a value for quantities of material upon which the buyer-seller difference exceeds established limits.

uncertainty See *degree of uncertainty*.

UNH Uranyl nitrate hexahydrate, $UO_2(NO_3)_2 \cdot 6H_2O$.

uranium Element 92, which occurs widespread in the form of an oxide. The element itself is metallic.

value The precious metals contained in rock, gravel, or the like; (in the atomic energy field) the uranium content of ore.

variance The sum of the squares of the deviations from the mean, divided by one less than the number of observations.

volumetric Chemical analysis based upon the reaction of a volume of standard solution with the material being analyzed.

yellow cake A uranium ore concentrate used as a refinery feed material. The term describes the general appearance of ore concentrate obtained by the precipitation of uranium as an alkaline diuranate.

Zircaloy Any of several alloys of zirconium in which the principal alloying material is tin.

INDEX

509